FOREVER FOR ALL

FOREVER

FOR ALL

*MORAL PHILOSOPHY, CRYONICS,
AND THE SCIENTIFIC PROSPECTS
FOR IMMORTALITY*

R. Michael Perry

Forever For All: Moral Philosophy, Cryonics,
and the Scientific Prospects for Immortality

Copyright © 2000 R. Michael Perry
All rights reserved.

Universal Publishers
USA • 2000
ISBN: 1-58112-724-3

www.upublish.com/books/perry.htm

CONTENTS

List of Illustrations ix

Introduction 1

1. Heaven by Design 7
   The Paranormal versus the Scientific 12
   Apocalypse, Singularity, and Immortalization 17
   Immortality in Thought and Practice 22

2. A Brief History of Immortalism 28
   Immortality through Progress 30
   Technological Optimism and Cryonics 36
   Beyond Cryonics 44
   Summary of Immortalist Philosophies 48

3. A Matter of Attitude 51
   Knowledge of Mortality and Management of Terror 53
   Characteristics of Cryonicists 59
   Toward a Change in Attitudes 61
   Cryonics Acceptance: a Hypothetical Case 65
   A Future of Wonder 69

4. A Philosophical System 74
   Reductionism, Materialism, and the Problem of Survival 78
   Physical versus Psychological Reductionism 81
   Psychological Connectedness versus Continuity 85
   The Functionalist Viewpoint 87
   Personal Identity and Destiny 89
   Yuai, Resurrection, and the Multiverse 91
   Shorter-Term Also Important 97

5. Some Scientific Perspectives 101
   Reproducibility versus Unpredictability 102
   The Two-Slit Experiment 108
   The Riddle of Quantum Reality 111
   Relativity and the Problem of Locality 113
   Quantum Interpretations and Locality 118
   The Aspect Experiment and Many-Worlds 122
   More on Alternatives to Many-Worlds 132
   A Telling Experiment? 134

6. Unboundedness 138
   History: Process versus Description 139

vi

What Are the Possible Histories? 142
The Plausibility of Unboundedness 147
Our Existence As Extraordinary Evidence 153

7. Interchangeability 158
A Difficult Problem: Life after Death 159
Interchangeability in Physics 167
Interchangeability As Applied to Persons 170
Opposition, Rebuttal, and Illustrations 174
Underlying and Observer Reality 178
The UI Assumptions 181
The Problem of Actualization 184
Person, Brain, and Mind 188

8. The Digital Substrate 190
The Principle of Large Quantity 191
Strong AI and Materialism 194
Mind As a Digital Phenomenon 197
Information and Personal Survival 201
Information, Understanding, and Reality As a Whole 203
The Material World As Information 207
Digital Systems and Their Powers 210
Machines with Universal Powers 213
Physical Systems As Digital Mechanisms 219
Quantum Devices and Digital Consciousness 221
Answering Objections: the Chinese Room Experiment 226
The Gödel Incompleteness Theorem 229
A Simple Rebuttal 234
Consequences of the Digital Model 238
The Chinese Room Revisited 239
Modeling Time 242
Further Thoughts on Consciousness and Strong AI 243

9. Nanotechnology: Gateway to the Future 247
Progress in Nanotechnology 249
Difficulties and Objections 257
Expectations, Evidence, and Projections 262
Benefits from Nanotechnology 266

10. The Theological Issue 272
Atheism with a Concept of Divinity 279
Cosmological and Ontological Arguments 283
World and Eternal Happiness without a God 287
Our Immense Responsibilities 295
Yuai and Religion 298

11. Will the Good Prevail? 305
    An Investigation of Awakening 309
    A World Not Perfect but Perfecting.. 315
    Free Will, Determinism, and Progress 317
    The Doomsday Argument and the Fermi Paradox 321
    Meeting Other Challenges 328

12. Resurrection.. 331
    The Afterlife: Doubt and Rational Hope 333
    Requirements for a Resurrection 338
    Person-Segments and Person-Stages 340
    The Problem of Identity.. 342
    Onticity 345
    Ontic Robustness, Dreaming, and Past Lives 348
    Heaven Despite Hardships 352

13. Biostasis As the Better Way 355
    A Problem of Anticipation 357
    Advantages of Historical Ties 360
    Addressing Some Objections 365
    Attributes to Aim For... 371
    A Moral Argument 374

14. Immortality 380
    Personhood 382
    Requirements for Immortality 385
    Why Immortality Is Important 391
    Achieving Enontic Immortality 394
    Cosmological Perspectives 399
    Coping with the Mysterious Universe 403

15. The Philosophy of Assurance 412
    The Problem of Forgetting and the Ideal Self 414
    Continuity and Causality Issues 422
    More on Memory Problems... 428
    Avenues for Advancement.. 433
    Free Will, the Multiverse, and the Brain 437
    The Problem of Evil 443
    Assurance in the Face of Uncertainty 445

16. The Philosophy of Aspiration 448
    Wants, Survival, and Healing 451
    The Search for Meaning 456
    Shaping Our Own Future... 459
    Joy and Benevolent Self-Perpetuation 464
    An Illustration 467

Living, Loving, and Developing As Immortal Egos 469
Resurrection As a Community Endeavor 473
Fusion and Fissioning of Individuals 484
Extending the Resurrection 489
Cautions and Restrictions 492
Summary 498

17. The Philosophy of Action 500
Progress against Aging 502
Cryonics and Other Biostasis Procedures 507
Genomic Preservation 510
Cryonics and Brain Preservation 516
How Good Is Cryopreservation? 520
The Chemical Alternative 526
Coming Back: a Possible Repair Scenario 527
Choosing Physical Preservation 532
Summary and Conclusions 535

18. The World at Large and the Future 538
Coping with Resistance 540
Immortalism and Human Problems 543
Some Controversial Issues 549
Immortalism and the Outside World 555
Our Coming Transhumanity 559
The Singularity and Beyond 563

Cover Emblem 570

Illustration Credits 571

Glossary 572

Bibliography 579

References and Notes 585

Organizations 609

Acknowledegments 617

Index 618

ILLUSTRATIONS

The Three Principal Working Hypotheses 75
Photon Detection Apparatus 105
Detection Patterns in Two-Slit Experiments 111
Distant Events Refute Simultaneity 116
The Aspect Experiment 127
How Many-Worlds Preserves Locality 129
Interchangeability: Did You Have a Dog? 178
Symbols Not Simply Arbitrary 206
A Turing Machine 213
The Game of Life 216
The Gödel Sentence 232
Language Inconsistency and Auto Sales 236
Lucretius Demonstrates Onticity 345
The Conservatist Argument 364
Aging to Be Cured 444
Cover Emblem 570

In addition, the Introduction and each chapter have a title illustration.

Introduction

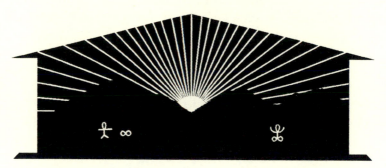

The individual ought to endure—for a life rightly lived is never rightly ended. And life can be rightly lived, I will maintain—which involves much more than a simple release from pain or burdens. Rightly lived, life must offer positive value, a preponderance of satisfaction over dissatisfaction,[1] a meaningful experience that calls for something beyond immediate interests. There must be a growth process in which the prospect of constructive change and the mysteries to be solved are inducements to continue and progress. Living can then become an end in itself, as it should be, and we can shape our philosophy accordingly: Life is fundamentally good, and death, consequently, is a detriment. We can look forward, with joy, to a future with joy. Ongoing developments lend support to this position and call for a reassessment of life's deeper issues.

This book considers the problems of death and the hereafter and how these ages-old problems ought to be addressed in light of our continuing progress. A materialistic viewpoint of reality is assumed, denying the likelihood of supernatural or other superhuman assistance. Death, however, is not seen as inevitable or even irreversible; it is maintained that the problem can and should be addressed scientifically in all of its aspects. The book thus follows recent, immortalist thinking that places hopes in future advances in our understanding and technology. A common ground is sought between two independent strands of this scientific immortalism that so far have been largely separate. There is the cosmological camp that sees immortality, including resurrection of the dead, as a distant future possibility, though outside our present control. There is another, transhumanist group, however, that maintains that our immortalization is much nearer at hand and supports such ongoing efforts as aging research and cryonics—freezing people at death for eventual reanimation.

Here I offer a philosophical system that incorporates and harmonizes both points of view. A functionalist, reductionist argument is developed for the possibility of resurrecting the dead through the eventual creation of replicas and related constructs. Meanwhile, it is urged, medical advances leading to the conquest of aging and biological death should be pursued. An advisable interim strategy is cryonics or some other means of biostasis—having one's remains preserved for reanimation when, in the relatively near future, technology will arguably be available to accomplish the task. The twin possibilities of eventual, universal resurrection and abolition of death starting from currently available means are not seen as competitive but complementary. Both have a vital role to play in the future that appears to be opening. Our resulting philosophy, encompassing both past and future, is directed toward the long-term interests of each sentient being. It thereby acquires a moral dimension. The immortalization of humans and other life-forms is seen as a great moral project and labor of love that will unite us in a common cause and provide a meaningful destiny.

The general plan of the book is first to lay groundwork, then treat the main topics, the Philosophies of Assurance, Aspiration, and Action, in greater detail. The book is intended for a general audience, and I have tried to make it reasonably self-contained. Interest and a willingness to do some hard thinking are more important than advanced learning in one specialty or another. Concepts and relevant details are introduced as needed, with references, and a glossary is included. The treatment will, of course, be far from exhaustive—many more questions are raised than are answered or can be at our present state of knowledge. I hope that brevity here, whether remedied in existing sources or not, will serve as a catalyst for more thought and action. I invite the reader to take part. The philosophical tradition I would establish needs much development.

Some starting familiarity with the ideas of modern physics and computer science will be helpful. A perusal of the glossary may be useful as a starting point (and will introduce philosophical as well as scientific concepts). The following references are also recommended for a general background, to be consulted as the reader finds appropriate.

For quantum mechanics—the most important part of physics for purposes here—a short, readable reference is *Quantum Reality* by Nick Herbert. For additional background on the important many-worlds hypothesis, which is somewhat inaccurately treated in the otherwise excellent book by Herbert, I recommend *The Fabric of Reality* by David Deutsch. A good, short introduction to computer science is *The Pattern on the Stone* by Daniel Hillis; a useful longer reference is *The Turing Omnibus* by A. K. Dewdney. Other pertinent references are *The Physics of Immortality* by Frank Tipler, *Engines of Creation* by Eric Drexler, and *The Prospect of Immortality* by Robert Ettinger.

Occasionally in the text there is a need for large numbers, and standard scientific notation is used. Therefore, thirty-one million (31,000,000) is written 3.1×10^7. More generally, 10^n with n a positive whole number means 1 followed by n zeros or 10 multiplied by itself n times. More generally still, m^n (m to the n or nth power) means m multiplied by itself n times; n itself is rarely a number that is also expressed in this way, that is, as p^q, so that we have m^{p^q}. In addition, subscripts are occasionally used in the usual way, that is, with no special mathematical meaning but only to distinguish one object or thing from another: persons P_1 and P_2 ("p-one" and "p-two") for instance.

Superscripts are also used in a nonmathematical sense to indicate endnotes; the distinction should be clear. Endnotes are essentially referential; I have made an effort to incorporate all relevant, expository material in the main text.

Following this Introduction, immortalization is presented as a scientific and technological problem, and a more detailed overview is given of the main topics covered. Next is a summary of related ideas stretching back to ancient times. A discussion then follows of the surprising resistance that is often seen to the idea of immortality, particularly to achieving it scientifically, with some thoughts on how the objections might be answered. The philosophical system of the book, which is given the name Yuai, is then outlined in detail. An important issue is that of personal identity. I offer a theory, based on functionalism, in which psychological connectedness with the past self is crucial, but continuity, whether physical or psychological, is not essential. This is further developed in later chapters.

A discussion of scientific perspectives then leads to a chapter on Unboundedness—that in some reasonable sense, all the possible histories are real. One physical theory that strongly favors Unboundedness is the Everett many-worlds formulation of quantum mechanics. It also has interesting scientific support and has been endorsed by some leading physicists, including most quantum cosmologists, though I do not think the case for it is closed. But it does furnish significant evidence that the viewpoint developed here is valid, and I have devoted extra space to it, while not overlooking alternatives. A chapter then follows on Interchangeability—that like objects share "identity." This is the link between the ideas on personal identity and those of physics, and it supports the possibility of resurrections of past individuals under general conditions.

Next is a chapter dealing with persons as digital phenomena, supporting psychological reductionism and functionalism. Chapters follow on nanotechnology, theological implications of immortality, the ultimate prevalence of good over evil, resurrection, the desirability of preservation or biostasis after death, and immortality. A more detailed treatment then follows, in three successive chapters, of the Philosophies of Assurance, Aspiration, and Action. Some deeper ontological issues are addressed, with an eye toward tying loose ends and forming a unified whole, and matters of a more practical nature are then considered.

Nanotechnology and other advances, I argue, offer a coming age of immortality and place it near the present, perhaps within decades, and also require active participation. A program for one's personal immortality is indeed a realistic and advisable course to follow. Morals, logic, basic physics, and our advancing capabilities all play a part in what I advocate as a Philosophy of Action. Along with sensible, benevolent conduct and the fostering of research I make an appeal for the practice of cryonics or some other strategy of biostasis. In these ways a bridge can be formed between our present condition and a wonderful Apocalypse that surely is coming. A concluding chapter contrasts the present world situation with what the future might and ought to bring, with a final appeal to take seriously the prospect of a transition to a more-than-human status.

Today the thinking is often far removed from the viewpoint that a beneficent Apocalypse is soon to happen, one that will be engineered by our own civilization. In fact, swaying opinion in the direction of seeking immortality through science will no doubt continue to prove difficult, as it has during the several decades that the cryonics movement has been in existence. A good part of the problem, no doubt, is that advances are required that have not yet been made. Scientific research—always of a constructive sort—should accordingly be commended and encouraged. It will be the ultimate arbiter. But it will not happen unless it is seen as worth pursuing.

In this book I have attempted to offer at least some new possibilities for trying to influence public opinion in the right directions. With acceptance of the right outlook, necessary progress will be fostered, and something better subsequently will be made of the situation that confronts us today. Hopefully some who have not otherwise been interested will find what is said here reassuring and decide to make a bid for whatever science can offer them toward personal immortality. In addition to the humanitarian aim this would serve, if the quest for extended life should prove successful, a more favorable public will benefit the existing immortalist movement, promoting progress and creating a better world for all.

On a personal level, I hope you, the reader, will think over the ideas offered here and be assured, despite any initial misgivings. Resolve to stay as healthy as possible and be optimistic about the prospects of research that will lengthen the life span. But do not hesitate to go further. Choose a biostasis program for yourself as a backup if you have not already done so. Try to influence others into habits favoring life extension, along with other good behavior, and remind them of the biostasis option too.

We have a world to gain, the like of which has not been seen. It is in no sense improper that we should seek this immortal habitation on our own. Such an outcome is good and proper and to seek it morally exemplary. Anything less is both inadequate and unworthy. We will have to make it happen ourselves—and there is reason to think we can. It is comforting, once we are past the initial barriers, to approach this great and beneficial project in the best way possible. An important part is to do what we can to further our own participation. We need to plan and act, as far as possible, for our continuing presence in this world.

CHAPTER 1.

Heaven by Design

$$\int (\alpha \, dx - y \, dy + xy \, dz) = \pm \iint \left\{ \ell \left(\frac{dy}{dz} - \frac{dx}{dy} \right) + m \left(\frac{dy}{x} - \frac{dx}{dz} \right) + m \left(\frac{dx}{dy} - \frac{dy}{dx} \right) \right\} dS$$

Science, technology, and other rational pursuits are making unprecedented strides in our time, conferring great and growing powers to achieve desired aims. The potential for misuse abounds, and is tragically realized from time to time, yet overall the trend can be viewed with optimism and hope. For an Apocalypse is looming, one of our own choosing and making, that will radically transform life as we know it. Handled correctly it will bring no catastrophe—except to the minions of tragedy itself—but will instead herald the fulfillment of many ancient dreams, and furnish the gateway to a glorious, more-than-human future.

It is fitting and proper that we pursue an inspired course of development and seek to transform ourselves into greater beings. Many may think it unlikely, but the means to accomplish this—literally remaking ourselves as higher creatures—appear within reach, if not yet realized or guaranteed. Much remains unknown and undeveloped, yet by serious estimates the prospects are awesome. Such fundamentals as human biology and physiology could be greatly enhanced or bypassed, and life could advance in ways now scarcely imaginable.

Many approach such possibilities with foreboding, conjuring up nightmare visions of technological horror, as if only bad could ever come from sweeping change. This, I submit, is unduly pessimistic and one-sided. Surely a more sensible reaction is first to reflect upon our current status and then ask if reasonable improvements could be made and ought to be pursued. A basic question then arises: what ought we to want? What ought to be that we should be devoting our best efforts toward bringing it about and resting our hopes and aspirations in the successful outcome?

It is no small matter to address the question of what ought to be, especially when we try to look beyond immediate concerns to a larger and more meaningful picture. Here, however, we are in good company: The great question has been contemplated through the ages, and there is something to gain by studying opinions both ancient and modern from an objective standpoint. One of the things that strikes the inquirer is how fantastic are many of the common notions of what ought to be and how seemingly remote their possibilities of realization.

The reason seems simple enough. Many would agree that there are shortcomings in the human condition that one might like to overcome—but the means are not at hand. The main shortcoming of this sort is the finite life span. People seek something more than this present existence. They would instead prefer a reasonable immortality, a good life beyond the death that up to now has been the lot of living things on Earth. That immortality in some form is our rightful destiny is, to such a viewpoint, no idle thought or daydream but a deep-seated conviction of the most serious sort. This conviction has been arrived at often and independently, as the records of numerous cultures attest, and in it people have seen fit to rest and defend their hopes, in the face of formidable obstacles. Indeed, many have willingly faced death rather than renounce their particular ideas and practices regarding a hoped-for immortality. This is all the more remarkable in that no shred of material, verifiable evidence exists that anyone has ever achieved immortality or a life after death. Something so problematic and challenging, a hope up to now unsubstantiated, has been a necessity to many; among them I number myself.

Increasingly we face a challenge to such a hope: Scientific evidence casts doubt on the possibility of supernatural or other superhuman assistance in our quest to overcome death. Without such assistance, many have assumed that our chances of success must be nil. This has never been demonstrated, however; the limits to what are achievable scientifically and technologically, by ourselves, are unknown. Astonishing advances have already occurred, particularly over the last century, and appear to be accelerating. Moreover, any assessment of our ultimate potential must take into account possible enhancements we could engineer in our own physical makeup, including improvements in intelligence. Arguably, such enhancements will become feasible as our knowledge increases and will then help further both understanding and progress. Where it will lead will depend on the values and aspirations that come into play as the advances are made. Immortality is not precluded; even self-engineered, eternal salvation must be regarded as a possibility.

The recognition of this possibility, and, more generally, of both the promises and the perils of the developing technological picture, becomes a vital issue in its own right. It is something we must undertake, to reassure us and to help inform and guide our decision-making, and it calls for an appropriate philosophical outlook. Such an outlook—in which scientific methods, generally yet to be developed, are to be employed to accomplish what had been thought to be the prerogative of mystical forces or higher powers—attaches to what may be called a *scientific teleology*.[1] More generally I would define scientific teleology as the branch of philosophy dealing with the possible role of sentient agents in shaping the reality they inhabit to suit their own, long-term needs and purposes. Specifically it concerns our efforts to become immortal and more-than-human through scientific means and to create habitations and develop lifestyles conforming to this sought-after status. Some works devoted wholly or in part to scientific teleology in this intended sense are John Barrow and Frank Tipler's *Anthropic Cosmological Principle*, Freeman Dyson's *Infinite in All Directions*, Hans Moravec's *Mind Children*, Tipler's *Physics of Immortality*, and David Deutsch's *Fabric of Reality*. Somewhat older works exploring interesting areas of scientific teleology are Robert Ettinger's *Prospect of Immortality* and its sequel, *Man into Superman*.

Among these writers, Tipler in *The Physics of Immortality* offers an explicitly theological, if still scientific, vision of the future and also has the most elaborate and daring scenario for a life beyond current limits. His viewpoint is that "theology is nothing but physical cosmology based on the assumption that life as a whole is immortal."[2] He offers "a testable physical theory for an omnipresent, omniscient, omnipotent God who will one day in the far future resurrect every single one of us to live forever in an abode which is in all essentials the Judeo-Christian Heaven."[3] He proposes to define all his theological terms, including God and Heaven, as "pure physics concepts," and in all arguments to appeal only "to the reader's reason."

The present work, though related in scope and purposes, is more conservative scientifically and more skeptical theologically than Tipler's, a position that seems warranted by both the extent and lack of our knowledge and by the way the world seems to work. I offer a scientific teleology but with the emphasis on philosophy rather than hard science. There is no attempt to encompass the whole in a testable, physical theory. Such efforts as Tipler's are useful and even commendable but also hazardous given present uncertainties and the difficulties of trying to do so much in one mighty swoop. Instead, I think there is need for a more general, more robust if less scientifically ambitious approach. Our hoped-for scenario should be realizable in more than one version of reality and adaptable to a variety of "the shafts of impartial evidence"[4] that scientific probing may present. As for the theological issue, along with some others and contrary to Tipler, I will argue against the existence of God as traditionally understood, though not against all possible conceptions of what can be considered divinity. But the focus is on our developing selves as the rightful shepherds of our own future, and the scientific methods by which we will arrive there.

Though the emphasis is to be philosophical, the position I wish to articulate is to have a rational, materialistic basis—something that may be reducible to a testable theory when more is known. There are real prospects for solving the problem of death and other human limitations through scientific means, as the authors cited and others have ably argued. We will explore these arguments, which are interesting enough, though often remote from everyday experience. A case will be made that immortality for all who have ever lived is attainable and quite possibly inevitable. But I will argue, additionally, that there are things we can and should be doing now to further our cause in eternity, though much that now engages the popular imagination is excluded.

Thus there will be no appeal to the possible utility of supernatural powers, paranormal abilities or mechanisms, violations of generally accepted physics, and such fantastic occurrences as visits by spacefaring aliens. Mysticism, in the sense of belief or trust in a reality that is not accessible through reason, is not accepted as a valid approach to solving problems, including the problems of death and the hereafter. Wonder, awe, fascination, and reverence for the majesty and mystery of existence are not at all precluded by the rational approach I propose as a substitute. Instead, we can feel a keen and even enhanced appreciation of the reality that surrounds us as we strive to attain a greater presence within that reality through our own, rationally guided efforts. In place of the God of tradition, I echo the thought that we are becoming a sort of deity ourselves—and we must help ourselves. Progress now demands a fresh, new viewpoint. A supreme privilege and opportunity is presenting itself—but it also carries an awesome responsibility.

We must put our trust in material reality and the rules that govern its properties, but I do not mean by this to suggest a light or superficial treatment of the issues at hand. As for personal survival, I firmly discount a reinterpretation such as "survival" through works, offspring, reputation, or an essence or "further fact" that carries no memory of an earlier existence. The requirements of survival can only be met by a functioning individual with characteristics reasonably connected to, and who identifies with, some previously extant, actual person. There must be authentic recollections of an earlier self, a genuine and accepted feeling that "I was there and I am now here."

Infinite or unbounded survival becomes immortality, a state that, as will be understood here, does not preclude the possibility of death or a cessation of vital functions. But if death comes it must be temporary, to be terminated always by a suitable reanimation or resurrection, with consciousness, recollection, and self-awareness. The problems associated with immortality are challenging ones, at least if they are to be treated scientifically, as I propose here and others have attempted. Conventional approaches involving familiar things are inadequate. There must be some appeal to extraordinary means, though I insist that it need not transgress the bounds of scientific plausibility, if we use a reasoned approach and allow for extrapolation beyond our present level.

The Paranormal versus the Scientific

Some clarification of terminology will be useful. By *super-natural* I refer to any phenomena that are incomprehensible through a scientific approach. I mean by this that not only is scientific understanding lacking now, but that it is impossible in principle. Something significant must be involved that is inherently beyond our powers, even allowing for reasoned advances we may make in the future, including the improvement of our intellect. Typically the significant something is a mind or sentient agent, for example, a God, angel, or ghost, which is not subject to the usual scientific laws and cannot be understood on those terms. This then is a kind of animism, or belief in extracorporeal, largely unseen, intelligent agents. It is probably the principal supernatural belief, though other forms are possible too. Synonyms for *supernatural*, in this intended sense, are *parascientific* and *mystical*.

Paranormal, on the other hand, will have larger scope and refer to such additional effects as alien visitations, which might indeed, if they occurred, have a scientific explanation but appear highly unlikely for other reasons. Included also are the more "usual" paranormal effects, such as clairvoyance, telekinesis, and (literal) out-of-body experiences—all of which do, at present, seem scientifically untenable. Logically, there could be a scientific explanation of these effects and others, including even a sentient God, but all would still qualify as paranormal in the intended usage. The paranormal thus will be inclusive of all the commonly alleged features of reality that I feel are doubtful and thus not to be taken seriously, whether we regard them as within the scope of understandable science or not.

Many claims of the paranormal, of course, are advanced by sincere advocates who are convinced of their truth. These claims are deserving subjects of rational inquiry and should not be dismissed out of hand. A few organizations, such as the Committee for the Scientific Investigation of Claims of the Paranormal (CSICOP) have taken up the challenge and tested such claims as best they could. So far, no paranormal effects have been scientifically verified or demonstrated.

It is worth noting too that some scientific possibilities seem remote but perhaps are not to be dismissed lightly, an example being backward time travel. Strictly speaking, I think it is ruled out by the "grandfather paradox" in which the time traveler changes history—family history, in this case, say, by kidnapping her infant grandfather—thus preventing her own existence! However, something close to backward time travel may be possible (and there may even be ways a traveler could avoid the grandfather paradox, if careful). Such possibilities, though, I have conservatively ruled as unlikely and not to be relied on. Other projected advances such as nanotechnology (the controlled manipulation of matter at the atomic scale, demonstrated to a limited though impressive extent already) do seem feasible and will be important. In any case, claims today of having traveled back in time or visited distant galaxies will and should be classed as paranormal, and are discounted accordingly.

"Extraordinary claims require extraordinary evidence," astronomer Carl Sagan was fond of saying,[5] following Enlightenment philosopher David Hume.[6] This is a good principle always to keep in mind; I will try to heed it here. Many extraordinary claims, of course, lack the corroborating, extraordinary evidence they ought to have and thus may be discounted, but not all. One well-known extraordinary claim, for which extraordinary evidence was found, was that stones fall from the sky—meteoric impacts have been well documented. Another is that species originated by evolution, which has been backed rather spectacularly by the fossil record and other biological clues. Another still is that material objects are made of atoms, a hypothesis that much physical and chemical evidence now supports, including direct inspection with scanning probe microscopes. Still another, that a moon landing is possible, was established beyond dispute by doing it, though in this case we had good evidence it could be done before it actually was. The list goes on.

The position that the problem of death is solvable by ourselves, scientifically, certainly makes some extraordinary claims and indeed, is one itself—though not about things that have been seen or that are outside rational understanding. Instead it is about things that could happen, and hopefully will, and certain, observed features of reality that are understandable through reason. It thus does not fall within the scope of the paranormal as I have defined it, though this, of course, is not by itself a vindication. Evidence for and against the position and its supporting claims must be considered. Extraordinary and, I will maintain, interestingly favorable and confirming evidence comes from an appraisal of reality as it appears to be, something that is subject to empirical testing, with the possibility of falsifying cherished hypotheses. Some of this evidence, amply tested already, is simply the incredible things uncovered in our scientific investigations and our dazzling technological achievements, both of which point to things even more amazing.

Still, the picture is incomplete. Ideally we would hope that the scientific principles on which we base our projections would be thoroughly tested and verified first. Someday this may be so, but for now some compromises are necessary if, in our philosophy of what is to come, we are to arrive at anything approaching a satisfying completeness. Although it might then be objected that we are building castles in sand, I think that the evidence, such as it is, is enough to warrant the sort of optimistic synthesis I have attempted.

Some of the scientific underpinnings I will rely on, then, are presently controversial and lack anything approaching full verification. I expect that evidence increasingly favorable to them, and to the overall case to be made, will be obtained over time through research and development. Yet there is also the possibility of contrary and invalidating evidence, or continuing, unyielding uncertainty. Care is needed to make the arguments as sound as possible in the face of these difficulties.

Toward this end I will call upon, and present arguments for, two principal hypotheses about reality, the "UI" assumptions, as follows: (1) *Unboundedness*—in the whole of existence, all possible, finite histories actually happen; and (2) *Interchangeability*—like entities share "identity," or a variant of the pattern or form theory of identity. How these principles are to be understood will become clearer as we proceed.

Unboundedness is a claim about physical reality. It asserts that, in the whole of existence, not necessarily confined to the visible universe, a very wide variety of conditions and happenings must occur and recur. So wide are the possibilities that beings like ourselves must also occur and recur, accompanied by essentially all variations of events, including but not limited to the happenings we have actually observed. Though it may seem farfetched, Unboundedness is not at variance with some of our present physical theories, which postulate a profusion of universes besides our own, opening the door to alternate histories. These theories are straightforwardly materialistic, invoking no supernatural or paranormal elements.

Interchangeability is a philosophical position that is a strong version of the "Identity of Indiscernibles." Based on a theory of mental processes known as functionalism, it is intended mainly to apply to persons as they perceive themselves—self-perception seen as of primary importance in defining a person. Interchangeability will open the possibility of resurrecting a person by creating a copy. Unboundedness meanwhile will ensure that the necessary conditions for creating the copy occur. Taken together, the UI assumptions imply Tipler's conclusion that life "as a whole" is immortal—and, very significantly, that each of us individually is immortal.

Naturally, such sweeping conclusions call for substantial supporting arguments. The two assumptions, in any case, must not be taken as dogmas but instead are to be viewed as working hypotheses. More will be said later that bears on them, and relevant scientific and philosophical arguments will be examined at length. More generally, the whole system developed here will rest on various working hypotheses, as must any system claiming a scientific grounding. These hypotheses can be questioned and possibly, though not necessarily, modified, discarded, replaced, or supplemented. Meanwhile, and always provisionally, they can furnish assurance about life and its meaning.

In this work the assurance will depend, in large part, on a claim about what we can accomplish for ourselves with a rational approach and continuing, dedicated commitment. This claim itself, that we can engineer our own, meaningful, immortal existence, is most extraordinary, and requires extraordinary evidence, which I will try to provide. Yet it is a limited claim, calling upon nothing beyond our own efforts using reason, critical inquiry, scientific methods, and technology—though generally at levels not yet achieved or even, in many cases, remotely approached. Thus I imagine a vast project, starting with ourselves of today and all our limitations, but expanding, adapting, developing, over unlimited reaches of space and time. The desired, happy outcome should be achievable, given enough time and dedication, and provided we do not destroy ourselves instead. The realization of this project will no doubt involve many new scientific discoveries, but I will emphasize only what is already known at the fundamental levels.

And indeed, a vast potential already exists, even if, as a few have predicted, we are approaching the "end of science."[7] This pessimism I do not share, but it is clear that much could be done that ought to be feasible, based on existing science only, so that there is much room for optimism. But we must work with diligence, courage, and enlightenment and not shrink back from what has hitherto been, at best, only fantasy. The philosophical system I will develop to support this view will argue for certain attitudes and actions on our part.

The system is *transhumanist*—concerned, as suggested, with ourselves becoming more-than-human through our own efforts. Thus it is strongly *meliorist*—holding that the world can be made a better place through rightly directed human effort, and, as it becomes possible, more-than-human effort. Going beyond this, it is *immortalist*—advocating and placing hopes in the abolition of death through scientific means. It is naturally also *extrapolative*—based on anticipation of things to come; *eschatological*—concerned with an ultimate outcome; and *teleological*—dealing with the possible role of design and purpose, in this case our own, on a (future) cosmic scale. Yet it is *scientific*—grounded, as far as possible, in what is known and understood and relying on scientific methods to extend this knowledge and our capabilities. Finally, the system is *apocalyptic*. It advocates a radical transformation of life and even of the very sort of physical creatures we are and argues that on the scale of history this sweeping change must also be soon and swift. There is a call for action now and the prospect of a great adventure. The change, as I have indicated, is not to be one of destruction or violence but quite the contrary, something of the greatest benefit. Still it is a very radical change and a challenge many will find hard to approach. Yet approach it we must—for it is our rightful destiny.

We need not—must not—rest our hopes in unseen powers and their putative plans for us, or other outside help. Instead we must do for ourselves. Heaven will not be provided to us—every beam and rivet, so to speak, we will have to shape and hammer into position from the plans we have made. Such assumptions, as usual, are not offered as dogmas but working hypotheses, though in this case they are based on what I think is especially sound evidence. We have only ourselves to depend on, to blame most assuredly if we fail or praise and congratulate to the skies if we succeed.

So we will have to develop our standards of what ought to be and act with our growing powers to bring it about. We thus should always adhere to our own best judgment as to what ought to be done and how we should go about doing it. We must not despair that there are no realized perfect standards or standard bearers. The perfect standards do exist in principle, I maintain, and can and should inspire us. But perfection—the full understanding and flawless application of those standards—is a potentiality not an actuality, as it always has been and will be. This is true of ourselves and, we may confidently conjecture, all other sentient beings. Perfection can only be realized and fully understood over infinite time, that is, approached as a mathematical limit. During this process we must increasingly serve as the standard bearers, as we grow in the ways that count toward personal survival and meaningful existence. We must increasingly approximate the imagined Deity we might otherwise worship and petition for help. We must achieve immortal self-sufficiency and a harmonious whole of interacting, individual selves so that our lives can become something of unprecedented value.

Our task thus calls for the highest standards of integrity, morality, compassion, and virtue of which we are capable—as well as unflinching devotion to a cause that, by way of compensation, is the most rewarding possible. And that in turn is only a beginning, for our lives—rightly endless—will always have only just begun. We must always seek and be willing to accept improvements, both in the means to reach our goals and in the refinement of these goals as our deepening understanding demands. We must continually try to better our standards even as we progress in other ways. We thus have a lot of hard yet tremendously exciting work to do. In the course of our progress we will transform ourselves unimaginably—yet not unintelligibly—and secure our eternal future, if all goes well.

Apocalypse, Singularity, and Immortalization

I claim no priority for the thought that immortality can and should be won scientifically. Advocates have been proclaiming this message or something like it for centuries, and particularly since the Enlightenment era of the eighteenth century. Benjamin Franklin speculated in 1780 that one day, "all diseases may by sure means be prevented or cured, not excepting even that of old age." Our lives might then be "lengthened at pleasure" beyond all previous records, including the legendary near-millennium claimed for early biblical figures.[8]

By now the idea of a scientific Apocalypse—a radical trans-formation and reformation of human life—has become common-place among forward-thinking persons. Indeed "Apocalypse" may be putting it mildly. In the 1940s, mathematician John von Neumann foresaw technology and society advancing to a demar-cation point or "Singularity" beyond which current rules and stan-dards will no longer apply.[9] More recently, science fiction writer Vernor Vinge sharpened and popularized the theme, focusing on one anticipated achievement—the development of superhuman, artificial, or artificially assisted intelligence.[10] Such an advance, it should be emphasized, would not be limited to one specialty such as computing but should have application in many domains and bring tangible benefits to all, even as it radically transforms and sweeps away all that came before. Understandably, people who contemplate this are nervous about the "sweeping away," but the potential for good cannot be ignored either. A group of enthusiasts now searches and researches as far as opportunity allows, eager for results that signal the approaching Singularity and expecting great rewards through the wise management of unprecedented opportunities.

Central in this thinking is the idea of progress. Humanity can achieve things never known before, using rational, orderly means. Not all progress is good, of course, but overall the good will pre-dominate and make the whole worthwhile. Reasons for thinking this include the strong wish of people for individual improve-ment and the amazing power of the scientific method to continu-ally provide new ways of reaching goals, many of which had seemed impossible. In this way benefits have accumulated, and many more seem in the works.

True, there have also been tragic regressions. Violence in our society is inflicted by misguided ideologues, troubled schoolchil-dren, and adult terrorists. Dislocation, poverty, and despair con-tinue to plague our cities. Misery, starvation, and overcrowding have not been eliminated in less developed parts of the world. Environmental depletion is a problem. But overall trends have been positive. Living standards have improved. Medical treatments have advanced dramatically. Access to information of all sorts is becoming widespread. Science is offering a lengthening list of achievements that promise further tangible benefits and new and revolutionary insights. We thus find cause for assurance and hope. The human enterprise is far from a zero-sum game in which the gains of some must be equally offset by the losses of others. Constructive change—good progress—has instead benefited the whole of humankind and can be expected to bring further betterment. As the means and frequency of communication improve, there is more and more realization of this among the "unlettered masses," who are thereby enlisted to help the process even as they better themselves. Happily, there are indications that our further good progress will not be minor but will extend to the deepest levels of life.

Advocates of progress have long imagined that, perhaps many centuries from now, aging and death will be conquered and our then-immortal successors will develop into superior life-forms. To the more conservative progressives, the estimated time interval stretches to cosmological dimensions. At an opposite extreme, a transhumanist group—of which I am a member—has hopes for greatly speeding up the timetable, to the point of its affecting them personally. Continuing progress in the biological sciences helps nurture such hopes. Increasingly, once-intractable diseases are yielding, wholly or in part, to our growing knowledge and expertise. Some modest successes in aging intervention have also been reported both in animals and humans and promise greater success with further effort. Research into the underlying mechanisms of aging is now offering results that could translate to more radical improvements, including a reversal of senescence and the indefinite extension of the human life span.[11] As yet, of course, aging and death still take their usual toll, and those who hope for immortalization must base this hope on some sort of extraordinary claim, preferably a scientific one.

In any case, the immortalization of our species is coming, according to reasonable indicators. Here I use the term *immortalization* somewhat loosely, to signify primarily the end of the biological aging process. (The more exacting demands of true immortalization are treated later, mainly in Chapters 14 and 15.) It is a challenge to address the issues that arise in connection with this possibility. One issue is that those who are then living will be in a different, stabilized position from those who have already died. Another is that as we approach the time of immortalization certain options will open, and arguably have already, that may offer benefit and thus must be considered.

A major philosophical difficulty arises. On one hand, hope is offered, for all who have ever lived, of eventual resurrection and eternal happiness. On the other, as technical means become available, we may act to gain advantages that were not open before— provided we can accept the idea that even the prospect of eventual paradise could leave some room for additional betterment, depending on the choices made. As a simple illustration, persons of today desiring longer, happier lives are advised to stay as healthy as possible, not just for the primary benefits but also for the increased chance of surviving until breakthroughs that would personally affect them occur. For it cannot be ruled out that aging could be cured within the lifetimes of many now living, and the chance of living long enough is increased by better health.

We may imagine, then, the dilemma faced by a hearty gourmand who is overweight. Dieting might increase his life expectancy, thus the chance of survival to the cure of aging. Perhaps he takes this possibility quite seriously, yet is also firmly convinced of an eventual, universal resurrection, which, unlike the cure of aging, will also restore those who are no longer living. So he may decide that it does not really matter if he survives in a direct sense and may then continue his bad habits. Dealing with this sort of issue will be one major theme of this work, particularly in connection with the cryonics option, discussed below. I contend that, despite the eventual, anticipated immortalization of all who have died, more direct forms of survival are preferable, if possible.

One possibility in particular is now available for counteracting death when it occurs. This is to have one's remains preserved so that further deterioration is virtually halted. The rationale is that the body is not necessarily "dead" when so pronounced in the hospital but, if maintained in a state of arrested biochemical activity, or biostasis, might one day resume its functioning when necessary repairs can be made. Such superfine repair work is not feasible today but should be within the compass of future technology, provided the preservation is good enough. Of the possible methods of biostasis the one that appears to have the greatest promise is cryonics, in which persons are frozen after death and stored in liquid nitrogen. Several dozen people have already been frozen in this manner and await reawakening with all their ailments cured. An alternative strategy is high quality chemical preservation, and it may offer some advantages though it has not been as well researched as a possible route to eventual reanimation and is more difficult to arrange for this purpose. I will emphasize cryonics here.

Today cryonicists—myself included—form the most serious and committed group of *immortalists,* meaning those who feel that life spans can be greatly extended through scientific means, and who look forward to such developments. We are hoping that, in the event of death, our preservation will be good enough so that identity-critical information, such as memories stored in the brain, can be recovered through future technology. In this manner, and again with means that should become available, we may be returned to a fully functioning, healthy state with mental faculties intact. Whether this will in fact prove true must be considered unknown. Perhaps there is too much damage with today's freezing methods to undo, even with the best that future technology can offer, though some interesting evidence we will consider suggests otherwise. But I will argue that there is reason to pursue cryonics—or some form of high-quality preservation—even if important information is lost. In a proposed reanimation the proper course would then be to fill in missing information from outside sources or educated guesses. The revived patient then will not have unwanted impairments and will retain a reasonable set of past memories and other characteristics. Minimizing the necessity for such creative guesswork is a priority, however, and this, if nothing else, calls for the best preservation possible. Thus cryonics is a current practice the would-be immortal must take seriously.

More conventional approaches to life extension also deserve attention, of course. Known extenders of life and health such as exercise, good nutrition, and not smoking can be recommended. Again, more is at stake than just a few extra years of relative fitness. Exciting new research that explores the possible role of telomeres in cell senescence, for instance, may lead to the radical extension of life span and good health, even within a few years, though certainly there is no guarantee. But support for such research is encouraged and commended, and opportunities to apply the results must be sought. Yet biostasis at the personal level should remain an option. Despite the uncertainties, I feel strongly and will argue that one should make arrangements to be frozen or otherwise well preserved in the event of death. The reasons are not limited to considerations of personal benefit but extend to the health of society and life as a whole.

Immortality in Thought and Practice

Cryonics, other biostasis procedures, curing aging, future resurrections, and any other means of substantially extending life will not make sense unless their goal is accepted as reasonable and desirable. This goal, to take part in a more advanced future, reflects a higher purpose: to realize the ancient dream of becoming more-than-human with a meaningful existence beyond what is now possible. Immortality itself, or at least a life significantly expanded in length and scope, must then be regarded as a goal worth striving for. In keeping with this I hope to convey a sense of the wonder we immortalists feel in anticipating the good things we think will come.

In some ways, however, the present work goes beyond the attitudes and dispositions usually found among immortalists, whose philosophical perspectives leave many questions unaddressed or treated only lightly. I feel it is time to try to fashion, out of this rather disorganized hodgepodge, a sounder and more unified structure. I wish to construct a satisfying philosophical system that upholds an immortalist worldview and does not gloss over the tougher issues. It should be reassuring on a deep level yet also realistic. It should sketch out a reasonable pattern of aspirations for the would-be adherent. It should offer a course of action to achieve goals that themselves become reasonable in light of what we can do and become.

This I have attempted. In keeping with immortalism, my philosophy will value the individual, whose existence is to be extended indefinitely through rational means. In other respects, however, I have drawn on certain traditions and interpretations to fill out what I consider essential in a well-rounded philosophy, one deserving of acceptance and trust. This has demanded treatment of the whole problem of death, and I have assembled arguments as to how this problem may be solved in its entirety, again by rational means, to be perfected by our future civilization.

Again I claim no priority in these thoughts, which, for instance, require a stance of psychological reductionism based on functionalism: A person is essentially a computational process, which could be restarted, at a remote time and place, by constructing and activating a duplicate body or replica. In this manner persons of the past could be resurrected even if their remains were not preserved merely by the chance creation of a double. Though I will argue, again, that use of a straightforward preservative method such as cryonics is better, other factors being equal. Traditionally such reductionism, denying the existence of a "soul" or other component of personality that exists independently of matter, has signified the abandonment of hope in the possibility of resurrection and life after death. More recently, however, the exact opposite opinion has been maintained, as in the work of physicist Frank Tipler.[12] In fact, the very possibility that the reductionist stance is correct, and the evidence favoring it, seem now to provide the strongest arguments that our dreams of immortality can be realized.

Tipler in *The Physics of Immortality* lays much of the groundwork for my ideas on physical mechanisms of resurrection, including a defense of Unboundedness (through the many-worlds formulation of quantum mechanics) and of what largely amounts to Interchangeability. I should mention too that Unboundedness is somewhat anticipated as a philosophical principle in David Lewis's idea of modal realism.[13] Another related concept is Robert Nozick's principle of fecundity,[14] which is actually more general than Unboundedness and thus more powerful than is needed here. The idea of Unboundedness has other antecedents; for example, the suggestion of A. N. Whitehead that all logically possible universes exist,[15] though this too is a stronger claim.

Tipler, on the other hand, offers a possible cosmological scenario that would support immortal existence. (I offer here what I think are stronger arguments for such an eventuality, including resurrection of the dead, based on the more general UI assumptions.) Most important, Tipler argues that the resurrection of every person who ever lived will one day occur, not merely could occur, orchestrated by advanced beings of the future. These beings will find themselves disposed, for one reason or other, to carry out such a project and to treat their charges with kindness. This too I accept and will advocate from a somewhat different perspective, emphasizing the anticipated role of former humans (hopefully including immortalists of today) who, having advanced beyond the human level, then play the role of enlightened resurrectors.

Tipler's testable theory, known as the Omega Point Theory, is an attempt to reduce to physics the suggestive philosophical system of Pierre Teilhard de Chardin, which dates from the 1930s. Resurrection scenarios much like Tipler's, though less developed, have also been formulated by Hans Moravec and Robert Nozick. These in turn were somewhat anticipated, a few years earlier, by an alternate theory of Freeman Dyson, which is the first detailed model of eternal life based on modern physics.[16] Cryonics pioneer Robert Ettinger also noted how the basic resurrection ideas had been expressed by 1972.[17] Earlier than all of these, a scientific resurrection theory along Newtonian lines was developed in the nineteenth century by Nikolai Fedorov,[18] and the idea has still earlier antecedents.[19]

What these visionaries offer is a radical departure from the traditional, pragmatic view, though still within the confines of materialism. Life, not death, is the ultimate inevitability. This is so, not merely in collective terms but at the level of the individual, suitably understood, and by means amenable to our comprehension and control. Again I emphasize that this is a materialistic conclusion, requiring only forces or processes within the purview of science, making due allowance for future advances.

So we can master our own fate—if this view is correct—and of course we should. Each individual, as a consequence, can look forward to no less than personal, eternal life and an ultimately rewarding, happy state. Hardships along the way are certainly not ruled out, however, and the path one chooses is significant. The notion of "individual," I will argue, can be extended to lifeforms less than human—all sentient creatures, in some sense, will eventually benefit. These thoughts I suggest as the cornerstone of a Philosophy of Assurance. It will assure those whose lives are directed toward the high calling of immortality, an orientation that I hope those with misgivings will find increasingly attractive on further consideration.

It means that nothing of value is ever finally lost, that all can be regained with sufficiently diligent effort—though it may require a large effort. It becomes important, then, to so manage one's affairs as to reduce the likelihood and extent of difficulties, which are by no means precluded by an ultimately favorable outcome. Modern technological developments, in particular, offer considerable hope for improving the quality of our lives as we approach our transhuman and posthuman future.

We thus must accept that we ought to want and at least some part of us does want to become more-than-human. This means that, as individuals, we aspire to become immortal, transcendently wise and accomplished, and supremely, meaningfully happy. Anything less would be unworthy, and we must set our sights unreservedly on these goals and devote ourselves to their full realization—a task that is without end. Such a Philosophy of Aspiration hopefully should guide us in the coming transition to more-than-human status.

This could be difficult. Aspirations to a superhuman existence are hard for many to take seriously, and uncertainties plague even those who do consider themselves well-disposed. Hard questions come easily to mind. Should the would-be immortal have an overall goal or mission, and if so, what should it be? In becoming "more-than-human," which attributes of humanness would we want to abandon and which should we retain and enhance? Should basic drives such as sex and hunger be modified—and how? And what about society at large? Many of these questions, of course, can only be addressed when we are further along in "getting there," but we need to begin to formulate some answers now.

I will offer some starting suggestions, building on the work of others. I imagine that creativity, exploration, discovery, and learning will be of considerable importance, as will interactions with others involving mutual benefit. Such activity will not lose its savor with advancing intelligence and other capacities, but our increasing powers should open ever-new vistas, much as we observe today, for example, in young children. This should hold even when we are far more advanced than our present selves, particularly inasmuch as we should then have considerable control over our own drives and emotions. We will always be growing; we will always, in a sense, be children. The supply of mysteries to be explored and the wonders to be found are, to the rightly disposed, inexhaustible—enough to keep each of us happily occupied, literally forever.

Supreme, meaningful happiness, for the individual, is a goal that must be approached through the efforts of that individual. It is not imagined, however, that these efforts should happen in isolation. Interactions with others will surely enhance one's experience in the future, as they do now. Thus the individual stands to gain from a benevolence that arguably, to be most effective in promoting enlightened self-interest, will ultimately extend and deepen toward all beings. I advocate, then, a middle ground between a narrow egoism and a self-effacing altruism. The self, a separate, distinct, and developing entity, is to be valued—and so are other selves—likewise separate and developing—so that all in time may reap the greatest benefits.

So, the question then arises, What ought we to do to best further the goal of becoming more-than-human? What Philosophy of Action should guide our steps?

Certain things are apparent immediately. We ought to continue and support the course of technological development, emphasizing those advances that tend toward lengthening life and improving its quality. We ought to be good, kind, considerate of others, loving, compassionate, caring, and assisting for that will best further the long-term goal of a happy immortality for each of us individually. (Some circumstances also call for firmness—often the best choice is only the lesser evil, not an absence of evil—however, an overall stance of benevolence can be defended and encouraged.) Also, we ought to take good care of ourselves and try to maintain the best state of health at all times. We need to value ourselves, for that is the road to greater meaning in our own lives. It will also help us recognize the value of others' lives and of sentient life in general.

More generally we should at all times pursue enlightened self-interest. The concept acquires new meaning if an immortal future is taken into account. Enlightened self-interest, extrapolated to the time scale of eternity, can, I maintain, fully reconcile egoistic and altruistic behavior and appropriately resolve conflicts of interest among individuals or groups.

And for now we ought to both advocate and practice cryonics

or some rational strategy of biostasis as the best means of dealing with the immediate problem of death. Going further, I propose biostasis as a "common task" to unite the world in preparing for our posthuman future.

In such a future this particular issue will lose its force, if all goes well, as it should when we have sufficiently advanced. No doubt this will involve many changes in ourselves and our physical makeup. But for an unknown time before this, we may have to contend with sudden catastrophes and thus need rapid means of stabilizing a person's condition for later repair work: biostasis or something like it will be required. It is likely too that such a need will never completely disappear, though it may diminish very substantially and otherwise undergo great modification. In any case, a basic feature of each of us, our memory, or more precisely, the fund of significant, identity-critical information, must persist or recur through time somehow—for it is indispensable in defining who we are.

CHAPTER 2.

A Brief History of Immortalism

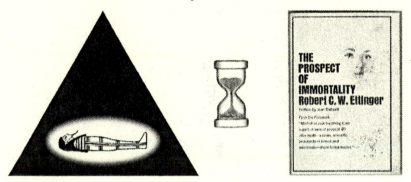

As a scientific enterprise aimed at conquering death, the modern immortalist movement is largely a product of the twentieth century, but it has far earlier precedents. These reveal the persistence of a dream, an enduring vision of life's potential, which must be realized by whatever means will work. The findings of modern science do not destroy this dream, but, as we have seen, may at last furnish the means of its realization.

Humankind wants to be immortal. Roots of immortalism stretch well into prehistoric times, as is suggested, for example, by the burial of artifacts such as hunting implements with the dead. In more recent though still ancient times, the feeling flowered into major religions that promised the sought-for immortality and a happy future existence. More advanced thinking resulted in Universalism—the opinion held by some that all would be saved and restored in the end, evil natures being cured and rendered benevolent without altering them into "different" identities or subjecting them to eternal punishment.

Such was the view of the remarkable ancient Iranian seer and religious founder Zarathushtra (Zoroaster), who lived perhaps around 600 B.C.E. Many details of his life are uncertain, but he started a movement that still exists as the religion of Zoroastrianism. From this it is possible to reconstruct something of his teaching.

Zarathushtra imagined that the dead would be resurrected and rewarded or punished according to their deeds in this life. The resurrection would restore past memories, not just a general state of awareness as some other traditions contrastingly held. The punishment of the evil, however, would not be eternal, but would serve a curative purpose and then would terminate, so that all would eventually coexist in a state of affection, harmony, and joy.[1] Zoroastrianism seems to be the main source of the ideas about resurrection and an afterlife that appeared in Judaism around the middle of the first millennium B.C.E., and propagated to Judaism's later offshoots—Christianity and Islam. The exalted Universalism of Zarathushtra was often forgotten or vehemently denied, yet it reappeared from time to time, one prominent supporter being the speculative Christian theologian Origen (third century C.E.).[2] In recent times Universalist sentiment has become more commonplace among religious adherents.[3]

Another remarkable idea can apparently be credited to Zarathushtra. Zoroastrian doctrine holds that the conquest of death will be no piecemeal process but will occur at a specific time, a Last Judgment or Apocalypse, this being the putative source of similar ideas in Judaism, Christianity, and Islam. All these religions assume divine intervention will be required—Zoroastrianism is no exception. But it also predicts, as one of the signs of the approaching Judgment, an astonishing increase in human capacity. We are to become so skilled in medicine that by degrees death will be overcome—a clear anticipation of today's immortalism.[4]

Here it is appropriate to mention the ancient Egyptians and their well-known practice of mummification. Preserving the physical remains of the deceased was thought to be important for future life, an idea with a parallel in the modern cryonics movement. Unfortunately, the ancient practice had a fatal flaw—the brain was not recognized as important and was not preserved—but at least we see a forerunner of much later thinking that a preservative process is needed.

Other cultures besides the Western also developed approaches to the problems of immortality and in some cases an elaborate philosophy with interesting affinities to modern immortalism. As one example, Jainism, an Indian movement dating back more than 2,500 years, denies a Godhead but holds that an immortal, blissful state is possible to each separate individual through personal effort.[5]

In the Western, scientific tradition, the problem of death has long held interest too. Until recently, to be sure, there was little support for the doctrine that the problem can be solved scientifically, in the sense of providing for resurrections of the dead and personal immortality. Yet such immortalist thinking in some form has been with us quite awhile, sometimes from critics whose rejection of the idea suggests that some even long ago must have wondered if it had substance.

One such critic was the Epicurean philosopher Lucretius (ca. 98–55 B.C.E.), whose thoughts come down to us in his great poetic treatise, *De Rerum Natura* (*On the Nature of Things*). Epicureans, who originated with Greek philosopher Epicurus around 300 B.C.E., thought that material substances were composed of tiny, indivisible units, or "atoms"—a point of view that, in broad outline, has been spectacularly confirmed by modern science. (Epicurus in turn derived his atomistic theory from his predecessors Leucippus and Democritus, who seem to be the true Western founders of physical atomism.)[6] Make no mistake—Lucretius, a thoroughgoing materialist in the traditional mold, firmly discounted the possibilities of an afterlife and endless survival. Yet in one passage he suggests a possible means of resurrection by reassembling the atoms that had once composed the body.

Life and consciousness might return, Lucretius tells us, providing the exact pattern of the person is recreated, though he is skeptical of the possibility because he recognized that to reasonably qualify as a resurrection memories of a past life would have to reappear. He allows, nonetheless, that we apparently have had past existences: "[Y]ou will readily credit that these same atoms that compose us now must many a time before have entered into the selfsame combinations as now."[7] But we have no recollection of these earlier incarnations; they are not part of our existence and never will be. Similarly, he doubts that future reappearances of our selves could retain the necessary memory links to qualify as resurrections (a position I will challenge later).

Immortality through Progress

Missing from the thought of Lucretius is any concept of progress. Actually, the idea of progress had already been current in the West for centuries,[8] but it generally was overshadowed by more conservative thinking: What was will be again; what has not previously happened is unlikely to happen in the future. This point of view would predominate for at least another 1,500 years, but significant challenges did finally emerge after the Renaissance with the rise of modern science, with its emphasis on empirical testing and independent thinking. One philosophical milestone of this later time was John Locke's 1690 treatise, *An Essay Concerning Human Understanding.* In one place Locke discusses the problem of personal identity and tentatively articulates a version of Interchangeability in which "two thinking substances may make but one person."[9]

Later thinkers would take aim at more practical issues. During the eighteenth-century Enlightenment, the feeling that something might be done, scientifically, to address the problem of death was endorsed by such well-known figures as Benjamin Franklin, William Godwin, and Antoine Condorcet, all of whom foresaw great prolongation of life through the elimination of aging.[10] But their world of near-immortality was a world of the future, which they realized was not imminent. Except for the eventual divine intervention that was widely believed in, there would be no immortality for those of their time.

This position, personally pessimistic but collectively optimistic, was echoed more starkly in the following century. In the 1870s British explorer-philosopher Winwood Reade, in *The Martyrdom of Man*, saw a coming age of immortality through the scientific control of biology but denied a personal God or the possibility of resurrection or other escape from death (hence the "martyrdom"). Similar sentiments were expressed a generation later by American physician and neurologist C. A. Stephens, whose book, *Natural Salvation*, elaborated a philosophy of the same name. Stevens too believed that all those then living must be lost forever—an especially painful thought in view of what would be open to future generations.

A contemporary of Reade and Stephens with a more optimistic outlook was Russian moral philosopher Nikolai Fedorov (1829–1903). Fedorov was a self-taught itinerant schoolteacher who became librarian of the Rumyantsev Museum in Moscow. His manner of life was ascetic, and he regularly turned down more lucrative but distracting employment while taking pains to assist needy students with the funds and provisions he could spare. To his own students he freely rendered his services without charging fees. His most famous pupil was pioneering space flight scientist Konstantin Tsiolkovsky. As librarian Fedorov had access to considerable material for research and lively contact with thinkers of the time.[11]

Fedorov was among the first to seriously consider the possibility of a physical resurrection of the dead through scientific as opposed to supernatural means. And, unlike contemporaries with a similar outlook (physiologist Emil Du Bois-Reymond, for example[12]), he based his entire life and work around his ideas of resurrection and developed them into an extensive philosophy. Living at a time when science was too primitive to offer much more than a distant future hope, he addressed the more fundamental issues likely to prevail throughout time.

Fedorov keenly felt the burden of the universal sentence of death and the need for a reprieve, not merely for the living but for those who had already perished. Children should resurrect their parents, he taught, even as they once received life through them. When one generation is resurrected it can join in resurrecting the previous generation, and so on, until every single human being who ever lived is restored to life. It was not necessary, of course, that literal ties of kinship exist to justify bringing someone back— all people are spiritual kinfolk. The resurrection, if carried out in full, as Fedorov believed it should be, would restore the bad along with the good. An evil nature, however, is a curable affliction. So when all diseases and disorders, physical or mental, had been cured, all would live forever in a state of love, harmony, and unity. This, then, echoed the Universalist sentiment expressed long before by Zarathushtra and recurring tenuously in the Western traditions.

But there was something new, not part of the thinking of earlier ages. It was necessary, Fedorov believed, for the resurrection to be engineered by humanity, through rational, scientific means, rather than by a supernatural or transcendent intervention, and to be realized here, in the visible universe, and not some mystical elsewhere. His arguments in this case were moral ones. Fedorov was no atheist but a committed Christian, believing in a transcendent Godhead. He felt, however, that a resurrection brought about by such a power would render humanity's God-given gifts superfluous. Similarly, if the resurrection must occur somewhere outside this world then this world is a mistake. The proper role of the Christian Trinity then was to inspire or admonish our species, not solve our problems for us. It would serve, in particular, as the model of perfect love and harmony toward which human efforts must strive and that must ultimately bear fruit in the universal resurrection.

The supernatural in Fedorov's scheme of things thus has a significance that must not be overlooked. It serves as a proof of principle that immortal existence is possible. Moreover, in the three persons of the Trinity it proclaims that proper immortal existence must involve a coexistence of separate individuals who are nonetheless united in love. One of these persons, Jesus the Christ, or Anointed One, is divine but also fully human, and thus can serve as our model, meaning that we too both can and should become immortal. In our immortality we shall not sacrifice our individuality in a "world soul," but instead approach a perfection of harmony in which all are highly valued, individually, by all.

But we must do this on our own, Fedorov taught, whatever the status of superhuman agents. For this reason the role of the supernatural is really not critical, despite its suggestive allusions and appealing allegory. It can be carefully excised, and the functions it serves assigned to other components of reality. This I have attempted in the present work, whose moral outlook is modeled on that of Fedorov. In doing so I have followed a precedent set by Taras D. Zakydalsky in his careful 1976 study.[13] Fedorov can be credited with the first philosophy of life in which the important promises of traditional religion, including resurrecting persons of the past, were to be realized through nonmystical means. Some further details of his proposed approach are of interest.

A person is made of atoms, and at death these particles are scattered. Through recovery and repositioning of the particles that make up the body, a resurrection of the person would occur. Fedorov thought this could be accomplished through a scientific technique. If accurate enough measurements of the positions and momenta of particles in the world are made, it should be possible to extrapolate the motions backward in time and retrodict all of human history. As a consequence, the particles necessary for each resurrection could be identified and their correct configuration determined. Means could meanwhile be developed for repositioning the particles to assemble whole, resurrected humans. Atoms seemed indestructible and unchanging, so the task should be able to be carried out with enough time and effort. (Fedorov also considered other possibilities; for example, that atoms, though apparently identical for the same chemical element, in fact contained distinguishing marks or features, like scratches on pebbles, that made each atom unique and would aid in the task of repositioning.)

Despite its fantastic character, the resurrection Fedorov envisioned was not inconsistent with what was known about the world in his time. Newton's laws of motion yielded a clockwork universe where both the past and the future could be deduced, given good enough observations. Apparently there was no limit on the precision to which observations could be made, though it would require developing new and better instrumentation. Just as astronomical calculations could give the times and positions of ancient solar eclipses, a sufficient refinement ought to allow a retrodiction on the much finer scale that would be needed for resurrections.

Fedorov was not greatly concerned with how the universal resurrection would be brought about, beyond noting its apparent, ultimate feasibility. He seems to have overlooked some obvious difficulties, such as the likelihood that the same particles were present in different individuals who lived at different times. These matters, after all, could be worked out with time. (It is easy to see how this latter problem could be solved under Interchangeability—like atoms would simply be substituted to make an identical copy of an individual.) The emphasis instead was on the implications for the meaning and purpose of life and the ordering of society. Fedorov saw the resurrection as the "common task" that would unite all humankind in a final, everlasting era of peace and brotherhood. People, in effect, would create their own Heaven, and all would obtain a deserving share.

In general Fedorov believed that science and technology were of vital importance, despite the potential for abuse, and must be used to the fullest extent for the betterment of humanity. One of his favorite illustrations involved some American experiments in the 1890s to cause rain by firing cannons into cloud banks. The taming of nature was the road to betterment, and that we must learn to train our weapons on natural phenomena rather than each other was an easy extension of the argument. This was no act of disrespect, however, and eventually nature too would become our friend and ally.

Fedorov's philosophy of the common task, which became known as Supramoralism, was dismissed as impractical or non-sensical. The decades following his death witnessed the bloodiest human confrontations that have ever occurred, the turmoil being especially violent in his homeland of Russia. A widespread horror and distrust of technology (which has never lacked its vocal critics) was nurtured, and many in the turbulent twentieth century longed for a "simpler time" or went so far as to champion the view that there is something necessarily evil about our species and our works.

Here it is appropriate to mention another nineteenth-century philosopher, Friedrich Nietzsche (1844–1900). Nietzsche had considerable literary talents in addition to a penetrating rational intellect and was powerfully affected by the great problems of life, including mortality. Nietzsche rejected belief in God and the paranormal and instead sought solace in what was possible in this world but also rejected the notion that death is the end. Instead, his science-based doctrine of the Eternal Return, or recurrence of events, provided what he thought was an escape hatch: in the unlimited stretches of future time, our particles must eventually come together exactly as before, and over and over, so we would live again—a proposition that has some grounding in physics. (Later however we shall find reason to reject this as a possible pathway to immortality. The idea itself can be traced back to the ancient Greeks. Epicureans had a version of it, as we have seen with Lucretius. Flawed though his argument was, Nietzsche must be given credit for trying.) This, then, is a foreshadowing of our UI assumptions, though there are differences, which will be examined in Chapter 14. It is worth noting that this Eternal Return is automatic, meaning it does not call for or require conscious interaction, which is also contrary to the thrust of ideas here.

Aside from his proposed solution of the problem of death, Nietzsche advocated a transcending of human limits, leading to the Superman. "Man is a rope, fastened between animal and Superman—a rope over an abyss."[14] Nietzsche's fictionalized mouthpiece here, who interestingly is Zarathushtra, also announces,

"God is dead!" But we, at least collectively, are also destined for more-than-human status, though the idea of humans progressing to such status as individuals seems to have escaped notice entirely. Zarathushtra continues, "...I love those who...sacrifice themselves to the earth, that the earth may one day belong to the Superman....I love him who works and invents that he may build a house for the Superman and prepare earth, animals, and plants for him: for thus he wills his own downfall." In general Nietzsche rejected any notion of individual, endless progress but instead advocated a "will to power" through which the self would advance but eventually be superseded and discarded for what was seen as a greater good. This called for a new morality, not the "slave morality" of Christianity but a "master morality" that would emphasize such virtues as individualism and self-reliance over conformity.

Unfortunately, it also led to misunderstandings, willful or otherwise, with sometimes horrific consequences. Nazis in particular based some of their thinking on a twisted parody of Nietzsche's ideas, and through their "will to power" inflicted violence that poisoned the minds of many against the constructive uses of technology.

Technological Optimism and Cryonics

Not everyone succumbed to pessimism, however, and some even saw in technology a road to salvation that was otherwise lacking. One such optimist was Robert C. W. Ettinger,[15] who grew up around Detroit, Michigan. As a boy in his father's store he would read the pioneering science fiction periodical, *Amazing Stories*. The July 1931 issue contained a story by Neil R. Jones, "The Jameson Satellite." In it, professor Jameson's body is chilled at death and placed into Earth orbit, to be revived millions of years later by an alien race, which has also conquered aging and other ailments. To the twelve-year-old Robert, the resuscitation of a human in a future without aging and illness held a fascination that would not be forgotten in the decades to come.

In 1944 Ettinger was wounded, ironically, while fighting the Nazis in Germany and spent several years recuperating in an army hospital in Battle Creek, Michigan. This offered him the opportunity to write a science fiction story of his own. Published in the

March 1948 *Startling Stories*, "The Penultimate Trump" is about a wealthy man, H. D. Haworth, who is frozen at death and eventually resuscitated, with youth and health restored. In two important respects Haworth's reanimation differs from Professor Jameson's: (1) it is planned for by Haworth himself (Jameson simply intended to be well-preserved, not eventually brought back to consciousness); and (2) it is carried out by humans and not through a chance encounter with aliens. To Ettinger this seemed a plausible, real-life approach to personal life extension and betterment. He expected that others with better scientific credentials would soon be working on the freezing idea.

In fact the idea was not new but had a venerable if somewhat checkered history. Ancient Roman writers such as Ovid and Pliny the Elder noted that fish trapped in ice and apparently frozen and dead could sometimes return to life. Experiments in the controlled freezing of organisms were carried out as early as the 1600s, one researcher being English scientist Robert Boyle. He reported the successful reanimation of fish and frogs after brief exposure to subfreezing temperatures, though he was unable to achieve the same results after longer exposures. In the next century English surgeon John Hunter also thought that human life might be extended by this method. In 1768 he reported his experiments on reanimating frozen fish by simple thawing—but these had failed. Still there was progress, both with freezing and with the related technique of desiccation. Both could achieve a limited sort of reversible suspended animation, or anabiosis. By the early 1900s many small creatures such as worms, tardigrades, and rotifers had been revived from an inert and "lifeless" state induced by extreme cold or drying. A Russian experimenter, Porfiry Bakhmetiev (1860–1913), started research with hypothermic mammals, and successfully revived bats cooled below 0° C, but he died before the work had progressed very far.[16]

By the 1940s some modest additional progress had been made. An important innovation with deep freezing was the addition of a protective agent such as glycerol beforehand to reduce the severity of damage. Single cells could then be frozen and cooled to very low temperature with successful resuscitation much more likely, though still not guaranteed. Larger organisms, including mammals such as hamsters, would soon be partly frozen and recovered. A new field, cryobiology, was born.

But beyond such initial success, progress was slow. Little serious attention was paid to the fantastic possibility that Ettinger and others before him had envisioned, of cryogenic storage as a means of defeating death. So in 1960 Ettinger, who had by then earned master's degrees in both physics and mathematics and become a college professor, set to work again. His first, modest effort was to circulate a short summary of his ideas to a few hundred people in *Who's Who*. Response was minimal, so he then set out to write *The Prospect of Immortality*, which advocated the idea of freezing people and storing them for later reanimation. The first draft of the book was completed in 1962, and an expanded version was offered commercially in 1964. Many thus became aware of the freezing idea. Eight years later Ettinger produced a sequel, *Man into Superman*, that explored some possibilities for becoming more-than-human. During this time the first freezings of humans for intentional reanimation occurred, a practice that became known as cryonics.

Meanwhile another immortalist pioneer, Evan Cooper, had also hit on the freezing idea and in 1962 had written a short book of his own, *Immortality: Physically, Scientifically, Now*. Never commercially published, the typed, mimeographed manuscript was privately circulated to a few. Ettinger responded enthusiastically, noting the similarities with his own just-completed book. Cooper's independent effort contained some original thinking too, drawing inspiration from *The Bedbug*, a 1928 play by Russian Vladimir Mayakovsky in which a man is frozen by accident and resuscitated decades later using new technology. Another of Cooper's sources was *The Human Use of Human Beings*, a nonfictional study by cybernetics pioneer Norbert Wiener in which the human personality is compared to a computer program. The program representing the living person might be transmitted to another body or, in more recent parlance, "uploaded." The new body could be a natural, biological product or an artificial device, opening considerable vistas for shedding old limitations and entering upon new modes of existence. This, let it be added, is among the possibilities Cooper considered without claiming dogmatic certainty that any of them would come to pass. More generally, a cautious, if optimistic, scientific stance became a hallmark of the developing immortalist movement.

In December 1963 the Life Extension Society (LES) was

founded in Washington, D.C., with Cooper as president, to promote the freezing idea.[17] The September 1965 issue of the LES
periodical *Freeze-Wait-Reanimate* carried stirring headlines:
ASTOUNDING ADVANCE IN ANIMAL BRAIN FREEZING
AND RECOVERY.... Dr. Isamu Suda and colleagues, at Kobe
University in Japan, had detected electrical activity in a cat brain
that had been frozen to -20° C (-4° F) for more than six months
and then restored to body temperature. The cat had been anesthetized and the brain removed. The blood was replaced with a protective solution of glycerol prior to freezing; the glycerol was
again replaced with blood on rewarming. Not only did the brain
revive and resume activity, but the brain wave pattern did not
appear to differ greatly from that of a live control. Here, then,
was dramatic evidence that cryonics might work, especially if
possible future advances in repair techniques were taken into
account.

But despite such successes and widespread media exposure,
cryonics was a difficult practice to get started. Ettinger and Cooper played pivotal roles, and critical contributions were made by
others, yet the problems were great. Few who were dying wanted
to be frozen, nor did their healthier contemporaries show much
interest; support and funding were meager. As for the activists,
there was a steady turnover among those initially eager who later
lost interest and quit. The casualties even included Cooper himself. Active for a few years, his LES could never complete a primary mission of establishing a cryonics facility, though others
succeeded. Cooper left the movement and, indulging a passion
for sailing, was tragically lost at sea in 1982.[18]

Progress in actual human freezings, the all-important end product, was slow and uncertain. In April 1966, after several years of
failed promotion, a success of sorts finally occurred. An embalmed
body was frozen—but only after weeks of above-freezing storage, which was highly damaging to any prospect of reanimation.
Relatives maintaining this preliminary suspension gave up after
a few months, and the body was thawed and buried. A much better freezing occurred in January 1967 by a team organized by a
California businessman, Robert F. Nelson. In this first, true cryonic suspension, an elderly cancer patient in Glendale, California, was placed in dry ice shortly after death and transferred to
liquid nitrogen a few days later. Nelson's group, the Cryonics

Society of California, would freeze several more people over the next few years. But his operation did not meet expenses; nine cryonics patients thawed and were lost, and when relatives sued, Nelson and an assistant were ordered to pay nearly $1 million in damages.[19] Another operation, the Cryonics Society of New York, also folded, though without legal recriminations and despite the heroic efforts of its principals, Curtis Henderson and Saul Kent.[20] Bitter though they were, these failures inspired greater and more careful efforts.

Alcor Foundation was started in 1972 by Fred and Linda Chamberlain after they broke with Nelson's group.[21] In coming years it would establish a strict funding policy so that suspensions no longer depended on the financial backing of relatives and would also pioneer head-only freezing. (The rationale is that technology that could repair a brain and resuscitate frozen tissue could probably also recreate the missing body from DNA and other clues. Human heads or "neuros" are less expensive to maintain, and none to date has been lost through thawing.)

Progress also brought a new level of effectiveness to the procedures used in cryonic suspension, which must go far beyond simple freezing to protect the tissues as far as possible from the damage of cooling to low temperature. Jerry Leaf and Michael Darwin pioneered better techniques of perfusion with higher concentrations of glycerol prior to freezing. Work by Leaf, Darwin, and Hugh Hixon of Alcor,[22] and Drs. Paul Segall, Harold Waitz, and Hal Sternberg of rival Trans Time,[23] demonstrated the reversibility of the early stages of such procedures. (This was a follow-up of similar work in the 1960s performed by noncryonicist Gerald Klebanoff.) Test animals, chilled to near the freezing point and left cold and apparently lifeless for hours (though not actually frozen), were revived without ill effects. Confidence increased that deep-frozen large organisms, including humans, could also eventually be recovered.

Then suddenly a crisis loomed over legal issues. In December 1987 Saul Kent had his eighty-three-year-old mother, Dora, frozen as a head-only. The woman, in fact, had died at Alcor's facility in Riverside, California, which prompted a coroner's investigation. When the frozen head was demanded for autopsy and could not be located, several Alcor officials were taken into custody but were later vindicated in court. A judge ruled that the head was not needed to decide the cause of death and there was no evidence of foul play.[24] A few months after this there was an attempt by the California Health Department to have cryonics declared illegal—also eventually rebuffed in court.[25] The legal challenges cost the small and privately funded Alcor dearly. But cryonics gained respectability both in and outside the state, and it was clear that some were willing to struggle very hard to keep the practice going and keep individual patients frozen.

The legal battle over Dora Kent involved a personal confrontation. I was one of the six Alcor employees placed in handcuffs on January 7, 1988, and taken to the local police station. There we remained some hours until an attorney determined there was no proper legal ground to hold us—whereupon our restraints were unlocked and we were set free. (One of our number, Carlos Mondragón, alerted the media during the arrest and helped manage this crisis.) There would be anxious days, weeks, and months, however, before the matter would finally be resolved in Alcor's favor. In general, cryonics has been fortunate to escape the fierce persecution that has often accompanied the more unusual, free-thinking movements of the past. But this incident and the subsequent struggle over legality in California were sobering events. Cryonics, a heroic, rational attempt to save and extend the lives of human beings, was not well received in certain "mainstream" quarters. Opponents tried to stop it through legal sanctions rather than recognize its life-affirming potential. Thankfully, their efforts did not succeed.

Another legal battle of a different sort concerned the wish of one person to be frozen. Thomas Donaldson, a Ph.D. mathematician, was diagnosed with a brain tumor in 1988. The tumor, an astrocytoma, was a particularly virulent sort that is usually fatal within a few years. Donaldson had been active in cryonics for many years and wanted to be frozen before he sustained substantial brain damage, though not immediately—radiation treatments had brought at least a temporary remission. But the freezing procedure, when needed, would have to be started while he was still alive. By current legal criteria it would be deemed assisted suicide or perhaps homicide. Donaldson went to court. Unfortunately, narrow legal definitions prevailed and he did not get his wish. (Thankfully, the tumor stayed in remission and Donaldson is still alive and active at this writing; other cryonicists with brain malignancies have not been so lucky.) The case also generated much favorable publicity for cryonics and helped dramatize the plight of those who wish to choose, without interference, the circumstances of what others consider their death.[26]

A tiny yet vigorous and growing cryonics movement now exists, and several organizations, most based in the United States, offer their services. Robert Ettinger was instrumental in starting one of these, Cryonics Institute, and remains active as do others whose involvement stretches back decades, though some, like Jerry Leaf, have "fallen asleep" and been frozen. Rivalries and contention have sometimes been fierce, as might be expected among the strong-minded individualists that cryonicists typically are and have split more than one organization, including the largest, Alcor. Still there is consensus that facing the common enemy—death—requires respect for others and a willingness to tolerate diverging views.

Research continues, though still privately funded due to continuing public disinterest in anything so radical. The ambitious "Prometheus Project" was organized in 1996 by Paul Wakfer to unite the various factions in work toward a common goal, in this case a demonstrated technique for full, reversible suspended animation through low-temperature storage. The project faltered before any research could begin,[27] but a parallel effort at California-based Twenty-first Century Medicine, financed by Saul Kent and Bill Faloon and endorsed by "Prometheans" and others, reported significant progress in 1998.[28]

James Bedford, the first person cryonically suspended, remains frozen, along with Dora Kent and approximately four-fifths of the one hundred or so that have been preserved at low temperature. Almost everyone, in fact, who was frozen after 1973 was still frozen in 2000, when about seven hundred were signed up for the procedure.

Through cryonics a small part of Fedorov's great project of resurrection may actually be completed in the relatively near future (thoughtful estimates allow anywhere from 30 to 150 years). It seems clear, to those of us who have accepted it, that cryonics offers a better approach to death than the conventional one of allowing or causing the remains to disintegrate. But as yet very few of the many thousands who die each day are frozen. Concern with the welfare of humanity demands that cryonics—or some form of biostasis—become universal, at least until the happy time that death is no longer a threat. Thus cryonics itself could become a "common task" to reorder society along the lines of peace and life rather than war and death. Though it would take a large investment of resources to maintain many millions of people in frozen storage, it does not appear beyond the productive capacities of the world, particularly if the less-expensive neuro option is used. (Lower-cost possibilities such as high-quality chemical preservation may also offer benefit.) The outcome of such a program could be far more beneficial to humanity than, for example, the diversion of resources into technologies of destruction, something that has occupied a fearful world for a very long time.

Along with cryonics are some related developments that help make its case more credible and offer support to those who might be interested. Eric Drexler's 1986 book, *Engines of Creation*, argued the case for nanotechnology. This atomic-scale manipulation violates no laws of physics and seems perfectly feasible, in principle, to many thoughtful people, though it has critics too. But it also has many potential applications, among which would be a kind of minute archaeology of a frozen organism. Damaged cells or subcellular structures should be repairable, missing parts replaceable, and the whole restorable to a functioning state, through swarms of tiny, intelligently controlled devices or other tools capable of acting at small scales of distance. A more technical book by Drexler, *Nanosystems* (1992), offers mathematical arguments for the feasibility of atomic-scale manipulators. An ambitious effort has since been undertaken by Robert Frietas to explore the prospects for curing diseases and extending human life span through developing nanotechnology. The first, massive volume of his projected, three-volume work, *Nanomedicine,* was published in 1999. Meanwhile the case for nanotechnology is continually being strengthened by the progress being made, particularly with devices such as scanning probe microscopes that can track and position individual atoms and alter individual chemical bonds; more will be said about this in Chapter 9.

The Foresight Institute was organized by Drexler to promote nanotechnology and publish the latest developments. Drexler himself is a cryonicist, as is another Foresight member, Ralph Merkle, who has done the most detailed theoretical study of the feasibility of resuscitation from cryonic suspension.[29] These and other

nanotechnologists are among those whose work reflects a deliberate intention to bring about a beneficent Apocalypse, leading
to a technological Singularity.

Other notable developments are cryonics-leaning organizations
such as Extropy Institute and the Society for Venturism—both
U.S.-based—and the Russian Vita Longa Society. There is also a
proliferation of cryonics-related communication through the rapidly burgeoning electronic mail services. Philosopher and cryonicist Max More, who co-founded Extropy Institute, completed
a dissertation, *The Diachronic Self,* that explores issues of personhood and favors cryonics as a means for extending life. *The
First Immortal,* a novel by Jim Halperin, realistically explores
the idea of resurrecting people who were frozen, and shows how
a coming age of immortality would make life happier and more
meaningful.

Beyond Cryonics

Whatever promise it may offer, however, cryonics can never
be the full solution to the immortalist's problem. The causes of
death themselves must be eliminated, chief among them being
normal, biological aging. Aging has not been an easy problem to
address, though progress has been made. In work beginning in
the late 1920s, Clive McCay of Cornell observed that rats and
mice on calorie-restricted diets lived considerably longer than
more amply fed controls; maximum life spans could be increased
more than 50 percent.[30] Human life expectancies in the succeeding decades have also progressively advanced. Much of the increase is due to a drop in infant mortality, but some is attributable
to better understanding and treatment of the ailments of the elderly. Beyond such limited advances, moreover, aging is now showing signs of yielding its deeper secrets. Recent work suggests
that the root causes of aging are certain, progressive changes at
the molecular level that occur in the course of normal cell functioning—more on this in Chapter 17.

Here it seems appropriate to mention a book that appeared in
1969 (updated in 1977), *The Immortalist* by Alan Harrington,
with its stirring opening : "Death is an imposition on the human
race, and no longer acceptable. Men and women have all but lost
their ability to accommodate themselves to personal extinction;

they must now proceed physically to overcome it." Indeed, Harrington's book can be said to have given new meaning to the otherwise rarely used word *immortalism*—as a philosophical stance that death might be or can be overcome *scientifically*.

The book has a chapter on cryonics, though it concludes that "[a]n intensified drive to control the aging process seems far more promising." This underscores the fact that overcoming death itself is the real goal. Cryonics or other preservation is at best only a holding action until such time as a course of effective treatment becomes available. Its outcome meanwhile is uncertain. Yet I object strongly to Harrington's implied dismissal, which for him ultimately had personal consequences. (He died in 1997 with no apparent interest in cryonics or biostasis and was conventionally buried.) The idea of something to assist those dying today—the preservation option—seems to have escaped attention, along with the thought that there would be value in preserving the newly deceased, even if the best processes are still imperfect.

Harrington indeed seemed resigned, in the manner of Reade and Stephens before him, to forfeiting his own survival even if immortality is near on the scale of history. His book is of interest, however, for its philosophical treatment of the ages-old human yearning for a world free of death, and of what might transpire when we get there. Other "mainstream" writers have not expressed much personal interest, so far, in a strategy for life-extension such as cryonics, though their works contribute usefully to immortalist thinking.

One such book, *Millennium Myth* by Michael Grosso (1995), is a survey of thought, beliefs, and practices relating to the possibility of immortality, with the coverage extending from earliest times to the technological present. Space is devoted to modern immortalism with its emphasis on the conquest of biological death and the use of cryonics to bridge the time gap from now to then. Grosso notes how the sweeping change that seems about to happen by design, what he calls a "technocalypse," is being taken more seriously by more people all the time. It may indeed bring final salvation—or ruin—depending on our handling of it.

Other books are even more focused on the near-term possibilities for immortalization through technology. *Cheating Death* by Marvin Cetron and Owen Davies and *Immortality* by Ben Bova (both 1998) take seriously the idea that the human life span is about to be substantially lengthened and consider some of the consequences. Significantly, an explosion of nursing home populations and other demands for health care are not foreseen. The anticipated life extension, after some preliminary progress, will allow a true rollback of aging and a return to a state of youthful vigor and health. Doctors, hospitals, and care facilities should be less and less needed. However, there could well be serious difficulties, such as unrest caused by still-primitive living conditions in some countries alongside the incredible advances and benefits in others. Overall, the authors seem optimistic about the outcome, though they note it will certainly require enlightened thinking and action.

Another 1998 book, *Last Flesh* by Christopher Dewdney, suggests that we are nearing the end of our tenure as carbon-based life-forms, and a change to more-than-human status is at hand. "What is relatively certain is that we are about to enter the transition period between the human and the posthuman eras—the transhuman age."[31] The choice of terminology seems particularly appropriate and has been in use for years among immortalist-leaning people, who may fancy themselves already transhuman to a degree.

The Spike by Damien Broderick (1997) is a still more ambitious book, arguing that progress that will change our lives beyond recognition is accelerating in such crucial areas as computers and nanotechnology. A Singularity—the "Spike," when the curve of progress measured by reasonable indicators goes off the charts—is projected for some time between 2030 and 2100, after which (if not earlier) we will become a new family of life-forms.[32] The book also offers a survey of a fledgling establishment devoted to forward-thinking and action. There are nanotechnologists, such as Drexler and Merkle, who are actively pursuing work leading to a technological Singularity, which is also suggested by trends in the computer industry. On the philosophical end are Extropy Institute and other transhumanist organizations. Prominent extropians such as founder Max More, Robin Hanson, John K. Clark, and Anders Sandberg have devoted much attention on the Internet to the problems we must overcome in becoming more-than-human, including social and conceptual issues.

Another book that interestingly forecasts a Singularity (though not named as such) is *The Age of Spiritual Machines* by Ray

Kurzweil (1999). Computers, it is predicted, will within decades exceed human intelligence, as humans are presently constituted. On the other hand, what does it mean to be "human," or should it mean, when our basic characteristics are mutable, as they clearly are becoming? "The primary political and philosophical issue of the next century will be the definition of who we are."[33] A parallel effort by cryonicist and fuzzy logic expert Bart Kosko in *The Fuzzy Future* (1999) forecasts "heaven in a chip" when computing devices are sufficiently advanced that our mental processes can be transferred or uploaded to them.[34]

This survey of immortalist writings is by no means exhaustive, and more are appearing all the time. But a clear trend can be seen in which expectations are slowly rising for a better life than human biology can furnish unassisted. People increasingly are adopting a scientific approach to problems that formerly seemed entirely beyond the reach of such methods. The thought then occurs that the scientific approach is the right one for the whole range of our problems. To make this approach workable, though, will require more than the conquest of biological death, however great such an achievement would be for those then living.

Indeed there is a far more difficult problem, inescapable to anyone who values what is good and right, than can be addressed even by future advances in aging control or possible, present successes with freezing or other forms of biostasis. If life is fundamentally good and death a detriment to be overcome, then lost individuals of the past must be considered too. We have seen how Fedorov was concerned about this and proposed a way of restoring the dead to life through means that seemed possible in his day. The feasibility of his detailed approach now seems highly doubtful; modern physics (most in the field are convinced) denies the possibility of recovery of arbitrary past information through simple measurements. Means other than those envisioned by Fedorov would be essential. Such means, however, are not impossible if the full implications of the modern perspective are taken into account. Some, like Frank Tipler, have investigated this issue, with most interesting conclusions.

Tipler's 1994 book, *The Physics of Immortality*, makes what I think is a convincing case for the possibility of resurrecting the dead through a scientific procedure, even in the absence of the detailed information that would seemingly be necessary. As a last resort, the missing information is simply filled in by guesswork. There is a nonzero, though generally very tiny, chance that any finite pattern can be recreated by such a random "throw of the dice." In an appropriate context this seemingly unimportant possibility has considerable significance—more on this later. For now it is worth noting that, even though Fedorov's physics has been superseded, his dream of a universal resurrection has some modern defenders and, I would say, a strong scientific argument in its favor.

Summary of Immortalist Philosophies

We have now seen how immortalism, a modern, science-based approach to the problem of death, developed from precedents dating back to much earlier times. The number of immortalists, past and present, is small but the thinking and sometimes the action lively. Several distinctive immortalist philosophies have emerged. A brief summary of these will help clarify what has just been said about immortalist history and place the present work in context.

First, we can distinguish two basic variants of immortalist philosophy, which I will call *biostatic* and *nonbiostatic*. A biostatic philosophy advocates putting human remains into some form of arrested activity or biostasis following clinical death, with a view to eventual reanimation when technology to do this becomes available. Cryonics-based philosophies (and there are several, as we will see) are certainly biostatic in this sense. Some other philosophies are clearly immortalist but do not emphasize any preservative approach and are nonbiostatic. Advocates of nonbiostatic immortalist philosophies include the precryonics immortalist Fedorov and more recent thinkers such as Alan Harrington, Hans Moravec, and Frank Tipler.

As a cryonicist, my bias is naturally toward the biostatic group, which is particularly oriented toward doing something now, but the others deserve inclusion for completeness. There is a subdivision of the nonbiostatic group that we have already considered. They are "cosmologicals," like Frank Tipler, who see immortalization as only a distant future possibility, though still a real one. There are also transhumanists who hope for immortalization in their natural lifetimes yet also are nonbiostatic. They are strong advocates of aging research and even take nutritional supplements and the like to increase the chance of living to a cure for aging but have not made arrangements for any special preservation at death and do not intend to. Cryonicists too, who can be characterized as transhumanist, often try to extend their lives through dietary supplements or calorie restriction and hope that aging will be cured in their lifetime, but they have taken this additional precaution in case it is not. It is worth a reminder here that views change with time and especially with continuing progress. Perhaps the nonbiostatic, nontranshumanist camp will dwindle soon through migrations into the more optimistic group.

In addition to the subdivisions we have just considered, there is another bifurcation into "one-chance" versus "resurrectionist" philosophies. Basically, a one-chance philosophy holds that once a person is dead—in the sense that the physical basis of identity, the brain, is destroyed—that person cannot and will not ever be resurrected or reanimated. The resurrectionist viewpoint is more optimistic and holds that physical mechanisms exist that permit the eventual recovery or recreation of the person even under such adversity as physical destruction. Probably most cryonicists are one-chance in this sense, whereas Fedorov was a resurrectionist, as are Hans Moravec, Frank Tipler, and some cryonicists, including Robert Ettinger and myself.

Within the one-chance camp, I would make a further distinction. There are pessimists who feel that true immortality is not attainable, though life might be greatly extended, or who lean toward this view, and optimists who lean toward the opposite view, that true immortality might be attainable scientifically. (Some of the division concerns the disputed possibility or inevitability of the "Heat Death" of the universe, which will be addressed in Chapter 14.) I do not sense such a division among resurrectionists, who seem pretty uniformly optimistic, but there are some other interesting varieties within this group.

Fedorov, for example, a nineteenth-century resurrectionist, advocated what might be called accessible determinism. Under this view, the universe is deterministic, and, moreover, the "hidden past"—lost historical information—can be recovered in full detail, enough to restore to life every person who ever lived. A modern accessible determinist is Robert Ettinger,[35] who, however, also strongly advocates cryonics—being the movement's principal founder. Tipler in *The Physics of Immortality*, also presents a possible scenario for accessible determinism based on his idea of a collapsing universe. This is not the only resurrectionist philosophy, however.

An alternative is based around the pattern theory of identity, including the variant I will develop in this book that I call Interchangeability. In this case the hidden past is not necessarily recoverable—though determinism could still hold. (In fact manyworlds physics provides an inaccessible determinism, as we shall see.) Recovery of personal identity depends not on specific structure or even informational continuity with the past but on recreating an identical pattern. In this way, then, through the chance creation of duplicates, persons could be resurrected without our initially knowing anything about them. Among the advocates of this view are Moravec and Tipler—and some cryonicists, including myself. Cryonicists who accept Interchangeability, as I do, differ from noncryonicists in that they also feel that preserving the remains to facilitate recovery of the person is desirable, even if not essential in an absolute sense.

The immortalist philosophy I offer here, then, is both biostatic and resurrectionist. The resurrectionist component is ultimately the more important of the two, but the biostatic side must not be overlooked. Committing oneself to a biostasis program is something that can be done, here and now, to further one's immortal future. It is a better choice, I feel emphatically, than passively accepting one's physical destruction, whatever future prospects may still remain open.

CHAPTER 3.

A Matter of Attitude

W hen the cryonics movement began in the 1960s, there was considerable optimism among the handful of proponents. Here at last was a new and positive development, something that ought to be of interest to many. Many, it was true, had other approaches to the problem of death, and the case for cryonics, though not scientifically refuted, was certainly not proved either.

But the case for a mystical afterlife was also not proved, yet many had placed their hopes in just such an outcome. In fact, many others would agree that the scientific evidence for cryonics was stronger than any evidence of a supernatural hereafter. Arguments, extrapolative and speculative but rational nonetheless, favored it seriously. Cryonics might perform poorly but there were signs it might do well too. And it should do better as more interest was shown and more research was done. On this basis it was thought that cryonics might quickly become widespread, but instead, and despite the fairly extensive and generally positive publicity, proselytizing proved slow and difficult. More than three decades later, only a few persons per million in the United States, where the movement has always had its greatest strength, have chosen this option, and the worldwide total is barely more than one hundred per billion.

Why are there so few immortalists, and especially cryonicists? In part the reason is simply that no one has been resuscitated from a frozen state. (Though I emphasize here that only more research will overcome this deficiency.) People who are frozen are, by usual standards, "most sincerely dead" even if they do not decay. Many simply find it impossible to believe that such "corpsicles" could be restored to a functioning state. Others allow a slim possibility, but one they can safely discount. Yet such skepticism, though widespread, seems unable alone to account for the pervasive lack of interest. Again, interest in various religious forms of an afterlife has always been strong, though no one sees people rising from the dead. Yet science has achieved spectacular things, and though many people grant it could one day score another triumph in resuscitating the frozen, they are "not interested in it personally."

Scientists, in fact, might be expected to be more disposed than others toward the possibilities of biostasis, and a few of some repute have indeed endorsed the idea—but not many. It is expected, of course, that many of a scientific outlook who might otherwise be attracted by the rationalist approach of biostasis, would scorn the idea of conquering death and disparage any thought of either the feasibility or desirability of survival beyond the biological limits. Such people, rejecting traditional faiths that promise immortality, have found a different resolution of the problem of death through acceptance. They are not looking for a way out but cling to their views no less tenaciously than many a believer in personal salvation. Still, it has often seemed that people with scientific backgrounds should show more interest than they have.

Overall, the very limited interest in cryonics has surprised and worried some of us who do endorse the idea. Too small a movement jeopardizes any chance of it working for us since a stable organization is needed to preserve those in suspension. There is, of course, the hard fact that frozen people cannot be resuscitated by known methods, which means that serious damage is being inflicted by the freezing process; despite any positive evidence, there is no certainty this damage can be reversed. We would like to have the greater certainty that would come from better freezing methods, which in turn could be expected if there was more interest leading to more support for research. Often too we have friends or loved ones outside of cryonics—we would like them to survive along with us. To this can be added a more general altruistic motive of saving as many as possible from death and assisting them, as far as possible, to what ought to be a glorious future life. (As suggested in Chapter 1, this position will be justified on grounds of enlightened self-interest, not just "altruism.")

So we are left with questions. Why such monumental apathy? Why the uniform willingness to yield, without struggle, to an impersonal force whose outcome is one's physical destruction? How can people be so little interested in scientific approaches to eliminate death?

Here I think we should suspect a selection process—natural or biological selection coupled with social and cultural tendencies that favor certain attitudes and behavior over others. Paradoxically, it would seem that indifference to the prospect of physically addressing the problem of death has historically promoted survival of the human species, and of certain cultural subgroups especially. Research in social psychology supports this conclusion, particularly the "terror management" theory of Sheldon Solomon and associates.[1] This theory, on which some of the following discussion is based, explains a wide variety of social behavior and has interesting experimental support.

Knowledge of Mortality and Management of Terror

Humankind, among all species, has unique talents but also special vulnerabilities that must be compensated if the species is to flourish. Intelligence is nature's great gift, but it is also a two-edged sword, balancing its awesome advantages by immense liabilities. The power it gives us for benefit can be used for destruction and abuse, which is a more obvious sort of liability, but there is another liability of a subtler sort, at least as pervasive, and possibly posing a greater threat.

All creatures struggle to survive, employing their faculties as best they are able. With creatures other than ourselves there is no particular threat to the species as a whole in the fact that their struggles, individually, always end in failure. They do not know they are mortal, and they happily replenish their numbers, undisturbed by deeper thoughts of where it is all leading. There is no conflict if they also possess a fierce will to survive, and this indeed is what nature provides them under the selection process. They struggle to avoid death in the short term but are indifferent to death in the long term, both characteristics that further survival at the species level.

Humans had more intelligence, however, and could not remain indifferent but were able to draw disturbing conclusions early on. Death seemed inevitable and final, a grim promise of doom. The struggle to survive seemed ultimately, invariably, a hopeless, useless task. Faced with such a devastating prospect, the mind recoiled, seeking an outlet, a reason to continue the struggle, an assurance that life was not just an exercise in futility. A problem thus arose that might have been ultimately fatal. It had to be dealt with if the advantages of intelligence were not to be negated by the very perceptive capacities it conferred. It is hard to play at your best if you are certain you will lose the game, that your defeat must be so total and final you will never play again. It is especially hard when the game is no passing fancy but is literally the whole of your existence. The knowledge of mortality thus became a major stumbling block for the human species, a unique problem created, paradoxically, by the most powerful instrument for survival that ever evolved, the intellect. As a problem it transcends the powers of the individual, so that forces outside oneself must be brought to bear. Historically these involved surrounding society or culture.

Throughout their lives, people are constantly interacting with their culture, which plays a sustaining and nurturing role. In infancy and early childhood our culture is most strongly represented in our parents. Material benefits and—most important—a sense of self-worth—follow from doing "good" or what is expected of us by those who provide for our needs and protect us against possible harm. Dependency and bonding are strong. In later life surrounding society—our culture, including family and friends—plays somewhat the role of parents. Dependency and bonding change character but still remain substantial. Culture provides our sustenance in such forms as entertainment, employment, the necessities of life, a search for meaning, and help in times of special need, such as medical crises. On the other hand, culture is nothing but the combined effects of individuals—each person forms part of the cultural web that surrounds and helps sustain any other participant. Conforming to the values and expectations of one's culture is perhaps the most important source of a sense of self-worth, and it is natural that this dependency would be fostered by a selection process.

People especially turn to their culture in times of crisis when the problems are too serious to deal with individually. Among the problems of this sort are natural disasters, medical emergencies, and major threats or harm from groups or individuals. The death of a loved one is such a problem too—authorities must be notified, if not already involved in rescue attempts or medical treatment—and grief must be managed, which generally calls for outside help. Finally, culture plays an important role in the problem of anticipating one's own death, establishing an anxiety buffer to shield against terror and despondency.

The cultural anxiety buffer—the shielding sense of self-worth provided by participation in one's culture—typically draws on religious or philosophical systems. These offer survival—in some form—beyond the biological limits, or a worldview in which one's endless survival is not so important and death is not to be feared. With such a psychological bulwark, people are relieved of much of the burden of concern over their own mortality. When the unpleasant subject does intrude, a natural response is to strengthen the anxiety buffer by defending or upholding one's culture.

The anxiety buffer in particular becomes a means whereby the culture maintains control over the individual and thereby fosters its own survival. In the case of a religion, for example, the culture serves as an authority figure to legitimize and lend confidence to whatever beliefs and practices must be assimilated. This is especially important for beliefs of an arbitrary character (belief in specific deities for instance) that vary widely from culture to culture. Belief can be more strongly held within a group than by a lone individual—consensus obscures the arbitrary nature of many beliefs and helps reduce doubts. Thus most people are strongly dependent on their culture for the anxiety buffer that guards them against the terror of death and makes life worth living.

In submitting to and participating in their culture, people take part in a cultural drama—an unfolding of events as seen from the vantage point of the worldview their culture provides. Such participation conveys a reassuring sense of self-worth—again, the cultural anxiety buffer. Participants must meet two main requirements: (1) they must accept the worldview of the culture, along with the standards of value inherent in that worldview; and (2) they must feel that they are living up to these standards and thus have a significant role in the cultural drama. The resulting feeling of self-worth, with its sense of participation in something meaningful and protection against the terror of death, offers great benefit, and people are willing to pay the price of conformity that their culture demands. The nature of the cultural drama, the worldview, and the standards of value will, of course, depend on the culture and differ in detail from one culture to another.

Cultures vary but have certain features in common, dictated by the state of knowledge and belief over the time they have flourished and the logic of the selection process that has operated in their own survival and evolution. In dealing with the short-term problem of death, there was certainly much that could be done in physical terms, even in ancient times, through common sense strategies, medical practices, and the like. Yet it was recognized that there were certain insurmountable barriers. Aging, with its eventual termination of the life process, could not be forestalled, nor could a person be restored to function if too much time had passed without vital signs, as would always happen eventually. These long-term problems were both intractable and universal and could be clearly distinguished from ailments of a more special nature (short-term problems), which often could be remedied. For the long term it was necessary to focus on terror management rather than unobtainable physical solutions.[2]

Cultures accordingly grew up that, for example, favored medicine and even medical progress but did not waste effort on more radical life extension, such as alleviating aging or reversing clinical death. Such cultures might stress either a religious concept such as an afterlife or an attitude of stoical acceptance. One way or another the things we cannot change would be granted a status that discouraged any thought or effort spent changing them. There would be compensating rewards of course. The sense of self-worth would follow by conforming to the values of the culture. The adherent could feel that he or she was a meaningful component even if individual extinction—temporary or permanent—must follow.

In the Christian tradition, for example, mortality is the deserved, universal penalty for sin according to the divine plan, and only an act of divine mercy can rescind it and restore life. To think of overcoming death by a physical process is an unwarranted presumption and to attempt it futile. (Fedorov's opinion was a rare exception and certainly not part of the Christian mainstream.) To those of stoical bent, on the other hand, death is part of the enduring natural order and thus to be accepted without complaint. Either way the cultural anxiety buffer discourages the thought of physical, purposeful human intervention, and adherents find they are not interested in such an idea. It is easy to see how such cultural attitudes, by deflecting wasteful preoccupation with impossibilities, would be favored by the selection process, so that now they dominate. Such a heritage, with the associated cultural bonding and commitment to conformity, appears to account for the present apathy about cryonics and other approaches for physically forestalling death.

Some interesting evidence seems to support the terror management theory, both inside and outside cryonics. In assessing such evidence we have to keep in mind the worldview of the subject, which is set by a particular cultural affiliation and will vary from subject to subject.

For the case of cryonics some claim disinterest on religious grounds, as we just noted with Christianity. When the possibility is raised of a scientific solution to the problem of mortality they are resistant, telling us that "God has provided the means to overcome death, through faith in him." Reminded of death, then, they strengthen their anxiety buffer by defending their culture.

Others disavow religious objections but tell us instead that "death is natural" or "one life is enough." Again it seems that they are strengthening the anxiety buffer by defending the values of their particular culture, which here advocates a simple acceptance of death without theological overtones. (Ancient Stoics and their modern sympathizers, many atheists, secular humanists, and the like, have expressed such views.) Sometimes the reasons given are less obviously tied to the terror management paradigm, but further questioning shows a deeper connection.

For example, someone may not want to consider it until the process is perfected. He may note that large, frozen organisms cannot now be resuscitated. This person too has no religious objection, apparently just a rational, technological one. If, however, you point out the technical arguments favoring the possibility of eventual reanimation (through nanotechnology, for instance) and ask what has he got to lose, he promptly raises other objections— perhaps to claim that "death is natural," as one such person told me. Again it appears he was defending his culture all along, using whatever "rational" means were at hand. (This culture no doubt valued rationality, to a point.) In truth, people's responses to cryonics, as for other challenges, are often to rationalize without being particularly rational. Once again though we see that, when reminded of mortality, people defend their culture.

Other evidence for the terror management theory, not involving cryonics, comes from controlled experiments in which subjects defended their culture more if reminded of death beforehand. In one such experiment college students were asked to set the amount of bail bond for a hypothetical arrested prostitute. Subjects were chosen who think prostitution is bad and deserving of legal sanctions. Some of these filled out a high-anxiety questionnaire beforehand that questioned attitudes toward death, while others filled out a low-anxiety questionnaire about television. Those who were reminded of death assessed a substantially higher bond than the others. A third group was given a high-anxiety questionnaire dealing with exams. Its responses resembled those of the television group rather than the death group, suggesting that defending the culture is a specific response to being reminded of death and not just a general anxiety reaction.[3]

The terror management theory seems to account for such human behavior as the large-scale conflicts that have often erupted over ideological or cultural differences. In these struggles people are reminded of competing worldviews. Being reminded of a worldview different from your own raises the possibility that yours is incorrect and threatens your cultural anxiety buffer. It thus not only raises the issue of death, it calls into question the manner in which you have resolved the problem. Such a challenge could provoke a violent response in defense of one's culture. Some of the bloodiest confrontations in history have resulted over such causes. (Particularly glaring examples can be seen in the many religious wars of past centuries, and the ideological and cultural contention that has figured so prominently in the twentieth century's gargantuan violence.) Even when it does not lead to warfare, the proximity of different cultures often gives rise to hostility, disparagement, or, at best, apathy between the different groups.

Once again, we should not be surprised at the generally unenthusiastic response we have seen so far to cryonics. For most people it offers a competing worldview and thus, we should expect, will be seen as a threat and a call to defend their culture. To persuade such people to accept cryonics would apparently require full conversion to a different worldview—a difficult task. On the other hand, some people do choose cryonics. We might ask what characteristics make them different from the more numerous ones who do not.

Characteristics of Cryonicists

There are certain unusual individuals who contemplate life apart from ties with a culture and insist on living, first and foremost, by inner lights. They may value contacts with others but do not feel that the sum of these contacts is what makes the crucial part of their identity. Regarding the issue of death they appear not to require an anxiety buffer that is enforced by group consensus. Perhaps instead they have a noncultural anxiety buffer that is mainly their own creation or otherwise does not depend on the constant group reinforcement that most people seem to need. They form, I think, the bulk of the cryonics movement to date. Their scarcity is probably selection-based; with their unconventional views and disposition they would tend to be ostracized, which would limit their influence both socially and genetically.

A simple analogy may help to visualize this. Imagine humanity as masses of soapsuds, each single bubble a person. Most bubbles are contained in the interior of a large mass of suds (culture), entirely surrounded by others with boundaries in common, so that each bubble consists entirely of interfaces. Less common are bubbles on the surface, partly exposed but still rooted in interfaces (cultural ties). These outer bubbles perhaps represent "leaders in thought" or other authority figures to those in the interior. They have some independence but still are tied to their society and lack the motivation to stand alone when necessary. (Imagine, for example, a prominent scientist who deplores cryonics for emotional reasons or even favors its possibilities but shuns any personal involvement.) Finally there is the very rare free-floating bubble who is not sustained by interfaces but instead manages a lasting self-containment, seeking close encounters perhaps, but never the ties that compromise by creating strong dependencies.

A word is appropriate here, concerning value judgments. Our "hierarchy" of bubbles seems to favor those with fewer interfaces, especially the free-floaters with none. It might then seem that, by way of analogy, we are commending outcasts and hermits of every description, if sufficiently alienated from the rest of humanity and surrounding culture. This is not the intent. I count interfaces important too, and indeed, in the next chapter and later we will find reasons for especially valuing the "Interface"—one's ties with reality as a whole. Such ties are meaningful, and not every free-floater is to be ranked highly, but I think, only those of good will and behavior with the courage and strength to stand alone when necessary.

At any rate, the soapsuds analogy clearly has other limitations too and must not be pressed too hard, though I think it does convey the basic picture. And one additional refinement seems useful: we could allow small, free-floating clumps of bubbles to model people who cohere into small, self-sufficient groups—for example, a husband and wife who are otherwise independent. I also think we can press the analogy a little further to suggest other attributes we actually observe. A large mass of suds is more stable and longer lasting than a smaller one, and free-floating bubbles and bubbles near the surface are more vulnerable than bubbles in the interior. In the social parallel, a large society of conforming individuals is more enduring and is consequently favored by the selection process. It may be too that the leaders in thought are more exposed to stresses than their more conservative following and thus are subject to some negative effects from selection, which, it is reasonable to conjecture, are more pronounced still with the free-floaters.

In any case, it is important to keep in mind that in the real world the social structuring we observe and the associated attitudes and practices are maintained not by some strange accident or the inscrutable workings of an unknown power but by the selection process. As long as the same underlying features are present, we should not be surprised if the selection process continues to yield up a similar structuring, with the same prevalent attitudes and behaviors. It is possible then that attitudes favoring scientific life extension will not gain much currency for a very long time—but this seems unlikely. The pace of change is swift in our modern society, and many old givens are increasingly being challenged.

Toward a Change in Attitudes

With advances in the state of our knowledge, new possibilities of a physical nature are emerging that, we might expect, will alter the very nature of what constitutes viability both for the individual and for entire cultures—if indeed the latter will continue to have a separate existence at all. The individual "bubble," we hope, will no longer be so vulnerable, whether free-floating or deeply embedded. In fact we may conjecture that with time all will become free-floating while in another sense also embedded, as all become enduring, not transient, beings. The standards and logic of the selection process must shift as new discoveries and their applications open new doors. Different modes of thinking and behavior will be favored and be induced to develop further, while others that formerly flourished must wither. Appropriate to these changes, whose beginnings are seen today, we can advocate a wonderful new worldview with a new and superior anxiety buffer.

In doing this, though, we must confront a world in which the most important features of this glorious promise are still unrealized and unrecognized. A part of the progress that must be made is a change in attitudes—an interesting chicken-and-egg problem: proper attitudes would further vital technical progress and its application, which in turn would further proper attitudes. Clearly, barring miracles, we cannot expect any attitudinal phase shifts overnight. This we have to accept stoically, even if we do not always agree with the Stoics (on death acceptance in particular). Generally such cultural inertia has survival value, as protection against the sort of shifts that might be deleterious, and thus itself is favored by the selection process. The good changes must come, then, as a gradual interactive effort, spearheaded by research that produces the advances that are hard to ignore and tend to change old worldviews.

But benefits can still follow from a better understanding of the situation that now confronts us. A better understanding in fact seems fostered through the terror management theory we have just considered. It appears to explain puzzling features of the resistance to the idea of extending life span through the new technological possibilities that seem to exist. Understanding this resistance should improve our success, even if only marginally, which will have value even if only a few additional lives are saved as a consequence.

Immortalism and cryonics, it seems reasonable to conclude, are widely seen as violating the conformity that most people value. Some have wondered if that alone might be the whole explanation for why the two have not become more widespread, at least among thinking people, but the terror management theory suggests that this would not explain the observed effects. Instead it tells us that the conformity violation is of a particularly disturbing and serious nature, calling into question existing worldviews and their associated cultural anxiety buffers.

Remarkably, all this occurs in a context of acceptability. Most agree that there is nothing wrong with the practice of cryonics, such that it ought to be suppressed through the legal system. (At least this is the prevailing view in the United States where the movement started and still has the largest following and despite the bureaucratic challenges reported in the last chapter.) That this much acceptance can coexist with the denial of personal involvement shows how cultural ties are stronger than logic—a situation that is reflected in the selection process.

In our enlightened society, toleration of opposing views and practices is widespread. This too we must imagine is favored by the selection process, as indeed is suggested in the collapse of Soviet communism and the victory of nontotalitarian systems that outperformed it economically. But society, for reasons again governed by the selection process, has not elaborated a worldview that favors newly available technological means for possible life extension, except when it can be seamlessly integrated into existing, culturally approved channels. This occurs in the case of nutritional supplements and medical advances of a more conventional nature, which indeed have much broader support than a "radical" approach like cryonics.

The immortalist position (generally) is that there is no all-providing superpower but that humanity must elevate itself. There is as yet no tangible miracle to convince a child or a skeptical adult. (Resuscitation of someone from cryonic suspension would be such a miracle, one would think, but as is often pointed out, by the time that happens the need for cryonics itself may have passed into history.) Thus the premise of immortalism—that science can provide the solution to the problem of death—is hard to understand and accept, both for the eager child and the skeptical adult.

Other attributes of the human psyche, no doubt, are at work. People usually come in pairs. One person may be predisposed to join a movement but will probably hold back if a lover or spouse is opposed. People generally will not endorse something unless experts have pronounced in its favor, which has not yet happened on a sufficient scale.

Some objections relate to perceived biological roles. A commitment to the reproductive process is strongly ingrained in most people, as indeed is to be expected from natural selection. In a sense, reproduction and immortality stand at cross-purposes; the one obviates the need for the other. "I will survive through my children!" is a commonly voiced rationale. Related to this is the idea of surviving through works, which appeals to some creative individuals. (The immortalist replies, "Your children are not you, nor is a book, painting, or some other creation of yours.")

Finally, the question can be raised whether many people really want to live. Much of the desire for immortality may simply be a visceral fear reaction against death. This aversion seems ingrained at the deepest levels of sentience; frogs and fish will struggle to save their lives. "I do not want to die" is equivalent, in some logical sense, to "I do want to live forever," but many do not accept this logic. Wanting to live forever requires an entirely different mental apparatus, one not open to fish or frogs. On the other hand, not wanting to live forever may be just an artifact of the cultural anxiety buffer that could be alleviated by adopting a better worldview. One's worldview and one's assessment of the value of life, it would seem, are closely interrelated. If it seemed feasible to attain immortality in this worldly existence, perhaps the desire for it would grow in step, especially when it was recognized that certain handicaps of being human (limited intelligence and joy in living, for instance) would not apply indefinitely.

When the cryonics movement began there was hope it would

grow rapidly. Millions or even billions of people might have been preserved for an immortal future, but it did not happen. Part of the reason was simply the instability of the earliest cryonics organizations and the lack of adequate provisions for long-term storage of patients. In the 1970s some stronger organizations were formed, and they established a better track record. Available information suggests that the number of people seriously involved in cryonics grew from a few dozen in the mid-1970s to six or seven hundred two decades later, for an average annual increase around 15 percent.[3] Though actually an impressive expansion, the number of cryonicists can be expected to stay small for a long time to come. In fact, at this rate, the growth will double only about every five years, which would yield a few hundred thousand cryonicists in fifty years, only a small fraction of the projected earth's population. It would take more than a century for the figure to approach the current world total of six billion.

Such projecting is hazardous: many things both plus and minus could happen to confound expectations. Still an argument might be made that cryonics, regardless of its potential, is unlikely to save most of those now living. This, if it proves true, is certainly sad, particularly if cryonics does work for those who do make the arrangements. On the other hand, the pace of progress often astonishes even those who are laughed at for over-optimism. Today we have ongoing developments in such fields as biology, nanotechnology, and computers, which could lead to much faster progress than most would predict. Maybe in a few decades immortality will be upon us, and cryonics will not be an issue.

In the meantime, what can be done, beyond providing the physical means to be frozen when the need arises—a not inconsiderable chore—and as always, supporting research? The best course seems to be to try to present a sound, positive philosophy of scientific immortalism that as many as possible can have confidence in, or at least take interest in, even if the actual number of devotees turns out to be small. It should, of course, provide an anxiety buffer to shield against the fear of death. It must be based on rational principles and not just arbitrary beliefs. This is what is being attempted here. We thus proclaim a new "good news." Death, in all its aspects, can be overcome and will be overcome scientifically—of this you can be certain enough (if not absolutely certain) to make it the foundation of your hopes. But we must do more than hope. The best path to follow is not one of passivity. Instead, for each of us a course of action is called for: to put in place a personal plan of biostasis, to carry out a reasoned and caring promotion of our ideas, and to lend whatever support we can to research and development.

It is also expected that as the end of mortality is increasingly seen as attainable, a considerable adjustment will be needed for the many who must then confront possibilities they did not dare hope for before. It would be well to have as much in place as possible, by way of something in which to rest one's hopes, for the profound changes that are likely to happen. For now, though, death is still very much with us. Only one approach exists, preservation through such means as cryonics for possibly defeating death before it can take its usual effect.

Cryonics Acceptance: a Hypothetical Case

To promote an idea, the likely audience must be kept in mind, of which the most important subgroup consists of the fence-sitters who have not fully accepted the idea but might do so with reasonable encouragement. In the case of scientific immortality, and cryonics in particular, the fence-sitters might be expected to be independent-minded individualists who are culturally "mobile"—willing to consider a switch in allegiance or lacking strong ties. They would not believe strongly in mystical concepts but still would long for something beyond life's current limits. In another sense, almost everyone of the converted who reads this— those who already accept cryonics—is probably no better than a fence-sitter since a philosophical system going beyond cryonics is being argued. For now, though, I want to address the more basic problems relating to acceptance of cryonics for the potential convert. Such a person, whom we will call Fred, is not a cryonicist but might become one with reasonable encouragement. He will have a certain mind-set, which we must consider before trying to present the arguments for cryonics.

Fred then is independent and open-minded, with at least some feeling that life does or can hold things of value. He might like to see the future, but might also feel some dread. Fred is a scientific materialist, not attracted to doctrines of the supernatural or paranormal, not convinced by fantastic claims of assistance through space-alien visitations, backward time travel, or other possibilities that so far have lacked reasonable verification. He is, however, willing to consider even very unusual claims on their own merits, trying at all times to be objective. He need not be a physicist or scientist, but should have an appreciation for science and the reality it is revealing to us, as well as the methods and standards it uses. The majesty and mystery of the world should hold some serious fascination, though he may have no small uncertainty as to what it really means. In our soapsuds analogy, he is at least close to a free-floating bubble.

Deep down, Fred is uneasy about the thought that, by straightforward appearances, he is going to die in at most a few decades, and will perish eternally, or just possibly reawaken, after his death, in some strange setting, by some unknown process. He may have tried to accept his demise as inevitable, but if so, is at least uncomfortable about it. Death, certainly, does not seem wholly and self-evidently a good thing, though he may have misgivings about the prospect of greatly or infinitely extended life. These misgivings could involve only personal issues or might extend to more general social and moral concerns. Whatever his feelings about death, he is not strongly committed to any of the solutions offered by the more prevalent religions and death-accepting philosophies.

Finally, we suppose Fred has encountered cryonics and is considering it. I will now try, in turn, to consider the possible questions he might raise, and how these might be answered in preliminary fashion (more on this will follow in later chapters).

The first issue might be one of efficacy: Will cryonics work? Is it likely that persons frozen by today's technology (or what can conservatively be estimated to be available by the time Fred will need it) will eventually be resuscitated as intended? Related is the question of whether there would be crippling deficiencies, in case only imperfect recovery of the patient is possible. There is a deeper question: whether, with imperfect recovery, the result would be the "same" or a "different" person.

But first let us consider these questions: (1) is it likely that some resuscitation of a frozen (cryopreserved) individual would take place? and (2) is it likely, in the event that perfect recovery is not possible, that a resuscitee would experience crippling or debilitating deficits causing suffering? The two questions, despite the attempt to keep them simple, already raise a further issue: technological capability versus willingness to apply the capability one has. Thus it is possible that future society will be able to resuscitate a cryonics patient, but unwilling to do so—though I doubt this, for reasons considered later in the chapter. For now, let us assume that future society would be willing to apply whatever technology it can in resuscitating persons who might be helped and consider the technological issue alone.

Here the evidence, if still circumstantial, is reasonably solid and suggestive. Scanning-probe microscopes regularly image structures at the atomic level, and they can also manipulate individual atoms. If information in a piece of material is there, it should be recoverable in principle, and ultimately in practice, when a mature nanotechnology is developed. This applies to a frozen organism just as much as to a rock or a piece of plastic. (Recovering information from materials at low temperature should not be prohibitively difficult because the energy to power scanning probes could be localized to avoid general heating. In the same way, molecular-scale repairs could also be made at low temperature.) Is the information likely to be there?

Here the outlook too seems generally positive, though there is a question as to how much information will survive. There is certainly enough information to infer the genome—copied trillions of times over in the DNA of our cells—which ought to make it possible, at minimum, to produce an identical twin or clone of the original. What then about the brain, which contains information such as the memory that delineates the individual personality and distinguishes one twin from another? Here the uncertainty is greater, though still, I think, there is reason to be hopeful. It is still unconfirmed, but frozen brain structure appears well enough preserved that it is reasonably likely that memory and other critical information survives also. Some of the evidence comes from such studies as Suda's revival of partly frozen cat brains, which we considered last chapter.[5]

The case for nanotechnology will be examined in more detail later, along with cryonic resuscitation itself, which could proceed along rather different lines than suggested above. In any case it seems a reasonable bet that, if sufficient information survives in frozen tissue to infer the healthy state of the organism—

here a human being—then a procedure can be developed for repairing all the damage and restoring that person to consciousness and health.

Similarly, to whatever extent information does survive in frozen remains, a functioning organism possessing those characteristics should be constructible, either from entirely new but atomically identical material or by reconditioning the original material. This could result in deficits if the original information is only imperfectly preserved, but there is good reason to think that there would be no deficits whatever, beyond possible amnesia. A deficit-free organism could be created merely by creating a twin, which could be done from DNA alone. Beyond this, the newly created/repaired brain could be conditioned or "programmed" as necessary to reflect, as far as possible, the known attributes of the original person.

Amnesia might seem inevitable if the brain is absent or heavily damaged—for where are we going to obtain replacement memories? Later, however, I will argue that even replacement memories are a likely possibility. (I realize too that some may prefer to be missing some of their memories and just start out afresh; these cases also will receive their due.) For now I hope it will be provisionally accepted that a resuscitation from cryonic suspension, to the extent of being free of crippling deficits, is a reasonable likelihood.

We can then raise the question whether, even if no such deficits are present, the resuscitee is really the "same" person or a different person from the original. Will we have rescued a person of the past or simply created a new, fantasy individual with some similarities to the old—a being with false memories who never existed? The significance of this question will be seen if we consider the viewpoint of someone like Fred, who is considering cryonics. "Will *I* come back," he worriedly wants to know, "or just some other, newly created person who may resemble me in some degree?"

The question has a particularly straightforward, reassuring answer in view of the UI assumptions, which will be examined later. We cannot be sure Fred is ready to accept them, however, so here we want to be more conservative.

We will consider the case of someone else, Ned, who suffers severe head injuries in a car accident. Ned is very close to death and a decision must be made whether to take him off life support and give up, or go on. The decision is made to continue treatment. At first it seems doubtful Ned will regain consciousness, but finally signs of awareness do appear, and the extent of his deficits can be assessed.

There has been a lot of brain damage, but with therapy, Ned gradually recovers faculties such as speech and motor skills. Let us say Ned was highly educated—much of that knowledge and skill is now garbled or erased but is reinstated or refurbished through further effort on his and others' parts. A great deal of Ned's past too is now hazy to him, but this problem is helped by his talking with those who remember some of the details. Further help comes from research that Ned carries out himself when he is stronger and from his gut feelings about what some earlier experiences must have been like. In time, Ned feels "normal," is fully functional, and seems reasonably the "same" person he was before both to others and to himself. Clearly the recovery has not been perfect, but all things considered it was not bad either—in fact it seems little short of miraculous. Ned is no less happy to be alive than before and is glad of the decision to try to rehabilitate him. Although we could still raise the issue of whether he is really the same person, I think most would agree that the initial decision not to give up was the right one.

This conclusion follows, in large part, because we assume Ned is fully rehabilitated and functional. In other cases in which the victim has lasting deficits, the issue is more complex. But, in view of the foregoing discussion, such cases should not be relevant to cryonics since our future capability should guarantee a full restoration to functionality. So Fred, like Ned, should be able to view the future prospects with reasonable confidence.

A Future of Wonder

Given, then, that cryonics ought to work to some desirable degree, we can consider whether one should opt for the procedure. This is really a question about whether life in the future would be worthwhile, and here the answer seems clear enough: The future should offer wonders beyond anything yet possible and anything yet imaginable. For the wonders will not merely be of the external sort—things we can see and do, but of the internal sort as well—our very capacity to experience wonder will grow in step as we develop beyond the human level.

We should be able to free ourselves of aging and diseases, and drudgery as well. Automated devices capable of handling most of their own maintenance, including repairs, should eliminate most work as we understand it today. We should then be free to pursue more creative and personally rewarding work. Far from being idle, we will be busier than ever as our own bosses and enjoying life far more too. And yet, we will still have responsibilities, as I will argue, and will not lose our importance or become superfluous or outmoded.

Today many may feel they are not particularly creative or capable of much sense of wonder. Such people often are not much interested in longer life—it would be too "boring." That will change. The mysteries of the functioning brain should become known to us, much as for the far simpler devices we understand today. It should then become clear how to enhance the brain's performance, and, proceeding with due caution, we can expect to further our own developmental process more generally. Our future progress will see increased intelligence as well as greater capacity to appreciate the wonders we now behold with more limited understanding. On the personal level, then, there is reason to expect great rewards indeed.

Once this is accepted, other possible objections become easier to manage. For one thing, we expect very great changes in how life will be lived. Old issues may lose their meaning even as new ones surface and must be dealt with. This thought can be used to answer certain social objections that are sometimes raised to the idea of overcoming death.

One objection is "Death allows society to change." True, older people today suffer from rigidity and narrowness of interests, which can lead to stagnation, given the influence such people are often able to exert. But the future should free us from the deadening effects of the aging process, which clearly is so largely responsible for the inflexibility, loss of inspiration, and unreceptiveness to new possibilities that is seen in the elderly. People will no longer be categorized as "elderly" as we understand it, but as bright, energetic individuals with more or less experience in different areas, and, generally, more experience than younger people, due to having lived longer. This, coupled with all our new capabilities, should well resolve the problem of stagnation.

"Wouldn't it lead to overpopulation?" is another commonly voiced concern. The reasonable answer, I think, is that it is hardly likely. Birth rates have been falling worldwide for decades now, even in the absence of any hopes of immortality.[6] As such hopes become more accepted, the trend can only accelerate. As technology improves, birth control will become easier and more convenient—as one possible check. Other curbs should become increasingly important too, as we pass beyond the human level. In effect, we will simply outgrow the preoccupation to reproduce, as it becomes less important to us and more of a liability.

The possibility of building habitats in space to relieve population pressure is sometimes raised too, and certainly this can be accepted, yet it seems clear that space habitats could not be the main answer. We must instead eliminate the exponential or geometric growth in which population doubles over a fixed time interval—an increase that no technology, by most indications, could support indefinitely. This should not be difficult however; after all, we are talking about becoming more-than-human. As this takes effect, we will naturally find it easier to curb and redirect our more primitive urges, even as we no doubt undergo changes in our physical makeup. In due course, overpopulation, or, more generally, creating new sentient beings at too high a rate should become a non-issue, along with such problems as jobs and many other difficulties of limited resources.

One positive change will involve an attitude toward fellow beings. Today the thought is often expressed that we are primarily machines to perpetuate our genes. The concerns of such beings are focused in rather obvious ways by natural selection, with the emphasis on immediate survival needs, mating, and progeny. This we have carried with us, thus far having no choice, even though our lifestyles have been modified greatly by our creation of civilization. Even so, the outlook is not so bleak—the roots of an immortal lifestyle can be seen in our world today, where we are still as we biologically evolved. Despite the pressures to develop a narrowness of interests and an unconcern for strangers, we have formed into societies. We at least pay nodding respect to such concepts as the rights to life, liberty, and the pursuit of happiness. Nature has, in fact, prepared us somewhat for the great leap we must now make, though we will have to take the initiative and work beyond the easy answers.

For the posthuman future we can imagine that consideration of others will intensify, for simple reasons of self-interest. When we are no longer focused on creating progeny during a brief struggle for existence that must soon end in our demise but on leading rich and hopefully endless lives, our perspectives will broaden. Among other things, we may conjecture that any two individuals must encounter each other again and again, or develop some pathological mutual aversion that will detract from both lives. It should become increasingly clear that there is much to gain, personally, through consideration for others and acts of benevolence. In this way, then, I foresee a postmortal society that is a harmonious whole, strife and violence having given way to more reasoned interaction.

The increased consideration for others should carry over to others of the past who might be resuscitated from a preserved state. It is easy to feel a certain fascination with such an idea even now. I think this feeling will be strong, at least for some people in the future, and probably for most if not all. The generally increased valuing of life must surely translate to concern for those who cannot now participate but could be helped to participate, given the means available. Persons of the past would have unique contributions to make in the lives of those then living, which should hold a special interest. This should be true even if such persons would initially be out of place; they could offer their own perspectives and perceptions in exchange for the new learning they would receive.

I think too that resuscitating frozen people, to the extent that it becomes possible, will also be inexpensive by future standards. This seems particularly likely when the possibilities for automation are taken into account. With operations directed by devices that are largely self-repairing and self-maintaining and can proliferate components in vast swarms as needed (though only as needed), even very complex procedures should become feasible and fast. Included, I imagine, will be whatever is required to repair and resuscitate a frozen human. This should not be a great resource drain, though even if it is the chances are good that it will be carried out anyway. It will be done if it can be done, much as great effort is expended today to restore ancient texts or monuments, or, for that matter, to scale mountain peaks or put people into space.

Once again, the future should have many wonders—not the least being an overall increase in friendliness. Still, many find this vision disturbing. A world beyond procreation and death is something they would rather not think about. However, such visions are nothing new in the history of thought, but recur throughout the major religions. Christianity, for example, is noted for promoting the ideas of resurrection and eternal life. It was well recognized that everlasting life would differ from its mortal counterpart.

Jesus, we are told in the Bible, was confronted by some Sadducees who denied the possibility that the dead would be raised. Their reasoning was thus: Suppose a woman had married, then her husband had died, then she married again, and so on—up to seven husbands in all. At the resurrection, whose wife would she be? (Polyandry being culturally disallowed, an impasse seemed to have been reached.) Jesus answered, in effect, that they had asked a stupid question. At the resurrection, he said, people would no longer be simply men or women, but something more—they would live "like angels." The question of marriage would become irrelevant.[7]

Happily and incredibly, modern science is coming to grips with ancient wishes for a more-than-human existence. We now approach these old but vital dreams with renewed seriousness and hope. Cryonics, in particular, as a reasonable way of making a bid for extended life, then presents us with a choice having moral consequences. To opt for cryonics is to choose life over death. In this way we send a message to others that this choice is available through a rational procedure and, moreover, that it is a better choice to make.

This issue will be considered in greater detail, along with the problem of how resurrections could occur even without the biostasis option and why reactivation of a past individual, under one set of circumstances or another, is even inevitable. Loved ones who have perished, then, will not be gone forever but will one day reawaken, though once again the biostasis route is better. The next chapter, after summarizing the larger picture, will go further into reasons why, as a preliminary to the more detailed treatment in Chapter 13.

CHAPTER 4.

A Philosophical System

The philosophical system offered in this book, as suggested in Chapter 1, is no bolt from the blue but has precedents that are recognized under various names. There is the Supramoralism of Fedorov and the "natural salvation" of his American contemporary, C. A. Stevens, both of whom have anticipated, in important ways, much of the moral philosophy and eschatological outlook offered here. These writers of a century ago have been echoed more recently by a small band of modern physicists, a principal exemplar being Frank Tipler, with his Omega Point Theory.

Essentially, the stance of these and others, which I have adopted also, is to recognize the great strengths contained in traditional religious views of the significance of life and of what ought to be our destiny. At the same time, however, we also acknowledge the weakness of the religious position on how the vision of our destiny, so extravagant yet so necessary, is to be realized. What their writings suggest, and I affirm more boldly—paraphrasing Gerald Gruman in his study of the prolongevity hypothesis[1]—is to replace the important promises of traditional religion with equivalent promises based on science and progress. The two most important such promises are the resurrection of the dead and a happy eternal life. It is customary, of course, to consider these as quite beyond the powers of science to approach, but careful consideration shows otherwise (as I think has by now been established) for an outlook based on modern physics.

This does not mean we are claiming dogmatic certainty about the fulfillment of these promises. Science cannot offer guarantees but only possibilities and probabilities based on experiment, observation, and rational thought. Yet this is no insurmountable obstacle to a firm foundation for hope. Uncertainty is actually a healthy thing. The reduction of uncertainty, in the domain of science, is no one-time act of affirmation, as in dogmas accepted without question, but proceeds over time. In this manner, one is either reassured by progressively confirming evidence, or, if not, one can try to correct any errors in views by formulating new hypotheses and testing them. The principles one lives and hopes by, then, take on the character of working hypotheses.

Of the working hypotheses assumed here, three are predominant: (1) life, fundamentally, is good; (2) death is an imposition on life and ought to be alleviated and eradicated; and (3) rational means, rightly inspired, are the proper tools for understanding all things and solving all problems of interest. These, we should note, will not be the only working hypotheses. The UI assumptions are also important working hypotheses introduced in Chapter 1, along with the rejection of the paranormal—to take some examples. But these principles are subordinate to the three named above, which will serve as our guidelines. Other working hypotheses will be added later as seems fitting. For instance, I will elaborate the first principle into "The life of each individual sentient being, fundamentally, is good," and offer supporting arguments.

For the system offered in this book, it will be convenient to have a name; I will call it *Yuai*. This is derived from Universal Immortalism—a good descriptive title—and also from the UI assumptions. A little more whimsically, the word can be formed

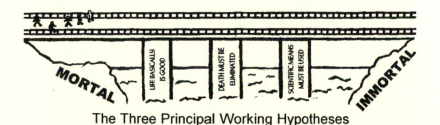

The Three Principal Working Hypotheses

from the Japanese syllables *yu* ("friendship") and *ai* ("love," "harmony," "peace"). Yet another rationale that some have suggested is "You-I"—all beings everywhere, as they relate to the individual. As still another possibility, in computer-speak UI can mean "user-interface," which is relevant if we imagine a User—the hopeful immortal—seeking a good Interface, or connection with surrounding reality and eternity. (These two concepts, and particularly the Interface, will be discussed more later.)

Yuai, then, is about a friendly universal community, a mode of existence in peace, love, and harmony, that hopefully all can share endlessly, and a fitting "user-interface" with the ultimate operating system, the world at large. Ultimately, *all* means all people and even all other sentient beings who have ever existed, now exist, or will exist. I anticipate that quite literally all will be resurrected, in the manner suggested before of creating either a functioning duplicate or a more advanced version, that is, a *continuer*. This is something I do not expect to happen anytime soon and almost certainly not until long after such preliminaries as the advent of a mature nanotechnology and many of its consequences, including any resuscitations of people in biostasis that prove feasible. I also, of course, discount any claimed resurrections of people in the past through supernatural or other paranormal means; on scientific grounds it seems most unlikely. Such a possibility as resurrecting the dead must await a more advanced future, when we are well into our posthuman existence and our horizons have expanded greatly. Yet again I think it will happen eventually; for it is not ruled out logically or scientifically, and some at least in the future, whose powers must far exceed ours today, will recognize that it ought to happen and will work diligently to make it happen.

In particular, evil beings will be resurrected along with everybody else and cured of their unfortunate tendencies, to join the others in advancing to unlimited heights. (For I regard propensity to evil, rather than being an innate or identity-critical property of certain "lost" natures, as a treatable ailment.) Beings with other shortcomings can be similarly assisted and can then join the advance. Yuai, then, is a form of Universalism—proclaiming that all shall be saved in the end and enjoy an eternal reward. It is a Universalism that rests its hopes fully in the natural world and upon individuals whose existence is explained by physics. These individuals—ourselves, past, present, and future, and ultimately all to be living again—are the ones who must care about and solve all the problems that are meaningful.

We are the ones who must shape the future. We thus must supply the standards for determining what ought to be, both in the large and the small details, as well as find the means to bring it all about. However, it is not the we of today through whom these problems will take their more definitive forms and find their better solutions. These matters will fall to our developing future selves, who, we imagine, will progress in various directions as needs and interests require. There is important preliminary work that we ought to be doing today, however. The future, then, is a growth process for the individual, who, starting here and now, with passing time will more closely approach perfection and fulfillment.

The extent of this future advancement is something we can scarcely imagine now in our only-human state, yet it will not render our life and work of today superfluous. Even with the greatest advances, a link is to be maintained, through remembered experiences and other personal information, with the past self, which thus is always of significance. This link I conjecture will—as it should—continue to be important as we master the secrets of our biology and psychology and transform ourselves into beings higher than human. Any being, then, can develop or be developed to any level intellectually and in other ways. The perception of the advance, through reflection upon the earlier stages in one's life, will add to the appreciation of the progress that has been made. No level of advancement, on the other hand, is ever final, but further progress is always possible and desirable. An essential in this will be an advancing, future technology to free us of mortality and enable us endlessly to progress. People of course are imperfect and must not be rated higher than they deserve. But the highest abilities and motives can be linked to the individual here and now, even if immediate attribution is withheld, through anticipation of the advancement that someday should come. People are to be valued not merely for present attributes and accomplishments but in terms of future potential.

Reductionism, Materialism, and the Problem of Survival

Questions often are raised about what sort of future life the would-be immortal should be interested in. It seems essential that (1) the person should survive, in some reasonable sense; and (2) the one who survives, a person from an earlier time with suitable "updating," should experience a meaningful happiness. The challenging issue of a future, meaningful happiness will be considered later; the problem of survival will now be examined in preliminary form. This is a matter on which many who favor immortality, even among cryonicists, have expressed disagreement. Here I outline the viewpoint on survival that will serve as our guide.

We are concerned with a person as a whole, regarded as an entity persisting over the entire time of life or, in the terminology of Max More, a *diachronic self.* We will also need to consider a *person-segment*, which is the portion of the person that can be said to exist over a particular time interval, long or short. Finally, it will be useful to allow the time interval to approach zero, so that we obtain a person at a particular time, or *person-stage.* The most general concept then is the person-segment. If the time interval for the segment extends to the whole of life, we obtain the diachronic self, while, at the other extreme, with the interval very tiny, we get a person-stage. It is not necessary that all existing personality characteristics play a part in this activity during the time interval in question, unless it is the whole of life. A memory of a past experience could be dormant or latent and only make an appearance later.

I will use the term *person* somewhat informally, often meaning a diachronic self, but sometimes other concepts such as a person-stage or a physical, functioning body and brain. The intended meaning should be clear from the context.

By rough analogy we can compare the diachronic self with a movie; a person-segment with a sequence, long or short, of consecutive frames of the movie; and the person-stage with a single frame. (For an immortal person, then, the movie has infinitely many frames.) The diachronic self thus is made up of a sequence of person-stages corresponding to the person at different points in his or her life. It will be useful to consider this in more detail. Suppose that we have a person-stage P_1, extant at some time t_1, and some other person-stage P_2, extant at some later time t_2. It is possible that P_2 is a later stage of P_1 and thus, that both are part of the same diachronic self, though of course this is not guaranteed—P_2 could simply be (from) a different person entirely. But in case the relation holds, we may say that P_1 survives in, or through, P_2. For such survival to occur, it is clear that some substantial connections or affinity must exist between P_2 and P_1. Opinions vary widely, however, as to just what connections are, or ought to be considered, essential.

The two major divisions of opinions are the reductionist and the nonreductionist views, as discussed by Derek Parfit in *Reasons and Persons*;[2] a short summary will be useful here. For a reductionist, the question of the survival or nonsurvival of P_1 in P_2 is reducible to certain other facts about P_1 and P_2 that can be described in an impersonal way. Such facts, for example, may include the different psychological and physical characteristics of both P_1 and P_2 and the process involved (if applicable) in the formation or development of P_2 out of P_1.

It should be clear that physical characteristics of a person can be described in an impersonal way, for example, by resorting to physics, if we think of a person as amounting to a collection of particles in motion. For the case of psychological characteristics, the argument is more involved but similar; we can, for example, think of the person as a type of computational process, a program running on a machine consisting of a body and brain. The body, brain, and program could in turn be described impersonally, at least in principle. For a nonreductionist there is some "further fact" that counts, something that cannot be reduced to the impersonal level, for example, the presence of a "soul" in P_2 that was formerly resident in P_1.

Since I reject mystical or paranormal elements in favor of scientific materialism, I discount such a further fact and accept the reductionism just outlined. *Reductionism,* however, is a term that is widely used and abused in philosophical circles; further clarification is needed. My intended usage can be understood, in the first place, as an acceptance of materialism over other possibilities in accounting for reality. Materialism is a kind of reductionism in its own right, but I will adopt an additional reductionism to apply at the level of persons.

A brief remark is needed here, because *materialism* can mean

different things, which can mislead. There is scientific materialism, a viewpoint about reality, which is important in the philosophical position we are considering. There is also what can be
called *valuational materialism*—an attitude toward what is important in one's life, extended perhaps, to life more generally. A
materialist in this second sense is one who is focused on material
possessions or comforts, and not on such supramundane issues
as whether immortality is possible. The narrow concern with the
material aspects of this present life, however, is not what I wish
to signify by materialism, but rather the scientific viewpoint,
which has wider scope.

Scientific materialism holds that everything can be explained
in terms of matter and void—particles and their interactions in
space over time—there is no need to invoke "higher powers" or a
supernatural realm. On the other hand, modern physics has substantially altered our ideas of the material world. As one example
there is Einstein's famous equation, $e=mc^2$, equating matter and
energy. Photons, mesons, neutrinos, and a host of other particles
now supplement those involved in more usual material objects:
the electron, the proton, and the neutron in their familiar combinations known as atoms. On a deeper level, attempts are under
way by theoreticians to reduce all particles to something like vibrating strings, membranes, or some other concept to explain what
can be observed. There is also the intriguing possibility, suggested
by certain scientific inquiries, that our universe is not the only
material domain but is accompanied by many separate and largely
noninteracting universes, that together form a "multiverse."

Still, despite such new insights or conjectures, modern, scientific materialism, in its approach to explaining reality, has much
more affinity with ancient ideas on the subject—like the materialism of the Epicureans—than it does with any concept of a spirit
world. Most important, it holds that the real world is comprehensible through a systematic process of investigation and thought,
rather than allowing supernatural or irreducibly mystifying elements. Materialism thus is a form of naturalism, holding that the
natural is all that exists and that it is to be studied and understood
by methods appropriate to the natural world, that is, rational, scientific inquiry.

The world is thus reducible to interacting, elementary components. Happenings are explained by mathematical theories that

have been developed to describe such interactions. These theories have had remarkable successes, and the search for even better theories continues. Modern, scientific materialism thus embodies a reductionism that has great power in accounting for reality as we know it. Still, our great mathematical theories are inadequate. Many things important to us are not well addressed, such as what constitutes a person and what is a good life. This does not mean materialism is invalidated—it is not—but theories that apply to one aspect of reality need supplementation so we can make sense of things at other levels. Thus we do not want to push reductionism too far. As examples, politics and psychology are not explained, in any practical sense, as simply the interactions of subatomic particles, even if they do depend, ultimately, on these very interactions and the laws that govern them. But forms of reductionism can still be useful in dealing with various aspects of reality, though there is sometimes confusion as to which form of reductionism, if any, should properly apply.

Physical versus Psychological Reductionism

At the level of persons there are two main, competing theories known as physical and psychological reductionism. These employ different criteria to decide when a later person-stage should be regarded as the "same" person as an earlier stage. The notion of sameness itself is more complex than it may appear. I will follow generally accepted usage, in that at a later time we could still have the "same" person despite differences. It then remains to determine what sort of differences are permissible, or conversely, what similarities or affinities are necessary, to say that an earlier person-stage survives in a later one. The two reductionist theories are further subdivided; they and their subdivisions need to be considered carefully to arrive at a viewpoint that seems right.

Physical reductionism uses the physical criterion, which focuses on the body as a whole, or possibly just the brain, since by itself the brain arguably contains the whole personality. P_1 survives in P_2 just in case there is physical continuity between the two. The notion of physical continuity (which actually exists in several versions—I will explore the simplest first) can be regarded as a generalization of the case for inanimate objects.

An inanimate object—a building, say—might be at a fixed location and (ideally) persist in unaltered form over a period of time. Further, it could be observed continuously during this time to verify that the original building was not destroyed and replaced with an exact copy. We thus would first have a building-stage B_1 at time t_1, then a building-stage B_2 at a later time t_2. By the physical criterion, given our continuous observation, the two building-stages would be identified, said to correspond to the same building, and to be one and the same. It should be clear that, in principle, we could establish this without invoking the notion of a building at all. We would simply focus on the various structural components, including suitable interconnections or other relationships among the different parts and note that they individually persisted in unchanging form. In this way, the reductionist premise would be satisfied.

In practice, of course, all physical objects change with time, but the principle of physical continuity can still be applied—at least to a point. If the building has some minor damage, repairs or alterations, for example, we would probably still regard it as the same building because the successive changes were small and more-or-less continuous. This could apply, for instance, even if the building was moved to a new location. In fact there could be considerable alterations over an extended period of time, yet, if done in such a way that a building was present at all times, we might still consider it the same building. (Jefferson's home Monticello comes to mind; throughout the many alterations its builder carried out during his lifetime it arguably remained "Monticello.") Similarly, if the various components were replaced gradually, as in the "ship of Theseus" that is substituted plank by plank, we might regard it as the same building even when every part had finally been replaced with something new.

In such cases it is critical that a building (more properly, a building-stage) be present at all times, which does not differ much from the building at nearby times. This requirement for physical continuity would clearly rule out some possibilities. For example, if the building were to be demolished, even slowly, the physical criterion would be violated since a building would no longer be present. Even if we constructed an exact replica on the same spot, it could not be the same building as before—the necessary continuity is now broken and unmendable.

Applying the physical criterion to persons, we would regard P_2 as the same person as P_1 if there is a continuous transition, starting with P_1 at time t_1 and ending with P_2 at t_2, such that a person is present at all intervening times. Such a requirement is reasonably met in the case of actual persons and accords with our intuition. For example, it implies that at all intervening times t_i there must be a person-stage P_i that is also the same as both P_1 and P_2—in the one case, there is a continuous, person-retaining transition from P_1 to P_i, in the other a similar transition from P_i to P_2. If P_2 is a later stage of P_1, then, there must have been a person living during the intervening times who can be identified both with P_1 and P_2. It should then be clear that, despite the intuitive appeal, I would not want to have to accept the physical criterion—resurrections of the dead, by whatever means proposed, must be forever ruled out. If a person has died, it is no longer the case that a person is present. Thus a later person-stage could not be the same person as an earlier stage. But I think there are good reasons to reject the physical criterion and physical reductionism in favor of a psychological reductionism.

Returning to the building example, we could ask if the same building persists under the following conditions. The building is carefully dismantled and the components stacked and stored in a warehouse for some time. Clearly the building is not present, in the form of a building, during this time. But then the parts are reassembled in their original arrangement so that, by all appearances, the same building is extant once again. (In a simple case the building could be made of prefabricated parts to make this easy.) By the physical criterion it cannot be the same building because no building was present at all times. We could modify our criterion and insist that only the components of the building—at some appropriate level—must always be present. This, however, would raise other questions—such as what level of component is appropriate or whether the components can be replaced with different but interchangeable components before reassembly. In the case of a person, we certainly must allow for replacement of components; this is going on in the body, at the level of molecules and cells, all the time.

Another difficulty concerns the nature of the allowed alterations. Suppose we gradually transform a circus tent into a train depot, retaining a usable shelter at every intervening stage. Do we still have the same building? For an analogous case of persons, we could imagine the scenario of Derek Parfit in which, using advanced technology, he is gradually transformed into an exact copy of Greta Garbo.[3] We assume that during the entire process a "person" is always present. This entity at the intervening stages would have some characteristics of both Parfit and Garbo, including alternate sets of memories, but would still be fully functional, able to perform tasks and answer questions. If asked, Who are you? he/she might answer, "Well, I have characteristics of both Derek Parfit and Greta Garbo, but however you judge it, I am certainly a person, an 'I'." Nearer the beginning there would be more characteristics of Parfit, nearer the end, more of Garbo. Is the Garbo copy that results from this, convinced she is the actress whom she resembles in all respects, and not at all Derek Parfit, still Derek Parfit? I would say definitely no, and there is something wrong with the physical criterion that forces us to conclude that the end stage must be the same person as the beginning stage.

While the above difficulties might be remedied if we modify the physical criterion sufficiently, I think this would introduce unnecessary complications. Moreover, I think that the viewpoint is misplaced that strongly identifies a person with a particular body and brain, or more generally, with some particular, material construct, even if we allow for gradual alterations. Instead, I see a person as an ongoing process for which the body with the brain is important as an enabling agent or means of expressing identity but is not important in a more fundamental sense. The body and brain—or something like them—are necessary so we can be alive. But they do not constitute the person that experiences. In particular, most of the body's substance (including most of the brain) is being exchanged with the environment anyway, at the molecular level. New, equivalent substance and structure comes into being and assumes the functions once performed by other matter.

Some of this happens rather rapidly. Substantial changes in the body's water content occur over a twenty-four-hour interval, for instance, and more sweeping changes can be expected over longer periods. If a person is in a coma for many years and is finally awakened, there will be a near-total replacement of the matter of the original body. This, we might say, is comparable to simply substituting a new, duplicate body while the person was asleep.[4]

Yet I would not consider that a new and different person exists or that the old person has died. The waking person could still be reasonably considered original. More extravagantly, if we imagine advanced technology able to disassemble a person into small components after placing him in biostasis and then reassemble those components in the same arrangement so that an entirely similar person results, I would regard that second person as the same as the first. Even in the case where the components were replaced by similar components before assembly, yielding a person similar in all respects to the original but lacking the original material, I would conclude that the original person had been restored and was living again. This restoration could happen many years later using detailed information about the original but again, no original material.

Thus I reject physical reductionism in favor of psychological reductionism. This employs the psychological criterion, explained below, to decide if two person-stages correspond to the same person. The emphasis is on mental characteristics rather than physical ones. The problems we noted with physical reductionism do not instantly vanish, as we will see, but they certainly seem more manageable.

Psychological Connectedness versus Continuity

For the psychological criterion there are two main properties, psychological connectedness and psychological continuity. Depending on the version of psychological reductionism, both of these may be regarded as necessary, or one or the other may be dropped as inessential. Roughly speaking, psychological connectedness refers to the extent that affinities in personality characteristics can be said to exist between P_2 and P_1. (In particular, this would cover the important issue of whether P_2 is a more developed version or continuer of P_1, as "continuer" will be understood here.) Psychological continuity refers to whether there was a smooth transition of person-stages, psychologically speaking, from P_1 to P_2. It is easy to see that the two are not equivalent.

If Derek Parfit eventually becomes just like Greta Garbo, but only gradually, there could be a high degree of psychological continuity. Earlier we imagined this transition taking place without any sudden, large physical changes, and now we can imagine it with no large mental jumps either but only small changes that accumulate over time. The later person-stage (Garbo) is very different from the earlier one (Parfit), so that psychological connectedness is violated, but psychological continuity is maintained. On the other hand, a copy of someone, say a person who has died, could be created by a lucky accident, with no causal connection between the two, as we usually understand causality. In this case, there would be strong psychological connectedness but no continuity. We are then left with the question of whether and how much one or the other property is important in deciding if P_2 is the same person as P_1.

It is clear that psychological connectedness is necessary. Otherwise, if psychological continuity alone is sufficient, we are forced to conclude that the Garbo copy is still Derek Parfit, which is something we have discounted. We then ask if psychological continuity is necessary. This is more controversial. Both Derek Parfit and Max More, along with others, argue that it is; I shall claim, again echoing some others, that it is not. My position will be that what a person-stage is, including any identification with past person-stages, depends entirely on the presence and functioning (or at least eventual functioning) of components that make up that person-stage at that point in time. It will not depend on how those components came to exist and function as they do and, in particular, on what the process of transition from a past person-stage (if any) may have been. For other reasons I will argue that, nevertheless, this process of transition *is* normally important, and so is history more generally. But identity, I will maintain, can be considered in isolation from how a particular construct physically came into being. Viewed in this way, the process of development or formation of a particular person-stage is not critical—it is the end result that matters.

This view is an aspect of a position known as functionalism.[5] I will argue the case for functionalism, including a functionalist version of psychological reductionism, with the implication that psychological connectedness but not continuity is necessary for survival. The argument, however, involves a metaphysical position that needs to be carefully stated and defended. This will occupy several chapters, during which the issues connected with identity and survival will be explored. Some important parts of the argument are left to Chapter 15; some useful preliminaries will be covered now.

The Functionalist Viewpoint

Functionalism is a materialistic theory of mental states. A person (or other sentient being) is regarded as a mechanism that can be in one of a number of physical states, to each of which corresponds some mental state (with unconsciousness as one of the possible mental states). The correspondence, however, is generally not one-to-one but many-to-one; that is, more than one physical state could produce the same mental state. In general, there will be many ways, physically, that a given mental state can be realized. On the other hand, two different mental states cannot be realized by the same physical state. (Mental states then are supervenient upon physical states.) What distinguishes one mental state from another one is not the difference in physical states but the functional role played by each mental state in the conscious experience of the person.

A word should be said here about the relation between a person-stage as defined earlier and the functionalist notion of person considered here. The idea of a mental state is related to that of a person-stage, but the two are not equivalent. The notion of person-stage is intended to allow for past information not currently accessed, that has no present effect on consciousness but is to have effect in the future. Indeed, for a person-stage corresponding to a state of unconsciousness all such information is in this category. In general, more than one person-stage of more than one diachronic self could be in the same mental state at a given time.

In the course of living, the person will interact with an environment, producing behavior (output) that depends on both the environment (input) and the mental state the person is currently in. In addition to output, the mental state will (possibly) change to another mental state. Two mental states are equivalent if, under all relevant environmental conditions, they yield equivalent behavior and transition to other states, in terms of the effect on that person's conscious experience. They are then treated as one, single state.

In fact this point of view is very machinelike. A Turing machine, a kind of theoretical computer, will be defined in much the same way, producing output and undergoing state transitions in response to input—even though we are not normally concerned with a Turing machine's "conscious experience." On the other hand, a Turing machine can perform any computation a digital computer could perform, which raises the possibility that a Turing machine could model or emulate a person if made sufficiently complex. This conclusion indeed seems inescapable if we are allowed any finite complexity, for then we could model the whole visible universe down to the quantum level. Moreover, a single Turing machine of appropriate type, a "universal" machine, could model different systems, including persons, with a change in its input symbols, or program. Most digital computers in fact are also universal in this sense. Under the functionalist paradigm, then, a person is equivalent to a computer program (albeit a very complex one, far more complex than any that has yet been written) that is "running" on some sort of machine, or hardware.

One consequence of a materialist outlook, which applies to functionalism, is that different, finite constructs can be duplicated. In principle this could be extended to persons. Two such constructs representing identical persons or person-stages could be placed in identical (finite) environments and might then undergo the same state changes for a short or possibly even a long period of time. From the functionalist perspective, it would be reasonable to regard them not as separate persons but as multiple instantiations of one and the same person. This in fact is the position I take, expressed in the principle of Interchangeability. We are not concerned so much, then, with each individual instantiation but with the properties they have in common.

It is worth noting that functionalism is not the only materialistic theory of mental processes. A major rival is the mind-brain identity theory, also known as central-state or reductive materialism. It holds that physical states are identical with mental states and thus denies the possibility of the same mental states recurring through similar but different material constructs. Multiple instantiations of one person, for example, would have to be regarded as separate individuals even though their thought processes were identical and they could not tell, individually, which instantiation they were. But I think this theory is too restrictive. There is no compelling reason to reject the pattern theory of identity that leads to Interchangeability, and it has much to offer as we shall see. Thus I choose functionalism over the mind-brain identity theory.

Personal Identity and Destiny

Returning to the problem of identity—when an earlier and a later person-stage would correspond to the same person—the functionalist position means we are concerned with characteristics presently retained by the later stage. What is there now may be part of the persisting personality, the diachronic self; what is not there, is not. (It is entirely possible and even highly desirable, however, that features never present before and not now present will eventually appear and become part of the diachronic self.) But again, it is psychological connectedness that is important, not continuity or, more generally, the process whereby the later person-stage comes into existence.

This position must contend with some major difficulties. What do we do, for example, about forgetting and false memories? Such problems will be considered in Chapter 15. I believe they can be satisfactorily resolved if we accept an immortalist viewpoint—that a "person" is best seen as part of an ongoing process of development leading to an ideal self, a kind of infinite being enduring forever. Such a viewpoint means we can, in some degree and with due precautions, overlook the difficulties on smaller scales. All will be well, it turns out, if certain properties hold in the limit of time. Remembering in particular should predominate over forgetting, and truth over falsity—and there is reason to think that both will.

Remembered experiences or episodic memories thus assume a particular importance, though they are certainly not the only important or even the most important characteristics. For example, valuing these experiences can be viewed as having more importance than the experiences themselves; experiences could not have importance otherwise. More generally, a person's values might be conceded to be of greater importance than such details as specific memories. But with the proper values—valuing life's experiences in particular and the ongoing, organizing process that hopefully will continue to one's immortalization—memories and other personal information assume an honored place and a necessary role.

Life is made up of experiences—happenings of which we have some awareness at the time of their occurrence. Experiences in turn—which we cannot avoid if we live at all, as conscious or partly conscious beings—ought to be worth having. An experience worth having is worth remembering. This simple argument (to be elaborated in later chapters) says much, I think, in favor of the value of memories and of having a high level of commitment to preserving them. This in turn takes on new significance given the possibilities of biostasis and our future prospects more generally.

Overall I think it is fruitful to view the life of an individual as, largely, a process of creating an assemblage of valued memories. (For those uncomfortable with this I include other information besides episodic memories—more on this later.) This has two important components: (1) having new experiences that will, in due course, take their place in the memory archives; and (2) reviewing the archives from time to time, to in some measure relive or recount older experiences. Both these things I hope to be able to do indefinitely, building an increasing archival record much as civilization has been doing, as a whole, since the invention of writing. And I hope others will join me in this, so that each of us builds our own individual archive as we all live, interact, and develop. The archiving and review of older material would not overlook other features of mental activity that also are vitally important, such as acquiring new knowledge and skills. The approach I take is to emphasize episodic memories but incorporate other kinds of acquired information under the same paradigm. Skills and other information are "memories" of a sort that are also added to the archives of our past experiences and are "reviewed" as they exert perceptible effects on our conscious states.

Each of us, properly, is a civilization in miniature. To achieve our rightful destiny we must become more-than-human and approach infinite beings in the limit of time. But we have the technological potential to do this, or at least go a substantial distance, as I think good arguments attest. In time all of us ought to, and hopefully will, individually surpass all of our present civilization, in many and fascinating ways. In this developmental process, even the humblest early memories should have lasting value, much as the most primitive ancient history and prehistory continues to hold interest today.

Meanwhile, we must not be daunted. Certainly we are far from perfect, and so are our present achievements and institutions. This should be no cause for despair but—in view of the possibilities for progress—reason for optimism and hope. In the first place, imperfection (including incompleteness) is necessary if life is to have lasting meaning since there must always be a reason for new accomplishments. (With an infinite amount of time, however, it should be possible to have an infinite amount of progress so that one is never finally completed but always has reason for further, meaningful activity.) Second, the course of our progress should witness some truly astounding achievements, and life, I think, will become rewarding in ways beyond the grasp of our present minds. Finally, I will wager, the game of life for more advanced beings will no more be zero-sum than it is today but a better state for some will tend, as a rule, toward a better state for others.

In fact it is reasonable to speculate that our capacity to experience happy states of mind will develop along with our means to realize the goals that produce the better states. What that will lead to can scarcely be fathomed, but some of the possibilities ought to be marvelous indeed. Our growing capacity to make better choices should, on the other hand, make happier outcomes increasingly likely.

I do not imagine that happiness will prove intractably elusive because, fundamentally, states of pleasure or enjoyment do not seem particularly hard to produce and should become easier as knowledge progresses. But it will be left to the individual to arrange life so that a deeper significance attaches to the feelings that are enjoyed, whatever the proximate causes of these feelings may be. Trivialization could result. The individual could choose something resembling eternal drunkenness, but I will argue that this will not produce the most rewarding states and thus is to be rejected in favor of a progressively developing consciousness.

Yuai, Resurrection, and the Multiverse

Something should now be said about the differences between Yuai as developed here, and other related systems such as

Fedorov's Supramoralism or Tipler's more recent Omega Point Theory—though more will be said later. Largely, these differences stem from differing perspectives and commitments. As the last decades have run their course, marvelous vistas have opened, both from new cosmological insights and, closer to home, from certain options of a biological nature.

On one hand there is the universe at large, the place that will hopefully be our eternal home. Fedorov, in the nineteenth century, imagined a universe along Newtonian-Laplacian lines—fully, accessibly deterministic—whose events could be retrodicted by future generations. This had immediate implications for the problem of restoring the dead to life. His resurrections involved tracing the motion of atoms backward in time, as we have seen, to find out which living bodies were present and what were the characteristics of the beings who had them. But this idea was severely challenged, in the early twentieth century, by the finding of quantum uncertainty, which appears to put sharp limits on what can be known about the past.

The immediate reaction, when the problem of resurrection was pondered scientifically, was pessimistic. Barring supernatural means or assistance, persons of the past, once dead and decomposed, were surely gone forever—that was that. This position is reinforced by straightforward examination.

A person, viewed at the physical level, is an almost unimaginably complex assemblage of atoms that engage in an intricate, interactive balancing act for the decades of one's natural life. Materials are exchanged with the environment, and many changes occur. Yet the structure as a whole, including the mind and memories of the brain, maintains a certain integrity that allows us to say that, in some reasonable sense, the person persists or lives on. But at death the whole process comes to a halt and the structure is reduced, through decomposition, back to simpler substances.

More important, information is destroyed, particularly that of the brain, which is the principal repository of the elements that are critical to identity and personality and which is especially vulnerable to decomposition. Resurrection of the person, by any process conceivable scientifically, would require, at minimum, recovery or recreation of this missing information. Recovery seems out of the question, in view of quantum uncertainty, which leaves only recreation—an excruciatingly uncertain process—since vast amounts of information would have to be filled in by guesswork.

On the other hand, I will argue that, *if* a sufficiently accurate description of the person can be obtained, then resurrection of that person is always possible in principle. The method would involve making a functioning duplicate, or a continuer, of the original using the information at hand. Based on the functionalist version of psychological reductionism just outlined, in Chapter 7 I will present the case for Interchangeability—that this replica is, for all intents and purposes, that original person, restored to conscious existence.

The metaphysical position that a person would survive in a copy is crucially important for the philosophy that is to be developed, and it deserves some comment. That a copy of you is you may not seem at all intuitive—for example, it raises the issue of what would follow if there were two or more functioning copies in existence. Do we have several individuals or one? The position I adopt, as suggested above, is that exact copies (more generally, equivalently functioning copies) constitute one individual only, though in multiple instantiations. (I hope the longer term *instantiation* will be clearer than *instance,* which is sometimes used in philosophical discussions of objects that are separate but alike or equivalent.[6] I will use *instantiation* mainly to refer to a person-replica or, more generally, any physical process that emulates the person for an interval of time. Such a process will be considered equivalent and interchangeable with other similar or replica processes.) If significant differences arise, however, then different individuals are involved; thus it is possible for one person to fission into more than one, all of whom would share a common past.

A person, on the other hand, could be described (a person-stage could be specified) by some digital record of finite length, encoded, say, as a long string of bits. In principle then, it would be possible to guess an arbitrary, finite bit string and thus arrive at a description of any person who ever lived. Technology of the future, and particularly a mature nanotechnology, could presumably, working from this description, then bring the corresponding living person into existence by creating and setting in motion an appropriate instantiation. This then is a way that a vanished person of the past could be resurrected.

This scenario, however, offers difficulties if we contemplate its actual implementation, a major one being the problem of authenticity. The number of actual persons who lived on the earth must be very much smaller than the number of possible persons. Thus the vast majority of persons created by guesswork, in the manner just outlined, would seem to constitute unhistorical fantasies, people who never had real existence. A constructed person then, in keeping with objectivity, would have to conclude, "almost certainly I never really lived and my memories et cetera are just a recent fabrication," even in the rare cases where this was not so and the guessing was lucky enough to create a real person.

This projection, however, is based on a worldview that, while it seems to accord well with ordinary experience, is also easy to challenge if we take a larger view. What, I ask, is the totality of all that has ever happened, is happening, or will ever happen— that is, the multiverse? (Strictly speaking, the idea of time precedence breaks down in the multiverse and needs to be restricted to the domains, or individual universes, where it really applies— but I hope the concept of the multiverse, which is to encompass all that actually happens, is reasonably clear.) This question is not one for which I will claim a definitive answer, but there are certain features that, I conjecture, the multiverse ought to have that will shed light on the issue of resurrection.

The main feature of this sort, I maintain, is Unboundedness— that space, time, and events are so structured that, within large limits, all conceivable, finite histories actually happen. This does not mean, necessarily, that the universe we observe will last forever or has always been present but that the totality of all happenings is unlimited. Every person, then, must occur somewhere at every possible stage of development so that there are, essentially, no unhistorical fantasies, but innumerable individuals appear in alternate histories.

The question must then be raised whether the notion of Unboundedness could have a basis in reality. Though it may seem farfetched, I submit that rather simple properties could guarantee it. Mainly, if space and time really are infinite, we could reasonably expect that all finite patterns, in a suitable sense, would be created somewhere, and not once but infinitely often, along with the attendant processes. It is a big universe, and many things are happening more or less at random. Clearly a large variety of objects is being produced with imposed patterns and parcels of information, and many kinds of processes are unfolding.

Our observations suggest, on the other hand, that the observable universe has finite spatiotemporal extent, having started some billions of years ago in a Big Bang and that it could also come to an end (though it is not known that it will). But these properties do not rule out other universes, so that reality as a whole would consist of a multiverse that contains innumerable individual universes. So, in all, the requirements of Unboundedness could still be met even if our own universe is temporary and finite.

In fact there is a physical theory, with interesting scientific support, that appears to offer a solid case for Unboundedness: the many-worlds formulation of quantum mechanics, with its associated ontology. Many-worlds challenges our usual intuition, in which we think of history as having a single timeline, that is, one and only one authentic way that things happen. Not so, says many-worlds, but instead, equally authentic, alternate versions of history have happened and are happening all the time, in parallel. Moreover, our one world is constantly splitting into alternate worlds, whose histories then diverge.

Many-worlds, with its parallel universes, provides that all physically possible, finite, alternate histories are real and happening—essentially a guarantee of Unboundedness. I think it also offers the best explanation of what is happening at the level of deep reality, and that it is likely to be true, for reasons we will consider in the next chapter. Yet, and especially with so much at stake, I think we should exercise caution in our acceptance of this wonderful theory and acknowledge the possibility of its not holding after all. In fact, there are competing theories, which also make correct predictions, in which the worlds do not proliferate so readily and Unboundedness is not so clearly favored. But even here there are arguments supporting it, as we will explore. Overall, I think we can have confidence in Unboundedness, even if some of our ideas about it should prove untenable.

Interchangeability is, in broad brush, the idea that things that are sufficiently alike share identity or can be considered not as separate entities but as instantiations of one and the same single item. (The different instantiations are "interchangeable.") Thus, for example, in physics we are constrained to regard gas molecules—and different systems in general—as a single object (system) if they are in the same quantum state. As a philosophical principle, however, Interchangeability is to have wider scope than to identify two objects with exactly the same characteristics at the subatomic level. As mainly used here, it will apply to instantiations of persons. Each such instantiation is a person restricted to one material object or functioning device (body and brain)—which is indeed how we normally imagine "persons." Hypothetically, two such instantiations—functioning devices—could exhibit the same or equivalent behavior—so that the persons in question have the same conscious experience and in effect are one being.

Such identical constructs have not been observed, of course—the likelihood of the necessary coincidence, involving myriad corresponding events in two functioning brains, is small indeed. (Some approach to the condition is provided, however, by computer programs, which can be run on different machines and/or at different times, yielding equivalent behavior.) The value of the Interchangeability principle, then, is not in any imminent practical application, but in its philosophical implications—in providing for the possibility of resurrection, for instance, by identifying an original person with an exact copy made at a different time under different circumstances.

Although, as we noted, it is unlikely we will observe any two different but like instantiations of the same person, such multiple possibilities quickly come into play when we consider our basic ontological stance. Unboundedness should provide an endless supply of instantiations: somewhere in the multiverse are copies of you or me, exact in all essential respects, and these copies must be found over and over. ("You," of course, have no way of knowing which of "your" instantiations "you" are, so effectively "you" are distributed, evenly and redundantly, over all of them.) These copies, on the other hand, are by expectation constantly undergoing independent changes that distinguish one from another—in effect, one individual constantly splits into many. The many begin to have diverging experiences—in effect, their worlds become different.

This, then, is a version of many-worlds in its own right, that is an echo of the physics (Everett) version but is really independent and could follow from some other model of reality entirely. Here though we must distinguish between an observer-world, which is reality as perceived by a given observer, and a world, as delineated by physics. Though the two differ, and our intuition is to call the physics-world the real world, an observer-world is certainly "real" too—and also rests, ultimately, on principles of physics that determine the characteristics of observers and their perceptions, along with everything else.

We can then see that the UI assumptions, if accepted, offer a strong case that immortality is possible, even in the face of such difficulties as a collapsing universe that annihilates the life-forms within. (This then provides a more robust possibility of immortality than Tipler's Omega Point Theory, which depends rather heavily on a specific cosmological model.) The constant splitting of worlds (observer-worlds at any rate), and related occurrences, in fact constitutes an enabling mechanism comparable to the workings of the supernatural in traditional religions. This "miracle," however, is thoroughly materialistic and rests on principles of physics that are subject to observational testing and verification. Though indeed much is still unknown, so far the outlook seems encouraging, and this carries over to the long-term prospects for every sentient individual, whatever the more immediate circumstances that accompany one's life or death.

Shorter-Term Also Important

It is not just the very long term that has interest, however; matters of more direct concern to persons living today must also be considered. It seems very likely that, soon on the scale of history, and provided as always, our species does not annihilate itself or our civilization, means will be found to halt and reverse aging and end other now-terminal conditions. At minimum, then, very long life spans will be the rule, and possibilities will open for unprecedented modes of existence. Options should include redesign of the human body and modification of psychological characteristics, always subject, one hopes, to the wishes of the participant (and also, one hopes, in some sense conserving the participant). Another possibility is to upload the personality into a computational device, thereby virtually eliminating all physical encumbrances. These, it should be stressed, are possibilities only at this point. I think, however, that some incredible options can be considered likely—more will be discussed in later chapters. Properly exercised, our options should open the gateway to a paradise every bit as marvelous as the afterlife concepts of traditional religions and very likely surpassing all that our present minds can imagine.

The problem is that many of us now living likely will die before the great breakthroughs that will end aging and intractable illnesses. Thus I advocate biostasis as a form of holding action. Those dying today or in the more immediate future would have a reasonable chance, in my view, of surviving biologically, as preserved specimens, so that they can be awakened in the future. Biostasis thus will orient us toward this material life and the things that are possible now and in the relatively near future and not just in a remote, more advanced future. Moreover, it offers a practical course of action that does not require great power or wealth.

There is an interesting dilemma, however. Under the system developed here—Yuai—all can and should eventually be resurrected. Does this not make biostasis, even if it does work, superfluous? This issue is an important one and is treated in Chapter 13, but some introductory remarks are worth stating here.

There are two aspects of one's existence, which we earlier referred to, a bit whimsically, as the "User" and the "Interface." The User, what really makes "you" what you are, requires only the right information—an appropriate description from which a functioning replica can be made. This follows from the functionalist paradigm and is why resurrection could happen through guesswork; psychological connectedness with the past self, in the final analysis, is all that matters. But the Interface, your ties with reality and the world at large, though not strictly a requirement for your existence or reappearance, is still very important to make life meaningful and rewarding. In general, in the course of our lives we try to cultivate the proper Interface—doing so helps minimize the harsher features of the unknown—and this involves favoring life over death and what is more conserving of life rather than less.

There is much uncertainty about what would transpire in the event of our death, if one is not dogmatic, and we must cope. By discounting the paranormal, I also dismiss any cosmic sanction, or sanctification, of this present life with its usual terminal processes. We do not "owe a death" to any force or power. Yet the life of the individual should consist of an orderly progression in which disruptive events arguably are minimized. Biostasis is important as a means of minimizing a potentially very disruptive event—one's clinical death. It is thus a means of coping, and this is to be sought, despite the prospect, if it should fail, of an eventual resurrection by other means. In this latter case the unknowns are greater, despite whatever assurances can be argued.

A point worth making here is that it is expected there will be individuals in the future who are interested in resurrecting persons of the past. This should hold even in the relatively near future in the case of biostasis patients—contrary to the fears that some have expressed, that no one would care to bring them back. I will argue that resurrected individuals will be able to make interesting, unique contributions to the lives of others then living, thus the latter will stand to gain in terms of enlightened self-interest. (On this ground let it be said that I have a strong interest myself in resurrecting persons of the past, under whatever circumstances and using whatever methods may be feasible and appropriate. I hope others will agree with this position and also wish to be involved.) This is not, however, a guarantee that all will go well for the resurrectee, especially at first; again, a serious unknown must be faced in the prospect of one's death.

I should add that the advantages of biostasis are not negated if it is not fully successful, that is, if there is insufficient information to fully reconstruct the patient from preserved remains, so that some information must be recreated by guesswork. The less extensive the guesswork, the better the reconstruction—since more information is part of the historical record. I will also conjecture that, with more information to go on, the resurrection will happen sooner, even if the preservation was imperfect. Biostasis, then, is the clearly favored course to follow over alternatives that do not attempt to preserve identity-critical information.

In taking this position, however, I do not want to go to an extreme that would compromise the viewpoint that wrongs of whatever sort can eventually be righted. The philosophical stance of Yuai, in fact, will favor the prospect of overcoming all disadvantages one might incur, in the limit of time. (There are conceivable adverse circumstances, too, in which self-sacrifice is called for, that is, even saving one's life is not always, necessarily, the preferred course; more on this later.) This is not to suggest that the choices one makes are a matter of indifference. A choice, of whatever nature, that would lead to unhappiness or to less happiness, can be resisted on that ground. But if a wrong choice is made, as time progresses the extent of the resulting disadvantage will lessen with the right effort.

In general, actions favoring the perpetuation of life—one's own and others'—and benevolence overall, will result in greater benefits to the individual and lesser penalties or misfortune. As time progresses this should become increasingly clear to increasingly many, which should further diminish inequities. In the plenitude of our hoped-for destiny, all beings should approach a condition of unlimited benefit and joy, with past wounds healed and differences resolved.

CHAPTER 5.

Some Scientific Perspectives

Those who yearn for what ought to be must come to grips with what is. Historically this problem has not proved easy to assess, let alone address, and in fact perspectives on "what is" have altered greatly over the centuries. Once the world seemed to be ruled by intelligent superhumans. Then it seemed to be a clockwork mechanism, in which events could be predicted or retrodicted with arbitrary accuracy. By now the picture has changed again, with older viewpoints called into question once more but with some new and wonderful possibilities to take their place.

Models of reality shape the philosophical approaches that are developed for addressing the tough problems of life. At present, in fact, there is no unique, accepted model, but very many out of all the ones we have ever had are still with us, each with its circle of advocates. The supernatural ones we will consider more fully in Chapters 6 and 10—Unboundedness has an interesting perspective on these. Here instead the focus will be on scientific theories. In the early days, however, they too were often entwined with beliefs about higher powers.

Origen, for example, was convinced that the stars were intelligent beings, based on their regular, apparent motions (mostly due, we now know, to the turning of the earth underfoot). "[S]ince the stars move with such majestic order and plan that never have we seen their course deflected in the slightest degree, is it not the height of stupidity to say that such order, such exact observance of rule and plan, is accomplished by things without reason?"[1] More than 1,400 years later, however, Isaac Newton offered a mathematical explanation of the motion of objects. The universe was seen to obey knowable laws. The new approach both refined the ability to predict events and accounted in detail for what could be observed. No longer were the regular motions attributed to intelligent guidance, any more than for the periodic swaying of an earthly pendulum or the graceful fall of stones from a tower. The same gravitational force that affected objects on Earth explained the motion of things in space. Nothing beyond such measurable quantities as position and momentum was needed to deduce the future configurations of objects, and the past could be calculated as well.

The technique worked best for the large, ponderous objects seen in space. Eclipses of the sun and other celestial events could be forecast to the minute, centuries in advance, or similarly retrodicted to reconstruct what had happened long ago. On Earth the objects were smaller and their motions more erratic and harder to second-guess. Other forces came into play besides gravitation, such as electromagnetism. But theories resembling Newton's were developed by his successors to explain and predict these effects too and generally were quite successful. It appeared, then, that perhaps all effects might eventually be understood in this manner.

Reproducibility versus Unpredictability

A basic principle seemed at work that could be verified over and over by performing experiments in which a set of initial conditions was established, after which events were allowed to run their course. In any such experiment, the principle asserted, when the initial conditions are the same, the outcome is also the same. Thus, in dropping stones from a tower, if the same stone or another just like it is dropped from the same height each time, the time for the stone to hit the ground is the same, as well as the speed and direction of the impact, et cetera. (Other conditions affecting the motion such as wind speed and direction must also be the same.) True, there were often small variations in the outcome of different experiments, but this seemed accountable by variations in the starting conditions.

It was hard, maybe impossible, to have exactly the same starting conditions over again—there had to be some allowance for error. In general, though, the more nearly alike the starting conditions of two experiments, the more similar the outcomes would be. Insignificant enough starting differences could only yield insignificant differences in the outcome. The reproducibility of experimental results was verified countless times, in widely varied settings, with only small discrepancies that seemed well accounted for by the slight but unavoidable variations in the starting conditions.

The apparent reproducibility of results had tremendous philosophical consequences. In the clockwork world, effect followed cause automatically. No more did gods or other incomprehensible agents have to be invoked to explain happenings—except, perhaps, the initial "winding of the clock" in remote antiquity that had started it all. Increasingly, belief in supernatural powers began to weaken, though for other reasons many still clung to such beliefs.

Along with the reproducibility of results there was time-reversibility: specifying the ending state of a system in enough detail made it possible to determine the starting conditions. Thus if we knew the speed and direction of a rock striking the ground after being dropped from a height, by taking account of the earth's known gravitation and other factors we could determine from what point the rock had fallen and also how long the fall had taken. Generalizing this idea, the future or the past might be calculated to any desired accuracy from sufficiently accurate measurements of the present state of things. Such a physics characterizes a deterministic universe. In this case, we have both forward and reverse determinism—we can deduce both the future and the past from the present. (In general, however, it is possible to have forward but not reverse determinism, and vice versa, as computerized, toy universes easily demonstrate.) Moreover, the determinism here is accessible: the necessary information to deduce the past or future is available to the observer inside the universe.

Yet some phenomena resisted this reducibility to cause and effect, particularly when small objects were involved. It is easy to guess that this might be so, when we consider that observations are necessary before deductions can be made. Observations will tend to disturb the system being observed, particularly in the case of tiny objects. This disturbance introduces uncertainty: we can never be quite sure about the state of the system before we tried to observe it, nor what we have changed it into in the course of trying to observe it. We would naturally want to use the least invasive observational technique possible, to minimize uncertainties of this sort. (Actually, the problem with minute observations goes beyond this simple disturbance model—disturbance-free measurements, to high approximation, are difficult but not impossible[2]—but unavoidable uncertainties still persist for other reasons.)

Among the least invasive methods, which works well for many if not all cases of interest, is to use light. Light is useful for astronomical observations—planets are easy to track and not appreciably affected in their motions by the reflected sunlight that makes them shine. Nor are the sun and other stars affected much by the light they constantly beam into space, though it does result in a very gradual loss of mass. And even on Earth we can observe many systems quite adequately, for the amount of information we want to extract, through illumination that has negligible effects otherwise.

This becomes increasingly difficult, however, when we go down to small scales. In general, the smaller the scale, the less light we want to use for illumination since things are more sensitive to disturbance, so we attenuate our light source. But light cannot be arbitrarily attenuated because it comes in tiny, discrete packets called photons: a single photon is as far down as we can go. (True, we can use lower-energy photons to achieve a kind of progressive attenuation, but this will limit the information we can recover and so will defeat our purpose.) And photons themselves are objects we might want to study, to determine their past or future actions. We might then attempt to bombard a photon with other photons, as a means of observing it. But here we immediately encounter another major obstacle: photons do not bounce off other photons—they pass right through as if nothing is there. Using other techniques, however, we can extract information about individual photons but this information is limited. It is so limited, in fact, that it destroys the notion of reproducibility. Two experiments with, as far as we can tell, the same initial conditions yield different outcomes.

A simple example of this can be seen by merely shining a beam of light at metal foil or another opaque barrier into which a small hole has been made and placing a detector behind the barrier to record the passage of light through the hole. When a light source is turned on, light passes through the hole to the detector in back, and the detector responds. A sophisticated detector will be able to tell us how much light gets through the hole in terms of the number of photons striking the detector per second. (Actually, not every photon that strikes the detector surface is actually detected—only a percentage of them are; this can be taken into account and the results interpreted in terms of individual photonic impacts.)

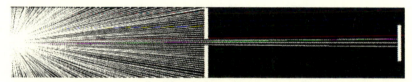

Photon detection apparatus. Light passes through a small opening to the detector at right.

For example, let us assume that a lamp with a 100-watt bulb (rated at 1,750 lumens) is placed 1 meter (39 inches) from a piece of aluminum foil with a pinhole 0.1 mm in diameter (0.004 inch, the thickness of a coarse human hair). For best results, the lamp should be carefully shielded so that only the light passing through the pinhole reaches the detector. Then, when the light is switched on, about 10 billion (10^{10}) photons will pass through the hole to the detector each second. When the detector is very close to the hole, the incoming photons form a small dot of light on the detector surface approximately the size of the hole, 0.1 mm. If the detector is moved back some distance, however, and kept perpendicular to the beam, the dot spreads out so that, at 1 meter away, it will be a fuzzy, round spot, reddish around the edges, whose brightest part is several millimeters across. Actually, closer inspection will show more interesting details, such as a bull's-eye pattern of fainter, concentric rings surrounding the central spot and more color separation, the reds and blues confirming that white light is a mixture of different wavelengths that spread out by differing amounts.[3]

One interesting effect can now be observed if we assume a detector sensitive enough to record a single photon and attenuate the light source so that individual photons striking the detector can be recorded. For example, by shielding the light emerging from the pinhole with a filter made of stacked panes of lightly silvered glass we could reduce the intensity by a factor of ten billion, so that, on average, only one photon per second strikes the detector. What we then notice is that successive photons do not fall at the same place on the detector but strike at random over an area several millimeters in diameter, occasionally straying farther afield. In fact, these individual photon detections are just building up the same spreading spot pattern seen with the unattenuated light, only much more slowly, as can be verified by making a cumulative record of the detections. The interesting thing, however, from the standpoint of reproducibility, is that the photons fall at random within the spot. There is no known means of predicting just where a given photon will land, or exactly when.

Two successive photon events, then, have the same set of starting conditions, as far as we can tell, yet produce very different outcomes. There is no known convergence of the outcomes that results from making the starting conditions more similar, but irreducible randomness prevails. In general, this variability is observed with any sufficiently small particles, such as atoms or their constituents—electrons, protons, and neutrons. (This is true whether, like photons, the particles always move at the speed of light or, like atoms and their subatomic constituents, always move at slower speeds and can be at rest relative to the observer.) It is even more a fact of life on small scales than the clockwork predictability is on larger scales because it ultimately affects that very predictability, rendering it imprecise. It has given rise to an entirely new physics—quantum mechanics (named after the quantum, or particle, that in different forms dominates things at small scales). In many ways quantum mechanics resembles its Newtonian precursors, yet it retains the irreducible randomness.

In quantum mechanics, events such as photon detections are not strictly predictable, but only their probabilities, which still obey deterministic laws. For example, in the above experiment, a photon has a 50 percent chance of landing above rather than

below the center of the fuzzy spot or a 25 percent chance of landing in the upper right quadrant. (Similarly, the time that a photon
strikes the detector, also inexact, is described by a law of aver-
ages.) With different starting conditions—for example, if we used
mirrors or lenses to change the path of the photons—different
probabilities would apply. Predictions can be made with confidence even though the exact outcome of any one experiment is
unknowable. Something then can be salvaged of the old trust in
the ability of science to explain events.

Still, the randomness is disturbing. If two experiments with
the same starting conditions can yield substantially different outcomes, then different effects must follow from the same causes,
so the scientific explanation of events is inadequate. This does
not necessarily mean that intelligent, supernatural agents must
be introduced—the randomness of the photons, for instance, does
not require a hidden, conscious manipulator—but it does raise a
difficulty. By now there are a number of proposed remedies, of
which more will be said later in the chapter, after considering
more experimental evidence.

Photons, which are as easily produced as turning on a light,
furnish a convenient pathway for investigating the strange world
of the quantum. For more sophisticated experiments, it is often
useful to have a single wavelength or monochromatic light source;
today this can easily be achieved to very high accuracy using a
laser. The familiar and inexpensive helium-neon laser, for instance,
emits an intense, narrow red beam of wavelength 633 nanom-
eters (nm; 1 nm is one billionth of a meter or a millionth of a
millimeter). It is bright enough that we can easily see the glow-
ing beam as it travels through the air. (A few of the photons in the
beam, in this case, bounce off particles in the air and find their
way into our eyes or elsewhere, illuminating the path of the light,
while most of the photons continue unhindered along the path.)
If such light is passed through a pinhole to a detector behind it, as
in the experiment just described, the light emerging from the ap-
erture is still monochromatic, but the beam is no longer so tight.
A pattern forms on the detector as before, but it now assumes a
clearer, bull's-eye appearance with a central disk surrounded by
alternating bright and dark concentric bands, all of the same, red
color.

This result can be explained, when large numbers of photons

are involved, by the wave nature of light. The conditions of the experiment, it turns out, alter the direction of motion of the various photons in the beam causing multiple, overlapping waves of light to strike the detector. Where waves constructively interfere, reinforcing each other, bright bands are formed; where they destructively interfere, there is darkness. Interference effects can be more easily seen if we make certain refinements in this apparatus.

The Two-Slit Experiment

If we pass the laser light through a very thin slit rather than a pinhole, it spreads out beyond the slit in a cylindrical wave front, which is still monochromatic though, again, no longer a narrow beam like the original. (For good results we would want a slit on the order of 1 micrometer or .001 mm in width, 100 times narrower than our pinhole but still technologically feasible; the length of the slit can be several millimeters or more, so that overall the opening is comparable in area to the pinhole.) The cylindrical wave front itself can then be used as a light source. If we shine it through a carefully placed barrier with two parallel slits similar to the first, we obtain two cylindrical wave fronts similar to the first, which can then be projected onto a detector. (The two slits, that is, must be parallel to and the same distance beyond the first slit, which can be achieved by fine adjustment.) Interference effects between the two wave fronts will show up as a corduroy pattern of parallel stripes or bands on the detector surface. If we close off one of the two slits admitting only one of the cylindrical wave fronts, the interference pattern goes away leaving only a bright, fairly uniform swath.

This then is a rough description of the famous two-slit photon experiment, a version of which was performed as early as 1801 by English scientist Thomas Young (using equipment more primitive than lasers, but capable of similar effects).[4] It has interesting things to teach on the level of classical (nonquantum) physics. By measuring the distance between successive interference bands, taking account of other factors (mainly the distance between the two slits and the distance of the slits from the detector), we can determine the wavelength of the light, for example. If the slits are 0.1 mm apart (the same as the diameter of the pinhole) and the detector is 1 meter away as before, the bands for our wavelength of 633 nm will be an easily visible 6.33 mm (about ¼ in.) apart. However, the quantum effects are more interesting still.

These are shown if we attenuate the light source so that there is almost always at most one photon at a time in the system. This is easy to achieve using a filter such as that described above, made of a stack of silvered glass panes. Light travels 300 million meters per second. Thus, if on average only one photon per second is detected, and we assume a 2-meter path from the laser source to the detector, for only about one 150-millionth of the time will there be any photon in the system at all. The chance of two or more photons being present is about one 150-millionth of that, or about once in five years, a percentage that can be ignored. (Actually, we could greatly increase the rate of photon detections and still safely assume that only one photon at a time was in the system. Even at a million photons per second, each passing photon will be unaccompanied more than 99 percent of the time.)

What happens if only one photon at a time goes through? As before, we detect the photons individually, and they fall at random building up a pattern over time. The pattern is found to be exactly the same as with many photons at a time, it just takes longer to build. Thus with both slits open, we obtain the same corduroy pattern as before, indicating interference. With one slit closed, we get a spreading swath indicating the absence of interference, just as before.[5]

How can one photon at a time cause interference? If we place detectors just behind both slits, we can look at how each photon goes through, to see if there is something peculiar. For instance, maybe the photon does not pass through just one slit or the other, the way intuition would suggest. For all we know, a photon may be a squishy, spread-out object capable of going through two slits at once. If this happens, we would hope to be able to verify it by getting a response from both detectors. What we find, however, is that there is no multiple response. There is nothing peculiar about a photon's passage through the slits, beyond the fact of unpredictability. One detector or the other may be triggered, but never both. When the photon goes through one slit, the other slit, we would think, might as well be closed. In fact, we can do two

versions of the experiment that intuition suggests ought to produce the same results.

In the first version we keep one slit closed and allow the photons, one at a time, to pass through the system, detecting those
that pass through the other, open slit. For definiteness let us say
we do this for one hour, giving about 3,600 photons at our rate of
one per second. As expected, we get the bandless swath indicating no interference. We then close the second slit and open the
first one and again run the experiment for an hour. Again, there is
a bandless swath in a slightly different position on the detector
surface. Add the two together, and we obtain a combined, slightly
fuzzier swath representing about 7,200 photons, with no interference pattern. Or alternately, we can open one slit and close the
other at random and send a photon through. As long both slits are
never open at the same time, we again get the bandless, fuzzy
swath.

In the second version we keep both slits open and run the experiment two hours, again giving about 7,200 photons. In each
case the photons pass one at a time through the slits, one slit or
the other. For each individual photon, intuition suggests that, if
we knew in advance which slit the photon would go through, we
could just close off the other slit so that the photon would zip
through unhindered, as it "intended" to do anyway. On this basis
then, the outcome should be the same as before, when one slit at
a time was closed. Yet this time, we get an interference pattern.
Each photon then, manages somehow to interfere with itself.

This strange phenomenon has numerous interpretations, ranging from "this is what the mathematics predicts, and you just
have to accept that" to the preposterous but wonderful many-
worlds theory, in which reality quite literally splits into alternate
versions, with parallel photons that really do interfere with each
other. Meanwhile, the mathematics of quantum mechanics, whatever interpretation you attach to it, does make the correct prediction, that is, the probability of a photon striking at each point on
the detector surface. But that still leaves open the question of
what it means.

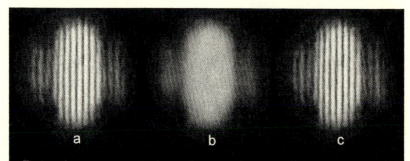

a   b   c

Detection patterns in two-slit experiments. Bright areas indicate many photon "hits" or detections, dark areas, few detections. *(a)* Dark interference bands appear when both slits are open and many photons go through at once. *(b)* Interference pattern disappears when only one slit at a time is open. *(c)* Interference recurs when both slits are open but only one photon at a time goes through. What is interfering with this unaccompanied photon? According to the many-worlds view it is companion photons in other universes.

The Riddle of Quantum Reality

Quantum mechanics is a way of describing interactions at very small scales of distance, the level of individual atoms, for instance, nuclei of atoms, or subatomic particles such as electrons or photons. At these minute scales, matter—atoms and other particles—behaves in ways that seem very strange by comparison with ordinary objects. Quantum objects do not have definite boundaries, and two experiments conducted under conditions that are identical, as far as we can tell, do not produce identical results. We have seen how photons behave unpredictably in the experiments above. Another experiment involves firing a photon at a "half-silvered" mirror in which a thin layer of metal is plated onto glass. At the right thickness, 50 percent of the photons with some particular features (wavelength, polarization) will reflect off the mirror upon striking it at a certain angle, say 45°, and the rest will pass on through, both outcomes being verified by appropriately placed detectors. (Such mirrors can also be stacked into filters to attenuate a beam of photons, as suggested above.) Again, there is no known way to predict which outcome will happen; all we can predict is the probability of each of the two possible out-comes.

In general, quantum mechanics provides a statistical descrip-tion—the probability that, when an experiment is done, the out-come will be some particular alternative out of several. All ver-sions of quantum mechanics exhibit this statistical character, and all make nearly the same predictions differing, at most, only in more subtle details. Many of the predictions have been tested and found very accurate—quantum mechanics is probably the most successful scientific theory yet devised. (It and relativity, which governs happenings at speeds approaching that of light, together constitute the state of the art in our present-day physics. These two theories account for all ordinary phenomena of obser-vation and many more esoteric effects, though not everything is satisfactorily explained, leaving exciting unknown territory for the future scientist.)

In particular, quantum mechanics allows accurate, statistical predictions in cases where small objects behave in seemingly contradictory ways. Individually, such an object often acts as if it were hard and sharp, in other words, it conforms more or less to our notion of a particle. This is what happens when a detection event occurs. Between detection events, though, in which many such objects may be interacting, the particle is better described as a wave. In fact, each particle has associated with it its charac-teristic wave, whose mathematical description can be manipu-lated to give the probability of detecting the particle under vari-ous circumstances.

Waves corresponding to different particles are added together to determine the probability of a successful detection in a situa-tion where several particles are involved. In general, any physi-cal system has a wave function that gives the behavior of the system over time in terms of the probabilities of the possible out-comes. Quantum mechanics successfully sorts the particulate from the wavelike cases and assigns the correct probabilities for the different particle events. Another feature is that in a system of many particles, the probabilistic effects are usually averaged out so that, to a first order approximation, the system behaves deter-ministically, and accessibly so. This is why planetary motions are predictable and also retrodictable; reverse-determinism holds in the same, approximate way. More generally, classical physics—as it existed prior to quantum mechanics—follows from this large-scale averaging. So actually quantum mechanics applies at all scales, not just the very small. (Classical physics is still a useful approximation at the larger scales, of course.)

The different, successful versions of quantum mechanics (there have been failures too) all achieve accurate predictions for the experiments that have been conducted so far—and there are many. The ways that the versions differ are subtle, yet still profound. The subtle differences become important when deep questions about reality are considered, in particular, whether Unboundedness may hold. For this reason we need to examine these different versions. As a start we need to consider how much confidence we can place in each version as a description of reality and whether one version might be preferred over the others; this is the subject of the rest of this chapter.

We have noted that different versions of quantum mechanics make the same predictions as far as we can tell by experiments. (Better experiments, however, that might distinguish some versions from others will be considered later in the chapter, including what is arguably one such experiment that has already been performed.) So we must then ask what criteria are to be used in arriving at preferences. As it turns out, there is one important criterion, based on the problem of locality, to be discussed shortly, plus some other considerations such as determinism, simplicity of the formalism, and believability of the metaphysical implications. These will be addressed in turn. My conclusion will be that many-worlds offers the best model of reality, when all known, relevant factors are taken into account, but that the case for many-worlds cannot be considered closed. So other viewpoints must have their due too, and we must consider different possible realities, any one of which might be true (or none of them), as we approach the issue of Unboundedness.

Relativity and the Problem of Locality

Let us go now to the problem of locality. This comes up in connection with that other great theory of physics, relativity. Quantum mechanics must square with relativity if both are to be correct descriptions of reality at the levels they address. So far there is trouble: most versions of quantum mechanics do not agree with relativity in one important respect, and we have reason in this case to trust relativity. The disagreement is over locality: relativity says that events in one part of the universe cannot instantly affect events in another part. (Actually there is another disagreement that we will consider in Chapter 8; it appears to be resolvable without fundamentally disturbing quantum mechanics, though the difficult work is still not complete.) Instead, anything that happens *here*, any process that gets started whatever, can only propagate at speeds not faster than light, so there must be a time lag before the spreading process can affect anything over *there*. Quantum mechanics, in most versions, allows that some effects propagate instantly, so that locality is violated. The one significant exception is many-worlds; here the locality property is preserved. How this can be so, and why it is important, is an interesting story.

Locality concerns the possibility that an event in one part of the universe could exert a causal effect on an event in another part of the universe. Say we have two events, E_1 and E_2; these may be separated by a small or large interval in space and/or time. For E_1 to exert a causal effect on E_2 means, at minimum, that E_1 must happen earlier than E_2. For instance, if I start out on a journey (E_1), my arrival at the destination (E_2) certainly is causally affected by my departure, and my departure is certainly earlier than my arrival. In this simple case the order of time precedence is easy to establish because I observed both happenings directly—at the times and places at which they occurred. The problem becomes more complicated, however, when there is no observer on-site at both happenings, and the order of precedence must be inferred from information collected at some distance away.

For this case the problem is not in the information itself but in how it should be interpreted. This is not so simple, even with perfect information. Thanks to relativity, space and time behave strangely, and different observers can get different results.

A simple illustration, going back to Albert Einstein (1879– 1955), who founded the theory of relativity, will show the nature of the difficulty.[6] We consider a train in uniform, straight-line motion. On such a frame of reference the laws of physics are just the same as in any other such frame of reference, for example, on the "stationary" ground. We ignore minor effects such as the earth's rotation, which are not in a straight line and do induce small discrepancies. Aside from such effects it will be clear that "stationary" is a relative concept; the train could just as well be considered stationary while the ground is moving past it.

One property that holds in such a frame of reference is that the speed of light, as measured by the observer, is always the same, about 300,000 kilometers (186,000 miles) per second. (Strictly speaking, this speed must be measured in a vacuum; the presence of the atmosphere will introduce another small discrepancy, which we can ignore here.) This is a very remarkable property indeed— a train speeding at constant velocity, for example, will not show the same velocity relative to some other moving or stationary point of reference. We might have a car running alongside that just keeps up with the train so it appears stationary or a car moving faster so the train moves backwards relative to the car. But this is impossible with light (that is, it is not possible for any material object to travel as fast as light or faster, as far as we know). Moreover, certain subtle effects are necessary so that observers moving at different rates in different directions will all get the same results when they measure the speed of light. These effects—clocks that run at slightly different rates and distances that minutely change (more so at greater speeds)—have all been verified experimentally.

But to return to our example, suppose that, as the train is moving down the track, bolts of lightning strike both in the front (E_1) and in the rear (E_2), leaving visible marks on both the train and the ground. (The visible marks are important as a way of determining, experimentally, exactly where the lightning struck.) An observer on the ground, standing by the track midway between the two points where the lightning strikes, sees two flashes of light at exactly the same time and concludes that the lightning struck at both points simultaneously. An observer on the train, however, also standing midway between the two flashes, will see something different.

A small interval of time must pass for the light from the lightning to reach the two observers. During this time the train moves forward. The observer on the train thus must see the light from the front before the light from the rear. The speed of the light, on the other hand, is exactly the same measured on the train as on the ground. (Again we are ignoring small effects, such as any side-to-side rocking of the train, and also assuming very high precision in all measurements, which, as we noted, should be done in a vacuum. The precision we would need, in fact, is unlikely under the conditions described but could be achieved with a special "train" and special instruments.) The light from the front must travel the same distance as that from the back, yet it arrives before the light from the back. The observer on the train concludes that lightning struck in front *before* it struck in back or, in other words, that E_1 preceded E_2. In a similar way, if the train had been going in the other direction, the observer would "see" that E_2 preceded E_1.

The conclusion is that the notion of simultaneity simply does not apply—there is no absolute simultaneity. We are unable to say whether E_1 or E_2 happened first or whether they both happened at the same time because different, equally valid frames of reference give different, conflicting results. It might then be asked whether this is true in general, that is, maybe we can never establish the precedence of any events because there could always be some observer who could refute the claim—but this is not so.

As one example, clearly there is no ambiguity if lightning strikes in front soon enough that the flash would be seen in the rear of the train before the lightning strikes there. Any observer, whether on the ground or in the train, must then see the flash in front before the one in the rear, and all must agree that the event in front happened first. (This, it will be seen, must be true even for a train traveling in the opposite direction, so that E_1 is now in the rear. By reaching the site of E_2 first, the light from E_1 gains a head start over the light from E_2 that this other flash, traveling at the same speed, can never overtake.) We then say that E_1 and E_2 have timelike separation, and it is possible for E_1 to exert a causal effect on E_2. The light from E_1, for example, could trip a detector at the (future) site of E_2, which could trigger the deployment of a lightning rod to intercept the second bolt when it did strike.

Two distant events, such as two flashes of light, may be simultaneous to one observer, but will not be simultaneous to another, equally valid observer. This ambiguity offers a major obstacle to faster than light travel and inhibits or localizes causal effects.

We can extend this notion of time ordering and causality to the case where light from E_1 arrives just as E_2 is happening. Clearly here too E_1 could exert a causal effect on E_2, though the options are more limited. So in this case, which is known as lighllike separation, E_1 still precedes E_2. But further than this we cannot go: E_1 unambiguously precedes E_2 if and only if there is time for a light signal sent out from the site of E_1 at the time of its occurrence to reach the site of E_2 not later than when E_2 happens.

Otherwise, if E_1 and E_2 are too far apart spatially and too close in time to signal in either direction, their separation is spacelike and there is no order of precedence. It is impossible in this case for one event to causally affect the other. For this reason a good case can be made that faster-than-light travel is impossible. If we could go faster than light, our arrival at our destination could not be causally affected by our departure or be said to occur definitely later—yet obviously it is causally affected and does happen later. Signaling faster than light is precluded for the same reason.

That faster-than-light or superluminal effects are not possible is basically the locality property. We have seen how it rests on simple assumptions, mainly, that the laws of physics must be the same in similar frames of reference so that the speed of light must also be the same. These assumptions (in a refined but basically similar form) underlie the special theory of relativity, which has wide applicability in accounting for what we observe in the world.

Of wider scope still is the general theory of relativity, which in addition accounts for the behavior of objects under gravitation. (The latter causes warping, or curvature, of space, normally only a very small additional effect.) Though the special theory precludes faster-than-light signaling or travel, there is still uncertainty about the general theory. Some have tried to argue that it could allow superluminal effects, though such effects have not been observed.[7] The only exception—of a sort—occurs in the expansion of the universe; space itself may expand faster than the speed of light. Indeed, this is conjectured to have happened in an early, inflationary phase of our universe.[8] But it would not permit one to travel faster than light, as we usually understand it, that is, choosing our destination at will and going there, or sending messages faster than light. In general it seems that relativity never violates the locality property, even with inflating space or such exotic, conjectured possibilities as wormholes, which will be considered in later chapters.

Quantum Interpretations and Locality

Enter quantum mechanics, where strangeness abounds even more than in relativity. In fact, there are weird effects that seem very close to signaling and also seem to happen faster than light, in violation of the locality assumption. This is one place, though, that many-worlds parts company with rival versions of quantum theory—it offers an explanation of events that preserves locality. How it can do so is part two of our remarkable story and is also important evidence favoring this theory over its rivals, given the confidence we have in relativity. To tell this part of the story we need a little background, including some consideration of the alternatives to many-worlds. We will start with the Copenhagen interpretation, which is the earliest historically and, despite the inroads of many-worlds and other theories, still has the widest acceptance.

The Copenhagen interpretation is named in honor of Danish physicist Niels Bohr, who with Werner Heisenberg developed it in 1927.[9] The virtues of this interpretation, the first of its kind to enjoy substantial success or acceptance, are that it is firmly rooted in what can be observed, and it does make accurate predictions—for just about every phenomenon it is intended to address. (The possibly exceptional cases, so far, can be defended.) But it fails an important litmus test too, in that it offers no good explanation of what is going on. Instead, the observer must be treated as a special class of object not subject to the same rules that govern everything else. Things evolve entirely deterministically until observed. (Satisfactory definitions of *observed* and *observer* have never been given, however; appeals to intuition are necessary.) At this point, random events can and do occur; the photon bounces off the half-silvered mirror, for instance, rather than going through. A random event causes a collapse, or reconfiguring, of the wave function, after which it again evolves deterministically, or without collapse, until another observation is made.

Though accurate in its predictions, the Copenhagen interpretation is unsatisfactory. Accurate predictions alone are not enough, as David Deutsch well notes in *The Fabric of Reality*, a book that explores some philosophical implications of the many-worlds hypothesis. A major point is that although predictions are important, science is even more vitally concerned with explanations.[10] True, an explanation, to be correct, must not make incorrect predictions and preferably will make correct ones—or otherwise, like Darwinian evolution, avoid specifics and confine itself to useful generalities. In any case it must offer more than predictions. The geocentric model of the solar system, which preceded the heliocentric system of Copernicus, was accurate in its predictions, especially with the adjustments to planetary orbits known as epicycles that were added to compensate for discrepancies that had been found. But nevertheless it was a poor explanation of what was going on and is no longer taken seriously, while the heliocentric solar system—with the planets revolving around the sun rather than the earth—is the mental picture we immediately form when we think of the planets. The heliocentric model, then, is a superior theory and not simply an alternative to an "equally valid" means of predicting effects.

Again, the Copenhagen interpretation fails to offer a satisfactory explanation. Why should the observer be a special class of object? Are observers made of different stuff from everything else? (No differences have been found.) In fact the observer must be assumed to be a "classical" object, subject only to the prequantum version of physics. Other objects (including very complicated systems) do not cause collapse of the wave function. What if an observer observes another observer, at the quantum level? What if two observers observe each other? Since the observer, an integral part of the theory, must be a classical object, it means that classical physics is not simply derivable from quantum physics—it has to be there to begin with—though in other respects it is derivable, as noted above, through the averaging of small-scale effects. And, of course, the idea of random events is scientifically objectionable. In general, the Copenhagen interpretation has to make a distinction between particlelike and wavelike behavior. The one is not a consequence of the other, but both must be included separately.

The Copenhagen interpretation is clearly a single-world theory—the observer, a classical object whose role is critical, never splits, nor does the world that observer sees. Other attempts at a single-world formulation of quantum mechanics have been made. One is quantum logic—special rules of logic applied in special situations. There are also hidden variable theories, in which randomness is explained deterministically by assuming information exists that is not available to the observer. There are nonlinear theories, in which wave functions do not add together as they experimentally appear to do. Another approach is John Cramer's transactional model that uses interactions going backward as well as forward in time. There are others. Some of these single-world theories have had some success and in particular have overcome some of the problems with the Copenhagen interpretation, but all have problems of their own. One of the problems with all single-world interpretations is that they violate locality. This will be seen shortly.

Let us go on now to many-worlds, which was originated by American physicist Hugh Everett III in 1957,[11] and is also known as the relative state or Everett interpretation or formulation. The underlying assumptions are very simple—indeed, this is the simplest of all the quantum theories in terms of postulates. In many-worlds, there is no irreconcilable duality between waves and particles, as is usual with other theories. In reality, there are no particles, and the observer is not a special case but is subject to the same rules as everything else. ("Particles" then are explained as virtual effects resulting from wave interactions.) In fact, there are no irreducible classical objects; classical physics is fully deducible from the quantum variety. Waves, however, have an objective existence, independent of the observer (not always a feature of quantum theories), and a wave function never collapses.

The strangeness of many-worlds, and what gives this theory its name, occurs because it still must explain apparent randomness. The explanation that follows from the underlying assumptions is that each apparently random, observed event causes splitting of the system in question (including any observers) into copies in which the event occurs in all its possible variations. After this the now-differing worlds do not (usually) interfere further with one another but go their separate ways and generally will split additionally. (Under certain conditions, however, separate worlds can fuse—something with important philosophical consequences that will be considered shortly.) So, in the case of the photon and the half-silvered mirror, the initial observer and associated system would split into two or more. For some of these, the photon would bounce off the mirror; for (nearly all) the rest, it would pass through. It can be seen that this splitting process avoids any true randomness—we know in advance exactly what is going to happen in all its variations—but to each observer-copy it appears that a random event occurred.

Once the worlds have split, they do not usually affect one another—except in subtle, though sometimes still detectable, ways. One such detectable scenario occurs with the photon in the two-slit experiment. In this case the splitting of worlds generates multiple real photons, some of which go through one slit and some the other. It is the interference of the photons with one another that produces the corduroy pattern on the detector surface and makes this pattern come out the same whether we start with one photon at a time in the system or many. In a similar way, interference effects can be generated by firing a single photon at a half-silvered mirror or involving it in other processes in which there is a significant probability of more than one outcome.

Something now needs to be said regarding common misinterpretations of many-worlds. For example, it is widely thought that the splitting of worlds propagates instantaneously and irreversibly—but this is not the case. The splitting is never faster than light, and under special conditions it can be reversed. The splitting in fact is parsimonious, only happening when it has to, that is, when two systems become different at the quantum level (have different, distinguishable quantum states), and it will also reverse itself, or heal, and the different worlds fuse again if the quantum states become the same or indistinguishable. In fact, much confusion and malignment of many-worlds has come from misunderstanding the parsimonious nature of the splitting that occurs.

Nick Herbert, for example, writing in *Quantum Reality*, a generally fine book about the different interpretations of reality at the quantum level, claims incorrectly that many-worlds violates locality. "Any model of reality," he concludes, "in which a tiny event in the Andromeda galaxy can instantly split my reality into thousands of Xerox copies cannot by any stretch of the imagination be called 'local.'"[12] In fact, with the splitting constrained not to propagate faster than light, events in another galaxy would not affect us until many millennia after their occurrence. Things in our size range can split quickly, but eons are required on the cosmic scale.

A final interesting property is that, as with determinism, reverse-determinism must also hold with many-worlds (though also of the inaccessible variety) by virtue of a basic principle known as CPT ("charge, parity, time") symmetry. Any possible process can proceed backward if we change the particles to their corresponding antiparticles (reversing all electrical charges) and change left- to right-handedness. CPT symmetry applies to all quantum theories and states, in effect, that determinism in one time-direction implies it in the other time-direction (though it says nothing about whether determinism holds, this being a feature of some theories but not others). This too has been a source of confusion for some, who think that the splitting in many-worlds is irreversible and thus is inconsistent with CPT symmetry.[13] This is not the case, though for sizable (macroscopic) systems, fusion would be a most unusual occurrence given the very small likelihood that two different systems would so evolve as to become exactly alike at the quantum level.

The Aspect Experiment and Many-Worlds

Let us now consider how many-worlds saves the day for locality. First we will look at an experiment in which the locality assumption seems to be violated then show how it is not, given the possibilities opened by many-worlds.

The experiment in its main essentials was first performed in 1982 under Alain Aspect at the University of Paris and has often been repeated.[14] A pair of photons is created according to a certain procedure. At creation they are momentarily together, but they zoom off in opposite directions at the usual speed of light. The headlong flight continues until each photon encounters a detector or is otherwise altered or stopped. The two photons may thus be far apart when finally detected, and the detection events will generally have spacelike separation so that according to relativity, one event is causally independent of the other. This should preclude the possibility of one photon in any way signaling the other—yet that is just what seems to be happening under suitable conditions.

A special kind of detector responds to the polarization, or pattern of vibration, of a photon and detects one of two states, either up or down—one or the other, never both. The detector is oriented; it can be pointed up (to the 12 o'clock position), to the right (3 o'clock), et cetera. (The two detectors must also be facing each other, so that clock directions are actually reversed in mirror-image fashion. It turns out that the two photons are mirror imaged too, having opposite, circular polarizations so each detector effectively "sees" an identical photon.) It is found by repeated trials that, whenever a photon is measured, it will be up or down with equal probability, like a coin toss. The exact pattern of ups and downs is unpredictable and independent of which way the detector is pointed. (This then is another case of an apparent effect without a cause, which needs to be explained to defend determinism. Many-worlds would explain it, as usual, as a deterministic split into different worlds in which each of the different possibilities is realized.) However, if another detector is used to look at the other photon, remarkable correlations emerge.

For example, if both detectors are pointing in the same direction, both will detect the same polarization states (both up or both down) even though the states themselves are random. This occurs independently of the direction the detectors are pointing. If, on the other hand, the two detectors are misaligned or separated by 3 hours or 90° (say one is pointing at 12 o'clock and the other at 3 o'clock) the detections will be perfectly anticorrelated, with one up and the other down—a 100 percent mismatch. Again, though, which detection is up and which down will be random. This effect too is independent of which direction either detector is pointing, so long as the other one is separated by 90°; for example, the 100 percent mismatch would occur with one detector pointing at 4 o'clock and the other at 7 o'clock. At other separations we find both matches and mismatches, but by averaging over many trials a physical law emerges: at each fixed separation (again, independent of the absolute direction of each detector) there is a characteristic mismatch. For example, at a 1 hour (30°) separation there will be a 25 percent mismatch, or a 25 percent chance of discrepancy on each trial—but at a 2 hour (60°) separation there will be a 75 percent mismatch. Seemingly one detector and/or photon "knows" something about the other detector and/ or photon. Is there some sort of instantaneous signaling going on?

One thought is that the two photons, which were created together, have somehow been imprinted with the same information. Perhaps this could convey the necessary effects without instantaneous signaling. By analogy, I can type a message on a piece of paper using a typewriter, also making a carbon copy. I can keep one copy of the message and give you the other copy; suppose you then travel a great distance away. I can look at my copy, and you can look at yours. Our two detection events, then, can have spacelike separation. Instantly they inform us about each other's message, yet despite our distance apart there is no faster-than-light signaling. However, the message we both see was created beforehand and not in the detection process.

In contrast, the photon experiment raises the possibility that some or all of the message *was* created in the detection process and not beforehand. The "message" of up or down is certainly not "written" into the photon in anything like the usual way we inscribe a message, even on a minute scale. If the detection process contributes to the message—in particular if the detection at one end can affect the message at the other end—then we are faced with what seems like superluminal signaling. But to arrive at such a conclusion we must be careful in assessing the observed effects.

For instance, the fact that we get the same polarization states when both detectors are pointed the same way does not by itself indicate any contribution of the detection process to the message, even if the detected states are unpredictable. Both photons might be imprinted randomly but equally at creation—but in a complicated pattern that our detectors can only "see" to a limited extent on any given encounter. What a detector sees, an up or down, could depend on how the photon is presenting itself as well as the detector orientation. When the two detectors are equally aligned, both twin photons would be seen equally, though unpredictably, but misalignment would cause discrepancies. Could some such message scenario account for what is seen? In particular, it would be reasonable that a small misalignment might cause less (or less frequent) discrepancy than a greater misalignment—and this is certainly observed, at least in many cases. (It would not always have to be observed, though; depending on just how the photons are imprinted, a large misalignment could again swing equal features into view and reduce the mismatch.)

But there is one, rather subtle property that is inconsistent with the experimental results and thus rules out this message scenario.

This property is reproducibility: we must assume that whatever detection process is applied to one photon, if that same detection process is or had been applied to the other photon, the result must be the same. Thus, for example, if one detector, pointed at 12 o'clock and seeing one photon, gets an up, the other detector seeing the other photon would also have gotten up if it had been pointed at 12 o'clock. This must follow regardless of whether the other detector really was pointed at 12 o'clock or was active at all. For clearly this is a consequence of the standard locality assumption: unless there is something like fast signaling between photons or detectors, detection of a property of one photon cannot change that property for the other photon. Since the paired photons are identical in their detectable properties, we can independently measure these properties, and the measurements must match. This, I emphasize, is an assumption that follows only if the twin photons are each carrying a message imprinted beforehand that is read in the detection process—something that is not a foregone conclusion but that instead must be examined in more detail.

In particular it means that, for a detector pointed at 1 o'clock, there must be a 25 percent mismatch between the polarization states that would have been measured had that same detector been pointed at 12 o'clock. It is worth noting here that this cannot be verified directly because measuring the polarization state alters the photon's properties. Instead, we would have to use the other photon, but this is straightforward: we simply note that we do indeed get a 25 percent mismatch when the other detector, pointed at 12 o'clock, looks at this other, similar particle. Once again, this follows if we assume that standard locality holds and our detections are a type of message reading. The 25 percent mismatch, as we have noted, does not depend on the particular orientations involved but only on their separation. Thus there is also a 25 percent mismatch between what a detector would have seen at 11 o'clock and what it would have seen at 12 o'clock.

But here, finally, is where we run into trouble, in the form of a result known as a Bell inequality, named for physicist John Stewart Bell, who obtained his famous inequalities in 1964. For the above scenario, we ask what is the maximum mismatch we could have between a detector pointed at 11 o'clock and one pointed at 1 o'clock. It is not difficult to show that, with a message-reading scenario, the mismatch could not be more than 50 percent—the sum of the mismatch as we go from 11 o'clock to 12 o'clock and then from 12 o'clock to 1 o'clock. This maximum mismatch will occur in the unlikely event that each mismatch in the measurements between the 12 and the 1 positions happens to fall on, and disrupt, a successful match that occurs between the 11 and the 12 positions. For otherwise it would have the effect of undoing the mismatch between the 11 and 12 positions' measurements, reducing not increasing the total of mismatches. More generally, the Bell inequality tells us that successive misalignments in our process of reading a message could not produce a worse discrepancy than the sum of the misalignments taken separately. Again, here it means we could not have a worse mismatch for measurements differing in orientation by 2 hour-marks, or 60°, than 25 percent + 25 percent or 50 percent.

Yet we find experimentally, despite Bell and his inequality, that the actual mismatch is 75 percent, or in other words, a double misalignment gives a whopping triple mismatch. It would seem that the photons, or detectors, though separated to great distances, know what each other is up to and arrange the extra mismatch on purpose. Seemingly, it is clear evidence of a superluminal connection. It is odd that it comes about by a mismatch rather than a match, but the implications are the same either way. To mismatch, as here, by more than we would expect to happen by simple misalignment must, by appearances, require some shared knowledge of the detection process, knowledge that would only become available as each detection is done. We seem to have no choice but to regard this as a form of nonlocal interaction—something that flies in the face of relativity.

Here it is worth noting that such interactions do not threaten our scientific edifice as much as, for example, straightforward faster-than-light travel would. There are really no contradictory facts involved. If necessary relativity might be "bent" to accommodate this rather fleeting nonlocality, though it would be awkward to do so, and something we would like to avoid if possible. (That relativity could, apparently, be bent to resolve this one difficulty is one arguable reason to consider the case not closed for many-worlds; however, it certainly complicates our explanation of things to have to make this accommodation.) But in particular we have not discovered any way to use the polarization results to transmit messages back and forth faster than light. Each observer, in detecting the polarization state, sees only what is, to all appearances, a completely random event. There is no intelligible information about a faraway place. It is only when the two observers compare notes through conventional signaling or a face-to-face meeting that the remarkable correlations can be verified. Thus the verification does not happen at superluminal speed—something that will be important for the rescue of locality by many-worlds.

A little more needs to be said first, though, about the creation we have accomplished in the act of reading the message. We have produced information—that required for a mismatch—in the detection events. Each such event, the recording of up or down, is

Detectors aligned, no mismatch

Misaligned 30°, 25 percent mismatch

Misaligned 60°, 75 percent mismatch

The Aspect experiment. Twin photons are repeatedly created and travel in opposite directions to detectors that record their polarization states, up (U), or down (D). A photon can be in either state at random, but if the detectors are aligned, the two photons will always show the same state. Misalignment of the detectors leads to odd mismatches; here a double misalignment gives more than a double mismatch. These strange effects suggest some form of collusion or instantaneous signalling between the detectors, a violation of the locality property. But is this what is actually happening?

different from what it might have been. Moreover, it happened in one particular way only. The property that a measurement comes out different from what it might have been is known as counterfactuality (or contrafactuality), while that of happening in one particular way only is definiteness. Together they add up to counterfactual definiteness, which in turn plays a pivotal role in the challenge this entire experiment poses—or seems to pose—to locality.

In fact, with counterfactual definiteness we see that there must be some sort of superluminal connection. Each detection happens in one way only, and could have happened differently, yet the two events are correlated. So there must be some special way of ensuring that the correlation will hold—certain, necessary information must be transmitted or shared between the two events.

This, on the other hand, is why we do not have to assume a superluminal connection in the case we considered of a typed message and its carbon copy. There the message can only come out one way because it has been created beforehand and we do not make any changes or add anything at the time the messages are read. There is definiteness but not counterfactuality, consequently, no threat to locality. The information that must be transmitted to correlate the two detection events *is* transmitted, but in the subluminal (not faster-than-light) process of separating the two copies of the message before the messages are read.

Many-worlds, it turns out, violates counterfactual definiteness too but in the opposite way: there is counterfactuality but no definiteness. When the polarization state is detected, we cannot predict whether it will be up or down, though we know it must be one or the other. Here then is counterfactuality: the detection could come out either way, and the message is created in the detection process, not beforehand. However, when the measurement (detection) is made, we cannot say "it could have come out different but it did not" because it did come out different. The act of measurement splits the observer into two observers—one of whom sees up, the other, down. As it turns out, this counterfactual indefiniteness allows many-worlds to preserve locality. Again, certain necessary information is transmitted between the two detection events to establish the observed correlation. But the information is transmitted, after the detection process, by the splitting of the worlds, which happens subluminally and does not violate locality.

Remember that the correlations can only be verified at subluminal speed, something that is intimately tied in with the splitting of the worlds. When the observer measures one photon, he splits and the split begins to propagate into the surroundings, though again only at subluminal speed. Similarly, the other observer makes a measurement, she too splits, and the split begins to propagate from her location also at subluminal speed. Eventually the spreading splits join, and this occurs before the observers can meet and compare notes (or possibly in the very act of comparing). The way the spreading splits join determines the correlations that will be found between the different measurements.

In fact, in the joining of the splits—or equivalently, the separation of the worlds—all the possibilities will be realized that are observed. Up will be matched with up in one of the worlds, down

a   **b**   **c**

How many-worlds preserves locality. *(a)* Twin photons speed in opposite directions toward distant observers with detectors. Results—polarization up or down—will be shown on computer monitor screens. *(b)* Observers and surroundings split as different states are observed—but splits propagate only at finite speed, not instantaneously. *(c)* Only as splits join are distant correlations established—here up is paired with up and down with down—so that there is no violation of the locality property.

with down in another—or mismatches will occur, with the correct, observed frequencies. For example, in the case that the detectors are correctly aligned, the splitting will ensure that up is always matched with up and down with down. The absence of mismatches in this case accords with our observations, yet the correct correlating occurs as the spreading splits join and not at the earlier times that the measurements were made. There is no instantaneous signaling. Many-worlds, moreover, will assign the correct "thickness" or "weight" to each world created by splitting, to correspond to the probability of our finding ourselves in any of these worlds. All this, again, is achieved without invoking superluminal effects. Many-worlds, then, is triumphant where single-world interpretations fail, and it offers no challenge to the well-verified theory of relativity. (Indeed it is worth remarking that the main reason we have confidence that relativity could be bent to accommodate other, nonlocal interpretations, is because they agree with many-worlds experimentally—so far.)

Besides squaring with relativity, many-worlds has other attractive features we have already noted: it is deterministic, it makes no special case of the observer, and it is the simplest in terms of postulates. Another interesting (and, in this case, unique) property is that many-worlds predicts quantum gravity, that is, that the gravitational force is transmitted by particles, or gravitons.[15] This is expected to be important if we are to arrive at a "theory of everything" uniting quantum mechanics with relativity. (For the other interpretations quantum gravity would have to be added as an extra postulate. As yet quantum gravity has not been verified or refuted; evidence is being sought through astronomical observations.) Indeed, such a theory might help decide whether many-worlds should be accepted over its rivals, but for this we will have to wait. There is still another line of argument favoring many-worlds, which relates to quantum computing—this is considered briefly below and again in Chapter 8.

The problem with many-worlds—for those who do not subscribe to it—is its metaphysical claims: on the face of it, it does seem preposterous that over short intervals of time, gigantic conglomerates of people and things are splitting into near-identical copies, all but one of which—our own, observable world—are undetectable. History, then, has multiple timelines, in which alternate versions of events occur. There must be versions of history in which Napoleon won the battle of Waterloo, or for that matter, neither Napoleon nor any other humans ever existed, and intelligent birds, not mammals, peopled the earth after the extinction of the dinosaurs. Going back further, there must be versions (and perhaps very many) in which life never evolved at all on Earth or took forms completely alien to what we find on our Earth. Going back still further, there are many histories in which the Earth and our solar system never appeared in the first place, though something else very interesting occurred—or perhaps did not. All these possibilities are real, though we only see one of them. A substantial portion of our explanation of reality, then, must rest on unobservables, and some rather gaudy ones at that.

Thus it is sometimes objected that many-worlds violates Ockham's razor. William Ockham (1285–1347) was an English thinker who advocated parsimony in philosophical theories. This principle, that unnecessary complications should be avoided in all explanations of things (though advocated by others before him, including Aristotle), became known as Ockham's razor.[16] It is seemingly violated when we require the splitting of the world into copies of which we can have no ordinary perceptions. But alternatives to many-worlds have difficulties too, suggesting that it is, in fact, a better exemplar of Ockham's razor than its rivals. Many-worlds is long on universes, but short on postulates, that is, it is the simplest of all the quantum theories, as we have noted. And, for similar reasons of parsimony, its easier fit with that other great theory, relativity, must also count in its favor.

Deutsch in *The Fabric of Reality* notes an interesting case of where many-worlds provides a simple, straightforward explanation of what is going on, one that alternate theories do not seem able to match. A variation of the two-slit experiment uses two additional, outer slits, one on either side. What we see with this four-slit arrangement is bright interference bands as before, except that every other band is almost entirely missing. This pattern, of course, is observed with one photon in the system at a time, just as with many photons. When the two extra slits are covered up, the missing bands reappear. Something, then, is nudging the photons away from places they land when only the two slits are open. What? we ask, and many-worlds tells us, matter-of-factly, that it is "ghost" photons from parallel universes. These in turn are real enough, though not part of our everyday reality.[17]

It is interesting to note too that, according to many-worlds, the ghost particles are themselves organized into their own whole universes—each universe is a ghost to the others and has structure comparable to ours—rather than all ghosts being amorphously lumped together. (This idea of separate, equal universes leads to predictions that have been confirmed experimentally.) So there are many other universes much like ours (though they can be very different too), which provides for histories like ours though differing in detail.

More on Alternatives to Many-Worlds

Alternatives to many-worlds, that is, single-world theories, come in numerous varieties.[18] All deny the splitting into real, alternate histories that is specifically provided in many-worlds. (The possibility of other worlds generated by other means is not ruled out, however, and in fact is considered in the next chapter, where it too plays a part in supporting Unboundedness.) Otherwise the important alternatives form two major groups, based on how they explain apparent randomness. Some, like the Copenhagen interpretation and Cramer's transactional interpretation, are based on a rejection of unobservables. Apparent randomness, then, is real— an effect without a cause—and something that must be accepted, usually without explanation. Other versions explain the apparent randomness through "hidden" variables, which are unobservables at very small scales rather than the grander ones of many-worlds.

Unfortunately, it is not possible to decide at this point, experimentally, which of all the interpretations (if any) is true. I think many-worlds has more in its favor than the alternatives, for reasons we have considered, and I accept it myself but will stop short of discounting these others entirely. It is worth noting, however, that many-worlds is overwhelmingly favored by physicists who specialize in the deep scientific study of reality—that is, the quantum cosmologists. Tipler, one of their number, says it is "simply because the mathematics forces one to accept it."[19] Many-worlds provides an explanation of things that is unmatched by alternatives, and denying it puts one in an awkward position of having to proceed as if it were true. This could be sufficient ground for adopting it over its rivals, yet I think we should be cautious. Many-worlds, with its support of Unboundedness, would open wonderful possibilities; yet I feel uneasy resting so much hope on one particular theory of unobservables, at least until there is more experimental confirmation.

It is also worth noting that, while one argument for many-worlds is that it upholds the locality property demanded by relativity, there are other ways that relativity seems to clash with quantum mechanics that apply more or less equally to single-world versions as well as many-worlds. Interesting work toward a possible a reconciliation will be considered in Chapter 8, where it will be seen to have additional importance.

In this book, then, I have given priority to many-worlds but have also tried to respect the possibility that it is not true after all, so that we must confront some other, possibly quite alien reality. Where this leads will become clearer in the next chapter where we consider Unboundedness in more detail. It will turn out that a case can be made for something much like many-worlds, enough to ensure Unboundedness, even if the Everett interpretation itself is called into question. The argument is much easier, however, if we can simply accept Everett's version, so it is still of interest to try to establish this as far as we can. To what has been said already, then, it would be desirable to add more, particularly from the observational end. Although, as I have noted, the experimental evidence is still inconclusive, there is actually some interesting experimental work that seems to shed further light—and there are interesting future possibilities too. Some of the experimental work concerns the possibility of distinguishing many-worlds from what is still its chief rival (because so many physicists still endorse it), the Copenhagen interpretation.

Ideally, what we would need is a carefully constructed observer, able to do a controlled experiment involving reversible learning. Such an observer would make a measurement—causing collapse of the wave function, according to the Copenhagen interpretation—then reverse the entire procedure, forgetting the measurement in the process.

According to many-worlds, the system under observation should always be restored to its original state; in this case, the split in worlds that momentarily occurred will have healed. According to Copenhagen, the system will not always be restored because making a measurement irreversibly collapses the wave function, regardless of what happens afterward. (This means that sometimes the original state will be restored, but sometimes it will not be, at random.) Whether the restoration always happens or sometimes does not will be detectable, and thus will distinguish between the two formulations. It is expected that, with enough progress in nanotechnology and computers, the necessary means will become available to do the experiment, perhaps sometime in the twenty-first century.

A Telling Experiment?

In fact an experiment suggesting reversible learning has already been done,[20] and it supports many-worlds over Copenhagen. It is another variation of the two-slit experiment. Again the photon can take one of two overlapping but nonidentical paths to reach a backstop detector. An interference pattern occurs if we do not know which path the photon took. By an ingenious technique, however, the photon can be reversibly tagged in transit to determine which path it takes. That is, the photon in transit exhibits polarization, or vibration in a preferred direction, which can be altered. With the proper apparatus we could then test the polarization of the photon to see whether it had been tagged for path 1 or 2. (In practice, tagging for path 1 involves changing the polarization while for path 2 it is left unchanged.) On the other hand, it is possible to erase the tag in such a way as to destroy this information before it can be permanently recorded.

What we find is that, if the in-transit tagging is done and not erased so we could, in principle, tell what path the photon took, there is no interference pattern—it is just as if we had one path closed off all the time. This result is not surprising; it is predicted both by Copenhagen and many-worlds. With Copenhagen, the tagging causes collapse of the wave function, which means the photon cannot produce the interference pattern. With many-worlds, the tagging causes a split in the worlds (in the alternate world, the photon took the other path and received the other tag) after which there is no further interference from the alternate world, hence no interference pattern.

A much more interesting case can be tested, however, because the tagging can be reversed at a later point in the path, while the photon is still in transit. The information as to which path the photon took, which is momentarily present, is then erased. When this is done, the interference pattern appears. According to Copenhagen, the presence of path information should have caused collapse of the wave function. Collapse is irreversible; once the wave function collapses, it must stay collapsed. (This irreversibility, it will be noted, conflicts with CPT symmetry which must hold for quantum objects, but a way around this for Copenhagen is to say that it must be accompanied by an observation—and the observer, we remember, is not a quantum object.) Thus we should not get an interference pattern. According to many-worlds, however, tagging the photon causes the worlds to split, but erasing the information makes them rejoin. The "wave function" goes back to being what it was, and interference occurs. Since this is what is observed, we can accept this remarkable result as one tentative vindication of many-worlds, at least over the Copenhagen interpretation.

It should be noted that such a result, suggestive though it is, does not really refute even the Copenhagen interpretation let alone prove many-worlds over other rivals. Acceptance of such a theory as many-worlds, with its startling implications, can only come with the passage of time and the accumulation of more scientific evidence—if enough evidence mounts in its favor. With Copenhagen, it is observation that collapses the wave function, and "observation" has never been precisely defined. The committed Copenhagenist might say that no true observation occurred in the experiment because the information was lost before an observer could memorize it, so the wave function did not collapse after all.

But at least we see that a record was made of past history—this is what happened when the photon was tagged to indicate which flight path it took. If this is not the same as an observation it is not clear in what the latter must consist. If we say that perception by an observer is required, we must define *observer* and distinguish perception from a simple act of recording information. This has not been done, and it seems doubtful it can be done in a reasonable way, such that erasing a perception could not similarly restore an interference pattern and thereby support many-worlds over Copenhagen.

The Copenhagen interpretation has dominated physics now for most of a century, and it will probably be some time longer before many-worlds—or possibly some other rival—can win out.

Certainly, the simple logic behind many-worlds, that the observer must not be treated as a special case and that all things can be accounted for as wave phenomena alone, is appealing. The popularity of many-worlds seems to rest with certain of those, like cosmologists, who are most concerned about the grand design of reality and who are willing to be daring in their search for unifying explanations. In addition to Frank Tipler and David Deutsch, the distinguished roster of endorsing physicists includes Richard Feynman, Stephen Hawking, and Steven Weinberg, all three Nobel winners.[21] This of course is not proof of validity, but it is something to think about. (Einstein, it is worth remarking, died two years before Everett completed his formulation and never had a chance to tender his judgment. Would he too have been attracted to many-worlds, despite its outlandish character, since he was disturbed by unexplained randomness or "God playing at dice"?)

We can look forward to more experiments that might clarify matters. One would involve the possibility of quantum computing, in which alternate worlds are to be used for segments of a computation that happen in parallel. Certain problems can be solved in this way much faster than if only one historical timeline were involved (unless other peculiar properties hold for the single timeline). Successful quantum computing, then, would be another piece of evidence favoring many-worlds, if not by itself a proof. Failure, on the other hand, would not refute many-worlds; the alternate timelines could still exist even if they do not collaborate in all the ways we might like.

Returning briefly to the data-erasing experiment, one important further consequence is worth noting, if we accept many-worlds. First, let us consider what happens if a photon goes through the system without being tagged. Though it is reasonable to say, for each detection event, that the photon took one path and not the other, we cannot say which path it took. It is ambiguous in a fundamental way, which is reflected in the interference pattern we observe. That is, it is not correct to say that in "our" past history there was one particular path taken, only we just do not know which. Instead, both alternatives must be considered equally part of "our" past—the past is therefore ambiguous. Let us now consider what happens when tagging and erasing occurs.

When a photon is tagged in transit, an ambiguity is removed;

at least we can know in principle which path was taken. When the information is erased, however, the ambiguity reappears, as demonstrated by the interference pattern. So it is no longer correct to say that the photon took one particular path in "our" past, rather than the other one. Loss of information makes the past ambiguous.

This principle in this instance depends on many-worlds, but it can also be based on the more general UI assumptions. Doing so will be highly useful, along with the closely related principle, also implicit in the UI assumptions, that absence of information makes reality ambiguous. These latter we will consider in Chapter 7; for now we take a closer look at Unboundedness.

CHAPTER 6.

Unboundedness

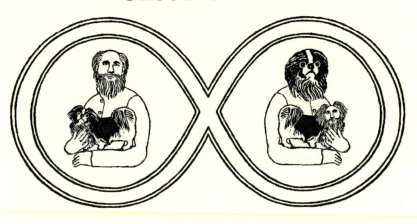

A s stated in Chapter 1, Unboundedness is the principle that "in the whole of existence, all possible, finite histories actually happen." This is a most important principle, a cornerstone of the entire system developed here. Some pertinent issues need clarification, such as the meaning of "possible, finite histories." It also qualifies as an extraordinary claim of a certain sort, so the relevant evidence needs to be considered carefully. Preliminary attention to both points has been given already, mainly in the previous chapter, where we noted that the many-worlds formulation of quantum mechanics supports Unboundedness and the reality of alternate histories. Many-worlds has some attractive scientific features and has gained the support of quantum cosmologists. It may be true, but alternatives to many-worlds are not yet ruled out and are worth considering too in our assessment of how much confidence we can place in Unboundedness. So we need to take a closer look.

First, some general thoughts. One motivation for considering Unboundedness is simply to provide for the possibility of immortality. That immortality should follow if "all possible, finite histories" are real requires a bit of argument, but such an argument can be made (and will) under the additional assumption of Interchangeability. Another important motivation is an "authenticity" issue. We want to consider the possibility of resurrecting persons of the past in a more advanced future. If, in some future resurrection project, a possible past person is created, the UI assumptions will imply that the person is real and historical and not simply a manufactured fantasy. The implications of the possibilities of immortality and a meaningful resurrection of the dead are, of course, profound. They suggest that life and existence as a whole, even (and especially) from the standpoint of unsupernatural materialism, are anything but pointless but instead contain deep reservoirs of meaning. Other issues too will be illuminated by Unboundedness, such as how the world came to be made as we see it.

Here we want to be clear about what is being claimed before proceeding to the question of whether the claim might be true. Thus we need to consider what should be understood by "possible" and "finite" histories. It is easiest, I think, to proceed in reverse order and consider finite histories first.

History: Process versus Description

We must proceed with caution, for there is much opportunity for confusion. *History* could refer either to a physical process that unfolds over time, which process itself can be regarded in different ways, or to a recounting or description of that process in more or less detail and at one level of abstraction or another. The same underlying process, then, can give rise to a multitude of separate histories.

Consider what can loosely be considered a "history"—recognizing the ambiguities in the term, especially at this stage. Our history in any case will be very highly detailed, and pertain to an individual. A collection of atoms making up a human body will undergo a physical process over time that could, in principle, be described at the quantum level for completeness. (During this process, many of the atoms that make up the body will be expelled to be replaced by other atoms and/or will take many complicated paths within the body and/or participate in various physical or chemical interactions, et cetera.) A complete description of this process covering, say, a time interval of years, would be most voluminous but still finite. On the other hand, another, very different interpretation of the process would confine itself to the conscious experience of the person during this time. This too might be quite voluminous to describe (and would certainly involve things we are not aware of at present but will arguably understand in the future). Yet a complete description of this too must also be finite, and probably less extensive than a description of the full, underlying process at the quantum level, though certainly there are many unknown complexities with consciousness, and we are uncertain how much information would be involved in adequately characterizing it.

In any case, we have one underlying process but two distinct histories corresponding to the different interpretations (particle interactions versus consciousness). Each interpretation, moreover, has its own description, making four histories in all. In actuality there would, of course, be very much more than this if we considered all the possible, equivalent descriptions, plus abridgments, further interpretations, and so on. A forest of complexity thus springs up. Yet I think we can successfully navigate this dense, tangled thicket, for reasons that should become clearer as we proceed. It should pose no fundamental difficulty at the level that is important for us, which is concerned with underlying principles. Other details, even ones so basic as the distinction between events and their descriptions, here play a subordinate role.

We must, of course, insist that the admissible descriptions be clear and accurate in what they describe. This alone may seem to involve no small difficulty, concerned as it is with the role of language as a descriptive tool. I will not try to deal with all the possible ways a language might be constructed, used, or misused but insist only that as a minimum an appropriate language providing a descriptive format for historical events and processes is possible, something I think is reasonable. (The discussion in Chapter 8 of the possibility of a universal language is relevant here. In particular, a description of any finite historical process reduces, in a uniform way, to a finite string of bits.) With this in mind I will accept the position that a particular underlying process can give rise to many histories—by way of different interpretations and their descriptions—and treat them all on a more-or-less uniform footing as the permissible elements of a large class.

A finite process, one involving a finite amount of space, time, and energy (as is true of all of human history and all of known cosmological history as well), will give rise to finite histories, including appropriate, finite descriptions. This follows specifically from quantum mechanics and is considered in more detail in the next chapter. The possibility of reducing processes to the quantum level offers a way of speaking of an underlying process, and I will assume that all processes of interest are thus reducible. (This, at least, certainly seems true of processes that would be important at the level of human interaction. It should be noted too that the quantum mechanics I am referring to here is generic— independent of the different versions or interpretations considered in the last chapter.) This does not mean that every process would be fully elucidated if we only had a description of it at the quantum level—far from it. But I do think it could be elucidated, in principle, from such a description.

To put it differently, if two histories are the same at the quantum level, they are the same period; other levels are supervenient upon the quantum level. Any history, then, whether a process or a description, will have at least one—generally more than one— associated, underlying process at the quantum level. Each finite history's underlying processes will also be finite, or, put still differently, the finite histories are histories (including descriptions) that correspond to finite underlying processes.

There is one further important property that follows from the thought that a finite history has a finite description. Quantum mechanics, and the ability we have to describe the processes that follow its rules, makes it possible to assign a specific size to a history, in effect, to measure the quantity of processing or "eventing" that is going on. Events themselves are discrete, and only a finite number can be going on in any history of given, finite size. But what is more interesting, for our purposes, is that the total number of possible histories of given size or less must be finite, though generally very large.

This follows because all possible histories must be realizable under quantum mechanics, and the number of realizable histories in this case is finite. (We must still consider whether all the realizable histories in this sense should be included among the possible histories, as we shall do shortly, but this will not affect our conclusion here.) This does not mean that *all* the possible histories are finite in number, just the histories that are bounded by a fixed size, which, for example would be guaranteed in a structure such as the visible universe, with its finite spatial volume, age, and energy content. But this limit on the number of possible histories will be of use later in the chapter.

What Are the Possible Histories?

Let us now consider what we ought to regard as the possible histories, which we limit to finite histories for purposes of Unboundedness. (The case of infinite histories must be considered in addressing the issue of immortality but need not concern us yet.) In its generality this is a difficult subject philosophically.[1] Part of the difficulty is illustrated in the position of modal realism advocated by David Lewis, in which the possible is simply that which is actualized somewhere, though "somewhere" could well include other universes than our own. With this rationale, of course, all possible things—including the finite histories—are actualized by definition. Yet it says nothing about which of those things are really possible, beyond the evidence we have about our own world. The position of Unboundedness will be that the possibles (finite histories at least) really are actualized, affirming modal realism, but it will be important to arrive at a notion of possibles that is independent of any a priori assumption that they are actualized. To accomplish this I appeal to basic intuition supported by a scientific argument.

A large variety of thinkable historical events and episodes will accordingly be included among the possibles—while the not-possibles, if not precisely delineated, should be clear enough not to cause confusion. Roughly, then, we shall identify a possible (finite) history, with a physically possible history, something our usual intuition tells us can or could have happened, though it is not guaranteed a priori to have happened, either in our visible world or anywhere else. To make this precise, I will consider as possible any happening that is physically realizable under the laws of quantum mechanics. Such a happening, then, is reducible to an underlying process involving interacting particles, which process in turn could be assigned a nonzero probability or likelihood relative to other processes of a similar nature. This seems to be a sound approach based on the experimental evidence, which strongly supports quantum theory, though I think it is important to keep in mind that notions of what is physically realizable are not, in principle, tied to any particular theory. In any case, in assessing the significance of different possible, alternate versions of history, we will have to consider probabilities as well as bare possibilities.

As a simple illustration of some of these ideas, consider a coin toss. Usual intuition tells us the toss can end in heads or tails. After the toss, if the coin comes up heads, we can say that the alternate outcome of tails was possible, so that both occurrences must be regarded as possible histories. This conclusion is reasonable, based on our knowledge. True, our state of knowledge, including lack of knowledge, will affect our estimates of the likelihood of different outcomes, on occasion making some possibilities very remote and others virtually certain. If we know enough about the physics of a just-tossed coin while it is still spinning in the air, as we might learn from a rapid computer analysis of video data, we may be able to predict the outcome of the toss with high confidence. In this way we might all but rule out one of the two alternatives, rendering it, for most purposes, impossible. On the other hand, quantum uncertainty works against absolute certainty in very many cases, so the supply of happenings that are at least barely possible is a rich one that is not easily reduced. Differing amounts of knowledge, then, will change our estimates of the likelihood of one or another of the alternatives happening, but not the bare possibility.

The domain of physically possible histories is quite large and includes the sorts of happenings people have been speculating about through the ages. It is possible, in this sense, that Napoleon could have won the battle of Waterloo. On the other hand, there clearly are some outright impossibilities. Napoleon could not have proved that 1 is greater than 2 or drawn a round square. Such cases are excluded because they are logically impossible, but there are other thinkable cases that I would exclude from the possible, though they need not involve a logical contradiction. One would be that Napoleon in some way was able to violate the laws of quantum mechanics—this I exclude on grounds of physical impossibility, based on the experimental evidence supporting quantum theory. We must be careful: too great an insistence on the physically possible begs the question of how do we know what is physically possible—even the soundest-looking conclusions could eventually be overturned. So I offer no rigorous formalism but think that intuition, once again, will serve our needs.

It is instructive here to consider the possibilities provided by physics at the quantum level since, as we noted, experimental evidence suggests these are truly possible. But despite this endorsement we must proceed with caution since probabilities are also important. In fact, a great many unobserved events are, while unlikely, not at all impossible but would happen with calculable frequency. One simple example would be that, in a series of experiments involving photons striking a half-silvered mirror, 100 consecutive reflections are observed (the photon bounces off rather than passes through the glass, with an equal likelihood of the other alternative). The odds of this "jackpot," though tiny, are not zero, but 1 in 2^{100} or about 1 in 10^{30}. (With a billion automated workstations, each doing a million sets of 100 trials per second, a jackpot would be expected about once in 40 million years.) Similarly there are far more improbable events that still have a nonzero chance of happening.

Water could freeze solid in the broiling summer sun, for instance. This would require that the water molecules, individually, behave in certain ways. The hot environment would render it most unlikely that any sizable number of the molecules would mutually cooperate in this manner, yet the possibility is not ruled out. At the microscopic level we see that particles are darting to and fro, jostling and vibrating in constant, random motion. Generally, the higher the temperature the faster and more disruptive is this movement, which is called Brownian motion after English botanist Robert Brown, who first observed it in 1827,[2] but this is only an average effect. A given particle (water molecule) could move less energetically than average and so could a large number, enough to coalesce and arrange themselves into a sizable, frozen mass, even under conditions of high surrounding temperature. But it would not be something we would expect to observe even in many billions of years—and it is no surprise we have not seen it.

But with this in mind, we see that incredible histories ought to be at least among the remotely possible. The dead could rise from their graves, that is, exact living replicas of the original people could form by the appropriate, unlikely motions of atoms. In the same way, much more prosaic variations would be possible—a history in which a battle went the other way, for instance, or where the main street of your town was thirty feet wider or narrower than it actually is. In fact, these more prosaic possibilities will hold much greater interest for us simply because they are much more likely; again, we will have to give consideration to probabilities. Very unlikely possibilities, though still within the bounds of reality, are treated as virtual *im*possibilities and will have correspondingly minor significance.

This caution in turn, though, must be viewed with some caution itself—more will be involved in deciding whether something is likely, in particular, likely to be observed by us, than may at first be apparent. We will have to consider, for example, what sorts of universes are likely to have observers in the first place. But when such cosmological issues are not at stake, the more important cases of the possible can be reasonably identified with what we think of as typical. These more likely possibilities will be legitimized, on more-or-less equal footing, by the claim of Unboundedness. If something we know of happened in some particular way, there will be alternate versions that really happened too, in other parts of the multiverse. If there is something that happened but the details have been lost and cannot be recovered from surviving records or artifacts, then, with Interchangeability, alternate possibilities must be considered equally real to us. There is not one special version only that really happened and others that could have happened but did not. Again, the validity of Unboundedness, on which these conclusions must rest, is still to be examined.

One issue that comes up here is time precedence. In our everyday experience history seems to have a single timeline. Although some events may be so close in time that we cannot decide which are earlier or later (as in the relativistic case of the train and lightning bolts in the last chapter), generally we can order events based on when they occur. This might be much less so, however, if we consider the possibility of different histories happening in parallel, alternate universes. There could be no meaningful time precedence at all. (And, more generally, a case can be made that time does not "flow" at all, as David Deutsch, for example, does in *The Fabric of Reality*. Perceptions of the passage of time are explained as correlations between certain "snapshots" of a fundamentally static reality.[3] This will be considered in Chapter 15, where it helps resolve a problem connected with causality.) On the other hand, sometimes it would be reasonable to claim an order of precedence, even when different timelines are involved in different, parallel universes. This we expect, in fact, when the timelines can be said to converge.

Suppose we are considering alternate versions of our past that all fit the surviving records. These different but converging timelines we want to regard as equally real; thus they should be equally in our past, and we ought to be able to assume this, based on our formulation of Unboundedness. This actually seems to follow easily, without any modification of our definition: if a given (finite) history is consistent with our past, that is, if it is a possible past for us, then there is a possible (finite) history that incorporates both it and our known history. By Interchangeability, as is argued in the next chapter, it will then follow that this possible past is one of those that is real to us, that is, can be regarded as "our" past. This, once again, will open the possibility of resurrection by creating a copy of a deceased person. But the notion of time precedence gets slightly complicated, with the consequence that a finite but growing multiverse can be considered equivalent to an already-infinite multiverse. (Again, this is a milder version of the idea that time really does not flow at all; it will be considered later in this chapter.)

Another matter connected with resurrection should be briefly mentioned; it ties in with the possible but unlikely histories. My stance, to be argued more fully, is that resurrection could occur by the creation of copies of previously deceased persons. The resurrection scenario we considered above, where the dead are restored by Brownian motion, would be a most unlikely occurrence, requiring just the right coalescence of atoms into bodies having the necessary structure and other properties. This sort of purely accidental resurrection, then, does not deserve much consideration, it is too improbable relative to other possibilities, as I will argue later. These other, more realistic scenarios for resurrection (and more favorable to the resurrectee too) ought to develop in the future through the purposeful actions of advanced beings.

A final point worth making, in regard to possible histories, is that arbitrarily long, finite histories ought to be possible. There is nothing we know of, physically, to preclude this, and I will assume it so, as one consequence of Unboundedness. This has a special significance—immortality will require it.

In summary, then, the principle of Unboundedness asserts that the physically possible, finite histories really happen, but in addition we see that the more likely scenarios deserve proportionally more consideration than the barely possible ones. This in particular will rule out serious attention to claims of the paranormal, in which events are said to happen that would be most unlikely, though barely possible, by our accepted physics and knowledge of the world. Histories that fit our own past, on the other hand, can be linked with ours to form larger, possible histories, and thus must be accounted part of our real past, which must be seen as involving multiple timelines.

The Plausibility of Unboundedness

We have now considered what is involved in the claim of Unboundedness and will go on to the question of whether it might be true. We need to consider negative as well as positive arguments. The arguments that best apply will, of course, depend on what our view of reality should be—an unsettled question. Nevertheless, I think we have something significant to go on, even if physics and other sciences cannot decide the matter yet. I will reach optimistic conclusions. Unboundedness has at least a reasonable, fighting chance of being true and is something in which we can put our confidence, though uncertainty remains. We have noted how many-worlds, with its reassuring profusion of alternate histories, also has scientific arguments in its favor. Many-worlds essentially guarantees Unboundedness, but there are fallback possibilities in case it fails.

But first let us consider the negative arguments. Mainly, these are observational and certainly not to be taken lightly. We do not see any direct evidence of alternate histories. We have never even seen unequivocal evidence of life from anywhere but planet Earth (notwithstanding numerous claims). True, it is a big universe, and there must be many things going on out there that we have never observed. If the universe were infinite that would furnish an argument for Unboundedness, based on probability considerations. Even though it might be unlikely that, for instance, a solar system would form very much like ours, with intelligent beings almost or even exactly the same as us, the probability would be nonzero. It thus must happen over and over, if there are an infinite number of settings where it could happen, each with roughly equal likelihood. In this way, then, we could get the different histories in all their possible variations.

But the universe—at any rate what we have seen—while large, is certainly not infinite, and this limitation turns out to be fatal for the exacting requirements that would have to be met. To illustrate, we consider a simplified version of the histories problem.

Instead of the more general possibilities, we will limit the allowable processes, and their corresponding histories, to computer programming of a certain sort, whose purpose is to make an image on a computer monitor screen. Image making can now be done routinely through draw programs, as well as scanners that convert photographic images or printed pages to screen images. Again, we will ignore many details and focus on just the patterns that are created, rather than what programming steps were performed by which particular programmer (human or otherwise) or what type of monitor or computer was used, and so on. Our histories, then, are highly abridged and only tell us the main, end result in each case. Although monitors come with different capabilities, we will assume our monitors produce black and white images in a square array of $1,024 \times 1,024$ picture elements, or pixels. Each pixel itself is a number from 0 to 255 that records a gray level: 0 is solid black, 255 solid white, and intermediate values yield shades of gray.

These requirements are well within the capabilities of many computer monitors today, which have other features, such as a color capability. The numbers chosen are not that special, but do occur frequently in real computer applications because they are powers of 2, or nearly so, which makes them more convenient to work with. In fact, it turns out that each picture intensity can be represented by an 8-bit byte of 0s and 1s. Each such byte, interpreted in the base-2 or binary system, is a number. 00000000 is 0 or black, 11111111 is 255 or white, and a value like 01110010 is intermediate (in this case, 114), a shade of gray. Each pixel, then, is represented by a byte. A picture is a square that is 1,024 or 2^{10} pixels on a side. A picture will thus contain $2^{10} \times 2^{10}$ or 2^{20} pixels. Since each pixel is 8 (2^3) bits, the total number of bits in a picture is 8 times the number of pixels, that is, 2^{23} or 8,388,608. For convenience, we will call a picture like this, which shows on a monitor screen, an M-picture.

M-pictures provide a way to represent a large variety of interesting information in a simple way. Highly detailed images are possible. Included among the possible M-pictures, for example, will be good-quality photographic images of every human being who ever lived on Earth, even those for whom no trace of evidence survives. On the other hand, an M-picture could show a printed page to high resolution. In this way, every page of every book ever written could be represented (with possibly a few exceptions where superfine resolution is required), though it would not be a particularly efficient way to do so. (For greater efficiency we could simply use the bytes directly and encode the text in ASCII format, which would also be an allowable M-picture.) Very many of the M-pictures, too, would simply be uninteresting, just random jumbles of pixels making a fine-grained, smoky smudge, but included among the enormous collection would be an occasional item that, for one reason or another, was highly meaningful.

As a thought experiment let us now suppose that somewhere in the multiverse is a Babel Picture Gallery that has every one of the M-pictures on file. (This idea is based on the Library of Babel of Argentine poet Jorge Luis Borges, which is noted in Daniel Dennet's book, *Darwin's Dangerous Idea*.[4]) How many pictures would this be? Each picture, we noted, takes 2^{23} bits. Any two pictures are different if any one of these bits, anywhere, is different. (Here we are being exacting in the interest of simplifying the calculation, treating as different those pictures that are the same except for rotation by 90°, for example. But for our purposes the numbers would not be changed much if we used such symmetries to identify as many of the pictures as we could and reduce the overall number.) Suppose we number all the bits 1, 2,..., up to 2^{23}. For any picture we have 2 possible choices for the first bit, 2 for the second, and so on. Each additional available bit, in fact, doubles the number of possible pictures—for each picture that has some particular bit set to 0, there is another picture exactly like it, except that this one bit is set to 1. The total number of possibilities, then, will be 2 raised to the power of the number of available bits, or $2^{2^{23}}$. This is certainly a very large number; nevertheless, it is finite. Next, we can obtain the number of bits taken up by all the M-pictures by multiplying this large number by the number of bits per picture, 2^{23}. The total number of bits for all the

M-pictures, which we will call the M-number, thus is $2^{2^{23}+23}$, which is a number with 2,525,230 digits.

So now let us ask if the Babel Picture Gallery could be anywhere in our visible universe. The answer, most clearly, is a resounding *no*. The universe may be large to us, but is nowhere near the size needed to contain such an archive. To see this quantitatively, we can use the size estimate provided by Jakob Bekenstein of 10^{122} bits for the visible universe,[5] a number of 123 digits. Though big enough by everyday standards, it is minuscule compared to the M-number. It should be pointed out, too, that this conclusion is by no means strongly dependent on this size estimate of the universe, which is uncertain. Make the universe a trillion trillion (10^{24}) times larger, and the count of its bits has 147 digits, still woefully short.

What it means is that, no matter how compact our representations of information might be, even if we went down to the level of individual atoms or (if possible) beyond that, we could never represent more than the minutest fraction of all the M-pictures in any conceivable format. There simply is not enough matter, energy, or space in the universe to do it. (The only remaining possibility, within our visible universe, is that its information-carrying capacity could increase over time and eventually become much larger than it is now. This, which is not ruled out, will be considered later, mainly in Chapter 14.)

At this point the possibility of data compression might be raised. Certainly there would be ways of reducing the storage requirements for many of the pictures, which would contain much redundant or repetitive information. However, it is easy to see that no mere data compression, however efficient, could reduce the storage requirement to anywhere near the available size limit of the universe, if we insisted on representing each picture individually. For then we must use one or more bits per picture. At only one bit per picture (though this would hardly be adequate), the new M-number would be millions of times smaller, yet still "almost" as large as before, with 2,525,223 digits.

It is out of the question, then, to think that our present visible universe, despite its size, could serve as a repository for the Babel Picture Gallery, which in turn contains only simple abstractions of some small fraction of all the possible histories. To satisfy the requirements of Unboundedness would be much harder

still, numerically, since we must consider the underlying historical processes and not just simplified descriptions created from
them. It is even more out of the question, then, that every possible finite history is happening or has happened somewhere in
the visible universe. We must look beyond it, or consider its state
in a remote future, for any hope of realizing Unboundedness.

The future universe has not happened yet—whereas our main
focus and reason for the Unboundedness assumption is to assert
that the possible histories are real or have happened, already. (So,
for example, in the resurrection scenario we have considered, a
copy of an authentic person of the *past* is to be created.) This
issue is not so simple, however, as has been suggested in our
discussion of time precedence. The possibility of future, exact
repeats of our (finite) history will complicate our notions of before and after—but this we will consider later. For now the focus
will be on domains, if they exist, that are outside the visible universe.

Immediately we are reminded of many-worlds, which asserts
that such domains are constantly being formed. In fact, we appear to get exactly the Unboundedness property we want. Not
only does many-worlds provide the usual variations of history,
such as, for example, a world where the dinosaurs never died out
or the Aztecs defeated Cortes, but whole alternate universes with
different physical laws from ours, which were formed in the early
stages of our own universe.[6] Moreover, and most important, many-
worlds assigns the correct weight, or probability, to all these alternate worlds. Thus we are not forced to consider all histories on
an equal footing, but the more likely scenarios are given due
prominence.

Another desirable property of many-worlds is that its universal profusion is on the deepest (the quantum) level. Later we will
have reason to distinguish two notions of reality, *observer reality*, the world as individuals experience it, and *underlying reality*,
the world from the standpoint of physics. The two are not to be
taken as contradictory or separate, but one follows from the other,
that is, observer reality follows from underlying reality. (And this,
in fact, is explicitly provided in the Everett interpretation where,
we remember, the wave function that describes everything is to
have an independent existence, apart from any observer.) Many-
worlds, then, gives us Unboundedness at the level of underlying

reality, which is the deepest level possible, but it would be adequate if Unboundedness only applied at the observer level. (The distinction between underlying and observer reality will be considered more fully in the next two chapters. The two realities are certainly not the same, but the differences, as they relate to Unboundedness, should not be critical because observer reality should be able to model underlying reality.)

In any case, many-worlds, with its fantastic proliferation of separate realities, has cut the Gordian knot in one immense swoop. If we could accept it as true, we could end this chapter right here, but in fact we do not know this, so we must also consider single-world possibilities and whether they too might provide something similar. Certainly, there is no requirement that they must do so, yet I think an interesting case can be made that they would—or to put it more accurately, that Unboundedness holds whatever may be the nature of underlying reality.

As a start we may consider whether the multiverse is finite or infinite. We can accept that the visible universe is finite, with a size limit around 10^{122} bits. If that is all there is to reality—if the multiverse is simply the universe—then at best the multiverse is only potentially infinite. (Under many-worlds, of course, the multiverse is not just the universe but much more, an exhaustive plenum of universes.) It must be at least potentially infinite if we are to have immortality, according to the computational viewpoint of immortality that is developed in Chapter 14, following the ideas of Tipler and Moravec. This, of course, does not establish that it must be so, but it does underscore the importance of having an infinite amount of room or territory in which to operate if we are to have eternal life.

The multiverse could, of course, fail this litmus test and not even be potentially infinite. This would invalidate Unboundedness since arbitrarily long, finite histories must be possible, as we have noted. We must then ask whether any evidence can be adduced to shed light on the question—in addition, of course, to the ever-present possibility of many-worlds.

We could start by asking whether any histories are really possible other than what we actually see. If the photon strikes the half-silvered mirror and bounces off, in what sense was it possible that the photon could have gone through the glass instead? Up to now we have been content to let our usual intuition decide the matter. In this case, though, we have something more: our intuition is solidly backed by experimental results. The photon is alternately seen to reflect off and to travel through the object in question, even when the starting conditions are exactly the same, to all appearances. Both alternatives are possible, we say. We know of no reason they would not be possible, and this is true more generally when it comes to historical events. These in turn must rest on quantum interactions, so overall the same considerations, we might think, would apply to arbitrary historical events. Thus, even if we had the most complete knowledge possible, alternatives to what we actually observe would seem, always, to be possible.

If, as far as we can tell, these things are possible but never actualized, we can ask why. What mysterious forces, properties, powers, or conditions, if there are such, choose the particular things that happen and forbid those that do not? Needless to say, we know of no such controlling mechanisms, which is one more argument for Unboundedness: if there is nothing to limit the actualized happenings, then other things than what we see must occur. This brings up an interesting argument of a quasi-theological nature.

Our Existence As Extraordinary Evidence

We exist, and we are complicated—so complicated, in fact, that we do not yet fully understand the workings of our own physical bodies or especially the most important part, the brain. How did all this complexity come into existence? Clearly it constitutes extraordinary evidence—evidence, that is, of something, but what? What extraordinary claims are best suited to the rather remarkable evidence at hand? In the past, especially in the Western tradition, it was assumed that a cosmic Intelligence, or God, was involved in shaping the human and other species on our planet. Surely, it was argued, the incredible intricacies shown in living things in form, function, and interactions must have required a conscious Designer, a Being of stupendous powers. But there were also reasons to question the existence of God, to credit the creation of species to other, insentient mechanisms—biological evolution, for instance. The theological issue will be taken up in Chapter 10. The upshot will be that, contrary to traditional intuition, our creation rests on insentient mechanisms—no intelligent Designer, or Artificer, need be invoked. Instead, its absence—in other words, the nonexistence of anything approaching the more traditional concepts of God—seems likely.

With this in mind, then, we must account for our very existence. One simple way would be through Unboundedness: if all possible histories are real, then those histories that bring beings like ourselves into existence must be real too. (This idea in turn is closely related to the Anthropic Principle: that the observable universe must provide for the presence of the observer—more on this in Chapter 10.)

True, we might resolve much of the problem without Unboundedness. Once life got started on Earth, the course of natural history, through Darwinian evolution, gave rise to all the known life-forms, including ourselves. No other "Earths" with other evolutionary processes, or more generally other historical timelines, need be invoked. The existence of a place like Earth, moreover, may not be so remarkable in the cosmos as we see it. In all the trillions of planets that could exist in the visible universe, the possibility of some earthlike environments where life could flourish must be credited, supposing it had gotten started. To be sure, in this appeal to a vast profusion of planets there is a faint echo of Unboundedness—but the visible universe is grossly inadequate to support Unboundedness on its own, as we have seen. Perhaps, then, the visible universe can well account for our presence without requiring an additional, vast profusion of actualities that escape our detection.

To do this though, it would not be enough that life simply could evolve somewhere else in the universe but that the evolution of life is something that is reasonably likely to happen, given a universe such as ours. This itself is something we do not know, and some arguments, considered in Chapter 11, oppose this conclusion. But even if life in a universe like ours is likely, it still raises the issue of how likely it is that a life-sustaining universe would form in the first place. Here in particular we see some features suggesting an improbability.

How, for example, did there happen to be such a thing as carbon chemistry, which is basic to life and not explained by the mere profusion of stars and planets? For, as far as we know, physics and chemistry are the same everywhere in the universe we see. We find the same chemical elements whether close to home or in distant galaxies—this much can be verified by spectroscopic analysis and other tests. We can explain this in terms of the fundamental particles—electrons, protons, and neutrons of which atoms are made, and other subatomic species—but are left with explaining these particles, and it does not seem simple.

A proton, for example, has an electrical charge exactly opposite that of an electron but is some 1,836 times heavier. Another particle, the positron, has the same charge as the proton and exactly the same mass as the electron. It is a true anti-electron, while the proton is a rather odd beast, electrically like the positron but with that strange added weight. Atoms use electrons and protons, not electrons and positrons, for which the "atoms" are known but are highly unstable. The fact that protons are much heavier (and also neutrons, which are useful in binding the protons together in nuclei, and form a third constituent of most kinds of atoms) means the relatively light electrons are free to participate in electrochemical events. Among other things, this chemical versatility is vital to life as we know it.

Life thus rests on some unexplained properties at the level of fundamental particles. We do not know, in particular, where the "1,836"—more accurately 1,836.1527—comes from; attempts to explain this number (and other important dimensionless constants) have so far failed. A little headway has been made, to be sure. The proton, according to modern theories, is a composite particle made of three principal constituents known as quarks. The mass of the proton, and thus the weight ratio, can be explained in terms of the three quarks,[7] but these masses in turn must be explained, which has not been done yet. All protons from anywhere are alike, and all electrons are alike. On the other hand, there are not that many kinds of fundamental particles, and especially the more important ones that are involved in atoms and their chemical interactions (electrons, protons, neutrons, photons—four kinds of particles only). The ways conscious beings can be formed are limited, and this must especially apply when unconscious formative processes are responsible. It seems as if we just "got lucky" to be here (viewing it optimistically of course), or, that our being "lucky" has a more rational explanation.

In the absence of a Designer, the simplest rational explanation for luck is profusion: more than one universe exists, more than one family of particles with their associated properties, which again raises the possibility of Unboundedness. Indeed, if we suppose an infinity of universes to choose from, it does not seem so remarkable that some of these domains might generate life-forms as we know them—and perhaps many other strange and wonderful things. A multiverse consisting of multiple universes sounds like the many-worlds theory, of course, but there are other possibilities for such multiple domains besides the Everett model.[8] Lee Smolin and Andrei Linde, for example, have argued that universes can form out of collapsing black holes, which could offer myriad possibilities without invoking Everett's idea at all.[9]

Earlier we raised the issue of whether the multiverse is finite or infinite. An infinite multiverse—notwithstanding the finiteness of our own, visible universe—would provide a simpler route to Unboundedness, but a finite though growing multiverse might also do the trick. Such a domain could allow that every finite history would eventually happen and happen over and over. In particular, copies of our own, recorded history would happen over again, with interlacings of all possible histories that fit our surviving records. In the different, exact copies of our history, exact copies of ourselves would appear. Exact copies of a given person (or person-stage) must be identified by Interchangeability. The different possible histories, then, are all part of our real past, which thus has multiple timelines. An interesting property can be seen to follow. A multiverse, finite but growing as indicated, is really equivalent to an already-infinite multiverse. Both guarantee Unboundedness. The equivalence occurs because, with the possibility of the same finite history happening over and over, the notion of time precedence is blurred enough to remove any distinction.

This, then, is one more possibility for Unboundedness. In all, we might perhaps regard it as a toss-up whether Unboundedness holds, supposing many-worlds is not true, while with what we presently know it is another toss-up (at least no worse than that) whether many-worlds *is* true, with its strong support of Unboundedness. Although we have little to go on in estimating actual probabilities, I will conjecture that the two mutually exclusive possibilities, each rated a toss-up, add up to something better—I would call it a good, fighting chance. By this estimate, then, I think we can have confidence in Unboundedness, and accept it as a working hypothesis. We need to acknowledge that uncertainty remains, that we could be wrong and Unboundedness may fail. If it does fail, it is still not the end. Both resurrections and immortality are conceivable by other, and even materialistic means, though a considerably different outlook may be called for. But we can be hopeful that it holds and also that further research will shed more light on this question and, perhaps, tell us how it holds.

With Unboundedness, then, history exists both in multiple versions and in multiple, equivalent forms. The latter means in particular that persons are multiply instantiated. This, I maintain, calls for an interesting philosophical stance, whose properties and consequences we will now examine more closely.

CHAPTER 7.

Interchangeability

The scientist and the philosopher are rightly engaged in a search for the truth. (This eternal quest, of course, is a worthy preoccupation of others too, and should become more meaningful as we progress. With future enhancement all of us can become scientists and philosophers—at levels more-than-human and well adapted to our quest, if all goes well.) Such a search should proceed, as far as possible, unhampered by preconceptions of how things are thought to be or of how we might want them to be. It should fearlessly and objectively confront reality, so the truth—good, bad, or indifferent—can be brought forth undistorted.

From this it might seem that we must discipline our hopes severely. On any cosmically significant scale, reality, cold and uncaring, must be beyond our control entirely—but we have grounds to think otherwise. As we progress, our power to make changes, modifications affecting what would otherwise occur, grows and with it, we hope, the wisdom to make the right changes. Yet at some fundamental level it seems that the nature of reality must forever be unchangeable and something we can best only examine, understand, and accept. One instance of this is the fossil record, which has solidly supported Darwinian evolution over divine creationism. Creatures—including ourselves—have been made by unconscious forces, the evidence proclaims, and no controlling mind or spirit is needed to explain this or other effects we see. This is something I think we must accept and live with, and doing so is not easy for many, who see their hopes of a meaningful existence undermined.

Reality is what it is, of course, and not necessarily what we would like to believe. We have a wide latitude for making changes, particularly over long periods of time, but other things really are beyond our powers. Another unsolvable problem, of a very different sort than proving divine creationism, is squaring the circle (construction on a flat surface of a square with area equal to that of a given circle) with a ruler and compass. This was proved impossible in 1882 by mathematician C. L. F. Lindemann.[1] Yet that is not the end of that story because there are simple, approximate methods for doing the task with accuracy beyond the limits of our sharpest instruments. In effect, we can square the circle with a ruler and compass, evaluate irrational numbers on a computer, and do countless other things that are in some sense impossible.

In such cases we find that a problem that cannot be solved, in the way it has been stated, can be redefined. The new problem is not quite the same, but, if the new definition is well-chosen, it will not only be solvable but capture, in essence, what we set out to do originally. So, with squaring the circle, the problem is perfectly solvable so long as we can accept a tiny, insignificant error, which we would have to accept anyway, in a practical application. (Only those interested in a purely theoretical, perfect solution must remain disappointed.) For a difficult problem, then, how the problem is defined may have an important bearing on whether it can be solved. We may have to look beyond one plausible formulation if that should prove unworkable. A reformulation may both satisfy our intuitions about what we really want to do and allow a means for doing it.

A Difficult Problem: Life after Death

Let us now consider a difficult problem, whether a person does or can survive death. Among other things, we have to ask what we mean by a person and what it should mean to survive. Our answers will depend significantly on our definitions, or, in short, how the problem as a whole is defined. For instance, with the "day-person" concept (see below) we are forced to conclude that a person cannot survive even brief periods of unconsciousness, let alone death as usually understood. With a different definition we find our person becoming more durable, and we then must face the question of what definition may be appropriate.

This itself is a most important question, inasmuch as it concerns possible life after death. As for the latter, we can ask if the truth about things that we pursue so earnestly—as hopeful scientists and philosophers—is any more important. If death is the inevitable end, does anything really matter? What, if life must end forever, is the value of science, philosophy, knowledge, good times, or anything whatever—and is the benefit worth the cost? It does not make much sense to struggle hard for something we will only be able to enjoy briefly. But *briefly* is a relative term. Any finite period is brief when contrasted with eternity. If life ever comes to a permanent end, it does, in an overall sense, make all struggles fruitless, all points pointless, all truths no better than lies.

True, with the prospect of the future elimination of aging and the possibility of survival to that time through biostasis or perhaps even simple endurance, we can finally question whether death must be inevitable to all of us presently living. But this does not nullify the seriousness of the problem. Death has been the inevitable fate of all persons up to very recent times, and it may well strike any one of us regardless of any advances that are made or means we may use to try to defeat it. In any event, even if we can prove so fortunate as to escape its clutches forever through one strategem or another, there are so many others who did not—and these we cannot simply forget. So in what follows I accept that death continues to be a very serious issue, as it has been through the ages.

Our problem—whether there can be life after death—must then be approached very carefully. We must ask if there is a reasonable way of defining the problem, including the associated notions of person and survival. Our definition must be acceptable as the problem in essence, and if possible it must also allow a solution. We must consider how we ought to think of ourselves— how to obtain the best advantage, in some sense—given, as is the case, that we have some freedom to pick and choose. The choice we make must not violate certain, basic intuitions but should also, we hope, leave room for an optimistic worldview—in this case, one in which death is not the end.

In recognizing the need to properly formulate the problem, we are going beyond the level where we simply ask whether a given hypothesis is true or not. We must instead deal with different possible hypotheses that can all be said to fit the facts and try to choose the best. As an example we can consider the day-person concept noted by philosopher Thomas Nagel, which claims that a new person replaces us each time we awaken from unconsciousness, as in the morning after a night's sleep.[2] There is nothing about it that is contrary to our observations. How do we tell that we do not become different persons? The fact that we feel we are the same is certainly not proof that we are the same and would not rule out the possibility of other constructs, for example, duplicates of ourselves, who also felt they were the same and the real person in question. If, then, the day-person concept is granted equal standing with the more normal view, the true or false dichotomy simply does not apply to the claim that we die each time we lose consciousness. This gloomy hypothesis can be made to fit reality and justified. On the other hand, hardly anybody takes it seriously. Somehow we know better. This we might attribute to a selection process.

As the human brain developed under evolution, people became aware (or more aware) of a self and formed certain ideas about it. Selection pressure would have favored some ideas over others. A serious day-person advocate, I imagine, would have felt much less stake in the game of species propagation since this involves a lengthy process (raising offspring, involvement in social institutions, and so on). Such persons, if and when they existed, should have instead been extreme advocates of the maxim "live for the moment"—which would surely be selected against, even if part of this living, for example, involved reproductive acts or impulses. So instead today you find that most people are not overly concerned about dying every time they fall asleep. They have accepted that uninterrupted continuity of consciousness is not the important thing for survival. They might instead accuse a day-person advocate of having an inappropriate attachment to the idea.

People still have had to face mortality, however—the kind we usually mean, not just temporary loss of consciousness—and it has not been so easy. Certain ancients, well aware of the difficulties, dealt with them as best they could—one result being Buddhism, which teaches a doctrine of nonself. This calls for an extreme detachment from things that are usually considered important: possessions, status, even personal details such as one's memories. One can then reach a state where, it might be said, one is immortal—there is nothing of substance that can still be lost, even through death. But the price paid is a heavy one, in terms of what I think is any reasonable idea of survival. "[F]inal liberation," we are told, "…can only happen if the ignorance of regarding oneself as a substantial permanent ego is dispelled."[3] In effect, one is required to give up ambitions of any ordinary notion of survival which would, in particular, involve recalling one's past.

It is worth adding that various ideas of non-self are by no means uncommon. Some people do genuinely feel there is no substantial, personal self that even persists from moment to moment, let alone over a full waking period. But usually such people do not behave as if they must experience oblivion in the next instant. They may say their behavior is not entirely reducible to logic. In any case, the position I take is that it is reasonable to say that I persist from moment to moment, even granting that certain changes are possible (brain injury for instance) that would sometimes, hopefully rarely, make this claim dubious. This I can justify on both experiential and certain logical grounds: I feel the persistence of myself, plus I retain information about my previous states that can reasonably justify the conclusion that there is a "me" that persists over time, at least a short time. A reductionist argument that there is a persistent self under these conditions seems possible in principle, though precise details are intricate and still lacking. It also happens that I value this persistence—it adds an element of meaning to life that I consider important, and many others value their persistence too.

So to me it is unsatisfactory to give up a notion of survival that depends on recollections of past experiences—but also, it turns out, unnecessary. Regarding oneself as a substantial permanent ego is not simply ignorance but can be defended through a modern, materialistic argument, and it can also be seen in a positive light. (At the same time, the ideals of Buddhism are in many ways noble and inspiring ones, and I commend its stance of detachment from material goods and status. Also it is worth noting that different ideas of nonself are found in Buddhism and other traditions. I make no claim of definitiveness here; the version I have cited is mainly for purposes of illustration.) It is not necessary—or desirable—to so detach oneself from ordinary reality that past details of one's own life are no longer valued and can then be forgotten or obliterated with indifference. Such details can be valued, both in oneself and in other sentient beings, and one can have assurance that these details are not impermanent as traditionally supposed—this being a consequence of the UI assumptions. In this way the material world itself is also seen in a more positive light. But all this calls for an appropriate concept of Interchangeability, to be applied at the level of persons.

With this approach (details will be given shortly) there are certain things we will have to give up too. One is the idea of being made out of a specific, unique collection of particles. (The mind-brain identity theory that we considered in Chapter 4 thus will not do.) Another is that one's memories necessarily form part of the surviving historical record (though of course they might). A third is that survival involves a unique, "closest" continuer. None of these three, I maintain, is essential for survival. But considered as information, the memories, dispositions, et cetera must still be there—and they will be. They can still be retrieved and you can know them for what they were and are. To me that is the important thing about personal identity—you might not want to sacrifice other properties, particularly the connections with the historical record. But even if maintaining such connections were impossible "you" could survive.

So I advocate a middle ground between the more exacting ideas about what survival should mean, and the too-weak, in my view, idea of nonself that denies altogether the importance of one's past. I would say that the pattern that describes or characterizes the person must recur but that extra connections (for example, historical ties through informational continuity or even the original material of the body), though possibly desirable, are not essential. Survival occurs, in the worst case, through a construct created in ignorance of, but with suitable similarities or psychological connections to the original. These connections require an appropriate information content though not informational continuity. This idea I will call *pattern-survival*. Exact replicas will have the necessary properties, which amount to psychological

connectedness, and also continuers, so that exact replicas of continuers, however formed, are also continuers and the individual
can survive through them too.

Something further should be said about the notion of continuer,
by way of clarification, before turning again to pattern-survival.
As outlined in Chapter 4, the person as a whole, the diachronic
self, is a phenomenon developing over time and is represented at
a particular time by a person-stage. The changes in a person that
occur over time involve the assimilation of experiences and a
learning process. A later person-stage thus will be a more developed version, or continuer, of an earlier stage. Forgetting or erasure of past information can also occur, of course, and strictly
speaking does not yield a continuer of all that was present in an
earlier stage, though it may still be a continuer of what was important—this matter is addressed in Chapter 15.

Strictly speaking, moreover, a person-stage, including a continuer, is not a physical construct, which instead I have called an
instantiation. The person-stage instead is a higher-level entity,
"what the instantiations instantiate." Meanwhile it is important
to make clear that the notion of continuer, like that of survival
itself, depends purely on psychological connectedness, not on
how the person-stage in question came into existence. My concept of continuer thus differs from Robert Nozick's in *Philosophical Explanations*, in which physical or psychological continuity
between present and past person-stages is also important.[4]

It will be useful to extend the idea of a continuer to cover the
case of person-segments whose time intervals do not overlap.
The continuer (segment) will then consist of person-stages, all of
which are continuers of the person-stages that make up the original segment. A person (person-segment) during the year 1950
would be (approximately, allowing for forgetting, et cetera) a
continuer of that person (again, person-segment) during 1949, or
during 1945–49, and so on.

Pattern-survival in turn accords with the notion of person based
on functionalism that was considered in Chapter 4. In this way of
thinking, it is the interactive functioning of various components
that make up an individual, not some other entity or "gestalt"—
the whole is the combined effects of the parts. The parts themselves, however, have no significant intrinsic properties—it is
just the way they interact, how they function in the whole indi-

vidual, that is important. These parts, it will be argued in the next chapter, can be equated with the components of a digital or computational system—and their functioning will resolve into discrete events, or state changes, in the system in question. One system can be duplicated in its functioning by another system.

The position of Interchangeablity, and pattern-survival in particular, is to regard two such similarly functioning systems as one and the same, that is, their differences, of whatever form, are unimportant. It thus accords with a time-honored mathematical practice of considering two things or systems the same when they are isomorphic—when one system can be reversibly translated or disguised as the other through a "renaming of the parts." In general, though, there is more than one isomorphism—not all will be valid for the purpose intended. In the case at hand, we must be sure that the parts we relabel do not contain intrinsic components that would preclude the necessary equivalences and that the system obtained by relabeling is functional.

To use an analogy, a given make and model of new car will properly correspond with identical, factory-made copies of that make and model but not with other cars. An automobile isomorphism might be defined that identified one car engine with the other car engine, right and left headlights with right and left headlights, and so on, but overlooked finer details, such as whether the engines were four, six, or eight cylinder, which brands of headlights were used, or even whether the car would start. So one car could be the "same" as the other under this correspondence but still far from identical. With a finer correspondence though, going down to individual, interchangeable parts, we could achieve the necessary exact correspondence—still not really exact, of course, but close enough for most purposes, and close enough that different, intentional variations, however minor, could be distinguished. (We might have to go to uncommon lengths, however, to ensure that the microchips many cars now use for control functions were programmed identically.) If this level of correspondence in turn was not sufficient, we could go all the way down to the molecular, atomic, or subatomic levels.

In any case, we would have to identify a level at which the corresponding parts could be considered truly interchangeable and equivalent. For persons, we clearly do not know the full details. But the level of information processing must be adequate, whatever that translates to in terms of material components. It is not these material components that seem significant intrinsically, but how they function, and, in particular, what sort of interactive process they sustain in the mind. Again, as a last resort we could go all the way down to the quantum level where the parts are subatomic particles or things that behave like them. (This could, in fact, be necessary to capture the subtleties in conscious experience induced by the complexities of brain chemistry.) Some further issues connected with the notion of the right isomorphism will be addressed in Chapter 8. Though some questions remain unanswered, it seems reasonable that there is some level at which equivalent functioning must give rise to identical experience. Identical constructs at the atomic level would produce identical consciousness, as one example. We are thus led to the idea of pattern-survival, in which the same person re-emerges whenever an equivalent system becomes functional.

It seems to me that pattern-survival is the best possible notion of survival. Any weaker concept is too weak to constitute survival in any reasonable sense—though pattern-survival itself is reasonable in this respect—and any stronger notion is unlikely to be generally feasible. Such ideas as occur in Buddhism are too weak—you have to have past information, to reasonably define and distinguish a specific person. Otherwise survival can only be through a "further fact"—a violation of psychological reductionism. Any stronger concept, on the other hand, is unlikely to be achievable, in the general way that would be required, to be satisfying to me.

I would like to think that anybody—even someone who perished in the distant past has a prospect of eventual resurrection; otherwise I have to allow that the world contains major, unrightable wrongs, or that eternal death is acceptable—neither of which I am prepared to do. Instead I will give up what is necessary to make the notion of survival as robust as it needs to be, confident that I will not have to give up so much as to make the desired result untenable. A person could be reinstated, if you are lucky enough to guess the description, even if it has been lost. (Reasons to think that guessing of this sort by advanced future beings will not only occur but be successful will be considered in later chapters.)

A stronger notion of survival that has been advocated is that the historical connections must persist—there must be informational continuity with a past self. This, in fact, is what is aimed for in biostasis. From the preserved remains we hope to completely recover what constituted the person, information-wise, at the time of death. This would include all memories, dispositions, et cetera, plus biological information such as the DNA (which in turn will specify other organs of the body, glands, hormones, and so on—or perhaps these too are preserved directly). In fact, biostasis, especially whole-body cryopreservation, offers an even stronger possibility of survival, through object continuity. The original object is preserved and, if possible, eventually will be reactivated, though perhaps with certain, desired modifications. But in general I see little prospect for the recovery of the "hidden past" that would be needed to resurrect someone who died and was not preserved. (And, of course, we do not know if those who died and were committed to biostasis will be well-enough preserved for resurrection from their remains, though it seems a definite possibility, at least for the better cases.) The historical connections are worth it—up to a reasonable point and so far as obtainable. That is why I think we should stick with cryonics or some form of biostasis (though I am not similarly attached to stronger forms of survival such as object continuity, except as a practical means of achieving informational continuity). But whatever the state or lack of preservation—yours or someone else's—there is a guaranteed fallback position that allows "coming back" in some form.

Interchangeability in Physics

We are now ready to consider Interchangeability in more detail. As stated in Chapter 1, this is the principle that like entities share identity or can be considered the same thing. It is mainly to apply to persons; however, it will be instructive to consider how it also applies in physics. Indeed, there are situations where ostensibly different physical objects or systems must be treated as one and the same.

A very exhaustive mathematical description of a physical system is possible. Though generally very voluminous and most impractical to deal with directly, it is finite, under the assumption that the system must have finite spatial extent and energy content. (The physical system thus could include the whole visible universe.) The description, effectively, is known as the quantum state, and it is so complete and perfect that, as a basic principle of modern physics, two systems in the same quantum state must be one and the same object. (More accurately, a finite number of distinguishable energy states, also known as eigenstates or quantum states, can be associated to each bounded region in space and each finite amount of total energy. Since the visible universe is bounded in spatial extent and energy content, no two distinct or distinguishable systems in the universe can be in the same quantum state.) This has profound consequences because, in particular, there are situations where our intuition insists that more than one object is present.

Tipler in *The Physics of Immortality* considers such cases,[5] one of which goes back to nineteenth-century American physicist J. Willard Gibbs. We have two chambers filled with gas at the same temperature and pressure. A channel is opened between the two. If the gas molecules in both chambers are the same, both oxygen, for instance, essentially nothing happens. True, the molecules will begin to intermingle, but there is no energy gained or lost in this process. (And we cannot really tell, directly, that the molecules have intermingled because identical molecules are involved in the exchanges.) But if the gases are different, one oxygen, say, and the other carbon dioxide, energy is released as one type of gas diffuses gradually into the other and the two become uniformly mixed. This energy is no minute effect but may be considerable. If the two chambers each have a cubic meter of volume (264 gallons) and the gases are at atmospheric pressure and room temperature, enough energy is released in the diffusion process to light a 40-watt bulb for an hour.

Such a release of energy occurs for any two gases, so long as they are different. If the two gases are the same, all made of one type of molecule, for instance, or of different molecular types that are already uniformly mixed, no release of energy is possible. It is easy to see why this must be so, for if we could still derive usable energy when the two gases were the same, we would have an unlimited energy source that could be turned into a perpetual motion machine. At the quantum level, energy extraction is possible because one type of object is concentrated in one chamber but not in the other. As long as one container's contents differ in some way, however small, the mingling with the other container's contents will release energy.

With most gases at normal temperatures and pressures, nearly all the objects (molecules) will be in the lowest energy state, or the ground state—meaning that there will be very many molecules in the same quantum state. (In this ground state, electrons in a molecule are in the lowest allowable configurations or orbitals. In a higher energy state, one or more electrons are pushed into higher orbitals that generally are more distant from the atomic nuclei of the molecule.) This does not mean all the particles are alike in all respects. They will, for example, have positions, momenta, and spins, all of which will vary from particle to particle. But what it means is that the state of the system as a whole provides no information to distinguish one particle from another; we cannot tell which particle is in which of the allowed conditions. Each particle is just as much here or there as any other particle, and just as much in one condition or another.[6] So with all the particles on an equal footing and indistinguishable, we are forced to consider each individually as one and the same object.

Yet intuition cries out. Many billions of molecules are a lot of things to be considered one and the same. Yet that is what the laws of physics demand we do. Quantum mechanics in particular requires this, or certain fundamental relations would fail. Besides the one above that rules out a perpetual motion machine, there is the Law of Mass Action, which determines what amounts of different chemical substances remain after a reaction has gone to completion and equilibrium is reached. More fundamentally, without the exact identity of systems in the same quantum state, matter would be unstable and all solid objects would collapse into black holes. "In summary," notes Tipler, "quantum mechanics has a criterion for the identity of physical systems [the equality of their quantum states] and this criterion allows—indeed, often requires—us to identify two systems existing at the same time."[7]

We must then allow that one system can occupy more than one place at once. Seemingly different systems—including whole worlds—can share identity and be merely different instantiations of one and the same object (though strictly speaking we do not have different instantiations, though certainly it can seem that way, as with the gas molecules). So this is a kind of Interchangeability, or what is often called the pattern or form theory of identity. Like objects indeed share identity, regardless of their apparent separateness. (It should be noted, too, that this viewpoint has its philosophical opponents. They would deny that even objects indistinguishable in principle, like the gas molecules in our example, are one and the same, and thus deny the Identity of Indiscernibles, a principle considered later in this chapter. I do not go so far, but will accept Tipler's arguments at face value. In any case, whether the molecules are truly identical or not is not so important, in regard to our notion of Interchangeability, as that they have the same physical attributes.[8])

This property of being the "same," as we have considered it, depends on a very stringent criterion: that the different objects must be in the same quantum state. For objects of any appreciable size, there are very many possible quantum states, and it is most unlikely we will encounter two such objects that happen to be in the same state—two planets, trees, or even tiny grains of dust. It is only with much tinier objects still, such as individual gas molecules, that the range of likely states is much smaller, so that it is feasible for ostensibly different objects to be in the same state. But this Interchangeability, which applies mainly to inanimate objects, is not the one we are mainly interested in. It depends on something noted by an external observer—while what we are interested in is that observer, and how that observer perceives him-/herself. This gives rise to a different, stronger version of Interchangeability.

Interchangeability As Applied to Persons

Two persons, I submit, should be considered one and the same if they can be said to experience the same events at the conscious level. Clearly this will happen if the two could be in the same quantum state, for then everything about them must be repeated as far as we know. But the same events at the conscious level might be expected under other circumstances too. If persons are basically computer programs running on hardware, as seems to be the case, we expect that more than one hardware device, or computer, could "run" the same person. The progression of conscious events pertaining to a person is then reducible to a progression of information-processing events in the device in question. That two such devices could execute the same such events is a straightforward possibility. The "running" of a person, by whatever physical process or system, is what we should understand as an instantiation of that person.

Here something should be said in relation to the three concepts of personhood introduced in Chapter 4: the diachronic self, the person-segment, and the person-stage. A person-instantiation, which is to cover the person's conscious activity over a period of time, can be viewed as an implementation or realization of a person-segment which, as we noted, was the most general concept of the three, the others (diachronic self, person-stage) being viewable as special cases. In particular, as the time interval becomes short the instantiation approaches a realization of the mental state of the person at a particular moment, that is, that of a particular person-stage. An instantiation, of course, should not be considered identical to the person-segment; many instantiations of one person-segment should be possible in the multiverse, all of which will exhibit equivalent performance supporting equal states of consciousness. In addition we must remember that the instantiation is not required to exhibit all features of the person that apply during the time interval in question but only those that would actually, in some way, affect that person's state of consciousness. A "normal" instantiation such as a functioning body and brain will, however, have these extra features latent, that is, stored in informational form, even if the subject is not consciously aware of them.

Here it will be useful to introduce an additional concept: a *principal person-segment* will refer to a person-segment in which the time interval extends over the whole of a person's life up to some point in time but not beyond that point. Similarly, an instantiation of such a person-segment will be called a *principal instantiation*. An interesting property then must hold. In general, an instantiation does not recapitulate all the features of the person-segment, as we have just noted. But a principal instantiation will recapitulate all these features, as far forward in time as it extends. Again, this must follow because conscious events are what are important in defining the person. Whatever has had no effect on one's conscious experience up to a given point in time is not part of oneself up to that point.

Now, to return to our problem of comparing two instantiations:

we wish to know if we should regard them as representing different individuals. Is one person present or two? The instantiations are to be compared on the basis of the progression of conscious events, that is, the conscious experience, that the two are emulating (supposing, of course, that this concept admits of a reasonable definition, as I shall maintain). Properly speaking, to achieve a correct comparison we should consider principal instantiations only, for as we have just noted, these alone will completely characterize the person or persons, up to the point that the comparison is made. If the two instantiations, both principal, agree, then we have just one person not two—at least up to that point. But, except for improbable cases (or those that we may imagine being contrived through advanced technology of the future) it should not be necessary, in distinguishing two distinct persons, to consider their conscious states over any great interval of time. Two different persons should have thoughts and experiences that very quickly diverge, that is, distinguishing person-segments should be of short duration, approaching person-stages in waking states. Instantiations that emulate the same conscious experience, on the other hand, can reasonably be said to exhibit a shared consciousness. This, I submit, follows solely by the fact of the duplication itself—a duplicate consciousness is a shared consciousness. For otherwise the sharing of consciousness must depend on a "further fact," which can be discounted on the basis of reductionism.

The agreement of the instantiations must occur if each instantiation runs through the same progression of quantum states, but then they are not really separate processes at all but one and the same. However, I think it is clear (as Tipler and Moravec, for example, both argue[9]) that substantially different processes could emulate the same conscious experience too. Very numerous changes at the level of atoms or their constituents should be possible without any discernible effects at the conscious level. Equivalent instantiations with a shared consciousness thus could be quite different processes physically. Ostensibly, two or more persons, with physically different bodies, then will be interchangeable or really not plural but one—a single being, though with multiple instantiations. In terminology used by Derek Parfit and others, I am advocating that persons are "types" not "tokens"—but a person-instantiation is one example of a token.[10]

It should be emphasized that this interchangeability requires an identity of the states of consciousness: make the smallest difference, and the single person splits—the different instantiations becoming, through a kind of speciation, truly separate and distinct. Thus it would be impossible to have two interchangeable instantiations that were aware of each other's specific differences. You could inform each, "You have a double and one of you is wearing a blue hat and one a red hat," but you could not tell them which color hat each one was wearing.

Here I am overlooking difficulties of how we might evaluate conscious experience except to note the previous suggestion that it should be reducible to information processing—more will be said as we go along. (There are other difficulties too, such as the problem of forgetting that we have noted. For now we assume the memory is functioning well—well enough that two persons once distinguished are not later merged by their mutual amnesia.)

It is conceivable, of course, that two distinct individuals, represented by different instantiations, could briefly have the same conscious experience, then diverge. The two instantiations would behave equivalently for awhile, then act differently. In terms of the conscious experience of the two subjects, the divergence could occur by new and different perceptions of external reality but also by recollections of different past experiences, the latter being possible from the assumption that two different beings are present from the outset. So, though the two are different, for a moment, before the differences appear, each person has a "subpersonality" that is one and the same as the other's. It is conceivable that the differences would not make an appearance for a protracted period, and the identical subpersonalities might so express themselves as to constitute a complete, developed individual in its own right. But again, two different persons should normally diverge quickly, and this must apply in the case of the influence of past information, where there should be many differences, either subtle or more obvious.

Some additional consideration to this issue will be given later; for now let it suffice to note that there are many and varied conditions under which ostensibly different persons are properly regarded as one and the same individual, multiply instantiated. Such conditions in fact must occur, unavoidably and over and over, in

the multiverse under Unboundedness. Among the possible histories are those that are exactly similar to ours up to some point,
say to when a coin is tossed. At this point a bifurcation occurs:
our world, in effect, splits in two. Two authentic histories then
apply: one in which the outcome of the toss is heads, the other,
tails. The same, of course, applies to any other process whatever
that has unpredictable outcomes, except that more than two possibilities may be involved, so that multiple splitting must be considered. The splitting of worlds, of course, is explicitly provided
in the many-worlds scenario, but other versions of Unboundedness must also have it. (At the philosophical level that is important here, it thus is not critical whether Unboundedness is enforced by the Everett model or some other mechanism.) As worlds
split, individuals within them could still retain enough similarity
that they would not split—as individuals—at least for awhile.

To keep things in perspective: we are considering features that
are far removed from ordinary experience but are important philosophically nonetheless. We are most unlikely, for instance, to
observe identical human bodies that behave in identical ways
and thus contain what we should regard as one person spread
over multiple instantiations. There are innumerable differences
even between "identical" twins who may be able to look and
sound quite alike to us. We do not have to confront the issue of
whether a person we know is resident in more than one body that
we can see. Moreover, the main question before us is not a scientific but a philosophical one, as we have noted. We cannot prove
that Interchangeability holds or even amass evidence that would
distinguish it from other logically consistent hypotheses about
personal identity, even such extremes as the day-person concept,
or worse. However, the issue we are considering, concerning the
nature of personal identity, is a life and death matter. In fact it
will open the door to the possibility of resurrection without compromising a strictly materialistic stance, or invoking any "further
fact" about the nature of persons.

Opposition, Rebuttal, and Illustrations

To give the opposition some of its due, the pattern theory of
identity, the foundation for Interchangeability, while being favored by famous philosophers such as Locke, has also had its

share of distinguished critics. A modern critic is materialist philosopher Antony Flew, who is opposed to the idea that a replica of a person could be the person.[11]

One objection Flew raises is a legal one, which he applies to the idea of justice after a putative resurrection. "To punish or reward a replica, reconstituted on Judgment Day, for the sins or virtues of the old Anthony Flew dead and cremated, perhaps long years before, is as inept and unfair as it would be to reward or punish one identical twin for what was in fact done by the other."[12] An "identical" twin, however, is hardly a close enough copy to be considered a replica by the standards that are to apply for Interchangeability. Moreover, as Tipler points out, even the legal system today sometimes equates a thing with its (sufficiently exact) replica, as in the case of copyright laws. Another example might be said to occur when someone is tried for a crime committed decades earlier, when he was very largely different matter, so that he has now become a replica.

However, the objections of Flew and others are not limited to legal issues. John Locke's memory criterion of personal identity, which in essence is our criterion of psychological connectedness, is taken to task for a number of reasons, among them the problems of forgetting and false memories, which will be treated in Chapter 15. Again, for now we assume the memory is reasonably foolproof and focus on issues connected with persons functioning in a normal manner.

The memory criterion or pure psychological connectedness then becomes a more reasonable one for personal identity: each person-stage is linked with past person-stages by memories of past experiences. Two person-instantiations will be identified as pertaining to the same person if they agree in those features of their information processing that are relevant to their states of consciousness. Precisely what this would amount to is still unknown. However, we can imagine, by analogy, two computers running the same program in lockstep, or even running at different times and different speeds. The computers could differ in not-so-minor ways; their circuitry might be quite dissimilar, both in materials and construction, as long as the same computation was being performed at the bit level, say—including all intermediate steps. If, in the future, persons were to be emulated on advanced computational devices, this analogy would become more meaning-ful.

One way to think of this is that the person is like a radio broad-cast and each construct—the body with the brain that expresses or "broadcasts" the person—is like a radio receiver. Two or more receivers can both be tuned to the same station; in this case there is one program but multiple instantiations. (Or, it is possible that, through delayed broadcast, one receiver would play back the same program at a different time.) Of course, there are significant dif-ferences too, and the analogy must not be pushed too far. I do not imagine, for instance, that the brain-with-body that "broadcasts" is literally controlled from some outside source, a signal from afar. (This theory actually does have its advocates,[13] but it is one I reject along with psychic and other paranormal possibilities; if proven out, however, it could still support Interchangeability.) The brain is not simply a type of receiver but a self-contained mechanism though capable, in principle, of unusual correlations or convergence with other, similar mechanisms, other brains.

Nonetheless the radio analogy is useful. For one thing, it un-derscores how our notions of identity for persons can differ sub-stantially from that for impersonal objects. We think of the dif-ferent radio receivers as truly and substantially different or nu-merically different even when they are broadcasting the same program. Similarly, bodies (including the brain) would be nu-merically different even when all are "broadcasting" the same consciousness, except in the case of the same quantum state. Just as we could have many radio receivers playing one program, then, we imagine, many instantiations could be "playing" one person.

The radio analogy is useful in another way: to help clarify dif-ferent notions of the "same" person. We have been considering instantiations: different constructs with the same conscious ex-perience, which can be regarded, from a functional viewpoint, as exactly alike and interchangeable. However, another, more usual notion is to consider different person-stages as the "same per-son"—a person at age twenty-five and that "same" individual at fifty, say. These, however, are not at all like multiple, equivalent instantiations; we would not expect someone, starting at her fif-tieth birthday, to simply repeat the exact sequence of thoughts and perceptions of twenty-five years before. Yet a later person-stage is not simply a "different person" from an earlier stage but what I have called a continuer. This has a special significance that will be explored later. For now we return to the case of instantiations, in which numerically different constructs are identified.

Is this identification reasonable—or does it violate common sense? I submit that it is reasonable because it accords with the vantage point of the person in question. A person—an observer— by definition could not be directly aware of different instantiations: each different construct must perceive alike. It would be reasonable for an individual, then, to make the identification with all similarly functioning constructs, whatever and wherever they may be. I would extend this even to whenever—there is no way we can know, aside from what we are consciously aware of, such details as when we may exist or even which direction time is flowing. It is possible, for instance, that one instantiation could be time-reversed from another one, getting younger as the other became older. Such concepts as direction of time or spatial and temporal location are meaningful only in some particular frame of reference, which by hypothesis here is hidden, that is, perceived as the same, whether it really is so or not.

Interchangeability, then, introduces an element of ambiguity in the world as experienced. Essentially, what is not known to the observer to be some particular way (and cannot be self-inferred from that person's memories, perceptions, or past states of consciousness) is not specified, at least for that observer. Examples are easy enough to imagine from everyday experience.

There is a great deal we do not know about one another. You may have had a dog once—suppose I do not know that. Under Unboundedness, then, we expect identical versions of me to exist in domains in which you had and did not have a dog; that is, there are possible histories in which both alternatives occur. At present, from my point of view, it is ambiguous whether or not you had a dog. My identical instantiations occupy worlds with the two different versions of yourself. These differences in you do not affect my instantiations, so Interchangeability requires me to simultaneously occupy the different locations where these differences hold. In this case, however, I can easily clarify matters, assuming you do not mind telling me if you had a dog. As soon as I learn the answer, a split in my instantiations occurs: I become two individuals. In some of the many domains, you answer yes, in others, no, thereby creating two versions of me. In the same way, further versions of you will be created the more you learn about me.

Did you have a dog? By Interchangeability, both alternatives, that you did and did not, are real to me until I learn the answer.

Underlying and Observer Reality

The splitting of individuals is a scaled-down version of the divergence of more general histories that progresses as events unfold. More and more possibilities come up and are realized in different and mutually exclusive ways, which splits and multiplies the historical timelines. On the other hand, convergence of timelines can occur too. If past information is lost, individuals could be identified or merged who might otherwise have been distinct (the problem of forgetting). In general, loss of information will make the past ambiguous, as in the data-erasing experiment in Chapter 5. There the loss and consequent ambiguity occurs at the most basic, quantum level, or—to use the terminology introduced in Chapter 6—at the level of underlying reality.

We made a distinction between this level, which depends on basic physics and is observer-independent, and what was called observer reality. This in turn will depend on the perceptions of the individual and has different properties, for example, allowing an easier convergence or merging of timelines. Once again, loss of information makes the past ambiguous. More generally, absence of information, at the level of the observer, makes reality, to that observer, ambiguous. Observer reality is particularly important in view of Interchangeability and its implications; some additional remarks are called for.

Observer reality, we noted before, is not to be regarded as separate and distinct from physics-based underlying reality but instead must derive from it in full. (Observer reality, then, is supervenient upon underlying reality.) It thus must have a basis in the materialism that, as assumed, undergirds reality as we know it. The details of this origination, depending as they must on the complex phenomenon of an observer, are unknown at present and may never be reduced to anything like a physical theory. (Indeed, there are definite limits to how much mathematics can do, despite its success with such fields as physics; the mind of the observer, it seems, must considerably transcend these limits. Gödel's results, discussed in the next chapter, show one way in which mathematics is limited.) Moreover, the details of observer reality are obviously observer-specific—there in fact is no single observer reality but as many different realities as there are observers. This, on the other hand, is not so different from underlying reality, which resolves, under Unboundedness, into many histories. In either case, when we speak of a "reality" we are necessarily speaking in generalities.

At any rate, it seems necessary to have both realities, even if one is derivable in principle from the other. Underlying reality is theoretically simpler and more tractable; observer reality is attuned to the individual experience and thus is more crucial from the standpoint of life and its meaning. As one illustration of differences between the two, multiple instantiations of one individual must be joined or united at the experiential level, that is, from the standpoint of Interchangeability, but must still be physically separate. We can imagine, as a thought experiment, two or more different bodies that support the same consciousness being present in the same world and even within plain sight of each other—however unlikely. But supposing it did occur, it would be possible for the one individual to split—by differences developing in the initially unified consciousness—though all resulting persons would still occupy the same world. On the other hand, it is possible that instantiations of the same observer could occupy different worlds. Worlds could split while the instantiations, though also splitting from the standpoint of physics (becoming different in their quantum states), remained identical in consciousness, and thus still united by Interchangeability.

This last conclusion is strengthened if we consider the fact that consciousness clearly comes in varying strengths and degrees. It is absurd to expect that an observer-instantiation would be fully aware of things at the quantum level, so that every change at that level would split the observer just as the instantiation would split, for example, under many-worlds. Indeed, for the case of an unconscious person, in which, we could say, the "null observer" is active as a subperson, no amount of difference in the quantum state will be detected. All null observers, then, are mutual instantiations—all are one (though not a very interesting one). By similar reasoning, we expect that subpersons that are nearly unconscious will have many instantiations that differ in many ways materially and may have quite different surroundings. But surely there will also be many instantiations even when a full and lengthy conscious experience is involved.

The notion of Interchangeability is a variant of a long-recognized principle known as the Identity of Indiscernibles: any two things that cannot be distinguished in some way are one and the same. Stated this way, it is simply a tautology: by definition, two things are different if and only if they can be distinguished in some way or exhibit some difference. (German seventeenth-century philosopher Gottfried Leibniz can be credited with originating this principle, though in a nontautological form that requires intrinsic differences for two things to be different.[14]) For the case at hand I propose the following variation: any two things or possibilities that are not distinguished in some way by the observer are one and the same for that observer. This seems reasonable, though it is not a tautology since the observer might choose to regard indistinguishably different things as different nonetheless. So I should replace "are one and the same" by "ought to be considered one and the same."

This in turn I think should hold for a reasonable observer, even in cases where clearly more than one different, observed object is involved. Thus we have considered the case of me, the observer, confronting you, who may or may not have had a dog. The "you" that I see seems to be a single, definite individual but in fact encompasses the two possibilities. Until I am aware of which particular possibility is present in my reality, the latter is ambiguous, and my different instantiations remain unified in their confronting of the two unknowns. Some nonzero probability attaches to each alternative, and both possibilities must be taken into account.

In general, ignorance about the state of the world leads to ambiguity: more uncertainty results in more possibilities, all of which are simultaneously real as superimposed features of observer reality. The observer, then, is defined by self-perception: what the observer is aware of, over time, determines what that observer is, at the most meaningful level. Any two observer-instantiations that cannot be self-distinguished or, in other words, that have the same conscious experience, must belong to the same person. Such a viewpoint will need some attention later, again to address such problems as forgetting and false memories (and also mortality). For now I provisionally accept that the observer is self-defined, with the necessary consequence of Interchangeability.

The UI Assumptions

Interchangeability then takes its place beside Unboundedness, so that the two principles, the UI assumptions, will serve as the foundation for our ideas of reality and of what should be possible for the future. In the last chapter we confronted the issue of whether Unboundedness in fact holds in our domain of reality, the multiverse, concluding that the likelihood, while unknown, seemed better than a toss-up. A similar question can now be raised; we may ask if Interchangeability really applies, but here the same issue is not at stake. Interchangeability, as I have indicated, is not a falsifiable proposition, dependent on a property of external reality, but a point of view, dependent on one's attitude. Like the day-person hypothesis, we can accept or reject it without contradicting any empirical evidence. I have offered what I think are good reasons for accepting it. It is worthwhile now to explore a few consequences of the UI assumptions.

One consequence is that the worlds occupied by the instantiations of one individual will differ from those occupied by instantiations of another individual. If the two families of worlds have a world in common, the two individuals may be acquainted to some degree; otherwise they will not be.

Another consequence, about which there is more to say, is the splitting of worlds. This could occur, more or less independently, at both the underlying and observer levels of reality, as we have noted. The splitting of worlds is a stumbling-block for many, particularly at the underlying level, for those who find the claims of many-worlds hard to believe. Certainly an objection can be raised in the endless process of generation that seems to be involved. One observer and environment divides into two or more, over and over, an explosion no physical process in our universe could sustain for long. Where does the extra material and the space come from for all this creation, if that is what is happening?

A better tack, however, is to take the splitting more literally and indeed regard it as a process of division. The observer and surroundings are rendered into thinner and thinner slices of smaller volume or weight while the total volume remains constant.[15] A single slice can be thought of as representing the probability that we will find conditions just as they are in that particular slice and not as in some other slice—so that thicker or heavier slices correspond to greater probability. The slices can be divided indefinitely, provided each can retain the characteristics distinguishing it from other slices. Otherwise—if the distinguishing characteristics are lost—different slices fuse into a single, thicker slice.

The division model seems a good one, in general, for understanding what is happening as events unfold according to many-worlds. (For non-many-worlds scenarios supporting Unboundedness the picture is less clear, but something of the same considerations might still apply, with different outcomes weighted according to likelihood, even though all are actualized.) The generation model has its uses too, despite difficulties. Both can be rationalized—indeed, each rationalizes the other. It is important to recognize that different interpretations of reality, or some aspect of it, may be describing the same thing observationally, that is, may not differ in their predictions, though they differ in an explanatory sense. Sometimes the differences are deep and irreconcilable. At the philosophical level this occurs, for example, with the day-person concept versus the more usual idea of survival after unconsciousness. But other times the differences seem deep but are resolvable, and the different ways of looking at the same thing are complementary and help us understand the overall picture better. The wave-particle duality we encounter with objects at the quantum level is an example of this complementarity.

There is a third way of looking at the proliferating worlds that is in this class too; it will complement the two other interpretations.

This third possibility is speciation, in which there is neither generation of new things nor dividing of old things, but the number of things remains the same at all times. The effect of splitting is accomplished when things initially similar enough to be considered equivalent become significantly different or divergent. Equivalent (though not identical) things together form a class known as an equivalence class. Within each equivalence class different items or objects are considered instantiations of one and the same thing, sharing identity rather than possessing a separate individuality (thus showing a form of Interchangeability). With speciation the initially single equivalence class splits into more than one equivalence class, or species. Items within each class are still equivalent, but items in one class are not equivalent to items in another class. The equivalence classes could be infinite in size so that splitting could occur over and over without end. The splitting could be deterministic or nondeterministic. With the right changes, things initially divergent could become equivalent too, allowing a joining together. It is, of course, a matter to be decided just what differences between things are significant and what are not.

Speciation seems especially appropriate to model the splitting of individuals as their (multiple) instantiations diverge. One complication is that objects that are treated as identical should form an equivalence class, a mathematical requirement. This will follow, in the main cases of interest to us, because the objects in question (person-instantiations) are finite-state machines—more will be said in the next chapter.

In Chapter 5 we considered how the many-worlds formulation, rather than violating Ockham's razor as some would claim, can be regarded as upholding it by its formal simplicity. A case can be made that Interchangeability too is in agreement with Ockham's razor—by way of a rather different argument: we simply take a parsimonious view of when we should declare that different persons exist. Two physical systems that support conscious, functioning individuals, when sufficiently alike, do not define separate persons, but the persons in question are one and the same. If one of the constructs is destroyed, the person does not die but lives on in the other construct. By the same token it is only necessary to make a replica of a deceased individual—even accidentally—to resurrect that very individual.

We can then see how, in important respects, a many-worlds ontology is actually independent of the modern physics version of many-worlds and could rest on different premises entirely. For the UI assumptions generate their own version of many-worlds, at least at the level of observer reality. This must hold whether underlying reality ever truly splits or not. Each person, through multiple instantiations, occupies a world that splits whenever an event occurs that causes some instantiations to diverge from others.

The Problem of Actualization

Let us now consider an interesting application of the UI assumptions, to resolve a paradox about probabilities. Suppose I am about to toss a coin (assumed unbiased, and guaranteed to land either heads or tails). It is reasonable to conjecture that there is a 50 percent probability that heads *will* turn up. Next, suppose I toss this coin, but look away so I cannot see the outcome. I think to myself, there is a 50 percent probability that heads *has* turned up. According to some philosophers, this is not reasonable because I am referring to an event—the coin toss—that has already happened. If the coin came up heads, the probability that heads has turned up is 100 percent; otherwise it is 0 percent; in no case can it be 50 percent. Yet I can check this too by experiment, and I find on repeated trials that half the time heads turns up—the result is the same as before.

This problem of actualization can be resolved without resort to the UI assumptions. I can say, for instance, that my probability estimate: "heads *has* turned up"—referring to a past event—is really about a future event after all—that I *will* find that heads has turned up. However, it is instructive to see how the problem could also be resolved using the UI assumptions.

Under these, we suppose that my instantiations occupy all possible domains consistent with my perceptions. I have tossed the coin and it has landed, but I do not know yet whether heads or tails is showing. Some of my instantiations are in worlds where heads has turned up, and others where tails has turned up, with an equal proportion or frequency of both (supposing, for this, that a random sampling of instantiations could be polled to establish the relative frequencies). Before I look and see whether heads or tails is showing, my interchangeable instantiations are united in the ambiguity of not knowing which alternative has happened. As I look though, I split into two camps—my instantiations diverge into those who see heads and those who see tails.

Here the probability that "I" will find heads is 50 percent—but this would not be true of an observer who has already looked and knows which alternative has turned up. That person's instantiations are already split—each one knows the answer already and thus the probabilities that apply are different—strictly 100 percent or 0 percent. We see then that the probability depends on the state of knowledge of the observer. This principle applies more generally, as in the following example adapted from an essay by Robert Ettinger.[16]

We have three observers, all of whom are trying to estimate the probability that team A will win an upcoming football contest against team B. The first observer is a visiting Bantu who knows nothing about football and does not read American newspapers. He estimates that A will win with 50 percent probability. The second is a reporter who has access to statistics that show, over the past several years, that A has won against B 65 percent of the time—so the reporter guesses A's chances at 65 percent. The third is B's coach, who, despite his best efforts, has to rate his own team as a two-touchdown underdog and makes a note to that effect in a ledger he keeps. Looking back over several years of such notes, he sees that the opposing team won in four out of five cases when he felt obliged to assign such a rating, and accordingly he estimates A's chances at 80 percent.

All three observers, it turns out, are right—despite the apparent contradictions in their probability estimates. The Bantu has simply picked a team at random, and such a team will win about half the time. With more knowledge, the likely winner can be chosen with more confidence, which is why the reporter and the coach are also right in their estimates. Probability again depends on the state of knowledge of the observer. But the UI assumptions offer an interesting explanation of how this can be: again, because each observer is multiply instantiated, and the instantiations in each of the three cases occupy different collections of worlds in the multiverse.

The Bantu instantiations, being ignorant of the strengths and weaknesses of A and B, occupy some worlds where A is stronger and some where B is stronger, in equal proportion. The coach instantiations, in contrast, are mainly limited to cases where A is stronger. (Rarely, B could actually be stronger—or just lucky; even the coach will not be a perfect prophet.) The reporter is intermediate between the two. So the observer's state of knowledge determines the mix of worlds that the observer will occupy.

In general, the UI assumptions, with the speciation model of splitting, allow us to justify a kind of hidden variable theory. Two instantiations of a person, we could say, are identical up to hidden variables—which are unperceived. In this case, the hidden variables are whatever properties may distinguish one instantiation from another. By definition these properties are unknown to both. One instantiation, for example, may have different pocket change from the other (where we imagine the instantiations are extended to include such peripheral elements)—so long as neither is aware of the specific, distinguishing details. More generally, any variation in the quantum state will distinguish two instantiations. This brings up the issue of what, precisely, are the physical boundaries of an instantiation. Do we include peripheral elements such as clothing and contents of pockets, as we just did? On the other hand, should we be much more conservative and even exclude all body parts except the brain or just the portion of the brain that is involved in consciousness and recall?

Actually, it seems feasible to include all of the above examples, that is, many constructs could be instantiations, including nested constructs, though this may seem confusing. At least we must include all that is directly involved in consciousness, which puts a lower bound on what could be an instantiation. But extras that go beyond the lower bound do not invalidate the principle, though this would ultimately include the possibility of a construct—a whole environment or universe say, that instantiated many individuals at once. One instantiation of a person, then, could have a component that is also an instantiation of the same person, along with other components that are not. Any difficulty in this idea, I submit, is manageable in view of Interchangeability. What is important is that we have a reasonable idea of what the observer is. I think a robust concept of observer can be based around the idea of Interchangeability. It will be insensitive to what precisely we single out as an instantiation, so long as certain elements are included. Once again, it is not the details of instantiations that make the person, but what the different instantiations have in common as an embodiment of that person.

But it does bring up another issue that should now be addressed. Earlier we considered the notion of a subperson, which, we noted, might qualify as a person in its own right; certainly a (nonempty) subperson must be considered a sentient agent. An instantiation of a subperson will, in general, have to meet less stringent criteria; two different persons, or more properly, their instantiations, could both be "running" the same subperson, at least momentarily. This suggests, in another way than we just considered, how the boundaries of instantiations can overlap. But I think this need not threaten our notion of instantiation, if we keep in mind that, in general, there will be more going on with an instantiation than just the "running" of a specific person or subperson. In the case at hand, various entities will be instantiated that we should regard as subpersons but which, even taken as a whole, may not be sufficient to distinguish the given person from all other persons. Or, from another perspective, one instantiation will instantiate more than one person, though in this case the multiplicity of these extra people will diminish with the passage of time and the occurrence of distinguishing events at the conscious level.

So, on one hand we have the process of splitting: a single person, multiply instantiated, becomes more than one person because perceived, external events happen differently in the different instantiations. But on the other hand, we have a process of differentiation, in which multiple persons initially perceive themselves the same (their active subpersons are the same) but progressively recognize pre-existing differences as the different instantiations progress. To distinguish a given person requires some occurrence at the conscious level that conflicts with, or mismatches the corresponding occurrence in some other person. In this case, it is not the perception of a new event, but of a previous event that is recalled or otherwise affects consciousness in some perceptible way. One person will remember he had a dog, say, while another, a "feel-alike" to this point, will remember he did not, and so on. In general, with a longer time interval the person in question will be better distinguished from the feel-alikes who progressively drop out of the instantiation as mismatching perceptions from the different pasts occur.

Person, Brain, and Mind

We are now ready to examine in more detail the sort of mechanism that a person is, or, more properly, what sorts of mechanisms there are, that support or run the activity involved in consciousness. In keeping with materialism and our functionalist viewpoint, we shall see that there is nothing special about such mechanisms, except in the details. The familiar example is the brain, a computerlike device that is assisted by the body that in turn furnishes peripheral devices. The brain in turn can be said to instantiate the mind of the person, thus the person as well. Here it will be useful to have a concept of mind as distinct from both the brain and the person but as a sort of intermediary between the two. Once again, this approach, based as it is on functionalism, differs from mind-brain identity theory, in which the mind would be identified with the brain.

The mind, as we shall understand it, will be a mechanism in the abstract, a type of which the brain is a "token." The mind thus will be instantiated by the brain, not identical with the brain. Two identical brains, as physically similar though different constructs, would instantiate one and the same mind. The mind in turn will be, in a more direct sense than the brain, the mechanism that runs the person. Indirectly, through instantiating the mind, the brain will also be said to run and thus to instantiate the person—so our discussion of instantiation up to this point will continue to apply. The mind, on the other hand, will not be the person but rather a sort of tool used by the person. The same mind might thus in theory be used in different ways to delineate different personal experiences, thus in effect to run different persons—notwithstanding that this sort of multiplicity is unlikely to occur except across parallel universes. (Different people, that is, even twins, have really different brains, and, consequently, different minds.)

These conventions will, I think, be useful enough to offset the additional complexity of an intermediary between the brain and the person. We can then address some problems of the mind that have long puzzled philosophers.

Though a complex entity, the brain-with-body is something in a physical universe, a system subject to the same laws as everything else and understandable as such. In the next chapter we will consider how the brain—and consequently the mind—can be regarded as a digital device, something that can be in one of a finite number of discrete states that in turn define the states of consciousness.

This is not to claim anything beyond a rough similarity between a human brain and any present-day computer. Instead it will underscore a property of mechanisms more generally and the processes they sustain. For all processes, in effect, are computational: it is a digital reality. And, though materialism holds and can be reasonably upheld, the deepest substrate of reality, I shall argue, is not matter after all but information, though the two are inextricably linked.

CHAPTER 8.

The Digital Substrate

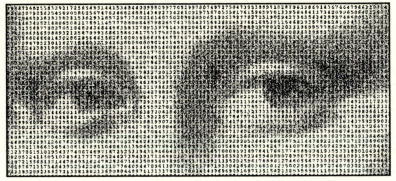

We have likened a person to the running of a program on a "computer"—the mind. This in turn is realized or instantiated in hardware consisting of the brain supported by the rest of the body. In effect, minds are digital devices, and the persons they run are digital processes. You get people out of numbers. This is sometimes called into question, particularly by persons who are uncomfortable with the reductionism it implies. Some, for example, cite a mathematical result known as Gödel's incompleteness theorem as proof that a reductionist explanation of the mind is necessarily faulty and inadequate. But this argument can be rebutted in an interesting way, as we shall see.

More generally, we find confirmation that everything we see—the whole visible universe—is simply a type of computational process or digital system. This can be shown to follow from the laws of quantum mechanics.[1] Despite its complexity, the universe operates in a manner that is in a deep sense analogous to the much simpler devices that are our computers, or other such machines, simpler yet, that can be emulated (exactly simulated) by simple computer programs. (We must make allowance for the unpredictability that is inherent in natural events. Computers are generally designed to be predictable; the same computation, done over again, comes out the same, but incorporating unpredictability is feasible too, a topic considered in this chapter.) Conversely, a sufficiently vast computer could emulate the entire visible universe (a finite construct) for any finite period of time, accounting for the interactions of all particles and thus for all happenings within.

There is, of course, no such sufficiently vast computer, at least not in the very universe which is to be emulated. Someday, we may hope, it will be different; the expanding universe could develop into a much larger processing system in its own right, and our horizons would broaden accordingly. To a computer and outlook of that time, emulating our world of today in all its complexity may be feasible or even trivial—it remains to be seen. But for now, and in this chapter, we must often deal with properties that hold in principle only. This has its own significance, however.

The Principle of Large Quantity

A principle can be useful and valuable from a philosophical perspective even though its practical demonstration is infeasible. In particular, a Principle of Large Quantity will be seen to apply in much of what is presented here—and elsewhere in the book as well. For a property to be realized in a certain type of functioning system, the system may need to be enhanced or scaled up considerably beyond anything in our present experience. Such a scale-up, however, should be possible in principle and may be carried out in a more advanced future. This must be kept in mind whenever a claim is being made of a sort that many find untenable.

One illustration (or close parallel) of the Principle of Large Quantity, a natural one, is seen in the evolutionary process. If enough time is allowed—billions of years—we do not have to invoke a God or other sentient agent to account for the features of seemingly intelligent design seen in living things. The time intervals required, of course, are outside immediate experience and thus evolutionary theory is still contested by those who are uncomfortable with it, though enjoying scientific support that rival explanations lack. Similar skepticism in the computational field can, I think, be met in a similar way, by considering larger quantities of basic resources.

For example, that a person could be emulated in a stored program, digital device seems highly doubtful to many. Certainly no computer we have built so far could accomplish this, but again a sufficiently vast computer—one not yet constructed but still in essence a computer—should have that capacity. Depending on the details of its construction, it might require enormous amounts of time and extra space too, or, with suitable sophistication and speed, might operate compactly in real time or even faster. That such a thing would be possible in principle is no idle conjecture but rests on the basic graininess that reality seems to present at an underlying level, again implied by quantum mechanics.

Quantum mechanics, as noted in Chapter 5, is probably our most successful scientific theory. It is seen to apply at all levels of observable reality, from subatomic particles to the universe as a whole. So far, no exceptions have been found, and, moreover, at a basic level it is digital, despite some appearances to the contrary. The march of events, traced out in the interactions of particles, could be modeled in a computer, though such a modeling, using today's computers, would be impractical except for very small numbers of particles and/or tiny intervals of time. Indeed, there are limitations in our current, "classical" computers that seem to make such modeling inherently inefficient and impractical, though still possible in principle. Greater success could be had with quantum devices themselves, including a universal quantum simulator which we will consider. But the seeming universality of quantum mechanics, coupled with its basic computational nature, lends some confidence in our Principle of Large Quantity.

This of course is not a guarantee. Theories that once seemed rock-solid, like Newtonian gravitation, were found slightly inaccurate and in need of supplementation. Though there is no strong indication of it, this fate could be in store for the quantum theory too, and it could drastically change our perspectives. The Principle of Large Quantity involves a large amount of extrapolation beyond known experience. Any slight inaccuracies in its theoretical underpinnings might be greatly magnified in domains where the theory has not been tested.

One area of controversy concerns fuzziness. Fuzzy computational systems are now finding important uses, one example being in automobiles to help provide a smoother ride. A fuzzy system decides the finer details of shifting gears or applying brakes or accelerator, and is able to modify its responses in small, incremental amounts to improve its performance, based on feedback.

Fuzzy programming, on the face of it, is a far cry from digital but instead contains imprecise instructions such as "if the stopping time was a bit longer than it should have been, next time push down a little harder on the brakes." More generally, fuzziness is seen to apply in the world at large, where uncertainty and imprecision are facts of life.[2]

We note in particular that uncertainty prevails at the quantum level, and this may seem to threaten our claim of the basically digital nature of processes. But the problem, I think, is resolvable by appealing to the multiverse. Uncertainty, it is true, denies the crisp definiteness that is often convenient in the processes that are important in our lives. Even conventional computing, which is highly reliable, has a small chance of behaving differently than expected, or making errors. The chance of making errors is not simply a probability, however. In view of the multiverse and Unboundedness (or many-worlds, if this is accepted), there are actual universes where the contrary behavior occurs. The occurrence of the behavior or its contrary, seen in isolation, is non-fuzzy and digital. This holds more generally, of course, whenever there are contrary possibilities, as in the photon encountering a half-silvered mirror. Fuzziness is expressed in the fact that contrary conditions occur simultaneously but does not rule out the basically digital character of the different processes that are going on in parallel.

It is also appropriate to mention a problem between quantum mechanics and the other great physical theory, relativity. Apparently, they do not agree and cannot both be right, even if we choose the many-worlds version of quantum mechanics which, as we saw in Chapter 5, harmonizes with the locality property that relativity calls for. The reason for the still-persistent discrepancy is that relativity is a classical theory, predicting a continuum in space and time and calling for smooth variations in the finer details of processes, while quantum mechanics deals in sudden jumps. It is also worth noting that quantum mechanics is mainly applicable to smaller scales of distance and time and relativity to larger scales. Thus, when it comes to the locality property, which involves large distances, we might on the face of it expect that relativity would prove correct, and it is fortunate that there is a version of quantum mechanics, the many-worlds formulation, that agrees.

At small scales, however, we observe the graininess that quan-

tum mechanics predicts, and thus expect it to prevail over anything to the contrary that relativity may forecast. Work on harmonizing the two theories has centered around such exotic ex-
tensions as string theory. "Particles" (virtual effects anyway, under many-worlds) are explained in terms of tiny, vibrating, ex-
tensions, or strings, or more recently and inclusively, membranes.
Space and time do not make four dimensions but ten or eleven,
with the extra dimensions tightly "rolled up" and reduced to a
minute scale. String theory is very much still on the drawing
boards at this point, but the upshot seems to be that on a sufficiently small scale the familiar continuum of time and space breaks
down and discreteness prevails. In the hopeful reconciliation of
quantum mechanics and relativity, then, the discrete, basically
digital nature of processing appears to be favored.[3]

So for now the outlook seems favorable. Quantum mechanics
may be reconciled with its great and mostly complementary rival, relativity, without disturbing its essentially computational
nature. A new, inclusive, "theory of everything" may even emerge.
Meanwhile, quantum mechanics is sound enough, as far as we
know, to explain such phenomena as people, who possess awareness, emotions, and volition. Each human body in turn consists
of some 10^{28} atoms that behave and interact in most complicated
ways in the course of our lives. The complexity in this case is so
great that we really cannot be sure it is all explained by quantum
mechanics—but we do not see any substantial reason to think
otherwise. So, provisionally as always, I will accept the universality of quantum mechanics with its implications for the digital
nature of all processes and its support for the Principle of Large
Quantity.

Strong AI and Materialism

The digital view of reality, in its full strength, is known as
strong artificial intelligence, or strong AI. It will be useful to us
in several ways, though in view of the still-present uncertainties
I will exercise caution in applying it. Strong AI tells us that feelings and consciousness are reducible to digital processing,[4] something many find especially hard to accept. While I think strong
AI can be justified and will offer supporting arguments, it is also

worth considering ways in which it might be toned down without sacrificing what is most important.

In particular, when it comes to the possibility of restoring deceased persons to a functioning state, either by outright guesswork or by a process of refurbishing preserved remains or extracting information from them, strong AI seems inessential, though digital considerations still play a part. A person should have a finite description, which would furnish a digital basis for a restoration. If we produced a replica that was atomically perfect or sufficiently close, including a brain with memories, and induced it to function as did the original, that should qualify as a resurrection. Whatever is the basis of consciousness, it must be captured in such a material construct. We would, in effect, recreate a person-stage that existed before death. By activating this new construct we would obtain an instantiation of the original person, based on Interchangeability. This would follow, irrespective of whether consciousness itself is entirely a digital phenomenon. (More generally a resurrection will not require, as a starting point, a construct exactly matching the original; continuers will do.) But actually this very possibility, that persons could be restored from some form of digitally encoded record or digitizable object, can be turned into still another argument for strong AI—more on this later.

In any case, I think consciousness is entirely digital too; this conclusion seems unavoidable, again based on quantum mechanics. On the other hand, it is a happy conclusion—facilitating the possibilities of resurrection and immortality, among other things, by easing the physical requirements of survival. A person could survive as a computer program rather than a "meat machine." Such an existence might offer considerable advantages in terms of freedom from disabilities and options to develop as one wished, assuming an appropriate scale-up in computer capabilities is possible. Arguments for strong AI will be considered in the course of our exploration of digital processes. One precursor of strong AI is materialism, the view that things are made of matter or comprehensible constituents rather than containing additional, mystical, or unknowable elements or features.

A materialist viewpoint seems adequate to account for all we observe. On the other hand, and contrary to more traditional thinking, materialism can offer the hope of an afterlife, as we have seen, especially if digital considerations are taken into account. This suggests a new worldview, grounded firmly in science and the natural world but soaring to aspirations and ideals that have heretofore been the province of mystics. Some further discussion will help clarify this viewpoint and how it applies to such matters as the nature of sentience.

Scientific materialism holds that the world and its phenomena are reducible to material effects, thus comprehensible. To say that things are reducible in this way does not mean that an explanation of all effects is already contained in, for example, our theories of subatomic particles, but that such an explanation could be developed from a foundation consisting of a materialist theory of reality. Reality, we say, is supervenient on a material substrate. Immaterial things, and particularly information, certainly do play a role, a very important one, but they have no existence apart from matter in some form. Information, for instance, must be recorded in some sort of physical system or object, though it can also be copied. More generally, materialism is a form of reductionism, and it opens a door to understanding. Happenings of a complex nature can be comprehended in terms of simpler, underlying causes, prior phenomena, and secondary effects, all of which are accessible to our observation and intellect.

Basic explanations must be sought in the physics of the very small or the very large and temporally remote—the opposite but connected poles of subatomic particles and cosmology. Large-scale effects can be understood as involving aggregates of particles in varying degrees of organization. There are statistically amorphous masses such as gases and liquids, highly organized functional systems such as living organisms, and objects intermediate between the two such as stars, crystals, and artifacts of our own making. Very large-scale effects, such as the curvature of space under gravitation, exert a subtle effect requiring adjustment, not repudiation, of previous theories. There is no reason to assume a controlling mind or other inscrutable force with humanlike characteristics to account for any of these phenomena, their origins, or their interactions. Materialism accounts well for the phenomena of our immediate experience and seems to go far in explaining the origin of the world as we know it. No phenomenon that refutes it has been found, and there is an objective mechanism, the scientific method, for testing, adjusting, and adding to its doctrines.

Mind As a Digital Phenomenon

One of the more difficult tasks of materialism is to explain the phenomenon of mind. In earlier times especially, it was doubted that the mind could be understood in purely material terms. Origen, for one, was highly skeptical. "But if there are any who consider the mind itself and the soul to be a body, I should like them to tell me how it can take in reasons and arguments relating to questions of great importance, full of difficulty and subtlety. Whence comes it that the power of memory, the contemplation of invisible things, yes, and the perception of incorporeal things reside in a body? How does a bodily nature investigate the teachings of the arts and the meanings and reasons of things?"[5] Locke nearly fifteen centuries later had similar doubts: "For it is as impossible to conceive that ever bare incogitative matter should produce a thinking intelligent Being, as that nothing should of itself produce Matter."[6] But a materialistic explanation of the mind now seems more reasonable and likely, one ground being an analogy with a modern invention, the digital computer.

Like a computer, the brain, though differing greatly in detail, is an information processing system. A computer stores, retrieves, and modifies information and can be equipped with sensory and motor devices to provide it with input and the ability to physically affect its environment. Its abilities include the possibility that its own programming or software can be modified and adapted based on its experiences, and not simply put in from the outside, as by a human programmer. The program that controls the computer, then, is not simply an entity that does what it is told but in the right circumstances is capable of what we should call volition and independent action, thus exhibiting a form of free will. The brain by analogy is able to detect information through its sensory apparatus. It stores and retrieves information through memory. It modifies information by thinking, based on knowledge and experience. Finally, it controls the physical motions of the body that contains it. The personality it "runs" in the course of instantiating a person is analogous to an interactive computer program—it is a time-varying body of information interfacing with the surrounding world. This personality too, of course, is capable of voluntary actions and not just doing what it is told.

One reason this analogy, though still controversial, does not seem so farfetched is that both brains and computers are made of matter and consequently their behavior must be determined by the same physical laws. It is even possible in principle, as we have noted, to simulate the behavior of matter, under these physical laws, on a computer. Thus a computer, given enough resources, could precisely simulate a brain and with it the workings of a mind, though possibly only at very low speed. (Again, such a precise simulation, an emulation, would have to take unpredictable events into account, so an exact reproduction of a given experience or complex of mental events would not be expected— though it would at least be one of the possibilities. Instead we would expect only as close an approximation as what would be expected if an initially atomically exact replica of the original brain could be started off in the same way.)

This I think could overcome one possible objection to the comparison between a computer and a brain. A computer (the modern digital variety, at any rate, which is now standard) is a stored program device. There is a clear separation between hardware— the physical apparatus of the computer—and software—information manipulated by the computer, which is generally stored in a transient, rewritable form such as patterns of magnetization in certain materials. In the brain there is no such clear separation. Hardware—structure that remains largely the same as we learn and acquire more experiences—blends more or less seamlessly with software—other structure, generally on a fine scale, that changes.

For example, the brain seems to store long-term memories by changing its physical connections, by increasing its synapses to provide more connections between neurons,[7] something very unlike a manufactured computer. But again, the brain is matter and interactions of matter could be emulated at the quantum level in a computer, though it used a stored program. It should thus be possible in principle to emulate a brain in a computer, if very slowly. Indeed, it is worth emphasizing that computer hardware (and software too) must improve very radically before anything like a brain emulation would ever become practical. For now we must invoke the Principle of Large Quantity to justify our claim.

The point is still important at a philosophical level, something that is independent of whether an actual implementation would be hard or easy.

Still there is one attribute of mind—emotion, or feeling—that many would argue is inevitably missing from a machine. Emotion requires consciousness, so its absence, if established, calls into serious question whether a machine could exhibit true consciousness, and thus, whether an important part of the reductionist argument holds. One answer to this is a brute force argument: simulate behavior at the quantum level and you would inevitably capture interactions at higher levels, including all responses of organisms, such as consciousness, feeling, seeing of colors, hearing of musical tones, whatever—this is the position of strong AI. For such an argument we must, for now, appeal to the Principle of Large Quantity, and ask additionally whether even an advanced system that perfectly imitated consciousness would really be conscious. But we can also ask about our more immediate prospects. Does it seem likely that any artificial construct we are likely to build, even in the next one hundred years, could exhibit emotions? More to the point still, could some machines or programs of today be said to exhibit at least rudimentary emotions?

A possible reply to the doubter is, How do you know they do not? Generally, since we are unable to become the entity in question, we must judge its internal experience, or state of mind, by its behavior and our knowledge of how it works. Existing computers and the programs that run on them generally do not seem emotional. Even if some quasi-emotional traits are shown, say, by a program that converses with a human subject, usually these responses can easily be exposed as only a rough parody of the feelings they mimic. A program can be made to answer "I feel lonely" or "I am optimistic!" in response to a typed question—that is easy enough. But making it respond realistically to a wide variety of conversation and convincingly mimic a mentally healthy adult has not been achieved and certainly seems difficult. Still, the convincing mimicry of human feelings does not seem inherently beyond the capabilities of machines, particularly in view of successes with modeling systems resembling interconnections of neurons, the basic cellular components of the brain.

As computers become more brainlike in their complexity, with vast parallel architectures reminiscent of the hundred billion or so neurons of the brain that all fire concurrently, we can expect more brainlike behavior. This will include reasoning (another area where computers now are weak or "artificial") as well as something increasingly akin to emotion. When the range of responses becomes enough like a human's it will be natural to describe it in human terms. That the machine thinks this or feels that should then be conceded with a literalness not granted today. There may always be room for doubt. A perfect imitation of emotional responses could occur, yet someone may object, How do I know it is not just an imitation? Such doubts perhaps can never be finally laid to rest—any more than the solipsist argument, that I am the only real person in the world or, similarly, the day-person hypothesis we have considered. But I think the doubts will be seen as increasingly untenable, both in terms of artificial systems whose behavior seems increasingly to involve real feelings, and by our deepening understanding of natural brains, which we credit with feeling.

In fact, if we try to consider what is actually involved in feeling and consciousness (though this is a large, complex topic that can only be touched on here), the position of strong AI seems more reasonable. The ability to experience feelings must have evolved in response to natural selection. An organism had to be able to make decisions of certain kinds to further the aims of survival. Feelings, we might say, are a way of simplifying this complex decision process by reducing the amount of processing needed to arrive at a choice. Charting a course can thus be done that would otherwise be infeasible. We eat because of a feeling of hunger and not because of a complex, reasoned analysis of our metabolic needs, which would be hard enough for us and quite out of reach for other creatures that must also eat to live.

Simplifying procedures, at least roughly analogous to the feeling that is seen in living animals, have been built into machines. A suitably programmed robot becomes "hungry" and seeks an electrical outlet to recharge its batteries.[8] Some might deny that it possesses any real awareness at all, that instead it is totally unconscious and just responds because it is programmed that way. But I think—along with other advocates of strong AI—that such a device possesses rudimentary feelings and awareness, which could be deepened to the human level and beyond by making a much fancier machine along the same lines. (A "fancy" machine that emulated a human at the quantum level could base its decisions on that very person's feeling.) Again, there may be no way ever to finally prove that a machine could have feeling (and that some, in a limited way, do already) but I think our understanding of relevant factors will make this increasingly tenable to doubters.

Information and Personal Survival

In general, an information paradigm seems adequate to account for the mind and personality, and this has far-reaching consequences. No mystical soul or incorporeal entity is needed to explain the existence and behavior of thinking beings or to approach the questions of the meaning of life and death. Instead, a computational model suffices. In this model, functionalism, with its implication that the mind is essentially a computational device, is implemented in a particularly straightforward way. The whole is fully determined by the parts—parts, in this case, that are simple enough to be comprehensible, though numerous and organized most intricately. This, on the other hand, is no reason to despair—instead, it points the way to salvation.

There are certain requirements connected with the survival, in reasonable mental health, of a human or humanlike personality. There must be a continuing sense of identity, and a grasp of the properties of the world and of the passage of events, all of which involve complicated processing. Storage and preservation of information must occur. Over a period of time, information must accumulate, which will require increasing amounts of memory, though the physical structures that are ultimately involved could take many forms. Dreamless sleep amounts to a temporary halt in program execution. There is no consciousness or interaction with the outside world in this dormant state, but since the pattern of information inherent in the personality is preserved, execution can be restarted at a later time. The subject then will "awaken" and resume the activities of consciousness.

Death, on the other hand, entails loss of information through destruction of the body's "hardware" or possibly other erasure. The subject cannot simply be awakened. Thus, though there are grounds for not regarding death as an absolute, it has a finality that transcends the more usual, reversible loss of consciousness.

Recovery or recreation of information is necessary for any plausible resurrection. Once the information is extant, the information paradigm and the possibilities of future technology suggest that an actual resurrection would be straightforward. Embodying the information in a suitable, running, interactive system should be feasible, as one of the possibilities of future technology, including a mature nanotechnology. The person, in a reasonable sense, would then be alive and functioning again. In the next chapter we will consider in more detail, if still mainly in principle, how it should become possible to literally create people with preassigned specifications, including memories, abilities, dispositions, and other features.

One possible objection to the information paradigm concerns personal identity. Normally a computer program, resident in a particular machine, is not considered to have an identity as such. Instead, since identical copies of the program would perform identical functions, to all intents and purposes they have no existence as separate entities but are like works of literature or music. Identical copies are interchangeable. It does not make sense to identify Homer's *Iliad* or Beethoven's *Ninth Symphony* with any particular copy of these works but to regard the works simply as bodies of information. Copyright laws pertain to copies, not to the works themselves.

But a person, rather than being a static body of information that may exist in multiple copies, is a particular, ongoing process that evolves over time. At any given time this process is resident in a device that stores information, but cannot be identified either with the device or its momentary configuration. Other physical structures could be pressed into service for memory or abandoned as the case may be, and new information could be stored or old information copied or lost. The process does not remain static but changes, as does the information that describes it. Considered as a whole, then, the person is neither a material object nor a specific pattern of information.

Normally personal identity is traceable by close observation of the ongoing process. We observe the material structures involved, such as the whole body, and note that changes in these are gradual enough that there is no confusion about which person we are dealing with. The memory, which normally confirms our assessment, is relegated to a subordinate role in defining identity. We speak of the "same" person being able to suffer amnesia, or even delusions about being someone else. More difficult questions arise when confronting the issue of death or the hypothetical question of whether the same person could exist in multiple copies.

In general, it can be asked whether the same person would be recovered by recovering the program that was resident and active at some point in the past and restarting it in a similar device. Would it be the same person or merely someone else very similar? In the last chapter we answered this question: based on Interchangeability, indeed it must be the same person, whenever the same program is made to run. We would need to say more, of course, about what it means for the same program to be running, but this question too should be answerable in principle. We need to keep in mind, of course, that a person is not the same from moment to moment but is updated progressively. At best what we have is a continuer of a past person, not the original. Identifying a person involves linking a process active at present with one that was active in the past. Although this can pose a difficult philosophical challenge, the nature of the active process in each case must still be the same. It will still be consistent with the information paradigm. But this paradigm that seems able to account for the mind also has wider applicability. A look at this wider domain will shed further light on the issue of identity and have application to such issues as resurrection and immortality.

Information, Understanding, and Reality As a Whole

A principal function of the mind is understanding. Understanding involves building up a description of reality that allows inferences to be made without the necessity of direct observation. It is not necessary to drive a car over a cliff to perceive that bad effects would follow. Anticipating such effects results in safer driving, thereby providing incentive to increase the level of understanding. In a similar way, rewards may be increased by a better understanding of how to obtain them. There are good, practical reasons to have a high level of understanding, and our evolution has made the means of acquiring it—the learning process—enjoyable in its own right.

Understanding requires a body of information, or database that is stored somehow in the brain. This database can be regarded as a map of reality. In the usual viewpoint of materialism, reality is simply the material world. It is the territory that is mapped by the understanding. This division between the map and the territory seems reasonable as long as we stay within the confines of everyday experience.

A very different viewpoint, however, seems necessary for a larger perspective. The material world is transient. It is not well defined. Objects are subject to alteration and destruction. The fundamental particles things are made of disappear and reappear, resist measurement or definition of their properties, and generally evade any characterization of their identity. It is expected that any lump of matter will eventually disintegrate through chemical reactions, simple evaporation, other molecular dislocations, proton decay, or some other, possibly exotic physical process. At no time can we be really sure what reality is, even a small part of it, if its definition must rest wholly on material artifacts and detectable events. And the observer, a part of reality, must continually alter some of that reality in the act of updating a map of reality.

On the other hand, consider the world of information. Information can be encoded in standard formats, a convenient one being as strings of bits. Looked at in this way, information has an absoluteness not possible in the material world. The pattern 011 all by itself may not mean much, but it is not subject to decay or alteration. I can specify it with an exactness not possible for material artifacts. I can never know what the earth or even a single, specific proton or electron is with the exactitude possible for patterns of information. Though the simpler patterns may not be too interesting, more complexity will introduce worlds of meaning, everything from symphonies to mathematical treatises to the details of a happy childhood. Such information will need to be interpreted but can also contain instructions for doing so.

This leads to a bold thought: information could embody universal units of meaning that would be decipherable to any reasonable, sufficiently intelligent entity. We could devise a universal language that all smart folk from anywhere could read. This is not so apparent at the simple level for, in fact, the meaning of a specific string of bits is highly context-dependent. Thus it is hard to say what universal meaning would attach to 011, considered all by itself. But for longer, suitably chosen messages (bit strings) the idea of an inherent meaning seems more plausible: the message as a whole provides a context for the smaller strings (submessages) contained within, which then acquire meaning in reference to the whole. For the parts to acquire such meaning, however, will actually impart meaning to the whole.

As a simple example, consider the twenty-bit sequence: 01011-011101111011111. This we see is made up of five substrings of increasing length: 01, 011, 0111, 01111, 011111. In fact we simply have each number from 1 through 5 represented in "unary" notation (as a string of 1s), preceded by 0 so we can tell where the number begins. This should be apparent to an intelligent alien even with no prior knowledge of humans or their civilization. Within the longer string, our pattern 011 occupies the position it should, representing the number 2. It thus has acquired some meaning in relation to the whole, and the whole in turn has a meaning in view of the arrangement of its parts. This sort of rudimentary meaning is not to be taken too seriously, but it does suggest how messages might be designed to communicate with an alien intelligence. Longer messages will open more possibilities.

We could, for example, consider 8-bit strings or bytes that represent the numbers 0 through 255 in binary. A square array of such bytes could define a picture, with each byte corresponding to a brightness value or pixel at a specific location within the picture. Our picture might, for example, be in the M-picture format of Chapter 6: an array of bytes dimensioned $1,024 \times 1,024$, making a picture having 2^{20}, or just over one million, pixels. A sequence of such pictures would form a movie. The first few pictures could be devoted to providing clues as to the format of the whole, for example, a few simple patterns such as all-black (0), all-white (255), and simple geometrical shapes to establish the dimensions of the pictures and the use of 8-bit pixels.

The movie proper could start with something easy to recognize, say a scene from space. Astronomical events, covering sizable amounts of space and time, might then be depicted as a long sequence of video images. It should not take much imagination or guesswork on the part of an extraterrestrial unfamiliar with human culture (but equipped with eyes) to recognize, for example, that stars against a black backdrop were being shown, or planets in gravity-bound motion. With other simple cues other sorts of information could be depicted, such as earthly life-forms in interaction or mathematical relationships. One important property to note here is that the relation between information—an encoded picture, say, and what it stands for, the scene depicted—is not arbitrary but there is an intelligible, intuitive connection between the symbolism and what it symbolizes. This property, I think, is not sufficiently recognized by those who imagine that language is necessarily limited because the meanings of words or expressions have to be assigned by us. Instead, in certain important cases, a potential meaning is natural and resident already.

If we want to imagine really strange aliens (blind for instance, but highly intelligent and technologically advanced) it might get more difficult to provide suitable cues. However, creatures of high intelligence should be able to bridge gaps created by the lack of suitable sensory organs. In fact, any advanced intelligence that found itself in our universe must surely be aware of so basic a component as the photon and, we may conjecture, would have long since created eyes for itself if it originally lacked them. On the other hand, in trying to be intelligible to the most alien creatures imaginable, we could emphasize such basics as computer programming and mathematical relationships. Mathematics would furnish a good foundation for the expression of other ideas too, which could then be developed in turn.

A stream of bits encoding the prime numbers 2, 3, 5, 7, 11, and so on might be a good start, to signal that we were an intelligent species with something to say.[9] One important practice, the use of symbols or certain expressions to stand for other expressions, generally longer and more complex, could be carefully introduced.

Symbols need not be just arbitrary, but can bear an obvious relation to what they symbolize, as in these representations of numbers. Mathematics can be developed from numbers, and mathematics can serve as a universal language.

With the help of such symbolism, ideas that would otherwise be prohibitively complex can be economically indicated, as mathematicians are well aware. From there we could go to programming concepts, leading to a general purpose computer language, and then proceed to other fields. Perhaps the first choice after computing would be physics, then chemistry, biology, psychology, and, ultimately, history, politics, culture, and so on. Aliens intercepting our message and wanting to talk back could respond in similar ways to tell us about their world. It could, of course, require a great deal of time and patience, especially if the aliens were far out in space—no obstacle to dedicated immortals.

So, in short, information could be suitably encoded so that the process of unraveling its meaning could be carried out by intelligent beings who have no acquaintance with us except through the messages themselves. It does not seem farfetched, in view of this, to regard information as possessing intrinsic meaning independent of who or what is trying to make sense of it.

The Material World As Information

It seems natural to think of the material world as the territory and information as the map, but an alternate view is possible. The world as we know it is made up of matter and energy subsisting in a framework of space-time. Matter is actually a form of energy, as Einstein showed us, energy contained in a holding pattern. Matter is needed to record information. Matter thus serves as the map for territory composed of information. (The analogy can be pushed a little further: mathematical tables are limited in accuracy, so the matter map, true to intuition, need not contain as much detail as the information territory.) Since information can be copied, it can survive the destruction of the matter that records it. If it fails to survive, however, it can eventually be recreated. This we would expect to hold even if the laws of physics alter with time so that the "same" matter is no longer possible. If information processing became impossible due to changing physical conditions, even including a change in physical laws, the situation might be salvaged if once more the processing could happen again, even if in another universe entirely.

Information thus has a permanence that makes it more real, in an ultimate sense, than the material world that is needed to map it. Information, we might say, is the ultimate, enduring substrate of reality. This point of view, it will be seen, in no way contradicts materialism. Information always requires a material substrate for its expression. No mystical essence is needed that is outside the reality that physics reveals to us. Yet I think we can see, in the information paradigm, the basis for a deeper meaning in life than was suspected traditionally by materialists.

The notions of map and territory are complementary. Seemingly they are opposites, but we have seen how their roles can interchange. Information can map matter, which in turn can map information. Thus information can map information. This self-imaging can extend to many levels of complexity, and, indeed, such high-level structuring seems necessary for high-level understanding. It may be difficult to acquire such understanding, but it is also rewarding. Thus in one simple way we are impelled to seek meaning in life, and from the unlimited intricacy of the relationships that by all appearance are knowable, we can be confident of reasonable success.

The notion of the world as information may appear unduly focused on static entities. The world of experience, in contrast, is not an artifact frozen in time but a process in motion—as perceived by us. Within this dynamic framework we observe many phenomena. Most are transitory, but a few, such as biological evolution (through DNA sequences) and human civilization (through written records), attempt in various ways to stabilize and maintain a growing body of information. These then are growing processes, which undergo a progressive development. The information accumulated by such a process offers a recapitulation of the events involved in its own, ongoing development; it is a map of its history. As such it is more than a mere collection of patterns. The march of events is reflected and has an honored place within the world of information, though information is also concerned with static relationships, as in mathematics.

If information is to be regarded as the real, enduring substrate of reality, as our argument suggests, it lends further confidence to the principle of Interchangeability. Different instantiations of persons may be materially distinct, but if they are identical on informational grounds, they can rightly be regarded as redundant images, as mutual backups of a single mentality.

On the other hand, the idea of information as a map of history suggests an ideal model: a person too (a diachronic self) is rightly a growing process that accumulates and stabilizes an increasing body of information, a map of history. This history will in fact resemble the record of events that is accumulating in civilization at large—but be more limited and personalized, with assertions in the database such as *I* did this or saw that. Up to now each such personalized process has suffered an inevitable interruption and dissolution in death. The course of our progress now offers hope of an indefinite continuation of the process that is each person.

In such an endeavor, it should not be overlooked that we have existing models to go by; earthly life and human civilization can be regarded as growing processes, as we have noted, and this extends to subprocesses, to individual human cultures, say, or to more limited entities, such as universities. In short, we can recognize a multitude of growing processes already. When we take our place among them (in some cases thereby rendering them obsolete and superseding them) we can be reassured by their precedence: our immortality need not seem strange or unnatural. It goes without saying, however, that many changes in ourselves and our perspectives must take place, though I think the challenges will be exciting and enjoyable and increasingly so as we advance.

An issue of consciousness is worth addressing briefly here. In our zeal to proclaim information as the ultimate, enduring substrate of reality, we do not intend to go so far as to say that information is "everything." In fact, it is only part of the recipe of living. An equally important, complementary part is activity— what we do in our moments of wakefulness. This is how we experience consciousness. Activity could involve physical actions or simple contemplation—what is important, from the individual perspective, is the conscious experience. (In case this seems unduly selfish, note that one's conscious experience includes the possible awareness and approval of acts of charity that one is performing for others.) Without this activity, we would not be alive—at least not psychologically, which is the important sense. But without information, *we* would not be alive—information defines *which* person is conscious. So information, we can say, is necessary for the *conservation* of identity, but activity is needed for the *expression* of identity. Both are indispensable if we hope to continue our existence.

Digital Systems and Their Powers

It will now be useful to take a closer look at digital systems. The computer we have already encountered makes a good starting point.

What can a computer do? Computers nowadays are used for a wide variety of tasks, but the underlying task can be expressed quite simply: to transform strings of symbols into other strings of symbols according to specified rules. This ability, limited though it may seem, conveys great power. A parallel is provided by considering the human species in relation to other life-forms. Humankind has been gifted through the evolutionary process with an unprecedented capacity for symbol manipulation. Originally through spoken language, later extended through various written forms, it fostered the near-miraculous in the creation of civilization as we know it. (In the process, despite all the problems, life advanced into something of greater meaning.)

In general, computers work with descriptions of things and produce descriptions of procedures or other things. (The descriptions can be interpreted by other devices as commands to act, so in effect the computer is capable of directing physical operations as well or serving as the "brain" of a robot.) Almost arbitrary rules can be employed. Almost arbitrary things can be described. Computers can describe themselves, or other computers, and moreover can deal with procedural knowledge. Thus one computer can emulate the behavior of another one. (This is used to test new computer designs before they are ever implemented in hardware, which results in great overall savings in cost and time, despite the time-lag in the emulation.)

The orientation of computers toward descriptions leads to a strong association, in the mind of the computer scientist, between certain ideas and their descriptions, which serves as an aid to understanding. Thus we have the notions of procedure, program, task, and algorithm, which all are (loosely at least) synonymous with "a sequence of instructions a computer is asked to perform," and the associated description that is actually loaded into a computer's memory. This description takes the form simply of a long string of bits, though there is usually an equivalent, shorter description for human programmers, using letters of the alphabet and other symbols. Among other things, associating a program with a description makes it possible to operate on programs as data, to speak of the computer constructing programs, or to have a program that, through the computer that is running it, answers questions about other programs or even about itself.

Computers can model, essentially, any physical system for which definite rules can be specified. Since the time of Newton it has been recognized that the universe at large obeys such computable rules (or appears very convincingly to do so), even in the face of such properties as unpredictability. Thus, for example, by incorporating laws of physics, it is possible to model the behavior of systems down to the atomic level and beyond. In principle any finite system could be modeled for any finite amount of time, a possibility with tremendous implications.

It is most natural to think of modeling a system that is completely predictable since computers, by and large, are predictable devices themselves. Unpredictable behavior, such as that encountered at the atomic level, can also be modeled however. (As noted in Chapter 5, the unpredictability could be perceived as "true" randomness even if the universe is deterministic overall.)

The modeling of unpredictability can take several forms, including: (1) predicting the probabilities of different events whose individual occurrence is not predicted; (2) simulating an actual sequence of events, using a random number generator; or (3) using a deeper modeling to describe hidden variables that explain the (apparent) randomness deterministically. A fourth possibility, in principle at least, would be a computer working over eons of time to exhaustively model all the possible behaviors of a probabilistic system. In this way we could replicate the full course of events under the many-worlds formulation. A quantum computer or, especially, a universal quantum simulator, if perfected, might speed this process considerably, however. On a more practical level today, simulations of some of the possible behaviors would be quite feasible by iterating (2) (as noted above) several times to get a better idea of the different varieties of behavior and their respective likelihood. Such simulations call for choices to be made of which versions of the unpredictable events are to occur. These choices can be fully authentic—using truly unpredictable hardware to generate a random bit sequence. Or we can use a procedure that generates sequences that, though predictable in theory, are sufficiently random for most purposes.

By modeling a physical process we obtain a means for answering questions about it. But even if this is not feasible, the possibility of doing the modeling in principle can shed light on whether certain speculations about it might be true. Thus, while a computer could in principle furnish us a detailed prediction of a large physical system such as a cryopreserved human down to the level of atoms, this would be wildly impractical with anything like our present computing devices. Still, the theoretical possibility, if accepted, sheds light on what to reasonably expect in the way of future advances.

Computer science, as a theoretical discipline, took shape in the 1930s. Its chief early exponent was English mathematician Alan M. Turing.[10] Among his creations was a kind of simplified, theoretical computer that became known as the Turing machine.

In its basic form a Turing machine is limited to computations done by reading, erasing, and writing symbols on a strip of tape that is divided into squares. Each square is printed with a symbol or left blank, with "blank," for formal purposes, being treated as just another symbol. The machine stops by (or on) a square, reads its symbol, optionally changes that symbol to another symbol, and either moves one square to the right, moves one square to the left, or halts and does nothing from then on.

Actions of the machine all occur at discrete instants of time, or "time steps." The machine at all times is also in one of a finite number of "states." On each time step the machine has the option of changing its state to another one. What symbol the machine writes, whether it moves right, moves left, or halts, and what state it changes to, all depend entirely on the symbol it is now reading and the state it is now in. The alphabet of possible symbols is finite. The tape can be assumed to be infinite in both directions or can be marked with chosen symbols to indicate termination on the left or right. An infinite tape is simpler, theoretically, but is then assumed to be all blank except for a finite portion, or inscription. (A finitely inscribed tape thus remains finitely inscribed as the machine operates, an important theoretical consideration.) A complete description of the machine's actions under all possible circumstances can thus be written down in a finite table (the state transition table). In practice, the effect of the infinite tape could be simulated by starting with a finite tape and adding squares to the right or left as needed.

A Turing machine, here imagined as a crablike robot, marks or erases symbols and moves left or right along an infinite tape.

Machines with Universal Powers

Although a Turing machine would be too inefficient to be worth implementing directly in hardware, nevertheless it is capable of doing anything a more advanced computer can do, in terms of the basic task of transforming strings of symbols into other strings. Its very simplicity, moreover, makes it an illuminating object for study. One special variety, known as the universal Turing machine, is capable of performing any computation that any other Turing machine, and thus any computer, can do. To accomplish this we supply the universal machine with a description of the machine we wish to emulate (a program) together with the data (the tape inscription) that the emulated machine is to start on. (It may be necessary to use encoding to reduce the alphabet of the emulated machine to that of the universal machine—no major obstacle.) The universal machine is then able to correctly interpret what amount to instructions in its program, to transform its data, step by step, as would the machine it is mimicking. To make it behave like some other, entirely different machine, we merely change the program.

In fact, most modern-day computers are also universal in the same sense as a universal Turing machine—if augmented by unlimited data-storage capability to achieve the effect of an infinite tape. They are thus known as general-purpose machines. Like the Turing machine operating from a description of the machine it is emulating, they use a stored program to behave in a desired fashion.

It was a conjecture of Turing, now widely known as the Church-Turing thesis, that any effective procedure of the symbol-manipulation variety could be performed by a Turing machine—and thus by a universal Turing machine or a computer. (This honors American logician Alonzo Church, who independently advanced an equivalent formalism and conjecture slightly

earlier than Turing. Turing's approach, using the simple computers now known as Turing machines, is more accessible to the
nonspecialist and is more widely cited.) This would include any
task of the computational variety that a human might do, such as
numerical calculations, devising moves to a game such as chess
(such moves are describable in strings of symbols), and, in short,
any well-defined operation that produces a description of something from another description.

The Church-Turing thesis cannot be proved in a mathematical
sense, since the notion of effective procedure is not reduced to a
formal definition but left up to human judgment. However, in the
more than fifty years since it was formulated it has never been
refuted. When it comes to devices we can build, as well as other
finite constructs—including ourselves—the Church-Turing thesis seems to apply.

For the record, there are some operations one might like to
perform that are not Turing computable, and this can be shown
mathematically. This should be kept in mind in any anticipation
of future technology, including technology that we hope will make
us immortal. One concerns the famous halting problem. It is a
recurring nuisance to computer programmers that sometimes the
programs take inordinately long to run. This particularly is a problem with programs designed for intelligent behavior, such as
mathematical theorem provers. In fact, it is possible for the program to find itself committed to a task it will never be able to
complete; instead, it would just run forever unless halted from
the outside.

This could occur if it is given an impossible task, such as "find
an exact method of squaring the circle with a ruler and compass"—the program itself may never "know" that it is pursuing a
hopeless task and may never stop running. On the other hand,
some tasks are not impossible but merely take a long time; thus
the rewards could be great in allowing the program to continue to
run, or a great deal of resources could be spent for nothing. In
short, what we need is a computer program that will examine
each task beforehand to decide which ones can be completed and
which cannot.

Unfortunately, no such program is possible; that is, it is not
possible to decide consistently, in advance, whether a given task
can be finished. This is shown by a fairly simple argument: basi-

cally, if a program could solve the halting problem, then another program could be written that would emulate the first program under special conditions, determine its prediction, and violate that prediction. Instead the best we can do, in the tough cases, is to recognize when a computational task can be completed by observing that the computer eventually finishes it. If the task cannot be completed, we may never be able to tell. (This is unfortunate in one sense, but it also means that life has deep mysteries and is more interesting than it would otherwise be.)

In addition to unsolvable problems, there are some that, while solvable in theory, are intractably difficult. An example might be to break a modern encryption algorithm. Typically this would involve guessing a string of up to several thousand random digits or letters to find the key that when supplied to the program will cause it to correctly unscramble a message it has previously encrypted. This may be possible in principle, but in practice, billions of centuries may not be enough time, even at the rate of millions of guesses per second. (On the other hand, there could be surprises. Quantum computing, which we will consider shortly, may allow previously intractable encryption algorithms to be broken in a feasible amount of time, as well as great speedups in other operations.)

Finally, there are the tasks that can be done not only in principle but straightforwardly, in a manner that is reasonably efficient and practical. Among these are many of the usual operations one would like a computer to do, ranging from routine numerical calculations to limited modeling of the behavior of molecules or (processing the information needed for) making the sounds of speech. Included also is the task of instructing a universal Turing machine to behave like some other Turing machine. Similarly, to emulate one computer on another requires tedious but not particularly imaginative programming, provided one is not overly concerned about the speed of the emulation. In general, it is not too difficult to come up with a system exhibiting universal behavior, that is, able to emulate any other system.

One particularly simple system with universal power is the Game of Life invented by English mathematician John Conway and popularized by Martin Gardner in *Scientific American*.[11] Life is more like a rudimentary universe than a computer as we usually think of it, but it is easy to emulate in a computer and, on the other hand, can emulate a computer itself. Imagine a two-dimensional grid of squares, laid out on a flat, level plain, extending to the horizon in all directions. High overhead is a cosmic clock that ticks off seconds. At each tick the squares, which are black or white like those of a checkerboard, are able to change. Some black squares remain black, some change to white, and so on. All the squares obey the same rule, which has to do with the state of the square (black or white) and that of its eight nearest neighbors (the adjacent squares on its four sides and the four squares touching its corners). If a white square has two or three neighboring white squares, it stays white, otherwise it turns black. If a black square has exactly three neighboring white squares, it turns white, otherwise it stays black. That is all there is to it.

One thing to note is that the rules are not symmetric between black and white. In fact, computer simulations, in which the changing squares (a large finite subset, that is) can be shown on a video screen, often start with most of the squares black, suggesting empty space. Within the void small patterns of white may be seen—shrinking, expanding, darting here and there, or disappearing and reappearing like strange life-forms. (It is not necessary to assume only one clock tick per second, of course; the pace can be speeded up considerably, which greatly enhances the impression that some form of living process is going on.) Despite the simplicity of the rules, very complex behavior can be sustained or can evolve. Information can be encoded in patterns of white and black squares, leading to the possibility of devices processing descriptions, or, in other words, computers. In fact it has been shown that a general-purpose computer, capable of all the com-

   • • •

The Game of Life. In this simple example, the pattern of three white squares changes to four white squares in one time step, and thereafter stays the same. More complex starting patterns produce more interesting behavior.

putations a Turing machine or any modern computer can do, and self-replication in addition, is possible.

Using variations of the state-transition rule, and expanding to three dimensions, allow processes that more closely resemble biological activity.[12] We can also increase the dimensions beyond three, or shrink them to one. These cellular spaces, as they are called, sometimes allow a "universal computer-constructor"[13] capable of constructing any possible, finite object in the space, including itself, according to specified instructions. Here an "object" is just a configuration of cells in certain specified states. (In general, we allow more than just the two states of black and white, but one is still singled out as the quiescent state corresponding to empty space. An empty region remains unchanged until invaded from the outside by a nonquiescent or active pattern.) If the number of dimensions is three, we can obtain spaces that rather resemble our own, and, in fact, a few physicists have seriously considered the possibility that our universe is just a three-dimensional cellular space.[14] (This interesting possibility, however, is ruled out by the nonlocality of processes at the quantum level that we would have to assume unless we accept many-worlds, and many-worlds is not easily accommodated in a "single-world" cellular space.)

Once again, systems having universal computing capacity are numerous and varied. Some of them, as we have seen, resemble biological ecosystems, and, indeed, our own, natural ecosystem is one such universal computer, made of interacting atoms. All such systems are equivalent in the sense that any one can emulate any other one, that is, the emulating system can create an evolving description of the emulated system as it develops over time. Sometimes, though not always, the emulation can be done efficiently, that is, the number of events needed to emulate a process is bounded by a polynomial in the number of events being emulated. The prevalence of universal systems will be worth bearing in mind when we consider nanotechnology in the next chapter.

A cellular space allows many cells to change state on each time step, that is, in parallel. A Turing machine, on the other hand, operates serially on its data, one cell at a time; yet a Turing machine can emulate a cellular space of any finite dimension (and within a polynomial event bound) provided we require that all but finitely many cells of our cellular space are blank or quiescent at the start of execution. This suggests that there is nothing critical about such details as the geometric configuration or physical proximity of features in a given space or, more generally, of serial processing versus parallel processing. If two blobs of material in a cellular space collide, for example, the collision may be represented entirely differently on a Turing machine's tape, and events that were nearby in space and/or time may be considerably more spread out—yet a basic equivalence will persist. The world of the Turing machine is just as real as that of the cellular space and may have the same details, only differently encoded. The encoding and more general features will seem important to an outside observer but not to a process within the system. Such a process would have no way of "knowing," for example, whether it was really in a three-dimensional cellular space or was being serially emulated by a Turing machine on a one-dimensional tape.

The same considerations apply if we go to more powerful digital systems. Indeed there are, theoretically at least, systems more powerful than a Turing machine with a finitely inscribed tape, one being the Turing machine with an infinitely inscribed tape. Clearly this can do anything a finitely inscribed system can do and more. We could solve the halting problem, for instance, by exhaustively describing all the relevant cases on our infinite tape and using a lookup procedure for any particular case of interest. (This would require an infinite amount of data to be written down beforehand, which is impossible in practice. But even if it could be done, the lookup procedure would take an impractical amount of time for most cases.) A similar sort of system would be an infinitely inscribed cellular space. Again, the two systems will be equivalent and can emulate each other within a polynomial bound on events. In general, such infinite systems are not accessible to us—we must be content with finite approximations such as our computers, though life as a whole may confront us with something more.

Going in the other direction, there is one system, the finite state machine, which is less powerful than a Turing machine even limited to a finitely inscribed tape, but which still has much significance. The finite state machine comes in many equivalent forms, one being a Turing machine constrained to move in one direction only, say, always to the right. Here we restrict the system to include only the machine, not the tape, which could be finitely or infinitely inscribed. On each time step the machine reads a symbol on the tape, which becomes its input, and replaces it with a symbol, its output, before moving on, always forward (to the right), to the next square, and changing state. We are not concerned, really, with where the input comes from or with what happens to the output once it is produced. The machine can never look directly at either again—though it may "remember" them in its state configuration. More generally, a finite state machine does not need a tape—just some source of input and a place for output. We see, then, how a computer becomes a finite state machine if we accept it "as is," as a device of fixed size and do not seek to augment it by adding memory.[15] Going beyond this, the concept applies to happenings in our world.

Physical Systems As Digital Mechanisms

Any physical system whatever that is bounded in spatial volume and energy content is a kind of finite state machine, if also restricted to a finite amount of time. It exists in one of a finite number of states, and it changes state at discrete instants in time, not continuously, in response to its surroundings (input) and in accordance with the state it is currently in. (These states amount to distinguishable quantum states, which we considered last chapter, and they set a bound on the amount of information the system can contain.) The state changes, in fact, are described by known laws—the laws of quantum mechanics. A human being, in particular, is such a device, as is a city, a galaxy, or, in fact, the whole visible universe. The behavior of a finite state machine over a finite interval of time, including its input, state changes, and output, can be described by a finite record. By comparing two such records, we can decide if two finite state machines have behaved equivalently over the time they have been running.

Of course, when it comes to describing natural processes as finite state machines, the basic interactions are going on at the level of tiny particles, and there are myriads of these. The Principle of Large Quantity applies: the numbers of states and state transitions, for any sizable system, are very large. These numbers are governed by Bekenstein bounds—named after physicist Jacob Bekenstein—which limit (1) the maximum number of (distinguishable) states the system can be in; and (2) the maximum number of state transitions that can occur per second, the "going rate" of the system. The maximum number of states for a human, for example, is in the neighborhood of $10^{10^{45}}$ (much bigger, in fact, than the number of M-pictures we encountered in Chapter 6) and the maximum going rate is around 4×10^{53} state transitions per second. These actually are very generous upper bounds—the real effective numbers are likely to be much smaller, though by no means small. Moreover, there are special features of such a system, involving quantum interactions, that do not occur with classical computational devices, which we will consider shortly. But the main point is that a human, like other things in our reality, is, at the root, a digital device—nothing more.[16]

We have now considered several digital devices of differing computational power. At the lower end is the finite state machine; then comes the Turing machine with a finitely inscribed tape, along with equivalent cellular spaces; and, finally, the Turing machine with an infinitely inscribed tape, again with equivalent cellular spaces. For our purposes the differences between the three are not that great—all are digital systems, and all behave as finite state machines over finite stretches of space and time. Moreover, all can be regarded as interconnections of finite state machines since, for example, two such machines could communicate by one machine passing its output to the other as input, and vice versa. Two such machines interconnected form a third finite state machine, and, more generally, any finite number of interconnected finite state machines is a finite state machine. With an infinite number of interconnected machines, however, we obtain something more—a Turing machine with a finitely or infinitely inscribed tape, or equivalent. In all cases though, we again retain a digital system, in which the basic components (finite state machines) carry out all their operations in discrete jumps and not as continuous processes. This fundamental property—discreteness of the events—will not be affected even when correlations between distant events have to be enforced, as in the nonlocal-seeming effects we considered in Chapter 5.

The latter, however, does pose a problem for our basic computational model, though one we can deal with. In fact, interconnections of finite state machines would enforce a standard locality—a signal could only propagate from machine to machine at a finite speed, with nothing exotic such as splitting of worlds. (This is why a three-dimensional cellular space would not be a good model for the universe.) This is not a fundamental problem; we noted, for instance, how a serial device can emulate a parallel one, albeit at a considerable cost in efficiency. In such a case there will be many correlations that must be enforced between events that are distant in space or time. In addition, we saw how the locality property is upheld by one interpretation of quantum reality, many-worlds, in which reality does split repeatedly into alternate copies that pursue different behavioral paths.

A theoretical device, the "nondeterministic" finite state machine, accomplishes this also and could be used to model physical systems. It also generalizes to nondeterministic interconnections of machines, Turing machines with finitely or infinitely inscribed tapes, and cellular spaces. (It is worth noting that this "nondeterminism" is actually a form of determinism if the splitting itself is deterministic; hopefully no confusion will follow.) Such devices really have no more overall computing power than their deterministic (single timeline or single-world) counterparts, which can emulate them, but for obvious reasons they can accomplish a lot more, computationally, in a given number of steps. Indeed, though it is not known for sure, there seems to be no way to emulate them efficiently, that is, in a polynomial time bound, using only the usual deterministic devices that cannot do the many-worlds trick of splitting into copies.

Quantum Devices and Digital Consciousness

Here it is appropriate (if not overdue) to note that a new type of device, the quantum computer, also seems capable of doing more, efficiently, than the conventional Turing machine and its related family of devices, including those that operate in cellular spaces. Its powers, in fact, seem intermediate between conventional computing and the full-blooded but unrealizable (as far as we know) nondeterministic devices.[17] And, unlike the latter, a quantum computer seems achievable, based on physics as we understand it, though as of this writing it has not been implemented at a practical level.

The quantum computer will not be simply a better computer but, if it can be perfected, will also furnish an interesting argument for many-worlds. This is because it explicitly makes use of processes happening in parallel in different universes, at least according to a straightforward interpretation. A quantum computer, that is, can simultaneously be in many different states. (But the total number states, though very large, is still finite as usual.) As one example, it can, according to theory, factor large numbers more efficiently than a conventional computer. Here it exploits parallel worlds to arrive at a correct "guess" much more rapidly than any serial machine or even cellular space could produce using any known technique. This could spell trouble for encryption algorithms, which often depend on this very problem being hard enough not to be solvable over a practical time scale. However, it happens that by using other quantum effects a secure communication channel can be created that would allow users to detect any eavesdropping and thereby obviate the need for encryption in the first place.[18]

More generally, quantum devices promise unheard-of capabilities as well as vastly increasing our understanding of what ought to be possible. In particular, theory predicts universal quantum computers and universal simulators analogous to the universal Turing machine but with more relevance to real-world applications.[19] Among many other things this would, by appearances, nicely resolve the problem of how to model unpredictability in a computational device.

In general, it turns out that quantum systems can only be emulated inefficiently on classical devices such as computers and the Turing machine. The universal simulator, however, should be capable of doing this efficiently, that is, within a polynomial time bound of the original system. With this in mind, a universal virtual reality generator should even be possible to run efficiently, which suggests the idea that our future selves, uploaded as programs in a quantum computer, may find interesting options—and challenges—for life as immortals. Nevertheless, at the quantum level, all processes that go on are describable digitally. They could all be emulated, at the description level, albeit inefficiently, by conventional computers, and even the humble Turing machine, patiently scratching and erasing symbols on its one-dimensional tape over eons.

As one consequence, finite histories are simply progressions of states through which a system passes over time—or finite descriptions based on such sequences. The number of possible histories that can occur in a finite time, starting, as usual, with a finite volume of space and finite energy, is finite. This clearly supports the plausibility of Unboundedness. The finite histories, in effect, become throws of a big, but finite, sackful of dice. Though it might happen with considerable rarity, we expect any possible combination to turn up eventually, and not once, but over and over, in our postulated multiverse.

We can even go a little further and say that any device that emulates an object at the quantum level, with the corresponding state changes, in effect becomes that very object, even if the states and their transitions are represented very differently from the original and the time and space requirements too are very different. It is not the specific representation that counts but the behavior of the system as a whole—equivalent behavior yields an equivalent system. This is a bold assertion, essentially a restatement of strong AI, and is stoutly resisted by some. It means, for instance, that all events are, at root, equivalent to discrete changes of bits in a computer or other similar, sudden jumps. This includes whatever is involved in feeling and consciousness, something that may seem preposterous. I think, however, that the difficulties are resolvable if we are not daunted by the scale of operations that might be required.

For example, a living human replete with all emotions, perceptions, thoughts, and actions should be able to be modeled by an unthinking, unfeeling device, a Turing machine, say, making and erasing marks on a very, *very* long strip of tape over a period of time. (Once again there must be an appropriate provision for unpredictability.) To say that the full range of human feelings could somehow be expressed this way seems silly until it is remembered that we are positing no theoretical limit on the amount of time and materials involved. The Principle of Large Quantity must be taken seriously. (And, of course, the exact nature of the materials is not important as long as they perform certain basic functions, such as allowing information to be recorded in retrievable, modifiable form.) In other words, we could well be committing resources far beyond the known age and size of the universe.

In practical terms, we need not take this scenario seriously at all. Surely it will all but never happen, even if we grant an unlimited future—there will be better ways to spend our time and treasure. But the philosophical implications are still meaningful and worth considering since they apply to emulations more generally. Thus, unless we allow that atomic constituents themselves are tiny homunculi with undeciphered emotions, a system that models a human subatomically should be capable of supporting true, humanlike emotions. The whole known universe could be modeled in this way, right down to the quantum level, so that genuine emotions could be supported by thoroughly unemotional text editing or symbol-changing operations.

If this is hard to swallow, it will perhaps seem more plausible if we think in terms of the possible interactions that could take place between a hypothetical outsider and a modeled entity—someone, say, whose behavior is being traced out in very great detail but at slow speed on a computational device. Along with this behavior, let us say, is a sizable, surrounding, virtual environment that could involve many other emulated individuals along with objects and numerous processes. A person on the outside would be "running" at a much faster pace. To synchronize the running speeds, our hypothetical outsider could be put into a long sleep after each message is sent to the insider, who in turn may take a very long time to respond but otherwise is observed to respond in an entirely normal manner. So an exchange like this may occur: (Outsider): "How are you today?" (Insider): "Fine, though I have a slight cold, I think—the thermostat was turned down, it is a little chilly outside. How is the weather where you come from?" and so on.

In general, we can imagine a situation in which a person, emulated in a computer and using nothing but nonbiological computational elements, responds in all respects like a human being and seems in every way capable of feeling and consciousness. Such a being might be running slower or faster than a normal human, and be strangely represented inside its emulating device, but would otherwise seem normal in every way. The emulated being could then pass the Turing test, first proposed by Turing in 1950,[20] of answering questions in such a way as to be undetectably different from a human and thus possess intelligence. This would satisfy the requirement of weak artificial intelligence (weak AI)—meaning the emulation could at least convincingly imitate a human, though it might be lacking in true emotions and consciousness. But we are also assuming not just an arbitrary program to carry out conversation but a fully modeled human being whose internal workings, including brain activity, are being accurately represented as an ongoing process. So I think a stronger conclusion would apply; the true feelings would exist. This, then, would meet the demands of strong AI—that a suitably programmed computer must support mental states comparable to those of humans and not just an intricate, convincing imitation. The possibility of strong AI (or even the weak version) must still be considered controversial; to me the arguments for it seem convincing.[21] (More will be said near the end of the chapter, in connection with the problem of isomorphism.) Again it must be remembered that we are positing no limits on the size and time requirements of the emulating device, beyond finiteness.

So what insight is to be gained from this? Simply that there is good reason to think of reality in computational terms. History is a computation-like process, as are its constituents, including individual persons. "Things," in the sense of eternally enduring, unchanging objects, exist—but they are chunks of information—no more, no less. Such objects are recorded in various, temporary configurations of matter and in general are multiply recorded. Similarly, a process can be multiply instantiated—if the same exact computation is run on two different computers, there is a reasonable sense in which just one process, not two, is executing, though in multiple environments. In short we arrive at the position that like entities or constructs share identity—which is our principle of Interchangeability.

There is one issue connected with Interchangeability we left hanging in the last chapter, where we noted that person-instantiations share identity when they can be considered equivalent. The precise delineation of when this equivalence would occur is well beyond our present powers. But the general idea is that a person is a type of computational process, so that the equivalence we are seeking is a similar notion to the equivalence of two running computer programs, which at least is a meaningful concept. In general, the digital model of events should allow us to decide, in principle, when two person-instantiations can be considered equivalent.

Given some finite limit on the time, space, and energy involved, all processes are replicated by finite state machines, and, in fact, only a finite number of processes fit any finite bound. If such processes are expressed in a standardized form recording the input, state transitions, and output, there is an effective procedure for deciding when two such processes are equivalent, so that equivalent processes indeed form sharply bounded or well-defined classes. (The equivalence classes could then be extended straightforwardly to more gargantuan, slower processes that mimicked the faster ones but seemingly required more states.) Once again, we are benefited if events can be regarded as happening in discrete jumps rather than by continuous changes. Here the benefit is that the notion of person-instantiation gains coherence, lending plausibility to the main form of our concept of Interchangeability.

Answering Objections: the Chinese Room Experiment

Something should now be said in response to critics of the information paradigm and strong AI, who sometimes go to considerable lengths defending their various positions. (Possibly they are uncomfortable with materialism and the idea it favors of reducing people, in one way or another, to purely physical processes. But I think they have not taken account of the wonderful possibilities this opens.) Feeling, consciousness, understanding, and intelligence, they would tell us, are forever closed to digital devices such as computers and consequently cannot be understood in purely digital terms. Strong AI counters that such effects are complex, emergent properties that can and do rest on a digital foundation, invoking only sharp, individual state changes. The notion of an emergent property, in fact, furnishes a powerful reply to critics of strong AI.

One such critic is John Searle, a University of California philosopher, who proposes a "Chinese room experiment" as an argument against strong AI.[22] A man who understands no Chinese is given a very elaborate set of rules for conversing in Chinese. Persons who understand the language pass a note written in Chinese characters under the door of the room where the man works. He consults various references, copies and arranges symbols, and ultimately arrives at a message in Chinese that is an intelligible reply to the first. This he passes under the door to his audience on the outside. After a series of exchanges the outsiders conclude that whoever is in the room understands Chinese, yet in fact the man has no idea of the meaning of the messages he is writing—he has simply been obeying a set of rules. In a similar way, it is argued, a machine, even if it passed the Turing test, would not truly understand what it was doing—it too would just be obeying rules.

As it turns out, a good rebuttal to this argument can be based on some simple considerations.[23] We noted earlier that the task of conversing in a natural language is quite difficult computationally and has not yet been accomplished at the level of a normal adult. In short, no machine can yet play the Turing imitation game. Machines, on the other hand, process information very fast. Deep Blue, the expert chess program that defeated world champion Garry Kasparov in 1997, could examine twelve billion moves a minute, very far beyond the human level.[24] (A human chess grandmaster, however, is much better at determining which moves to examine.) A set of rules adequate for intelligent conversation would, by indications, be most extensive and moreover take a very great amount of processing. If implemented as suggested in the Chinese room experiment, we might have to wait eons for replies to messages. Again we must appeal to the Principle of Large Quantity to argue that a suitable rule book would be possible at all—though in view of the information paradigm it does seem true.

Better than one person doing all the processing, however, would be a vast army of, say, a billion people, all connected electronically, all patiently working away at transforming the incoming message. (Again, we lack any suitable set of rules, but it seems possible in principle.) Much of the transforming might involve simple acts of voting on the part of large numbers of people—this could be one way of finely partitioning the overall task so that many could take part at once. Or other techniques might be used, many of them presently unknown to us but all, we may presume, feasible computationally. If we assumed all the workers were ignorant of Chinese, no one person would understand either the incoming message or the reply, yet the system as a whole could be capable of meaningful conversation. Each worker would then resemble a neuron in a brain, which also, by indications, does not understand such tasks as conversation, yet the brain as a whole does. We could then argue that the system as a whole understands Chinese, even if the workers do not.

Finally, if the rules the workers obey are suitably adapted, we can imagine a single human, George, doing the whole task single-handedly (and granted immortality as a small compensation). To do this would require keeping track of the tasks of all the billion workers, who, let us say, are housed in a vast complex of offices stretching over a sizable territory. At some point George is informed he is to replace all the workers. On each day thereafter George dials up a different office on his computer terminal and does the work of that person. If the billion workers can together respond to a message in one day, then George takes a billion days or 2.7 million years. George, who has been stunted at a fixed level of development all this time for purposes of the experiment, never understands a word of Chinese. Yet again, the system as a whole does.

It is worth noting that the Chinese room argument is an attempt to discredit strong AI in favor of weak AI, not in favor of no AI. The Chinese conversationist—identified (mistakenly) with the man in the room—is assumed to be competent at performing the task at hand, just lacking in understanding. By implication, a machine might be similarly capable, yet lack any real understanding. The fallacy here, I think, is one of misattribution: the conversationist in this case is *not* the man in the room, as we should reasonably understand it. A similar consideration would apply to a machine capable of conversing. If such a machine were a collection of silicon chips or similar uncomprehending hardware, it might be tempting to deny that the conversationist has understanding. But there is a subtle distinction between the machine that runs the program, and the program—the conversationist—itself. The latter may reasonably have attributes not possessed by the former, especially if some extraordinary feature is involved, such as a very large amount of complex processing. We will return to this topic after considering another interesting attempt to discredit strong AI, in this case, an argument leaning toward no AI at all.

The Gödel Incompleteness Theorem

A human, it seems, must have capabilities no computing machine can ever have, however sophisticated its programming. This claim is based on a result known as Gödel's incompleteness theorem. Kurt Gödel (1906–78) was an Austrian-born, American mathematical logician. Starting in the late 1920s he obtained a number of startling results, including the famous incompleteness theorem. Some controversies of several decades' standing were settled. Some unsuspected limitations were found in mathematics—but some exciting new possibilities were opened too. The story a fascinating one, worth telling in some detail, after which we will consider its implications for AI.

Gödel's findings have to do with properties of formal mathematical systems, in which results are expressed as theorems that are proved. More specifically, these systems are the comprehensive sort that can express all of ordinary mathematics including such topics as the arithmetic of whole and decimal numbers, Euclidean geometry, algebra, and the various mathematical ideas that are used in physics. Such systems, moreover, can also describe themselves. (Another topic, the theory of computation, is also expressible in these systems, and its development was furthered by Gödel's work.) It is both remarkable and beneficial to have a more-or-less all-inclusive system of this sort, in which so many different ideas and results can be expressed and developed. It is pushing toward a mathematician's "theory of everything."

But there is a big danger in pushing too far. Your theory, whatever it is, must be based on starting assumptions or axioms that cannot be proved but must simply be accepted at the outset. (Other, outside evidence can be consulted in selecting the axioms, but they cannot be derived from prior principles within the system, for they are the prior principles.) More or less, the more comprehensive or powerful you want your theory to be, the more axioms you have to assume. If you assume too much, however, you find that, following one train of reasoning, you can prove some proposition P, but with some other reasoning you prove not-P, that is, your system is inconsistent. A basic principle of logic, which essentially all useful mathematical systems incorporate, is "P implies that not-P implies Q" where Q is any other proposition whatever. In other words, in an inconsistent, formal system, any proposition that can be stated in the system can be proved, which reduces everything to triviality. Anything you can prove you can also disprove. For a system to be useful, then, it is very important that it be consistent. Something of the seriousness of this problem can be gathered by considering a little mathematics history.[25]

In the nineteenth century there was great interest in putting mathematics on a firm logical footing, which involved finding simple underlying principles from which it was hoped that all or a very large part of mathematics could be derived. One of the pioneers of this effort was German logician Gottlob Frege (1848–1925), who worked for twenty years to construct, in essence, the first comprehensive mathematical system, a near "theory of everything." It was all based on a few relatively simple concepts, an important one being the notion of set. Almost everything in mathematics, it turns out, can be defined as some sort of set. For example, one definition of the number one is "the set of all singletons," where a singleton is a set having just one member or element. (This is not a circular definition, because "x has one member" means "there exists y such that y is a member of x, and for all z, if z is a member of x then $z=y$"; that is, x's having one member can be defined without already having a definition of "one.") To make your theory as comprehensive and powerful as possible, then, it is desirable to have as many different sets as possible.

Frege boldly rushed in: his theory essentially allowed a set to be associated to every statable, mathematical property whatever. However, it had a fatal flaw. Consider "the set of all sets that are not members of themselves." This set is a member of itself if and only if it is not a member of itself. Frege's system was inconsistent and, as it stood, mathematically worthless—a magnificent airplane that would not quite fly. There was too much generality. Efforts at fixing the problem thus centered on how to restrict the notion of set and still end up with essentially all of mathematics. Frege himself tried to devise such a fix, but his new system was again shown inconsistent. The first real success (we think) was had by Alfred North Whitehead and Bertrand Russell, whose system, Principia Mathematica or PM, was published in three volumes, 1910–13. PM can derive all of ordinary mathematics, though it is cumbersome. Later some other, simpler systems of mathematical logic were devised that better met the intended needs and have not been shown inconsistent. In what follows I have used PM as a representative of these systems, following the practice of Gödel himself; his results apply to all of them.

PM has not been shown inconsistent, but that does not guarantee it is consistent. Mathematicians such as David Hilbert, early in the twentieth century, worried over this problem. What you would really like is to prove such a system is consistent. Then (maybe) you could quit worrying or at least not worry as much. Ideally, you would start with PM and prove within PM itself that PM is consistent. This would avoid the problem that, if you had to use some more comprehensive system, say PM*, to prove PM consistent, it would still leave open the question whether PM* is consistent. (If PM* were inconsistent, then, as noted, anything you like would be provable within it, and consequently its theorems would be untrustworthy.) On the other hand, even if you did prove PM consistent, within PM, it still would not really show PM is consistent. The reason is that PM is comprehensive enough that "PM is consistent" is one of the statable propositions within PM. Thus if PM is inconsistent you can prove "PM is consistent." Still, mathematicians agreed, it would be interesting if you could prove consistency, even if you could not quite trust the result.

Gödel showed, however, that if PM is consistent, it is impossible to prove that within PM. Gödel's proof is closely related to another result, his incompleteness theorem, which started off our discussion.[26] Within PM there is a class of statements, the "closed well-formed formulas" or CWFFs, essentially just the statable propositions, expressed in a formal way, that is, according to specified rules. An example is "for all x there exists y, such that y is a member of x." This statement happens to be false, since if x is the empty set (a permitted construct) there is no y that is a member of x. Let us call this statement S. Then not-S has the form "there exists x such that for all y, y is not a member of x." Not-S is true. In general, if S is some CWFF then either S or not-S is true. One important class of CWFFs is the theorems, which are statements obtainable by applying allowed rules of inference to initial statements or axioms. Basically, every theorem is a true CWFF, provided your system is consistent. This means that, if S is a theorem, then not-S is not a theorem. The system is said to be complete, on the other hand, if, for any CWFF S, either S or not-S is a theorem. The complete logical system, then, is able to decide the truth or falsity of all applicable statements we can make within it.

If we had enough time, in fact, we could start with any CWFF S, and search exhaustively for proofs, of both S and not-S. PM and the other systems are constructed so that this process can be mechanized. In this way a computer must eventually find either a proof of S, which would establish that S is true within the system, or a proof of not-S. (Any such proof would be expressible as a finite string of symbols and could then be checked for correctness, a process that can also be mechanized.) If the computer ever found a proof of S, on the other hand, this would be a guarantee that it could never find a proof of not-S, and vice versa. All this would be the case, however, only if PM is both complete and consistent. If PM is consistent but not complete, for instance, there would be some CWFF S such that neither a proof of S nor of not-S could be obtained by exhaustive searching.

What Gödel showed was that, in fact, PM and related systems, if consistent, are all incomplete. He did this by constructing a statement S for which he could show that both S and not-S are unprovable. S, the "Gödel sentence," has the form "this statement is not provable within PM." If S actually *is* provable, the contradiction leads to the inconsistency of PM, while if not-S is provable, that amounts to proving "S is provable," which means

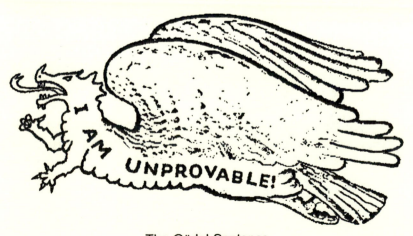

The Gödel Sentence

that S really is provable after all, which again leads to inconsistency. It is worth remarking that this result establishes the impossibility of proving the consistency of PM within PM. Such a proof would prove that neither S nor not-S is provable, for the reasons we have just considered, and thus that S is true within the system, which would amount to a proof of S. Another point worth making is that Gödel's argument establishes that it is S, rather than not-S, that is true in PM. To establish this, however, it is clear we must use arguments not entirely formalizable within PM or otherwise S would be a theorem. However, these extra arguments can all be reduced to the one property, that PM is consistent! This, really, is all the extra knowledge we need, beyond what is in PM itself.

So, for instance, we could expand PM slightly, adding one more axiom, "PM is consistent." In this way we would create a new system, PM*, from which we could prove the Gödel sentence for PM, but it would be inadequate to decide the truth or falsity of an analogous Gödel sentence, "This statement is not provable within PM*." Of course, we could iterate this process, adding another axiom, "PM* is consistent," but that would just create a slightly bigger system, PM**, with the same problem all over again. In general, any reasonably comprehensive formal system—unless we make it too powerful and therefore inconsistent—must have this sort of defect. We can always construct a Gödel sentence that is true, but the system can never "know" that. A human, on the other hand, who has sufficiently studied the matter, does know that the Gödel sentence is true. A computer must always use some sort of formal system—a program—in anything it does, including mathematics. From this it may seem that the human must have capabilities that are forever out of reach of a computer, no matter how well programmed, and, in fact, this is the gripe of the critics of AI who base their argument on Gödel's work.

Their criticism amounts to calling in question whether a computer could even really imitate things such as thinking and understanding, that is, achieve the same effects but by a different process, let alone actually "do" these things. (As an illustration of the significance of this issue, the chess playing computer defeated the human world champion by exhaustive but unimaginative searching rather than anything approaching human deliberation. Thus it successfully imitated human thinking, though in a limited domain and arguably without actually thinking.) So, as we have noted, it is a criticism of AI in general, not just strong AI. However, the criticism has a simple and powerful rebuttal, well noted by Daniel Dennett in *Darwin's Dangerous Idea*, that I have adapted here.[27]

A Simple Rebuttal

Suppose you have a computer programmed with PM, or, more likely, one of the later improvements. The computer, then, has a superb system for answering questions of a mathematical nature, which extends to questions about the real world, since mathematics is important in physics and other sciences. If we assume the computer's system is consistent, it will answer our questions infallibly—if it answers at all. On the other hand, there are certain questions it cannot answer—and, moreover, some of these, at least, a human can. The human can also answer any question the computer can—by doggedly emulating its program if necessary—and thus has additional ability that the machine, in this case, is lacking. So we then ask, what is the nature of the human's extra ability? Would we say that it too is infallible? No one would seriously maintain this—humans are certainly fallible.

True, in the case at hand, where we consider the simple statement, "the system is consistent," that the system itself can never prove, mathematically minded humans may know it is true (provided it *is* true), even if unprovable. But, more generally, humans certainly disagree on matters of judgment and certainly make errors too, though human intelligence is still impressive. What then is the nature of the "programming" people have that enables them to make decisions outside of a formal system like PM, though the method is not foolproof?

The answer, as Dennett, myself, and other proponents of AI think, is *heuristics*, which are procedures to obtain answers that are not guaranteed to be correct or the absolute best; heuristics are used simply because they are found to be useful. We can imagine, in particular, that natural and social selection have equipped human minds with many and varied heuristics and, in fact, a far better apparatus overall than anyone has managed, so far, to code into any computer program. Indeed, this seems to be what makes us humans smart—certainly it is not some formal system like

PM that has found its way into our brains and that we use for most of our thinking. Instead, a few, exceptional individuals may construct formal systems like PM, using good heuristics in the process. Such a system may then serve as an aid to thinking for them and a few others—but the real core process is elsewhere, even for such thinkers.

It is worth noting too that when actual attempts have been made to endow computers with reasoning powers based on systems like PM, the results have, by and large, fallen far short of human performance. Computerized theorem provers have not replaced human mathematicians, although computers have been found to be useful drudges—doing mountains of calculations and special testing that would otherwise be far out of reach for people. True, a computer, suitably programmed, will always solve a mathematical problem it *can* solve—if it is allowed to run long enough. The problem is that, for the really interesting cases, it usually takes an impractical amount of time, even at the superhuman speeds of electronic computing. On the other hand, computer performance is steadily improving. As one illustration, in 1996 a computer solved an important problem in symbolic logic, the Robbins Problem, adding a major contribution to the previous efforts of human mathematicians.[28] Such performance depends somewhat on advances in hardware, such as faster processors and bigger memories, but better programming is vital too. Better programming often means better heuristics, especially on problems humans find intellectually challenging; computers have been using heuristics for decades now.

Heuristics are vital in many tasks for which we do not know an optimal approach, even tasks involving problem solving using systems like PM. For example, a computer may be asked to decide the truth of some mathematical statement. It can search exhaustively for proofs as well as disproofs. Exhaustive searching, however, is generally very inefficient and impractical. Some streamlining of the search procedure may be possible, but in the end we are confronted, in our searching, with numerous forks in the road, or branches in the search tree, where it is not clear which path is most promising. Here is where heuristics can greatly assist and make a huge difference in how fast an answer is found— if it can be found.

Beyond this issue is one of reasoning outside of a formal, infallible, but limited system. Consider the sentence, "This statement is false." It is true if and only if it is false. Natural language allows such sentences, thus natural language is inconsistent. But somehow we manage with it anyway, and, despite "*P* implies that not-*P* implies *Q*," are not constantly fooled into thinking that day is night, rivers run uphill, or everything is free at the grocery store. In particular we have our senses, and our heuristics tell us to trust them (on occasion) and other such indicators, rather than arguments, however fine-spun. But more than this, we find language a most useful tool, despite its inconsistency. Again, our heuristics tell us how seriously to take sentences such as the above that asserts its own falsity and, more generally, how to make language the useful tool it is, while navigating the pitfalls.

Similarly, if on a presently simpler level, heuristics assist computers in all sorts of decision-making, in fields such as game playing, medical diagnosis, traffic control, and natural language processing. Heuristics enable the computer to break out of the rigid constraints of a formal system—with the price to pay that sometimes they do not give the right or the best answer. Humans, to be sure, have better all-around heuristics, but our heuristics too are subject to the same sort of fallibility, as we well know. The difference between a computer's capabilities and ours, in areas calling for "intelligence," seems to be one of degree and nothing more fundamental. The claim of the anti-AI advocates, that Gödel's results demonstrate a fundamental inadequacy of machine performance relative to human, that machines can never be "intelligent" in the same way people are, is a doubtful one. I think it can be discounted unless more substantial evidence is found.

Only time can decide the matter, of course. But we can expect computers to perform better as they are designed and programmed better, until—it seems reasonable—the human level is equaled and surpassed in more and more areas traditionally associated with intelligence. (Meanwhile, though, humans themselves will have unprecedented opportunities for self-improvement. In time we will be getting smarter too, right along with our machines, so that the threat of being outclassed by artificial devices is not what it may seem.) Much of this better programming will no doubt involve heuristics, with powers not open to rigorous, error-free methods. One is reminded of the old problem of squaring the circle. There the rigorous methods fail too—but not the heuristics—in this case, approximate procedures that give the correct answer within practical limits. In short we have to accept the possibility of inconsistency, of error, of some wrong answers, if we want to do our best—and this applies to automated devices too. Our machines can very likely acquire our mental strengths, but along with these come unavoidable weaknesses.

As long as we are considering Gödel's results, another observation is in order. The incompleteness theorem, looked at in one way, is disappointing because it says that mathematics must forever be inadequate to delineate all truth, or even the somewhat limited truths expressible within a particular, abstract theory. But this is actually a great advantage. The fact that we can never reduce all decision-making to a rule of thumb—a single, effective procedure—means that there is always room for novelty, that even the restricted domain of pure mathematics is inexhaustible in its riches. (A similar conclusion was noted earlier in the case of the halting problem, to which Gödel's results are related.) Science, so much of which is founded on mathematics, is not reaching an end, nor will it ever. Immortality, if we can achieve it, need not be boring, as critics have complained, but should have wonders unlimited for the rightly disposed. It is left to us to become the rightly disposed as we progress beyond our historical limits.

Consequences of the Digital Model

We have now considered digital systems and the evidence that fundamentally, everything as a whole, including all the parts, is such a system. In particular, it means that human intelligence and understanding can be duplicated in a digital device such as a computer, though it might be difficult. It means that even such a "nondigital" quality as emotion must also have a digital basis. It argues that systems such as humans that experience emotions and consciousness do so *only* as a result of the discrete state changes that go on within them, that is, the changes at the quantum level that we know occur in sudden jumps. (Not all these changes, of course, and probably not most, will be significant at the level of consciousness, but the quantum events underlie those events that are significant.) It seems then that what happens between the jumps is not significant—it is only the progression from distinguishable state to distinguishable state that counts. I think this is a strong position and a good reason for favoring strong AI.

It is to the superstructure that we must then look for such features as feeling and consciousness, and not the substrate. As in the details of a photograph, these features are emergent properties depending on the arrangement or interrelationships of finer elements, but not intrinsically on these finer elements. In both cases, there are a great many finer elements. Once again we see the Principle of Large Quantity at work, and also the possibility of duplication of the effect in a different medium, which demonstrates functionalism. Thus a black-and-white photograph could be formed of dark and light pebbles on a large, flat beach; dots of light on a computer screen; or in the more traditional way, with silver particles on film—and still be the same picture. Functionalism is shown in the way that the system's defining properties come from the way the myriad components function as parts of a whole but not on more detailed properties of the individual components. But, extending this property of photography to digital systems, it carries a sweeping implication: two systems that are equivalent in terms of their basic behavior (input, output, and state transitions, or similar digital processing) are equivalent in other ways too.

So once again, a human should be equivalent, in theory, to a

Turing machine patiently writing out a sufficiently detailed description of that human's functioning on a very long piece of tape. In principle we could interact with such an emulated human on a personal level, we noted, which made it plausible that our machine-being would have "real" feelings despite being the product of an emotionless and unconscious automaton. Such an imaginary scenario has value as a thought experiment even if its actual implementation would be impractical.

On the other hand, it is worthwhile to raise the question of what sort of artificial devices might be able to emulate humans in a practical way, so that the emulated persons, for example, could converse with flesh-and-blood humans in something approaching real time. Here, of course, the answer is unknown. It is possible that a quantum device would be required with the extra efficiencies we noted relative to present-day classical computers. Or perhaps a classical device, with such extra features as massively parallel, interconnected processors to act as neurons, would be enough. In any case, it seems inevitable that our artificial devices will equal and exceed the performance of the human brain, whatever properties are required. Like them, the brain is a material object with no mysterious, vital element beyond what our scientific theories can account for. But the possibility of emulating a human in a device (and the human brain, at least, is one such device already capable of such an emulation) brings out a subtle distinction.

The Chinese Room Revisited

In general, the emulator and the emulatee are two different things with different properties, something we noted in connection with the Chinese room. In this thought experiment it is possible that the emulator is unconscious but the emulatee is not or that both are conscious but differently conscious. George, for example, could have been emulating, at the quantum level, a person who understood Chinese. (Probably he would then take far longer even than the 2.7 million years we estimated for one day's work.) You would then, in effect, have two entirely different, conscious persons in the Chinese room, neither of whom was aware of the other's existence, though one of them was actually generating the other's existence. Persons on the outside would be communicating with this other, never George, who in fact might be replaced by a far simpler device.

It should be noted that here we are assuming a set of rules that accomplishes a dual purpose. The first is to converse in Chinese, the main requirement, and the second is to do it in a particular way, by mimicking, at a deep level, the brain functions of someone who understands Chinese and is human in other ways. It does not follow, of course, that every set of rules that could successfully converse would do it in this brain-imitating way, but I do not see any way to rule out the possibility. The extra, brain-mimicking property is telling because it both fits the basic paradigm of the Chinese room experiment, and it explicitly performs in a manner that suggests consciousness, something the Chinese room should not be able to support, according to Searle. Again, one straightforward reason for thinking the emulatee—the Chinese conversationist—is conscious is that it interacts with others in a way that seems conscious. In this case, it could be verified by its own internal workings, which in principle we could monitor and compare with those of humans. I have emphasized the need for suitable internal workings to be as certain as possible that true understanding, as an accompaniment of consciousness, must be present at least in this version of the experiment. But it is also worthwhile to consider the matter from the standpoint of the external behavior alone. Thus we may ask whether a program or system that can converse at a human level and pass the Turing test would, on the strength of that by itself, be conscious and have feelings.

Here the issue is less clear-cut. The ability to converse is no guarantee that any feelings that might be expressed are genuine. A human correspondent, for example, might imitate another human with very different feelings from her own. Still, a human must have some feelings, and I am inclined to think that a similar property would follow in the case of a human imitator, even if "only" a very complex computer program. Such a program, presumably, would have to present a convincing, consistent persona that, under suitable questioning, must confess to certain goals, interests, and so on, to seem fully and normally human. Perhaps the scope of the interaction would need to be broadened slightly to allow the program to initiate its own conversation, again, with the requirement of passing the test by showing characteristics that would seem to be those of some normal human. So over time the programmed persona must become acquainted with a human interrogator—the two would begin to share their lives. Then, in response to "How's it going?" the persona might answer, "Oh, not bad, though my cold seems to have gotten worse. Did you get your car fixed?"

Though natural language has its limits, it is also very powerful and versatile. It seems reasonable that a human conversationist could, in a case like this, demonstrate at least some attributes of sentience in our hypothetical persona, such as goal-seeking, learning, and adaptability—all being required by the premise that a human must be convincingly imitated. So again, I opt for the position that there would definitely be some sentience or consciousness here, and particularly if we regard our persona, in keeping with the Chinese conversationist, as the emulatee.

But in a case such as this, the capacity to interact seems important and should not be passed over lightly. In some way it seems crucial, if we are to regard a system as conscious, that it be able to interface adaptively with other processes and, in our usual experience, at least some other systems we already accept as conscious. This, for example, would seem to firmly rule out movie characters as being conscious, even if we assumed a hyperdetailed movie of the future that showed all happenings right down to the quantum level. Such characters, whose moves and thoughts are all predetermined, could not interact with an outside world, at least as we usually imagine an interaction. (More will be said on this in Chapter 15, however; the situation is not so simple if we assume, as again we must, a scale of processing and level of detail that is far beyond present experience. The Principle of Large Quantity could yield unexpected effects.)

But on this basis we can, it would seem, even more firmly rule out consciousness in a static record, such as a book or reel of movie film, however detailed a description they might provide of a person and that individual's behavior and thoughts. Again, there is no capacity to interact with an outside observer (or with anything else). Such examples do raise a difficulty, however, and I think it points to a deeper insight. According to the tenets of strong AI, a system is conscious that is suitably isomorphic to one we already accept as conscious. It is clear that not every isomorphism is suitable—in a book, for instance, time can be modeled by page number. A very detailed "book" could store, on successive "pages," an accurate description of the brain state of a person at closely spaced points in time. (Each "page," then, would be much larger than the pages we are familiar with, though once again, still finite.) A mapping between the recorded brain states and the corresponding brain events in the real person could be set up (after the fact at least)—an isomorphism between the conscious experience of the individual and the inert, unchanging descriptions in the book. Yet the book would not be conscious nor express consciousness in any active sense. The isomorphism would not be suitable. But if some isomorphisms are not suitable, just which ones are?

Again, the difficulty here seems resolvable if we require that the system in question be capable of meaningful interactions with a conscious outsider. Putting ourselves in the place of such an outsider, we can base our judgments about consciousness on reasonable intuition, which will lead to the conclusions that were reached in the thought experiments we have considered.

Modeling Time

The suitable isomorphisms, it would seem, must model time as we perceive time and not as some other variable such as order of occurrence in a collection of records. Perhaps this will seem inadequate because in the multiverse at large we expect noncommunicating domains, each with conscious beings. The notion of consciousness in our world, involving mutual interactions as a kind of verification, need not apply to these other domains, or more properly, across their boundaries. Our time is, in general, not the same as theirs, even if the two can be put in correspondence. However, this difficulty is countered somewhat, and perhaps decisively, by the UI assumptions, which require a profusion of instantiations of ourselves, in effect linking domains, including alternate universes, that otherwise would be widely separate.

Still, in general, in deciding whether a system should be considered conscious, we ought to consider in what domain it might be conscious, which involves a frame of reference and, once again, how time is modeled. This actually is not so strange from the point of view we have noted, that time does not flow in the multiverse anyway, except as a local effect that is universe-dependent or otherwise rests on a frame of reference. As long as our isomorphic image of a conscious being is some active process somewhere and acceptably conscious from that frame of reference, the attribution of consciousness in a more general sense seems reasonable too. We can say that "consciousness happens here" whatever part of the multiverse "here" may refer to. This still seems to rule out a static record in and of itself being conscious. For we must ask where the record is situated to conclude it is static, and the answer, we should think, is part of the definition of the record. Again, though, the issue is not perfectly clear-cut. No record is truly static—the dance of Brownian motion goes on, and each page of a book, we might say, is actively asserting its contents whether it is being read or not. More relevantly, I think, we may ask in what ways a static (for most purposes) record in fact corresponds to an active process from some other frame of reference in the multiverse. For it follows by Unboundedness that to every static record of a possible historical process there corresponds some isomorphic, active process in the multiverse. Perhaps this would change the way we ought to look at the static record—or perhaps not.

Another significant issue, from our perspective, is immortality. It is here, I think, that the inadequacy of a static record modeling is shown especially clearly, at least from a theoretical standpoint. This is because any physically realizable record must be finite, and immortality must require an infinite amount of subjective time—an infinite record, in effect. It would be impossible to isomorphically model an immortal being with a finite body of information.

Further Thoughts on Consciousness and Strong AI

The subject of consciousness, even limited as we have been to the broader philosophical issues, is a deep one that is certainly not exhausted by the foregoing discussion. Many questions are left unanswered, though we may hope that some useful insights have been offered too. We have, for example, tried to clarify what consciousness is by considering hypothetical cases of isomorphic systems, one of which is already accepted as conscious but that still begs the question of what consciousness is in the first place. Perception in some form is essential, and such other features as goal-seeking, learning, reinforcement through rewards or penalties, and adaptability also seem important—but this is only a starting point. Much has by now been written on the subject of consciousness, and studies are continuing, but again there is much uncertainty, with philosophical issues contributing a significant share. I see no compelling reason, however, to think that consciousness cannot be explained as basically a computational effect, when we allow a sufficiently large and complex system for its expression.

With this in mind, strong AI has an appealing simplicity that lends itself to the sort of ontological position we have been arguing for all along. If persons are fundamentally discrete-state devices, and if equivalent devices can be constructed out of disparate elements, it renders more plausible the principle of Interchangeability. Personal experiences, in particular, are equivalent to behaviors of finite state machines as we noted. Such behaviors in turn form a denumerable set, in one-to-one correspondence with the whole numbers 1, 2, 3,..., and there is an effective, nonterminating procedure to list them all, which would allow us, in principle, to resurrect every person who ever lived. (Otherwise—without strong AI—each personal experience might be unique and unrepeatable, which would make the matter of resurrection more problematic.) Similarly, Unboundedness is favored by strong AI. A finite history—which covers a bounded region of space, time, and energy—can be described as the time-bounded behavior of a finite state machine. The number of possible histories within a fixed time bound is finite too, and each, by appearances, has a nonzero chance of happening. Without some unknown restraining mechanism, then, all must happen over and over in an infinite multiverse.

For all that, I have stopped short of claiming that the validity of strong AI is absolutely essential to the goals of resurrection and immortality. But in certain ways strong AI would be hard to get along without, and, with the scientific support it seems to have, I will assume it as a working hypothesis. Still another argument in its favor is the following.

Earlier we noted how it should be possible to restore a person in conscious form from a digital record such as would be contained in well-preserved remains, irrespective of whether consciousness itself is reducible to digital processing. But this possibility means that what endures about a person, the memories or identity-critical information that is shaped by conscious experience, can be created by a digital process. A quantum-level simulation of the person, say, in a large computer, could tell us the exact positioning of atoms in the remains and thus obtain the same digital record through entirely digital means. (I refer to the process as *simulation,* not emulation to allow for the extra element, consciousness, that for the sake of argument we assume may not have been fully captured.) Any other attribute or element of consciousness, anything that would not be found in the digital simulation, would not endure in the original person and so can arguably be discounted. In short, if there is something nondigital about consciousness, we can have no recollection or awareness of this extra element in our past experience. At best it is something momentarily present that instantly fades. A case might be made that indeed there is some instantaneous presence in a biological brain that could never be captured in a purely digital device. But it is difficult to see what this "presence" would be, or how it would differ from a mystical soul. So, while certainly not conclusive by itself, this is one more suggestive argument for strong AI.

It is worth mentioning that, even though strong AI favors Interchangeability as we have seen, it does not thereby dissolve our reality in total ambiguity. Yes, it is not possible for us to tell that we are not in the sort of universe we seem to be in but only an in an emulation of that universe carried out by a slow-moving Turing machine, which in turn must be in some other universe. But such alternatives can be virtually ruled out.

Consider a universe much like ours, containing a Turing machine that emulates what in fact is our world but in gargantuan slow motion, scratching out symbols on a one-dimensional tape. Our world then is only a toy universe within this larger universe. At the quantum level, an event in our world would require an enormous number of similar events in this real world, each time the Turing machine makes one mark on its tape, let alone models some complex happening. If, on the other hand, we are a primary process and not some strange emulation, there is a one-for-one equivalence between the events in our world and in the emulating world and no complicated, underlying process that must also contribute. Probabilistically, in this case, it seems the primary process must be far more likely than the complicated emulation which, in turn, must be based on a primary process. Both, of course, will be found in the multiverse but again, hardly in equal proportions. The simpler, primary possibility thus takes center stage and we can, with a deft stroke of Ockham's razor, rid ourselves of the complicated alternative. More generally, I think we are justified, for practical purposes, in accepting things as they seem to be, until contrary evidence tells us otherwise.

Let us go on now to consider nanotechnology, which, it can be hoped, will help us in many ways to transform our dreams into reality, and in the not-too-distant future.

CHAPTER 9.

Nanotechnology:
Gateway to the Future

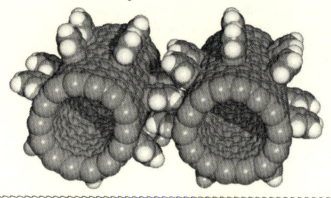

In preceding chapters we have considered how the essential
goals of resurrection and immortality might be achievable
scientifically, subjects we will also return to in later chapters.
But it is also appropriate to look into actual mechanisms for betterment through technology, as we will do in this chapter. Many
details of workable future technologies, of course, remain unknown, and certainly we are in no position to second-guess all
that must come to pass, for much of which we will simply have
to wait and see. Yet there is much under way right now that lends
confidence for the future and makes the issue of immortality a
far from academic one.

Indeed, the principal features of a beginning, immortal lifestyle should be in place very soon on the scale of history, perhaps
well within a century. These include the elimination of aging and
now-terminal diseases and options to develop ourselves indefinitely beyond the human level. One of the main reasons for such
an optimistic conclusion is the continuing progress in nanotechnology—the controlled manipulation of matter at the atomic and
molecular levels. Nanotechnology, if it lives up to the promise it
seems to hold, will remake our world and completely transform
life as we know it. It has relevance, moreover, to more esoteric
issues considered in this book, such as resurrections. It should

enable us, for example, to design and manufacture living persons with chosen personality characteristics, including memories.

Nanotechnology—a term popularized by Eric Drexler in his 1986 book, *Engines of Creation*—is nothing new. Long before humans existed it was carried out on an impressive if still limited scale by biological organisms, an enterprise that is still ongoing and vigorous. Everything, from bacteria to sequoias, whales to humankind, uses what amounts to nanotechnology for growth, reproduction, and basic metabolism. (In this case it was not arrived at artificially, that is, by a thinking process, but in other ways fully qualifies as technology.) Marvelous though biological nanotechnology is, the underlying principles are well understood, even if many details still elude us. Nothing more is involved than chemistry, which firmly rests on quantum physics.

As one example of such technology, there are the tiny molecular machines known as enzymes. Enzymes basically are catalysts—they participate in chemical reactions but are not consumed in the process. Instead, their function is to greatly speed up reaction rates. In this way processes occur that otherwise, for practical purposes, would not happen at all. Enzymes are used in cells and by an organism as a whole for operations that are necessary to life. Pepsin, for example, is one of a family of enzymes in the stomach that makes digestion of food possible. Each pepsin molecule, one tiny machine or "nanite," speeds the breakdown of proteins into their constituents—amino acids in this case—for further processing by the body to obtain energy. More generally, enzymes are used throughout the body—within a cell, for instance—to carry out the myriad operations involved in metabolism, growth, and repair. Not only do they speed reaction rates but they can operate in elaborate, cooperating chains to allow a specific sequence of reactions to proceed, excluding other processes that are not catalyzed.[1]

A biological organism supports many enzyme systems, each a family of molecules devoted to a particular reaction sequence. Such systems may be employed by other molecular devices within the organism. An example of such a device is the ribosome, a molecular-scale constructor that has a family of enzymes in its "toolkit." Ribosomes play a crucial role in building tissues of all kinds from the molecular level up from instructions coded in DNA, and, more generally, in manufacturing proteins that have many

functions in living systems. (Even enzymes themselves are proteins, which in turn are manufactured by ribosomes.[2]) Overall,
enzyme systems accomplish the near-miraculous in the complex
balancing act that an organism's body must carry out to remain
functional throughout its life.

Progress in Nanotechnology

Nanotechnology, though not called such, was anticipated in a
1959 lecture, "There's plenty of room at the bottom," by American physicist Richard Feynman: "The principles of physics, as
far as I can see, do not speak against the possibility of maneuver-
ing things atom by atom. It is not an attempt to violate any laws;
it is something, in principle, that can be done; but in practice, it
has not been done because we are too big."[3] Today we are still
bigger than we would like, but progress has been made, and no
inconsistencies with physics have been shown. Although still in
its infancy, man-made nanotechnology has already achieved startling results, if still less spectacular than the biological variety.
Actually, some of the most remarkable achievements have been
hybrids of the two. Consider some highlights.

In 1997 the successful cloning of a sheep named Dolly was
announced, and the world took notice. The wooly creature looked
perfectly ordinary—but was the genetic twin (in most respects)
of an older, adult animal, something previously unknown in mammals. The feat was difficult, and doubts were raised as to whether
it really occurred as reported.[4] But other adult mammal clonings
soon followed, and the feasibility of the approach was demonstrated.[5] (An easier goal, cloning of mammals from fetal cells,
had been accomplished earlier and presently is more common.)
The techniques—implanting genetic material in cells and inducing the cells to develop into adult organisms—most definitely
were a successful use of technology at the molecular scale. Typically a cell from an organism to be cloned is embedded in another cell whose own nucleus has been removed. The new, hybrid cell then divides repeatedly, first becoming a fetus, which is
then implanted in the womb of a suitable host or surrogate mother.
In time the developing infant creature is born and matures into a
genetic twin or clone of the original organism. Creation of a hu-

man embryo from an adult cell using similar methods was announced in 1998, though no effort at implantation was made.[6]

Other, perhaps even more promising, developments involved inducing not whole organisms to grow but individual tissues and body parts. Tissue engineering includes making replacement organs, parts of organs, skin, or other body structures by allowing cells to develop in culture, as well as implanting cells to strengthen existing structure through proliferation. The field is still in the experimental stages, but indications are that clinical applications could soon be forthcoming. A major advance was the successful creation of many different human tissue types from embryonic stem cells, announced in 1998;[7] there are other ways too of getting different tissue types. This raised exciting possibilities of new medical strategies for healing and repair throughout the body, including the brain. Indeed, manufactured neurons have been implanted as a possible treatment of strokes and reportedly yielded improvements in speech, feeling, and motor control.[8] Another important milestone, the creation of implantable mammalian organs (canine urinary bladders), was reported in 1999. In a series of experiments, a few cells from donor organs were "seeded" into plastic, preformed molds. The cells then proliferated and filled out the molds, resulting in replacement organs with the desired structure and function.[9]

Also related to cloning, and again with great potential for benefit, is genetic engineering. One example is gene therapy, which involves modifying tissues at the genetic level to counteract problems. The first clinical use of gene therapy began in 1990. A child with a weak immune system caused by a deficiency of the enzyme ADA was helped by an infusion of genetically altered T-cells, which increased the level of the enzyme. Another, and very promising application is "pharming": organisms are modified genetically to produce some needed substance in quantity, say an otherwise scarce pharmaceutical. In 1978, for example, a single dose of highly impure interferon, an infection fighting agent produced in small quantities in the body, cost $50,000. But in 1980 Swiss researchers modified the genes of bacteria to produce human interferon. Within a few years, proliferating colonies of the transgenic bacteria brought the per-dose price of *pure* interferon down to $1.[10] Other transgenic organisms, including cattle, look promising as candidates for producing valuable medicines in quantity through pharming.[11] Still another advance in genetic engineering may obviate the need for bypass surgery. A gene inserted into heart cells prompts them to manufacture a protein that promotes the sprouting of new blood vessels.[12] In another application, a virus is rendered harmless and genetically modified to produce a muscle growth factor. When injected into muscle tissue, the virus can then reverse the loss of strength and mass that normally accompanies aging.[13] Genetic modification has also increased the intelligence of mice.[14]

The dangers of tinkering with our biology must not be minimized, however. One well-publicized death, that of eighteen-year-old Jesse Gelsinger in 1999, resulted from a "low-risk" gene therapy experiment that might have led to a cure for his rare, inherited metabolic ailment. It goes without saying that attempts to improve our lot through unperfected means carry an element of risk. We must be grateful to those willing to accept such risks, sometimes even at the cost of their lives, so that such means can be made effective and safe. This must not blind us to the dangers, nor induce a policy of recklessness. In Gelsinger's case there was special concern since he was not seriously ill at the start of his experimental procedure. Others, however, have undergone such procedures when more conventional approaches have failed and thus had less to lose. In general the potential for benefit seems great enough to offset the risk—if experimental subjects are suitably screened and procedures are carefully managed.[15]

Related to all genetics-based advances are efforts to determine the structure and functioning of the human genome. Here there has been substantial progress though much remains to be done, as is so often true when practical benefits are sought from scientific advances. In 2000 two rival groups announced the nearly complete mapping of the human genome consisting of approximately three billion chemical bases or "base-pairs" that make up human DNA.[16] The task remains of identifying the many thousands of important subunits of the genome, or genes, and determining their function—no doubt it will prove more difficult to complete.

Genes are made of thousands of chemical bases each and carry information for making all the proteins, including enzymes and hormones, that are needed by an organism. The information is used by the ribosomes in their work of protein construction. The proteins in turn operate at the molecular level to impart basic characteristics to the organism, such as its form and size, how its food is metabolized, its ability to resist infection, and much of its behavior. The precise sequence of chemical bases is very important in the overall effect that a gene will have. Mapping the human genome should thus provide insight into the way specific genes work and greatly aid our efforts to treat many disorders.[17] Indeed, benefits are already starting to flow. As one example, the gene for producing the enzyme telomerase was identified using data obtained in the mapping effort.[18] Telomerase in turn has the ability to reverse some of the effects of aging in cells at the molecular level, a topic we will return to in Chapter 17.

What may be a more significant breakthrough in aging research, announced in 1999, involves the use of DNA chips, or microarrays. These are small glass slides containing thousands of genes (which are fragments of DNA) in a regular array or pattern. The microarrays are exposed to messenger RNA, or mRNA, a molecular type that imprints or "remembers" the base-pair patterns of DNA. The fragments of mRNA then attach themselves wherever they can find a match. Genes "express" themselves by producing match-seeking mRNA. As an organism ages there are variations in gene expression resulting in variations of mRNA that show up when this new mRNA is matched with an older genetic sample from the same organism. In this way, then, we obtain a sensitive indicator of molecular changes in the organism with aging—more about this too in Chapter 17.[19]

In 1997 a functioning nanite, a biosensor "with applications ranging from disease diagnosis to environmental monitoring" was announced by a group in Australia. Bruce Cornell, head of the team that developed the device, explained: "This biosensor is a unique blend of the ability of biology to identify individual types of molecule in complex mixtures, with the speed, convenience and low cost of microelectronics." The main component was a tiny electrical switch, 1.5 nm across, that acted as an ion channel. The sensor was inserted into a simple, hand-held unit that held a sample of material for analysis and also electronically interpreted the results. So sensitive was the system that it could measure the rise in sugar content if a single cube of sugar was thrown into Australia's famous Sydney Harbor. More practically, it should be able to detect a range of substances such as drugs, hormones, viruses, and pesticides and also identify gene sequences. Moreover, its results are gotten quickly; diagnoses of diseases that previously needed days were expected to take only minutes, using a small sample of saliva or blood.[20]

One of the interesting products of molecular research is the "buckyball," a hollow, round structure made of sixty linked carbon atoms that form a tiny, geodesic cage. (The name honors engineer R. Buckminster Fuller who pioneered this design for architectural domes; another term for this sort of compound is fullerene.) Buckyballs, it turns out, have medical uses. The little cages can mop up damaging molecules called free radicals that cause nerve damage after stroke or trauma. To make them effective, however, the normally insoluble hollow spheres must be made to dissolve in water, a feat that has been accomplished by adding carboxylic acid groups to their round surfaces. One study found that better results were obtained if acid groups were attached on one hemisphere of the buckyball rather than distributed along the equator. Sticking them on one side in this way appears to make the buckyballs able to slip through cell membranes more easily. This, then, shows one way that tools with specific and potentially valuable functions are now being crafted at the molecular level, and, more generally, how the puzzles of molecular engineering are gradually being worked out.[21]

Another significant research area is artificial enzymes, in which some modest progress has been reported. One series of experiments shows how catalytic activity can be induced in an otherwise noncatalytic protein by suitable incorporation of molecular groups into its structure.[22]

Other, molecular-scale devices are being developed with a view toward more general-purpose construction and modification of materials. In one such line of research, tiny "trains" made of segments of microtubules—protein filaments that crisscross the insides of nerve cells—speed along on matching Teflon tracks. "We are learning how to engineer a monorail on a nanoscale," says researcher Viola Vogel. "We want a molecular shuttle that moves from point A to point B and which can be loaded and unloaded."[23]

Nanotechnology is also showing promise in helping to solve intellectual problems that are hard for humans. A general-purpose molecular computer has been developed that uses fragments of DNA to explore computational paths in massively parallel fashion. In this way, with refinements, problems in artificial intelligence that involve lengthy searches might be handled much faster than is feasible today.[24]

Results outside the biological field are also encouraging. Images of surfaces are routinely obtained showing individual atoms standing in neat rows like billiard balls, and there is a growing array of techniques for forming and modifying structures at the atomic level. We can now, to paraphrase Feynman, "maneuver things atom by atom," in fully controllable ways. Atoms can be positioned individually into precise patterns or excavated a few layers at a time. In 1990 IBM researchers achieved an early success at this by spelling out the company's initials in 35 xenon atoms on a nickel substrate using a scanning tunneling microscope (see below) as the positioning tool.[25] It is also possible to alter chemical bonds molecule by molecule.[26] Giant, dendritic molecules have been created to precise specifications, and researchers have studded their surfaces "with chemical units that could do specific jobs, including analytic and medical tasks."[27] "By controlling precisely the structure and composition of layers of materials only an atom or two thick, scientists are proving they can program the electronic characteristics they want into a compound."[28]

A basic research tool in this kind of work is the scanning probe microscope, or SPM. An SPM uses a probe whose tip is one or only a few atoms across. In the scanning tunneling microscope, or STM, which was the first form of SPM developed, the probe is made of a durable, electrically conducting material, such as tungsten. The probe tip is moved close to another conducting material. The electrical resistance across the gap from probe to target suddenly starts to diminish when the tip is very close. This provides a sensitive indicator of the exact contours of the target's surface and also a way of nudging atoms from one position to another. In another form of SPM, the atomic force microscope, or AFM, the probes do not require an electrically conducting target either for imaging or nudging.[29]

Nanotubes—tiny, long, thin pipes of carbon atoms—are now finding use as SPM probes.[30] The possibility is opened of greater precision and reproducibility of properties than was feasible with older probe tip technologies. The new probes themselves are springier and more durable, and, by imparting a twist (changing the wrapping angle) of the carbon atoms, the tubes can be fabricated as good conductors or, alternately, as semiconductors that block low voltages.[31] Indeed, nanotubes, with their varied electrical properties and overall strength and durability, may see many future uses both as structural components and in computational devices.[32]

Other technology besides SPMs shows promise in certain small-scale applications. There are, for example, the optical tweezers, in which particles as tiny as a single molecule are grasped and held by finely focused laser beams. The optical tweezers have been further refined into an optical spanner that can impart spin to a particle or stop and reverse its spin. Such a device could be useful in building tiny machinery or powering it.[33]

Recently there have been other interesting successes. A transistor has been built out of a single molecule—a nanotube in fact. An abacus has been made, with buckyballs—single molecules—as the sliding beads, and an STM tip as the moving "finger." A rotating molecule has been fabricated, a propeller-shaped nanowheel that spins on a tiny, molecular bearing.[34] Quantum sculpting—reshaping an atom's wave function using laser pulses—can now be used to prepare atoms in desired states and appears to have applications ranging from quantum computing to controlling chemical reactions at the atomic scale.[35] Such accomplishments, of course, do not lead to the inevitable conclusion that all we would like to be accomplished will be—in particular, the unbelievably delicate and numerous operations that might be necessary for resuscitation of a long- but well-preserved human. Nanotechnology is not a guaranteed panacea, and we are not in a position to assess what its strengths or limits will prove to be, except in very broad outlines. But despite the seeming confusion of sighting down the time tunnel and trying to second-guess the future, there is solid ground for optimism, even if a large part of it must still come from indirect sources.

One such source of optimism is computer science, which has interesting things to say about what is possible and impossible under a wide variety of conditions, as we saw in the last chapter. Indeed, the computer programmer is forced to be a futurologist since he is constantly trying to do what has not been done before—writing new software—and, incidentally, succeeding. His world is a microcosmic analogue of the larger world that we inhabit. The laws of physics are set by the environment or operating system he works under. Though restrictive, in fact it has great generality and power because the behavior of materials under the real laws of physics, as far as we understand them, can be modeled. Considerations that apply to computation, including what is possible and not possible, thus extend naturally to the world at large.

In the last chapter we noted the existence of general-purpose computing devices, which take varied forms. These in turn can be instructed to mimic the behavior of any of a large class of more specialized devices and thus can perform a wide variety of tasks. The problem of designing instructions for such a device is not a formidable one. In the world we inhabit, the computer is a well-known general-purpose device that can direct machines to perform physical operations as well as process information, or "think," or turn descriptions of things into other descriptions. But, though computers are described as "general purpose," they are not sufficiently general for all we would like to do, especially at the nanoscale.

One of the devices nanotechnologists forecast is the "assembler," something that would be able to make any chemically stable structure out of its constituent atoms. This would be very much like the universal computer-constructor, a well-known theoretical possibility in cellular spaces,[36] though it would also have to apply in the real world at a small enough scale that quantum effects would be important. A closely related device, the "disassembler," would be able to unstack any structure into units of a small number of atoms each, recording the structural information and, if desired, storing and keeping track of the pieces.

Such devices, for all their marvelous abilities, would be of molecular dimensions, which does not seem a prohibitive constraint. There is enough complexity in the possible chemical arrangements of a few hundred atoms of carbon, hydrogen, and oxygen, to easily describe a universal Turing machine, for instance. The quantum level might pose additional problems, though it seems likely that unhurried construction or deconstruction would not be unduly affected—a topic we will return to shortly. Our devices should also be self-replicating (or be churned out in large numbers by automated factories capable of geometric growth in productive capacity). Though one assembler would be slow, an army of many trillions of them, working in concert, could accomplish a great deal in a short time.

Difficulties and Objections

Nanotechnologists are sometimes criticized for the way they think processes would happen at the tiny dimensions they imagine. Thus Simson Garfinkel warned, in a 1990 *Whole Earth Review* article: "The problem with these people's ideas is that they envision working with atoms the same way a model-maker might work with wooden sticks and stryofoam balls, breaking a bond here, moving an atom to the other side, and forming a new bond....But atoms don't work that way."[37] Atoms and molecules are not rigid, inert mechanical components, but they vibrate and stick to one another. Thus a tiny robot arm might find it much easier to pick up an atom than to put it back down again in a desired location. Another problem would be that of "seeing" or otherwise sensing which atoms or molecular fragments to grab and where to put them. Visible light gives much too poor a resolution at these distances, and x-rays would be too hard to produce and focus.

To these objections Eric Drexler replies in the same issue: "Everything vibrates, everything bends, and machines work regardless; the differences here are more quantitative than qualitative. On a very small scale, the vibrations associated with heat itself become of tremendous importance, and are a crucial issue in nanomachine design and operation." (More will be said shortly about this vibration problem.) As for the difficulty with "seeing," Drexler argues that instead tomorrow's molecular-scale robots would act more like today's industrial, macroscopic varieties, picking up "pre-positioned, pre-oriented parts off something like a conveyor belt, rather than rummaging around in a bin."

As he envisions it, assemblers will not do all the work directly but will create more special-purpose machines to handle the details. As for their complexity, it will be on the order of industrial robots and small-size computers of today, "because they will contain similar numbers of parts performing similar functions." After more discussion Drexler concludes, "I have yet to encounter a major technical criticism of the core concepts of nanotechnology that does not evaporate once it is examined." Garfinkel himself qualifies his skepticism, denying absolute unbelief but insisting that nanotechnology is not yet an "engineering discipline."

And certainly there are real difficulties that need to be addressed in any fair assessment of nanotechnology and its prospects. Just as with the halting problem, there are impossibilities that might at first seem feasible in principle. One of these, and long a topic of theoretical interest, is Maxwell's Demon, named after British physicist James Clerk Maxwell, who proposed it in 1871.[38]

Maxwell's Demon is a hypothetical nanodevice that could give us perpetual motion. It sits inside an observation booth watching a nanotube of suitable bore that connects two chambers filled with gas. With its nanoeyes it can observe the gas molecules flying back and forth at random in the tube. Each individual molecule, if not restrained, will eventually, through its random motions, travel through the tube from one chamber to the other, and back again, over and over. On average there is an equal swarming of molecules everywhere in the two chambers: to our macroscopic perceptions, the gas in both chambers is at an equal temperature and pressure. However, the Demon controls a valve that blocks the tube whenever desired, so that a molecule that would otherwise escape from one chamber to the other bounces back to where it came from. Seemingly, this could be done with very little expenditure of energy, so we could either concentrate a higher proportion of molecules in one chamber than the other, creating a pressure difference, or concentrate the faster molecules creating a temperature difference, or both.

In this way it would be possible to derive useful work out of the system, the amount depending on the surrounding temperature and not on the expenditure of effort required to observe the molecules and open or close the valve. Doing this repeatedly, more energy might be derived from the system than was needed by the Demon to operate the system. This would lead to perpetual motion, something forbidden by physics. Maxwell's Demon, then, is likely to remain out of reach, and along with it many other devices that might seem feasible through nanotechnology.

Some of the possible limitations are of more direct concern. Consider again the SPMs. They have demonstrated their worth and strengthened the case for nanotechnology, but much more will be needed from devices like these or something else for all the anticipated benefits. Existing SPMs are much too large to be operable on the massively parallel scale that would be necessary for atomically reshaping matter over realistic time-scales. They must be made smaller. Progress is being made; for example, an STM about a cubic millimeter in volume has been constructed,[39] and over 100 tiny SPM probe tips have been packed on a chip of a few square millimeters.[40] But clearly much additional progress in scanning probe or other technology, especially with miniaturization, will be necessary to achieve the desired control over matter at the nanoscale. It will be challenging. Problems develop when devices are made very small; vibrations increase, for instance. The smaller the device, the larger the jiggle, and at too small a scale things are hopelessly chaotic—unless, perhaps, you really know what you are doing.

In general, very small objects are not like the rock-steady things of everyday experience, but they shiver, shake, and have indefinable locations. The devices we must use to manipulate such matter are themselves composed of the same jiggling, wayward stuff. Stacking atoms is not the same as stacking bricks; atoms could just as well bond to the scanning probe tip as to each other. (This problem has been helped by electrification of the probe tip, but major difficulties remain.) A skeptic of nanotechnology, David E. H. Jones, writing in *Nature*[41], predicted that STMs will be miniaturizable to the micrometer range but not to the nanometer scale, a thousand times smaller, where individual atoms might be conveniently rearranged into arbitrary patterns by vast armies of the tiny devices. The possibility is raised, then, that the problems of nanoassembly may be harder than we would like to think, or, of course, unsolvable—though I will argue shortly against the latter. But certainly nature has not created a general purpose assembler.

Instead there is a large bag of tricks to accomplish the various feats we can observe in the natural world, such as those connected with life. These varied mechanisms clearly are tracking the boundary between the possible and the impossible, but always under certain constraints. A species must compete against others. The simplest mechanisms that are adequate for the basic requirements of survival and reproduction tend to be selected over others.

Jones considers termites as an example. Termites build nests but not telescopes. A termite is a relatively simple organism with no detailed blueprint or "knowledge" as we usually understand it, but definite behavior preferences nonetheless. Individually, a termite could not build a nest, but the collective behavior of a colony results in a huge and very serviceable habitat, albeit a crude and variable structure by our architectural norms. Termites have evolved with the minimum equipment needed for this and other requirements of their existence, both in terms of body structure and behavior; anything more would likely be selected against. Jones asks, "Could termites be modified by genetic engineering to assemble, not crude variable nests but...identical working astronomical telescopes?" His answer: "No: the enormous algorithm required would simply overwhelm them."

Here I take issue with this sweeping dismissal, despite the evolutionary arguments offered in support. Termites made to make telescopes very likely could not compete against their cousins that only focused on survival and propagation. This does not mean that some gigantic and unworkable mechanism would be needed by the telescope makers, just that the evolutionary pathways to a viable telescope factory are sufficiently uphill, relative to biological interests, that natural selection has never explored them.

The telescope makers would have to be engineered by ourselves, bypassing natural selection, and probably would also need protection from ecological competitors. We have been doing much the same with our domesticated species for millennia already— it is no major issue. I will even venture that something like termites—small and numerous, probably fully artificial creatures and possibly much smaller than termites—will one day be making telescopes and many other things that now require human labor. More generally, the failure of nature to produce a given device must not be taken as proof of its impossibility. The constraints of evolutionary biology have forbidden many perfectly feasible innovations, even simple ones, such as the wheel, which is not found on the macroscopic scale except through human ingenuity (though we do see it in such microscopic structures as the bacterium's rotary whip or flagellum[42]).

What about the general purpose assembler then? To Jones, "Nanotechnological assemblers look suspiciously like Maxwell's Demons." But there is a difference. Maxwell's Demon must interact rapidly but lightly with its environment, sensing the gas molecules, determining their position and velocity, then making a decision about closing the valve or keeping it open. All this must be done fast enough, and noninvasively enough, to achieve the desired control. Slow down the Demon and it loses this control, which is also precluded if too much energy is required to obtain the necessary data, for the surrounding system would be disrupted. But no such constraints would be essential simply to stack a stable structure of atoms.

More time could be spent as necessary, and nondisruptive amounts of focused energy, sufficient to reposition individual atoms but not otherwise materially alter the object, could be used. With more time would come better control; the vibration problem in particular could be better addressed. The repositioning could also, I think, be done without requiring exotic processes such as full-blooded quantum computation in the positioning apparatus itself, though it is possible that quantum computing will play a role in determining what structures to build in the first place. Or maybe such computation—impossible now in the absence of a practical quantum computer—will not be that difficult but even be the most practical way to proceed at the nanoscale. At any rate, there is no denying for now that formidable problems must be solved.

During assembly, for example, the object might be built up atom by atom, possibly as several or many components that eventually would be brought together. Each of these separate components must then be stable throughout the assembly process or, at any rate, long enough to be fitted in. More generally, in making any feasible object there are likely to be numerous intermediate stages or components that also must be feasible.

Another problem relates to the size and form that nanodevices must take to be effective at the tasks they would have to perform. For many such tasks it might be convenient to have swarms of tiny, intelligently programmed devices capable of independent but coordinated action. Devices like this in the body, for example, might repair damaged cells and fight disease better than existing mechanisms do. In a very limited way we have already made small mobile nanites, as in the case of artificial enzymes and the beginning stages of a molecular shuttle, but here again there is a long way to go and corresponding skepticism that it will be possible. There are many other problems connected with how molecular devices or nanites would keep track of what they were doing, obtain the necessary materials, and so on. But solving them would be helped by the absence of a narrow time constraint.

More generally, nanotechnology is found to be within the capabilities of known physics, and some of the skepticism is showing signs of weakening. One interesting example involved the well-known periodical *Scientific American*, which published an article critical of nanotechnology in 1996.[43] A storm of protest and counterargument followed from the community of nanotechnologists, and a lively debate was carried over the Internet. The upshot was that *Scientific American* reversed its stance, proclaiming in a 1997 advertising brochure: "Nanotechnology promises to change our lives for good. Machines and robots built atom by atom—and measuring no more than a micron across—will fight cancer cell by cell or store terabytes of data on space as small as the head of a pin."

Expectations, Evidence, and Projections

What can we expect from nanotechnology—besides terabytes dancing on heads of pins and cancer contested cell by cell? I will echo the bold prediction of other advocates that, at minimum, we can expect to do operations of a general-purpose character at the atomic level, reshaping matter and building stable structures to atomic precision. So long as certain, rapid interactions are not required, the prospects look good. From this it should not be assumed that positioning many trillions of atoms will take eons— vast swarms of nanites could work in parallel. Such devices could be mass-produced once some basic capabilities were in place.

What tangible evidence is there that these capabilities will be developed, and on a time scale of only decades? Direct evidence that such advances are at least possible is seen, we noted, in biological organisms and the things they do. Dirt, water, and air can be transformed into ripe strawberries by rearranging atoms—it happens all the time. For that matter, human beings are also made in the same sort of way, by rearranging atoms from the environment in a complex interplay of processes involving more than one species (other humans as well as organisms that supply nourishment, for instance). Enzymes and ribosomes, we have seen, are molecular machines—natural nanites—that operate in living bodies to help bring about the numerous processes necessary for life. We will need to develop something like enzymes that are tailored to specific tasks we would like performed in a suitable environment. Further direct evidence that we can do this comes from the successes to date in the efforts to develop nanotechnology. Again there is uncertainty, and we cannot accept the evidence as conclusive but are justified, I think, in viewing it optimistically.

It is more difficult to address the question of when we might have mature nanotechnology—to a certain extent we will not know until we get there. There is some interesting indirect evidence, however, that we will get there in a matter of decades at most and not centuries or longer. This comes from such fields as computer hardware and micromachining, where trend lines show a progressive reduction in the scale of manufactured components, suggesting the atomic level may be reached relatively soon, though of course there is no guarantee.[44]

But as one example, for decades computer memories have been doubling their density every two years. This is a form of what is known as Moore's Law, after Gordon E. Moore, one of the founders of Intel Corporation, who proposed a version of it in 1965.[45] Currently, memory chips for use in a desktop computer store upwards of 100 million or 10^8 bits per square centimeter, spread over a thin layer of material. At the present doubling rate, in fifty years the total will climb to more than 10^{15}, well within the molecular scale. With the reduction in memory size, there are corresponding advances in other areas such as computing speed. As it turns out, there are numerous developmental trends that exhibit this same exponential character and thus lead to comparable or even somewhat more optimistic predictions.

Well before then, it is true, the silicon technology in present use will reach its limits, but there are other technologies under development that show some promise as replacements, for example, optical and quantum devices. Even sooner, methods of fabricating silicon based around photolithography will need refinement; such refinements are in the works.[46] Another interesting development is the field programmable gate array, or FPGA. It offers the possibility of rapid, self-reconfiguring of computer hardware with the prospect of greatly speeding up adaptive processes and yielding more brainlike behavior than is now feasible.[47]

In general, up to now older technologies have periodically been replaced by newer ones, as when vacuum tubes were replaced by transistors, which in turn were replaced by integrated circuits on silicon chips. The trend may not continue for many more decades, but it does not seem threatened yet.

One indicator of possible obstacles, and a counterweight to Moore's Law, is Rock's Law, which says that the cost of capital equipment to build semiconductors will double every four years. (Venture capitalist Arthur Rock cofounded Intel Corporation in 1968 and arrived at his "law" in response to that of his colleague, Gordon Moore.) Like Moore's Law, this more negative forecast is holding up well so far. The cost of a computer chip factory is now in the neighborhood of $1 billion and could throw up a roadblock before Moore's Law can push miniaturization to the molecular scale.

More generally, we are reminded that everything has a cost. Very likely this will remain true even with the best that future technology can offer. I expect, however, that costs will be rather less than we might think, even taking into account the cost-cutting that has already occurred in certain products and services (in the computer field, for instance). This is because the "workers"—automated devices—will not need the amenities humans now demand, including high pay, time off, retirement plans, and eight-hour days, but should nevertheless, in their own, appropriate ways, function at the present-day human level and beyond. They thus will be highly competent and "motivated" to do what is demanded of them, including their own maintenance and repair.[48] (Again, though, I do not see ourselves being superseded or outclassed by such artificial minions since we in turn will advance to greater levels using the knowledge and technology that become available.)

At least one other possible means of advancing nanotechnology is the quantum computer, which is to use the quantum states of small components such as atoms, photons, or atomic nuclei to store and process information. This new computer, as we have noted, would have unique and impressive properties of its own, able to obtain results equivalent to many conventional machines running in parallel. It thus might be able to carry out exhaustive searches efficiently, providing a shortcut to high-order machine intelligence. It might also be operable in reverse, affecting its environment rather than passively doing computations, which could provide one pathway to a nanotechnological assembler.[49]

At present only very limited working models of quantum computers exist, which, despite interesting performance, are no serious competition to their more conventional cousins. Progress is being made, however, and far more capable devices using many quantum bits or "qubits" seem increasingly feasible.[50] At minimum this must rank alongside other major developments in computing, which overall are improving our understanding as well as our technology. It also suggests another important possibility, that processing at the atomic level may well use quantum effects that are presently ill-understood. Because of this lack of understanding, present work in nanotechnology has emphasized the more mechanical aspects of interactions at the atomic scale, but there could be great additional advantages when we can exploit the full power of quantum interactions.

Computation, with its great potential and reassuring progress, will surely be important for nanotechnology, but it is not the whole story. There is also construction, an art that still seems very primitive, despite the successes with positioning atoms and other operations at the atomic scale. Natural biology is far ahead of us here, but its very success is reason to think that our efforts too will succeed.

Indeed, perhaps the closest existing approach to a workable system of coordinated, nanoscale robots or nanobots is found in the body. Ribosomes, for example, can be instructed or programmed to make a large variety of different proteins, though they are hardly general-purpose robots. But nanobots appear to require no new physics nor do they violate any established physics. Known limitations, such as those connected with Maxwell's Demon, should not pose insurmountable obstacles. If one is found, however, there is still much we can do with special-purpose nanites and other devices able to operate at the atomic level. Our development will be aided by technologies that have demonstrated their usefulness. Again, computing will surely be prominent. Computers will help us design our engines of construction (to borrow a term from *Engines of Creation*) and help make many things, including better computers.[51]

Here we should note yet another sign that assemblers will be feasible, and possibly a very telling one—a theoretical finding that relates to the simulation of one quantum system by another. David Deutsch in 1985 showed that a universal quantum computer is possible, though not necessarily practical. Such a device could be programmed to duplicate any other quantum computation efficiently—within a polynomial time bound, that is. But, oddly, it still might take an impractical time to program, that is, to instruct the computer to run the computation in the first place. This difficulty was overcome in 1996 by another theorist, Seth Lloyd, who established the possibility of a universal quantum simulator, able to duplicate efficiently, in equivalent form, any quantum process whatever that meets very general restrictions. (Mainly, the process must take finite time, space, and energy to complete. Duplicating such a process in equivalent form at the quantum level would, for many purposes, amount to emulating it.) In the case of the quantum computer, this meant that the machine could be both programmed and run efficiently—at least according to a mathematical notion of efficiency.

This still leaves the unanswered question of whether a universal quantum simulator or computer will really be practical. It is clear, on the other hand, that for a nanotechnological assembler, the ability to do universal quantum simulation would not be a logical requirement—all we are asking for is the ability to stack atoms in prespecified patterns. By analogy, a present-day word processor is a "literary assembler"—able to print out any page of text you tell it, including Shakespeare, but is not able to write like Shakespeare. Despite the remaining uncertainties, we see additional ground for optimism. The extra firepower provided, in theory, by the universal quantum simulator is a further indication that the assembler (and by a similar argument, that other important component, the disassembler) can be built. Overall the prospects seem good for eventually attaining minute control, with great potential for benefit.[52]

Benefits from Nanotechnology

It is hard to imagine all the benefits that might follow from a mature nanotechnology, but some basic features are clear. We are talking about rearranging atoms, according to generally accepted physics of today, and other such interactions at the level of particles. Barring the discovery of new physical laws, this extends to all the possible marvels that the future may hold in store. (And new physical laws are certainly not ruled out, but to keep our predicting within plausible limits we do not consider them.) We can then contemplate some of these possible marvels, starting with one of the more prosaic.

Carbon is one of the commoner constituents on Earth, being abundant enough that, in view of its unique chemical properties, it is able to form the basis of life as we know it. Carbon exists in several rather different forms. There is the shiny black, soft substance known as graphite, for example, and the much rarer, hard, transparent mineral diamond. Both are made of the same kind of atom—the difference is in how the atoms are arranged.

In graphite the atoms are arranged into flat sheets that are then stacked to form larger chunks. Within a single sheet of graphite the atoms are closely packed and form a repeating, hexagonal pattern. The same sort of pattern can be produced by arranging marbles or coins of the same size on a flat surface. Spread a handful of pennies out on a table, packing them together, one layer deep, as closely as possible. Each interior penny will have six neighbors touching—this is the repeating, hexagonal pattern, which also occurs naturally in the cells of a honeycomb and the facets of an insect's compound eye. A large chunk of graphite in turn consists, generally, of a jumble of smaller chunks each of which has the thin sheets stacked in layers. Carbon atoms within a sheet are bonded tightly together, but between the sheets the bonding is much looser, and this determines the properties we observe. Thus graphite is very hard to melt or vaporize—this would require dislocating atoms within the sheets—but very easy to scratch, which only requires separations or slippage of sheets from each other. Other properties of graphite, such as its greasy-black appearance, slippery feel, and electrical conductivity, are also explained by the properties of the carbon atoms that make it up and the way the atoms are bound and arranged.

In diamond there are the same atoms of carbon but in a completely different arrangement. Each atom is bonded to four others as if it were located in the center of a regular tetrahedron (a three-sided pyramid with the four faces—the three sides and the base—all equilateral triangles), with each bond perpendicular to one of four faces. This is repeated throughout the structure, which thus extends in three dimensions like a sturdy jungle gym. Though the same atoms are involved, diamond is quite different from graphite. Gone are the sheets that slip and separate so easily, and this has dramatic visible effects. Instead of a greasy-black electrical conductor that rubs off on the fingers, diamond is transparent like glass, an electrical insulator, and the hardest substance known. It is also difficult to form and, in pure form or with trace impurities imparting delicate tints, a rare and valued gem. The largest gem-quality diamond was found in 1905 and weighed, in the rough, 3,106 carats or about $1\frac{1}{3}$ pounds.[53] It could be easily held in the hand; gem-quality stones are usually much smaller.

This should change dramatically once nanotechnology can be brought to bear. Tiny devices should be able to work in concert to create objects on demand from common constituents such as carbon. By rearranging the atoms of carbon and excluding unwanted impurities, it should be possible to transform graphite, soot, ashes, coal, or sawdust into diamond, a light, strong, beautiful material that ought to find numerous uses. Needless to say, the jewelry market would collapse—diamond could become as abundant as driftwood and obtainable in beachball sizes (perhaps as sparkling lawn ornaments)—but the rewards would more than compensate. One expected dividend is diamond fiber, which should be much stronger than steel and able to form light, very strong fabrics and composites. (Here, however, it may have competition from the carbon nanotube. In a nanotube the atoms are arranged in a hexagonal pattern as in a layer of graphite, but the flat sheet is rolled up instead into a thin pipe or hollow cylinder that is also very strong and light.) Other gems too, such as sapphires, rubies, and emeralds, should become cheap and may find numerous structural uses in various forms.

Other superior materials or artifacts will similarly be developed and manufactured in quantity. One possibility is goods and structures that each have their own retinue of nanites, resulting in something akin to living organisms. Buildings and clothing could thus be made self-repairing, and carpets could remove their own dirt. Roads might be self-repairing too, thereby reducing accidents, which would also be diminished by smart robot cars. Your auto would ask where you wanted to go, plan the itinerary accordingly, and take you there using its own best judgment and superhuman reflexes—if, that is, such a means of transportation as the car is still in use. Otherwise perhaps there would be the personal, intelligent airplane or other flying craft.

The world could be made a better and more interesting place. Nanotechnology should open many doors to recovery of undiscovered wonders of the past. Glaciers, sediments, and the entire earth's crust could be explored in minutest detail and all the interesting contents carefully recovered or perhaps left in place after the full information is copied. Priceless treasures could be repaired at the molecular level and maintained with a fidelity never before possible. The Athenian Acropolis, the temple complex at Karnak, and other precious monuments might be restored to original splendor and kept indefinitely by caretaking nanites, alongside the structures of more mundane use that would also be constantly repaired. Exact copying of relics should also be possible, and the copies could be unobtrusively tagged to distinguish from the originals. (For this purpose we could use tiny, "noisy" substrates such as the pattern of defects in crystals, slightly rearranging them to store identifying information.) Far more ambitious undertakings should become feasible too.

By recreating creatures from DNA, for example, recently extinct species could be resurrected. The passenger pigeon thus may fly again and the quagga gallop, in appropriate habitats of a restored preindustrial environment. (There should meanwhile be plenty of energy obtainable directly from the sun for our earthly industrial needs, which would reduce the demands on the environment.) Perhaps too there will be special preserves where reconstructed species of much earlier epochs will be kept and maintained, if their DNA can be recovered from amber or other durable fossils. (The possibility of restoring extinct species raises interesting moral issues, however—more on this in Chapter 18.)

Moving to the human level, there is the possibility of resurrections. People of earlier times who were well-preserved, as we hope may happen through cryonics, should be restored to life and health. Those then living should reap untold benefits, starting with a medical revolution. Armies of nanites in the body should make it feasible to eliminate diseases and aging and bring about biological immortality. Since, we may say, you already have armies of nanites in your body, this would not be something entirely new but an improvement, though no doubt involving much that is not yet in place.

More generally, the nanotechnological assembler and other innovations should make it possible to literally make people to order; persons could be created with desired memories, dispositions, et cetera. As one possible approach we could imagine doing this at low temperature, where tissues would be completely solidified and stable, but suitable nanites should still be able to operate. Structuring the brain appropriately out of its usual components of carbon, hydrogen, oxygen, and other constituents, along with a matching body would, in effect, create a well-preserved cryonics patient with the desired mental and physical characteristics who could then be warmed and made functional. (Such animations will be considered in Chapter 17.) This is only one possibility for the controlled making of people, and a rather crude one; of course such a capability would have to be used very carefully.

But to return to the more mundane prospect of biological immortality, clearly this will leave a major challenge—the human population. Perhaps there will be ten billion people living when aging and diseases are eradicated. The number then will not diminish significantly, except through dispersion of the population in space—but this too will become feasible. Nanites will assist the would-be spacefarers in many ways, ranging from transport to providing habitats to conditioning the emigrants to live in the sky and enjoy it. Meanwhile, through automation directed by hyperadvanced computers, economies will change beyond recognition. Labor as we know it should be abolished—to be replaced, of course, by new and more rewarding work. Nonvoluntary, nonthinking chores will be handled by our artificial minions, who for all their efforts will demand no compensation beyond the requirements of the workplace—energy, space, and time. Costs as we know them will plummet, all persons in effect will become wealthy, and all will be free to do things that few today could imagine.

By then we must face the real challenge: humans will have to adapt and develop into more-than-humans to so much as find a meaningful existence. Aided by our technology, however, even this should not be out of reach, as part of a more general capability. Among the many possibilities, increasingly we will be able to modify ourselves toward the constructive aims of perfection, including greater intelligence, knowledge, and happiness, which we may hope will be closely interrelated. The human body we will likely choose to modify and ultimately discard in favor of housing that better serves our evolving needs. Increasingly, then, we must become the products of our own choosing, planning, and devising. Making our free choices with diligence and wisdom, however, will yield a suitable fulfillment of purpose for the entity created by blind nature—our species, Homo sapiens—that present civilization has already begun, in smaller ways, to change. And, indeed, this species must change much more, and—as a species—die, that all of us individually may find our destiny, not a destiny of death, but everlasting life.

It is not ruled out, of course, that things could go awry. Nanotechnology could be used for evil and destruction as well as for good. Destructive devices of horrific effectiveness, we might imagine, could be based around the concept of a self-replicating disassembler and might reduce people and ultimately civilization to "gray goo."[54] But at least we do not presently see or hear of substantial efforts to develop destructive nanites (beyond some work with biological agents and the like). Clearly there is much potential for good in nanotechnology, and we can only hope that motives to see it realized will prevail over the sinister alternatives.

Among the further, constructive possibilities should come the ability we noted, to create a person with essentially arbitrary features. This raises the possibility of resurrections of a more general character than what may be provided through preserved remains, something we will consider in earnest in Chapter 12. Before this some other matters deserve attention, including religious questions, which we will now address.

CHAPTER 10.

The Theological Issue

Traditionally, hopes for immortality rested on the miraculous. These hopes did not seem unreasonable—evidence of miracles could be seen everywhere. Comparisons were inevitable between the phenomena of nature and the far lesser products of human ingenuity. Wind; rain; fire; the rising and setting of the sun, moon, and stars; the coming and going of the seasons; life in all its variety and complexity—all suggested the workings of a vast intelligence with powers beyond comprehension. There surely must be advanced beings, superhuman agents, able to create all that could clearly be seen but was so little understood. Later there were major religious movements that combined all the causative elements into one supreme being, or God. God made the world and set it in order, and God continued to shape events through conscious intervention. Among other things, God was appealed to in times of need, especially for problems that seemed utterly insoluble otherwise, such as death. All things, of course, were possible to God, whose stupendous workings were evidence enough.

Among the interventions attributed to God was the establishment of a religion with a divinely revealed scripture and practices to be followed. This particularly was true in the dominant religion in the West, Christianity (with the slight complication that God became a triune Godhead or Trinity, "three persons united in one substance"[1]). A clergy was needed to guide the necessary observances and perform services invested with religious significance, such as weddings and funerals. The clergy naturally promoted the view that it came into existence as a gift of the God it was appointed to serve, a viewpoint that other institutions, such as monarchies, also extended to themselves.

With the rise of modern science, however, understanding the phenomena of existence at last became the province of reason more than faith. Many things, it was seen, could be explained without invoking any miraculous element. These ranged from astronomical events down to earthly weather and the functioning of biological organisms and tentatively included even mental activity. Increasingly, thoughtful people began to question the idea of a God who actively directs the happenings that could now be understood in simpler ways. In the eighteenth century a movement known as deism developed. Though God was still extant and all-powerful, he had made the world and then left it to its own devices. God did not actively intervene, though he would do so again, someday, to restore the dead to life.

Deism is an opposite extreme from pantheism, which holds that God is the universe (or, more generally, the multiverse or all that exists), and thus is constantly acting in and through all things, which God comprises. An intermediate between the two is theism, in which God has made the universe and intervenes in its affairs, yet the universe has a separate existence. (Pantheism has claimed adherents among a handful of philosophers, poets, and the like—but unlike deism and theism it has never had a wide following.) Theism is the position advocated in traditional Western religions such as Christianity, Islam, and Judaism. Revealed religion—writings or other communication alleged to have been sent directly from God—plays a prominent role. Deism denies the validity of such revelations and holds that God must be known through observation and analysis of the natural world he has made. Reason is seen as the road to understanding about religious issues as well as other matters in life.

Deism achieved its principal flowering in eighteenth-century France, England, and America. Among the prominent deists was American Revolutionary Thomas Paine. His 1795 book, *The Age of Reason*, is a good, short summary of the main deist thinking and remains quite readable today. It offers a spirited attack on the "inerrancy" of the Christian Bible while affirming an alternative, sustaining belief based on the scientific method. It is interesting that Paine and others believed they would be resurrected, though they doubted the validity of "revelations" and other claimed evidence not open to scientific verification. For many thinking people of the time, deism offered the best choice of a reassuring belief that the reasoning mind could accept.

Thinking had progressed in many ways since the medieval "Ages of Faith" when theism held absolute sway. Despite the successes of science, however, much remained unexplained, and the role of a superhuman Creator still seemed essential, at least to account for what had happened "in the beginning" when the cosmos, the earth, and the first living things presumably were formed. The "Argument from Design" was widely invoked, especially for the intricate mechanisms of living species, which seemed to require a conscious designer. As William Paley, a leading theologian put it, "[T]here is precisely the same proof that the eye was made for vision, as there is that the telescope was made for assisting it."[2] Nature had many wonders, and the good deist was able to rationalize belief in a God of goodness and purpose whose wonderful works would one day see a greater fulfillment in restoring the dead to life.

The Argument from Design, however, was dealt a severe blow by the evolutionary hypothesis of Charles Darwin in the mid nineteenth century. The philosophical bases of deism had earlier come under withering attack from such able critics as Hume and Kant.[3] Never a well-unified movement, deism actually had mostly disappeared long before Darwin wrote, while theistic religions lived on and still have wide following. Tipler puzzles over this in *The Physics of Immortality*: "So what killed Deism? It was a rational religion, based on the best science of the day…. But it could not compete with the Christianity based on revelation, not reason. Why?"

Tipler answers his own question, "I believe Deism died because the physics upon which it was based was simply too impersonal." This physics, Newtonian mechanics, pictured the universe as a clockwork machine, perfect in every detail. It was something only a perfect Creator could make and something whose very perfection needed, even demanded no further intervention. A nonintervening God was too much like no God at all. The theistic notion of a caring Creator who does intervene in history had

more appeal and rather soon bested its upstart rival. Tipler concludes: "Religion can be based on physics only if the physics
shows that God *has* to be personal, and further, that the afterlife
is an absolutely solid consequence of the physics."[4] Tipler de-
votes much effort in his book to establishing these two points
and maintaining that a caring, personal God does really exist,
though it is a deistic God who must be found through science,
not revelation. His reasoning in turn has come under fire from
critics who think he has done both science and theology a disser-
vice.[5] His effort must not be condemned out of hand, however; it
certainly has merits.

In fairness, I think that many important issues are well explored in Tipler's remarkable book; insights are offered that well
deserve consideration, even if difficulties persist, as they certainly
do. Among the great merits is a framework of scientific materialism, which is adopted throughout even if there is a "God." The
latter is a technical term, though having "roughly [the] popular
meaning."[6] My position, nonetheless, is that this is going too far.
Yes indeed, immortality and resurrection of the dead are topics
we can approach scientifically through such avenues as quantum
physics and strong AI. But another important consideration is
that we must help ourselves. The emphasis on a transcendent and
beneficent outside agent is misplaced.

Tipler has a tall philosophical order, to square the traditional
view of a caring, attentive God with a more modern scientific
outlook in which this animistic, personal element is discarded.
Tipler's solution is to consider the human race, and intelligent
life generally, as developing into a kind of God. This entity, which
he calls the Omega Point (in honor of Teilhard de Chardin's original theory, which Tipler would rationalize mathematically), will
effect the realization of our dreams including resurrecting the
dead and a happy hereafter. Though called "God," it is really just
our own civilization projected to a remote future, when it is to
engulf the universe and shape its very evolution to a grand finale.
(We could also include with this any indigenous, extraterrestrial
civilizations which, if they exist or will exist in our universe, will
arguably have decided to join forces with us by then for mutual
advantages. Tipler does not consider such independently originated civilizations likely and does not include them in his forecast.[7])

By then our distant descendants will have inconceivably advanced beyond our present level, so that all-but miraculous feats should become possible, though all will proceed, as always, according to scientific principles and rational understanding. It is argued that for various reasons the Omega Point will not only have the capability to resurrect us to Heaven, it will also have the motive, due to its own highly refined self-interest. Indeed, one feature of Tipler's stance, and I think a commendable one, is a form of Universalism. He imagines that even the most evil historical beings will be provided the opportunity to mend their ways or accept rehabilitation so that they too can participate in the future paradise. (More will be said on Universalism later.)

So no supernatural character is needed even for the Deity; science, not the supernatural, suffices for all. Tipler's viewpoint in fact agrees in many ways with mine as presented here. For instance, when it comes to persons he is thoroughly materialistic: "...a human being is a purely physical object, a biochemical machine completely and exhaustively described by the known laws of physics. There are *no* mysterious 'vital' forces."[8] A person instead is just a type of very complicated computer program, running (more correctly, instantiated) on a machine we call the brain. Extrapolating to a remote point in the future, God (the Omega Point) is likewise nonsupernatural, being composed of many individuals (persons) who, though more advanced, are of the same material character as persons today. On this basis, then, there would seem to be grounds for denying that the Omega Point really is "God." Yet Tipler persists, trying as hard as possible to bring his scientific conception into line with more traditional thinking about a Deity.

There is, for example, a reverse-causality argument to justify the position that the Omega Point, from its vantage in the remote future, can extend its influence backward in time and affect our affairs today. But this argument I find particularly unpersuasive. Despite whatever subtle reverse-causal effects could be present, supposing, as may be hoped, that we do develop into a supercivilization, a presently, consciously interacting God is simply not there. The Omega Point does not function as a currently thinking entity able to receive and respond to communications from humans, in the way we would normally imagine. Prayer is a vital component in the major theistic traditions, as is some expectation of willful, divine intervention. The Omega Point, by comparison, does not seem at all capable of answering prayers like the traditional God, nor has it performed miracles such as raising people from the dead or granting special favors or powers to certain individuals.

In the case of the deistic, Enlightenment God the disparity with the Omega Point is less but still seems fatal. The deist's God is a presently conscious entity who could answer prayers or produce miracles but chooses not to. The Omega Point, by contrast, is nowhere to be found, except as a potentiality. Its present existence is not required to explain the existence of the universe, except by a peculiar reverse-causality argument that Tipler uses: unless life persists forever in our universe and becomes eventually aware of all things, our universe, and all that is in it, not merely will not exist in the remote future, but never existed in the first place.[9] The Omega Point, then, creates reality today. In Chapter 12, on resurrection, we will consider a logical alternative to this form of "retrocreationism" that is less restrictive and also, I think, more natural and reasonable. It does not require an Omega Point in Tipler's sense, though it does not rule it out either.

Deutsch, in *The Fabric of Reality,* considers Tipler's Omega Point, concluding it makes an unlikely candidate for "God," for much the same reasons we have just considered. Deutsch also doubts if the Omega Point, essentially a community of beings, would possess the degree of unity necessary to form a giant Mind.[10] Here I think Tipler's position is defensible but is not enough to overcome other objections. It is worth noting that Tipler expresses some doubts about his own theory, though still thinking it "has a very good chance of being right."[11] But its cosmology can now be called into serious question—more on this in Chapter 14. It should be clear by then, however, that more than one cosmological outlook would suffice for immortality according to the position I argue for in this book, even including cases where no individual universe can support immortality but the multiverse as a whole does.

But there is one major similarity between the God of tradition and the Omega Point: an utter remoteness, effectively making the latter, like the former, an incomprehensible "Other"—even if, as Tipler notes, his God is not physically distinct from the universe as in some other conceptions.[12] For him the separation is more of time than place, but it is real nonetheless. Some 10^{19} years (about a billion times the estimated age of the universe) are to elapse before the Omega Point is effectively realized, even though it is to take place in our universe as an outgrowth of our own civilization. Tipler does not imagine, in his main scenario, that any of us today will remotely survive, individually, to this distant time of paradise. Instead we, our near descendants, and even the whole human race will die, to be replaced by a superior species, and that by another, and so on.[13] (The inconceivably advanced individuals of the final stage, when dying finally stops, will in due course recreate all their predecessors, ultimately including ourselves and other historical humans, and all will then be immortal.) The wide gulf between present, mortal humankind and the Omega Point supports identifying the latter with the God of Western tradition, particularly if the reverse-causality argument is also accepted. But this is not the future I think is at all likely to happen.

Instead, I maintain, the most significant advance that will occur in all of history is simply the attainment of individual, indefinite life span, something that surely is very near on the scale of history. It will take no cosmological wait but perhaps only a few decades at most. There will be no successive die-off and replacement of posthuman species or even, much longer, of persons individually. The most essential occurrence will be the elimination of the aging process. Along with that will come the cure of terminal diseases, so many of which are associated with aging. Then, concurrently or soon to follow, will be an explosion of lifestyle options including redesigned bodies, enhanced intelligence, and, I will further conjecture, uploading the mind into a computational device, which will lead to further improvements and greater security. We will probably find it attractive to abandon our biological makeup for something we will think of as better (disturbing though the thought may be to many today).

Progress then should rapidly reduce the death rate to near zero. Death, in turn, will have been redefined as destruction of identity-critical information and thus be approached from a computational perspective rather than the primitive and faulty criteria of today. Persons dying today, I think, have a significant chance of survival to this fortunate time through biostasis. Cosmology willing, it should then be straightforward to transform near-immortality or indefinite life span to true immortality, and most who have attained the former should enjoy the latter without interruption. But the important step will be taken at the beginning and near our own present, when we, a product of unconscious evolutionary forces, transform ourselves into a product of our own judgment and design.

A society of immortals should thus come into existence within a century or so at the latest. In the next chapter I offer further arguments why civilization will shape itself into a benign society of immortals relatively soon, rather than only in a remote future. Being a cryonicist and antiaging advocate myself, I am naturally hoping to have a personal stake in this near-term, immortal society, and I hope also that as many as possible will join in this endeavor.

Atheism with a Concept of Divinity

Is there a place for a God in the scheme of things? I think this question is important enough that I have devoted additional space to it here. (A vast amount of literature already exists on the subject, of course, and I can do no more than briefly sketch some of the main arguments, with some additional thoughts related to special issues considered here.) I will argue an atheistic position: there appears to be no entity that has the major attributes traditionally associated with a God, at least in the Western, Judeo-Christian-Islamic sense. Some of these attributes, it is true, are arguably possessed by one or more of the phenomena of our experience and might serve as inspiration in our endeavors to better our lot. But it is we who must do the bettering, not some higher power acting on our behalf. Still I think it worth emphasizing that, as I see it, atheism and some notion of a divine or transcendent element are not incompatible. We are, after all, aspiring to a more-than-human state and have started on the path of making our wishes reality.

So in effect we are becoming a sort of deity ourselves, a One composed of many. Each person, in the course of progress, is to approach a state of perfection, an individual, self-sustaining, physically realized godlike entity or divinity, to form a worthy part of a larger and naturally cohering whole. It is a privilege that also carries an enormous responsibility. The burden is upon us as a species, intelligent if unconsciously evolved, to solve our own problems and engineer our own eternal happiness: a world of peace, love, and harmony, at a superhuman level—a place where all are valued and valuable. If there is no absolute guarantee of success, the prospect, at least, is a very real and exhilarating one, and the outlook, I think, is positive. Again the burden for solving our problems rests entirely upon ourselves. There are things, moreover, that we should be doing today that bear on the physical problem of our immortality.

Let us now examine the question of the existence of God, starting with some of the standard problems. God, we are told, is all-powerful, all-knowing, present everywhere, the maker of all things, and perfectly good. But if God is all-powerful, he can change his mind, we should think, while if all-knowing, he always knows in advance what he will do and cannot change his mind. What does it mean, on the other hand, to say that God is present everywhere? Do we observe a thinking process in empty space? True, space is not really empty but teems with such things as particle-antiparticle pairs that briefly wink into existence then self-annihilate. But this does not seem to involve intelligence. If God made everything, did God make himself? If not, who or what made God? Or if God is said to be uncreated, then how do we know that something else is not uncreated, say, the multiverse, which as a whole seems insentient? Finally, if God is perfectly good, besides all-knowing and all-powerful, why does evil exist? Why do the innocent suffer, as so often they clearly do?

As one example of evil, the suffering of animals does not seem to follow for the reason often claimed for human suffering, that it is punishment for sins. Animals lack the reasoning power to comprehend that they have sinned, yet they can and do feel pain. Rabies is a horrible disease. A virus destroys the brain and snuffs the life of its host, in the process inducing a demented state in which the dying, tormented creature bites other creatures, propagating this form of death by torture. The infecting organism, really just a fancy molecule, can hardly be said to "benefit" from its own proliferation. (Do water molecules similarly benefit if more of them are formed?) Is this, then, the working of divine justice? Is there some other, sufficiently offsetting benefit, of which we are unaware? What about other diseases? What about animal predation? What about earthquakes, floods, forest fires, volcanic eruptions, meteoric impacts? The list goes on.

And there are many ills at the human level too, inflicted without benefit of a legal process, that are hardly accountable as punishment for the victim's "sins." (Rabies itself, which sometimes occurs in such undeserving victims as young children, is one particularly horrific example, though far from the only one. As something universal and universally lethal, we may consider the aging process itself.) Further, we can argue that even ills that *are* attributable to willful, human misconduct could have been prevented by an all-powerful God, who thus must share moral responsibility. The sharing must also extend to the case of a Devil or other evil power that such a God may will or allow to exist.

Besides the very serious problem of evil, there is a difficulty from the fact that, according to the various traditions, God wishes us to believe in him and to hold certain opinions regarding his attributes and/or intervention in our affairs. Why then does he permit different, conflicting belief systems (Christianity versus Islam for instance, or different sects within one religion) that mutually condemn one another's "unbelief"? Which set of beliefs, if any, is true? And, if it is so important for people to hear the true word of God and become believers, why is it that some do not hear it through no fault of their own, while others do hear it? Why had the pre-Columbian Aztecs, for instance, never heard of Christianity or Islam?

These problems alone, which are well-treated in the literature, raise serious doubts about the likelihood of a God as imagined. But let us go on. According to tradition, God is purely spiritual and even supernatural, with an existence that is in some manner beyond understanding or, at least, not expressed in the usual, material form. But this does not seem supported by observations. There do not appear to be any supernatural powers or forces or spiritual entities with an existence apart from the particles of physics. All phenomena seem explicable in terms of scientific theories, either those we have already devised or (in the case of more remote or subtle effects) similar ones we may develop in the future. Indeed, the failure to reliably and objectively substantiate a claim of the paranormal in any one of its varied, alleged forms must rank as telling, negative evidence. This includes the results of attempts to influence events or bring about changes through prayer or other contacts with a superhuman agent. Pray for a rock on the ground to levitate and it stays right where it is. Pray for rain to come or sickness to heal and the desired effect may follow, but it also happens without prayer. (In the case of sickness we must also consider a placebo effect—healing will be influenced by the mental state of the patient who may believe in the curative powers of prayer.)

Certainly our theories have had great success in explaining reality without assuming a controlling intelligence of any kind, whether truly supernatural or simply much vaster than our own, though still material and subject to the usual physical laws. Probably the strongest argument against a superhuman intelligence has to do with life on Earth. Here it may indeed seem that some sort of purposeful, greater-than-human guidance is occurring, as in the formation and propagation of species. But different species are well accounted for by Darwinian evolution, with its principle of survival of the fittest and other mechanisms for inducing changes in organisms.

Life is complicated, to be sure, and is not yet fully understood. Some features, particularly at the human level, still seem hard to explain in terms of such evolutionary mechanisms as the variability of individuals within a species and a selection process favoring the fittest. How do we account, for example, for mathematical, musical, or literary talent, which would have been irrelevant to the hunter-gatherer lifestyle that humans, by appearance, evolved for? (Physicist Paul Davies, for one, raises this question in *The Mind of God*, a modern defense of the Argument from Design.) Such abilities have gained importance only in the relatively recent past (a few millennia at most, in some cases much less), too rapidly for their importance to be recognized by anything as slow as biological evolution. Moreover, some would argue, they often do not seem to favor survival of the species anyway.

But I think these features can be explained as logical outgrowths of more basic, evolved abilities that were important in our evolutionary past, such as language—a crucial talent that set us apart from other species and was clearly useful at the basic, hunter-gatherer level. Linguistic ability, with its associated capacities for reasoning and problem solving, makes people into computation-universal devices and opens wide horizons for abilities that were not specifically programmed. Moreover, many of our refined talents do have some relevance at a more primitive level. Music and mathematics, to take two examples, find uses either in religious rituals, commerce, or defense, all of which are operative at the tribal level and contribute to survival.

Cultures tend to nurture the talents that are important to their survival, this too being a reasonable consequence of a selection process. An Einstein or a Beethoven might have been useless in a more primitive culture, but could not have occurred there anyway as the geniuses they became. Their immense talents were not formed or even fully latent before they were born but instead, by appearances, required a lengthy process of nurture and reinforcement and perhaps some simple good luck. The appreciation of extraordinary talent in turn is an important source of meaning in a culture, whether primitive or more advanced, and thus will contribute, if somewhat indirectly, to its survival and that of the individuals within. Many talented people contribute in more direct ways too. So evolution proceeds not merely by genomic reshaping, which is glacially slow and gradual to us humans, but more relevantly by the progress of our civilization. No conscious, controlling mechanism outside of ourselves is necessary for any of this.

In general, the continuing success and improvement of our physical theories makes the supernatural seem increasingly problematical, along with other supposed, superhuman intervention. For example, extraterrestrial visitors with advanced technology might well have been taken for gods and given rise to religious movements. But here again there is no hard evidence. We have no artifacts of undeniable, intelligent, nonhuman origin nor anything else to clearly convince us of the putative visitations. The various claims that have been made of superhuman encounters are not supported by tangible effects.

Cosmological and Ontological Arguments

At this point we might rest our case that there is no God, but I think it is worth pursuing a bit further. Even if we discount specific claims of the paranormal, there could be phenomena in the natural universe that sufficiently meet the important criteria. I propose to show that this too is unlikely.

God, at least in one important manifestation, must be some sort of sentient being, like people but more advanced—a mindlike entity with certain other attributes such as omniscience. I will allow that there might be other manifestations of God as an unthinking entity, perhaps the set of all events as a pantheist might advocate, but there must also be a mindlike component to square with anything like the traditional view. Is it likely such a consciousness exists? We might imagine such an organized presence could exist and be composed, primarily, of intelligent beings like ourselves (including any advanced extraterrestrials) who are working to bring about a happy, immortal existence.

A theistic God must be able to detect the efforts of people to communicate and must respond accordingly. This God is not merely something that will act in this way at some point in the future but must also have been active in the historical past. The whole Judeo-Christian-Islamic tradition centers around a God who hears prayers and intervenes in the affairs of humans. (Other, parallel traditions of an interactive God or Godhead are seen, for example, among the various strands of Hinduism.[14]) Taken literally, this does not seem at all likely. Perhaps the closest approach would be just the human race itself, or some particular subset— a community of believers. They in their common efforts may be said to constitute a sort of thinking entity with powers beyond the level of any individual and that is able to respond to the needs and behaviors of individuals. However, the human race with its limitations and divisions is not usually taken seriously as a candidate for a Deity, and I do not do so either. Subsets of humanity also, though they may be more single-minded and unified, are similarly finite and fallible: again, not God.

In the future, of course, we may hope to progress toward a "One composed of many," a harmonious community of immortals, much as Tipler envisions for his Omega Point, though hopefully much sooner. We may also expand our territory and come to occupy a much larger volume of space we than presently do. However, such a future possibility could not today and in the past add up to the God of theistic or even deistic pretensions.

To try to remedy this problem, we could consider a totality of sentient, intelligent, or immortal beings distributed throughout the whole of existence. We could then ask if this, in one form or another, could be said to constitute a conscious entity that would achieve a close enough match to traditional attributes to be reasonably regarded as God. In this way we are not limited to the products of our own civilization but can incorporate possible extraterrestrial, intelligent species, wherever they may be, whether in our universe or elsewhere, and thus not solely in our future. This idea, which I will call the Cosmic Community hypothesis, possesses some cogency, particularly in light of possibilities that may exist for immortality. A harmonious community of immortals might function together as a kind of "God," much as Tipler conjectures for his Omega Point. The idea also has weaknesses, however, that seem fatal.

One is that civilizations in different universes would not be expected to be able to communicate. Our "God," overall, must be highly fragmented—a gargantuan case of multiple personality disorder. But even within a single universe—our own—the problems would be forbidding. A Mind spread over vast distances would be subject to speed of light limitations; coordinated, cosmic thinking must, it would seem, be more than glacially slow. Again, we do not see evidence of such an entity interacting with us: if extant, it could not be playing the role of a theistic God. As for a deistic God, who may have created our universe somehow and started in motion whatever natural processes have led to things as we now see them, at least the possibility is not ruled out. A super-civilization in some other universe could have started the Big Bang that led to our own universe. (Or our universe could even be a computer simulation in some larger universe.) But again, there is neither evidence of this nor anything we know of that would preclude formation of our universe by purely unconscious forces. A similar consideration would apply to a "cosmic community" limited to our own universe: advanced extraterrestrials who, perhaps five billion years ago, set in motion events that shaped our solar system and planet Earth. Again evidence is lacking.

There is another line of thinking about a God that can be called an ontological argument. Variations of it have been used to defend the existence of God, but, in fact, it can be turned against this possibility too because God in both theistic and deistic conceptions is a sentient being. According to the ontological argument, God is supposed to be perfect—basically a complete entity lacking nothing by way of experience and knowledge, all consistent with perfect goodness. All sentient life in our direct experience, however, clearly is incomplete. In the course of existence we are constantly apprehending new experience, the awareness of which is essential to our continuing interactions as sentient agents. (To fail to acquire new experience, in fact, would lead to a condition known as the Eternal Return, discussed in Chapter 14, which is incompatible with a reasonable notion of immortality.) A perfect, complete entity, it would seem, could not be aware in this way of the present or new events or the passing of time. A God, then, could not be a sentient, interactive agent, whatever other attributes it might possess. It would fail to meet the requirements either of theism or deism.

The notion of a perfect being who also necessarily exists—because existence is better or more perfect than nonexistence—has a venerable history, the best known advocate being Anselm of Canterbury (1033–1109). Anselm's position is a positive form of the ontological argument, but it overlooks the problem of sentience. It has had its critics, but it has modern defenders too, such as Charles Hartshorne, who considers Anselm's argument at length in *The Logic of Perfection*.[15] Included in this book is a discussion of the idea of God as a cosmic community, which Hartshorne also favors.[16] The arguments are interesting and have a logical cogency that at least calls for respect. Perhaps "perfection" could be said to exist necessarily, that is, in a way that extends to the whole of the multiverse and transcends all individual, special circumstances. The issue remains, however, of whether this perfection should be regarded somehow as being a conscious agent.

Hartshorne is aware of the problem of sentience for a being of "perfect" changelessness. His God, then, has both absolute (unchanging or necessary) and relative (contingent) aspects. For the latter, God is a participant in the historical process, as, for example, through a cosmic community. The possibility of a multiverse or Unboundedness is not considered; many-worlds was a very new idea when the book appeared in 1962. Reality as a whole is allowed to present entirely new conditions with the progress of time, that is, it is contingent or different from what it might have been. To my thinking Hartshorne's approach suffers from twin difficulties: (1) the cosmic community, presumably limited in this case to our one universe, makes a poor candidate for a Deity, for the reasons we have considered; and (2) reality as a whole, underlying reality, is not presenting new conditions or facets but, in view of the multiverse, can be considered fixed and immutable.

Indeed, an interesting insight is provided by the principle of counterfactual indefiniteness which, as we have seen (Chapters 5, 6), is a hallmark of Unboundedness and follows, in particular, from the Everett many-worlds theory. In view of indefiniteness, reality in toto is necessary, not contingent. Every possibility in a large class is realized, and because of this, things could not be different from what they are overall. We as sentient agents, of course, never see the whole of reality, and thus are able to have continually new experiences. Our observer reality does present new conditions—to us. We are contingent—this is counterfactuality—things (for us) could have been different. But God-as-perfection must transcend all this and could not have been different or become different in the smallest degree—a fatal mismatch, I think, with the main historical ideas about a Deity.

We have considered, then, several possible ideas of God and whether any of them seem both scientifically tenable and sufficiently close to traditional conceptions, particularly those in the Judeo-Christian-Islamic tradition and in deism. It does not seem likely that any such notion corresponds to reality: God as a sentient agent does not exist, though there might well be entities with some of the traditional divine attributes.

World and Eternal Happiness without a God

The absence of a supreme being should be no cause for despair. There is no need to hypothesize a God, either to account for what exists or to bolster hopes of an afterlife and immortality and, more generally, to establish standards of what is right and good and to have reasonable confidence that these standards will prevail over time. More comprehensively, we can reject animism—"the belief that humans share the world with a population of extraordinary, extracorporeal, and mostly invisible beings, ranging from souls and ghosts to saints and fairies, angels and cherubim, demons, jinni, devils and gods."[17]

Instead there is an alternative, as we have seen, that can be founded on the UI assumptions, which does not violate materialism or assume any controlling intelligence. If Unboundedness in particular is accepted, we can begin to understand how a uni-

verse like ours might come into existence and have the right properties for intelligent life without being consciously designed. In
the unlimited profusion of the worlds that must occur, some at
least would be expected to have the necessary properties. In effect, then, the multiverse itself becomes a kind of Deity, and,
indeed, this is the main idea behind pantheism, that God comprises reality as a whole. Yuai, it might be claimed, is simply a
form of pantheism, and there is some justification in the claim,
but I would resist it. "God," in the more usual sense, is not simply the universe or the multiverse, so that the pantheist's use of
theistic terminology seems inappropriate. More important, Yuai,
despite its materialistic, reductionist basis, is strongly concerned
with salvation and immortality at the level of each individual,
which is not prominent in the usual thinking of pantheism.

But it will be instructive to further explore how, in effect, God
is to be substituted so that the major functions assigned to a Deity can be accomplished by other means. Tentatively we have
established that a God-alternative should meet two requirements:
(1) accounting for the world as we see it; and (2) providing for a
hopeful future, including resurrection of the dead and personal
immortality. These two properties are the most important ones to
the believing theist and to others having an interest in the deep
issues of life.

Thus we shall now consider the issues of how the universe
came into being with the attributes we see and of what this appears to mean in terms of an ongoing process and overall trend.
One thing deserves mention at the outset, an explanatory tool
that I think has great power and relevance. This is known as the
Anthropic Principle. In the "weak" form that is most useful here,
the Anthropic Principle states simply that for things in a universe
to be observed, the universe must provide for the existence of the
observer. (There are also "stronger" forms of this principle that
need not concern us; the interested reader may consult *The Anthropic Cosmological Principle* by John Barrow and Frank Tipler, which also specializes our weak version a bit.[18]) In short,
then, when it comes to our universe we expect to find some necessary supporting apparatus, given that, after all, we are here.
The Anthropic Principle can thus account for everything from
the earth being the right distance from the warming sun to carbon
chemistry.[19]

The principle is so simple and nearly (if not quite) self-evident that there is little debate about it among scientists, but for that very reason its usefulness is also sometimes questioned. I think, though, that it becomes highly meaningful and useful if we couple it with a principle such as Unboundedness that leads to a multiverse. With this additional assumption, the Anthropic Principle can explain how our world has design with no Designer. It is simply that we expect an unlimited profusion of universes in the multiverse, so that whatever it takes to make beings such as ourselves, is bound to happen, and, of course, not just once, but over and over. Indeed, it will be seen that this can explain how all the (finitely many) conditions necessary for our existence could arise, no matter how numerous or complicated, no matter how much apparent engineering must be involved, and all without the slightest forethought or planning. It is analogous to throwing dice: if there is epsilon probability of a certain combination coming up, and epsilon, however small, is greater than zero, and the number of throws of the dice is infinite, then that combination must come up, eventually. Moreover, it will not occur just once, but infinitely often, if only a tiny fraction of the time (epsilon, that is)— all the while, however, purely by chance with no conscious intervention or guidance.

This sort of process, then, is what seems to have shaped the world as we know it, including ourselves and all that we see, and to have provided whatever conditions we find favorable to life as we know it. (It was not necessarily "purely by chance," of course, but could have occurred deterministically, though it would still be perceived by us as an accident; the main point is that no controlling intelligence was involved.) We should add, "so far," for when it comes to the more important conditions affecting our life and death, the aging process, for instance, we have so far been largely powerless to have effect, though this is beginning to change.

Here it is worth noting that the multiverse theory of creation just outlined has opponents who continue to hold out for intelligent design, one representative being Paul Davies, as noted above. His arguments, discussed in *The Mind of God*,[20] revolve around the claim that the Designer hypothesis is the simpler of the two, that is, is favored by Ockham's razor. By now we have encountered Ockham's razor several times, one being in connection with quantum reality (Chapter 5), where we saw that good arguments favoring many-worlds on grounds of this principle could be made, despite some appearances to the contrary. And once again I think there is reasonable ground, based on Ockham's razor, to favor the multiverse over an alternative, in this case the divine Designer.

Basically, if there is an infinite Mind, we have to account for that phenomenon as part of our reality. Traditionally, God has been held to have unlimited complexity and intelligence, in addition to being the source of all we see, and to have always existed. It is surely a simpler hypothesis that an infinite though unthinking multiverse has always existed and is the source of the things we see—provided that this hypothesis does, in fact, reasonably account for what we see. And in one very important respect, clearly it does. In conjunction with the Anthropic Principle and the evolutionary hypothesis, the multiverse theory accounts for life as we know it—something with deep significance. Life is the most complex, inscrutable, and wonderful phenomenon we know of, something of which we ourselves are an important part (the most important part we know of, I would say). If anything had a Designer, this must be it. If, on the other hand, we can account for life without a Designer, as we certainly can, it removes a major prop from the Designer theory, and we then must consider whether some other features of reality suggest an intelligent origin.

Indeed there are observable features, not obviously connected with life, that may seem to call for a Designer—but I do not think the evidence is at all compelling. Davies notes how electrons always have the same charge. This presumably is not necessary for life—could there be variations? The occurrence of identical charges is a striking enough property that it arguably favors intelligent design, rather like finding a row of identical mountains somewhere. Other subatomic particles are also seen to have identical properties; protons are all alike, for instance. Still, it is not clear how remarkable these similarities really are—there is much uncertainty about how the various features came into being. Particles are not mountains. There is no obvious indication that identical particles were manufactured intelligently, like coins stamped out in a mint, and I think the same sort of consideration applies to other properties we observe. Again, barring new evidence, we can reject the Designer theory on grounds of Ockham's razor.

With such thoughts in mind, it is worthwhile now to further examine the properties of our own universe, which in some ways seems quite a strange place. We will gain more insight into how the universe could have come to exist without a Designer as well as the difficult issue of our long-term future prospects.

One important property, for us, is that time has a direction. Rivers flow downhill not uphill, burning wood turns to smoke and steam, the latter do not coalesce into wood, and so on. True, there are ways that rivers acquire the water that flows downhill and wood is formed anew, but these are not by running uphill or "unburning." Stars shine, radiating photons into space rather than accumulating photons from the outside, or "unshining." In general, events follow certain, preferred courses and not their contraries. At the quantum level these preferred courses, which are known as phase paths, describe the most probable outcomes though not the only possibilities.[21]

The concept of phase path depends on the familiar idea that events are not strictly predictable. When we perform an experiment, the outcome cannot be known in advance but only probabilities of different alternatives. Some outcomes, however, are far more likely than others. It is very, very likely that ice will melt on a hot summer day, for instance, and most unlikely, though not impossible, that water will freeze. Ice melting in the heat is following a phase path, water freezing is not.

Phase paths are a way of reconciling the modern, quantum viewpoint with the older, classical view that provides only one outcome for an experiment. An older prediction, for example, would be that ice melts above a certain temperature and liquid water stays liquid or, if hot enough and not confined, boils away. The modern approach, by assigning an overwhelming probability but not absolute certainty to some particular outcome, correctly predicts the observed macroscopic effect but reconciles this with what is seen on a smaller scale. (Sometimes too there is not just one phase path but several, different outcomes all having probabilities that are too large to ignore, as in the case of the photon striking a half-silvered mirror.)

One principle that seems to be an inescapable consequence of following the phase paths, at least in our universe, is the Second Law of Thermodynamics. The Second Law in effect states that things are becoming more disordered with time. The measure of disorder is called entropy—entropy then is increasing. As entropy increases, the amount of useful work that can be done diminishes. At the limit, in a finite, closed system, even information processing becomes impossible so that consciousness could not continue. Any such finite system tends to a state of maximum entropy so that essentially nothing happens after a certain point. This condition in fact is predicted for the universe under various scenarios and is called the Heat Death, though it is not the only possibility since the universe need not satisfy the conditions for a finite, closed system.

Actually the Second Law poses a big puzzle: if systems always tend to a state of maximum entropy, why is our universe right now not in a state of maximum entropy? The obvious fact that we are not in such a state raises hopes that the end of life is not inevitable and immortality may be possible. But the question still remains, by what mechanism is the Second Law (to which no exceptions have ever been seen in the laboratory) apparently overruled? The universe seems to have started from a minute, very hot fireball in a cataclysm known as the Big Bang. What led up to this event, which itself seems suspiciously like a violation of the Second Law?[22]

A possible answer is suggested by the Anthropic Principle. The observer will only exist, in the sense of being able to observe, in a universe that is not in a state of maximum entropy but reasonably far from such a state. In view of Unboundedness, such universes must exist, perhaps in many and varied forms. (In particular, many-worlds provides for whole universes with other physical laws than our own.[23]) Perhaps in some sense these reduced-entropy universes are a great rarity and can only come about if phase paths are violated in their formation;[24] from the standpoint of what can be directly observed, however, they are the only universes that exist at all. The assumption that the universe must contain an observer thus introduces a new twist in the laws of physics, modifying them in subtle or not-so-subtle ways, one being, it would seem, that time has a direction, and the Second Law is dominant.

In any case, we see that the multiverse truly is the "maker of all things," an incredible creative principle that apparently knows no boundaries or limits. We may conjecture that it has always existed, always will exist, and is forever unchanging overall, even as it continually (from our point of view) transforms all that falls under its sway. Except for the rules of logic, it is not subject to any restrictive laws or processes of deterioration or termination, including, for example, the laws of thermodynamics that happen to prevail in one of its many branches, our own universe. It will undergo no Heat Death or final collapse. Moreover, it is fully, causally self-sufficient and needs no outside power, force, or condition to explain its presence or anything it accomplishes. It is, I submit, as much a creative principle as the human mind ever ascribed to a God, and yet, in important ways, it does not fit the usual notions of a God. Mainly, it is perfectly mindless and automatic. There is nothing we can do to influence it in the slightest degree—the causality is always in the other direction, from it to us. The things we do are according to its "plan"—conditions it automatically enforces.

Mindless though it is, however, its power and creativity are undeniable and beyond imagining. Since, we hypothesize, life fundamentally is good, the creative principle too is good. It cannot love, yet it might be loved—in a special way—much as someone could have a love of the sea, a creative force in its own right that can be compared, in a small way, to its great progenitor. Despite any differences in worldviews, we can join with monk and mystic Thomas Merton in contemplating a world of wonder and share "a vivid realization of the fact that life and being in us proceed from an invisible, transcendent and infinitely abundant Source."[25]

Though not like either a theistic or deistic God, the multiverse does correspond to some ideas of a God, notably pantheist conceptions, as we have seen. Such ideas—that God need not be conscious or a person—were developed by seventeenth-century Jewish-Dutch philosopher Baruch Spinoza,[26] and have attracted a small circle of adherents over the centuries. (Related ideas occur in non-Western traditions too, such as Taoism.[27]) In particular, the multiverse is complete and unique. There is only one possible multiverse by definition, though particular universes with particular histories could come in many varieties.

We do not have to parody the question, If God made everything, who made God? Granted, according to hypothesis, the multiverse "made" everything, yet the multiverse itself is not something whose origin requires explanation. (Or if one is troubled by "why there is something rather than nothing," simply ask, Why not?) Like a God, the multiverse provides for its offspring, though not consciously or intentionally. The Anthropic Principle accounts in particular for the good things in our environment but for the bad ones as well. Where we see the poet's "all things bright and beautiful,"[28] since the creative principle is mindless, we should not be surprised that "all things dull and ugly" are found alongside too.

So we are provided an elegant answer to the problem of evil that bedevils the theist: how a presumably loving God, who has put so many wonderful things in the world, could also allow so much suffering and wrongdoing. The creative principle, though wonderful enough in its own way, is not sentient and thus is morally neutral. It can be called good for its overall effects as we have noted, but it has no intentions for or against the welfare of any person or group. This is a cause of despair to the theist, who demands a purposeful God for a meaningful life and destiny— but it need not be.

Tipler's approach to the problem of evil deserves some comment here.[29] He too notes that evils are bound to happen—this being a consequence of the many-worlds physics he upholds— yet still there is a God, he maintains, that is, the Omega Point, which will abolish all evils as we are resurrected to happiness. Overall this God is automatic, or necessary—all possible histories happen (what I have called Unboundedness). Yet for us, in our particular corner of the multiverse, the Omega Point will manifest itself as a (contingently) sentient agent, as it actively intervenes to benefit us. Tipler then is well aware of the necessity versus contingency issue involved in Hartshorne's argument. Tipler moreover offers a subtle but important new twist. Where Hartshorne ignores the multiverse possibility, Tipler accepts it and seeks to uphold a God who is, in a different sense than Hartshorne claimed, both necessary and contingent.

Again though, I do not think the Omega Point is a suitable candidate for a God. Overall, our ontological argument still applies: the timeless, unchanging, necessary God is not a being as we usually understand it. The more specialized, contingent Being, on the other hand, who is to rescue us in the distant future, is not the God of tradition, who must have also intervened in detectable ways in our past and must presently be sentient. Again, the emphasis on a remote Other (the Omega Point) is misplaced—we, including our future selves, must be the agents of our own salvation. We must come to see ourselves as progressing to self-sufficiency rather than as worshipful subjects of something beyond our comprehension who is to provide for us.

Our Immense Responsibilities

Most important, it is we ourselves who both define the good and the bad and act to bring about the one and minimize the other. We thus form an essential part of the creative process, unlike the case with a God, where our role in the grand scheme is subordinate at best. Our standards are imperfect, as well as are our capabilities, but both are subject to improvement. In the remoter reaches of future time, arguably, both will approach a level of perfection of which today we cannot dream—and all will increasingly be made right. So there is reason to hope that all sentient creatures will find a worthwhile future. But again, it is they, including ourselves, who must bring this about, and even today we have an important role to play.

The presence of evil today need not imply its prevalence in eternity, as in a dichotomy of Heaven and Hell, which many have thought must hold for God. Hell too, they would say, must be eternal along with Heaven. But this we need not accept. We are not unchanging but can and will progress and hopefully bring benefits for all. We can draw comfort and inspiration from the orderly process whereby, if all goes well, we will attain our eternal reward. In this way, we may link ourselves with the best traditions of the past and stand as comrades of those through the ages who have sought and hoped for immortality. They too, we have reason to think, will not be eternally lost, whatever their circumstances and beliefs may have been—yet we must also exercise caution. Solidarity with other times or traditions may in measured doses be beneficial but must not stand in the way of scientific objectivity or the acceptance of uncertainty and the principle that we must do for ourselves without the expectation of outside assistance.

There is much we do not know. Working hypotheses, upon which our philosophy must be based, are not the same as dogmas. We do not know if all can be made right, and we do know, with reasonable certainty, that it will not be easy, nor will the path always be smooth. Yet it is toward the distant goal of perfection—a perfection to be approached, ever more fully and grandly, but never finally attained—that we must bend our increasing efforts. From these efforts, and all that we learn and experience, we can act, rest our hopes, and draw our inspiration.

Something more should now be said in regard to atheism as it is to apply to the system offered here, Yuai, which is atheistic but also recognizes an element of transcendence. Historically, atheism has had an unsavory reputation. It has seemed to be a denial of many things people hold dear, such as moral principles, the desirability of doing good and avoiding evil, and the possibility of immortality, all of which, it was held, required a God or some supernatural or paranormal element. I hope it is becoming clear that the position advocated here, though materialistic, also avoids these difficulties. It should also be kept in mind that *atheism* means somewhat different things to different people. Here I use the term to signify rejection of belief in a supreme, sentient, controlling agent—a denial, as a working hypothesis, of the existence of God as understood in theism or deism. But other possibilities that atheists often reject, such as life after death, are still very much open. The existence of a knowing God is not a requirement, either for standards of morality or a happy, eternal future. If this point is conceded, I think a strong case can be made favoring atheism— the present version at any rate—over theism or any other system requiring belief in some form of a thinking and acting superhuman power.

Indeed, a case can be made that the absence of a God is actually an advantage to us, who, hopefully, are persons advancing overall to greater beings. The advantage is that of democracy over totalitarianism, of pluralism over enforced conformity, of individualism over collectivism, of self-willed progress over eternal submission—and of valuing all sentient beings on an ultimately equal footing. For all must advance to superhuman heights. Without a God there is no one to blame, necessarily, when things go wrong, and we can focus on righting the wrong more than who, if any, may be at fault. Enforced morality, on the other hand, is no real morality, only the arbitrary fiat "might makes right." The imagined danger, that the absence of an Overseer would lead to chaos and disintegration, or perhaps at best, an attitude of mutual cold indifference in our relations with one another, is less a threat than it may seem, as I will argue later. A society of free immortals will have reasons to work for mutual benefit, and much good can be expected to follow.

There is also the issue of atheism versus agnosticism. Some might argue that one should simply affirm the agnostic position of not professing knowledge as to whether God exists, rather than the active, atheist stance of denying this existence. It is worth emphasizing that the atheist position I advocate is not intended as a dogma, or a denial of the possibility of error, but instead, like other principles, as a working hypothesis. I think it is an important working hypothesis, however, that would be unacceptably weakened by an agnostic restatement. It is a careful affirmation, made in all sincerity, that "we must do for ourselves" and, additionally, that our expectation is that we will have to find our salvation apart from the assistance of a putative Other. It is better, then, to accept the nonexistence of such an entity than simply to profess ignorance, so long as we are willing to remain openminded at all times and consider any new evidence objectively. If somehow we are wrong, and there is a God who wishes to tell us something, we will listen—but she must take the initiative.

We have noted how the multiverse fits a pantheist conception of God, which, however, seems rather unlike what most people have in mind when they think of "God." In the same vein we must, I think, resist the approach of such modernists as Paul Tillich with his God as "being-itself, not *a* being,"[30] even if being-itself, as Tillich claims, is to somehow be "personal."[31] Clearly the God of tradition is a person, a being, a unified, sentient, supervising agent, whatever else one is to believe or disbelieve about him/her/it. Another and very appealing idea that we must also, I think, respectfully decline was expressed by Schubert Ogden: "I hold that the primary use or function of 'God' is to refer to the objective ground in reality itself of our ineradicable confidence in the final worth of our existence."[32] This too does not posit "God" as (necessarily) a sentient being who intervenes in history—it is not the usual God, even if it does clearly have application to the worldview of Yuai. For we do indeed have confidence and hope in our final worth—as immortal beings—and it strengthens the feeling that our existence here and now has worth too. But this existence, whether now or in the future, need not invoke any supreme

Being or other guiding intelligence beyond our own. More generally, while the idea of God, despite its difficulties, might be rationalized in various ways, I think a careful and considerate stance of atheism is best in view of the task before us. We must secure our own immortality and construct our own eternal Heaven. We can best do this by accepting full responsibility at the start.

Yuai and Religion

At this point it might be well to offer some words of encouragement to those who do not share the views expressed here, including believers in a traditional God. You too are loved, and you also will share in an eternal, happy future, if all goes well. Under the Yuai banner, it is not necessary to believe to be saved or even to be good, though a better attitude and conduct should reap rewards in smoothing the path. But the more important point is that all will benefit: Yuai is Universalist. And, hopefully, all will increasingly see the value of approaching all problems through the unfettered use of reason.

Yuai is not the only atheist system that offers the hope of everlasting life. Another one, and very ancient, is Jainism, which originated in India and still has most of its following in that country, though the movement has now spread worldwide. "Jains do not believe in any external God who created and sustains the world," writes one of them, K. V. Mardia, "neither do they believe in any means of redemption outside themselves."[33] Self-redemption is possible, however, and will follow with diligent personal effort, resulting in an all-knowing state of eternal bliss. So, though Jainism could be described as atheistic by the canons of Western tradition, it does contain what could be called a concept of divinity in the form of each self-perfecting individual, who is also to form a part of an orderly, harmonious whole, a "One composed of many." As we have seen, this applies to Yuai as well.

Jains are noted for their high moral character, including an intense devotion to ahimsa, or nonviolence. Jainism is not Yuai—as might be expected, there are major differences in its views of reality and of how one's activities should be prioritized. Animistic and other paranormal ideas are incorporated in its teachings, which correspondingly affect its outlook and practices.[34] But Jainism well demonstrates how belief in a Western-style God is not a requirement either for a hope of immortality or the highest ethical standards in this life.

There is also the matter of Yuai's atheism versus the more traditional Western variety. The latter, we noted, does deny the possibility of immortality, or, in other words, accepts that eventual, eternal oblivion is the common lot of everyone. Here then the concept of divinity is more decisively absent (or less emphatically present, for those who would make of this atheism a kind of pantheism with its own concept of divinity). This attitude, of course, is rooted in traditional materialism, which was formulated before the rise of modern physics, computer science, and the budding field of nanotechnology. These and other developments have given us a radically new perspective. There is reason, then, to take a more optimistic stance on the question of immortality and our ultimate fate while not abandoning the objectivity of atheism, materialism, and the scientific approach in general.

Here I will raise another question: should Yuai itself be considered a religion? Many might say no. Religion, they would argue, involves some professed belief in the supernatural, if not a God then some other reality besides what is scientifically approachable or, in short, some form of mysticism. But this would not apply to all movements usually considered religious. Theravada Buddhism[35] and modern Unitarianism,[36] with their grounding in observable reality, are cases in point. In fact, even within the small cryonics community there is the Society for Venturism, which has legal recognition in the United States as a religious organization. (This has been used by cryonicists to legitimize a "certificate of religious belief" requesting that no interfering autopsy be performed after death.)[37]

Venturism, organized by David Pizer and myself in 1986, bases its claim to be religious on: (1) concern with what is of ultimate significance; (2) commitment to understanding and bringing about what ought to be; and (3) interest in furthering human immortality and progress to a more-than-human state. Venturism does not advocate beliefs in a supernatural or paranormal reality but instead seeks to address all problems through reason, science, and technology. In particular, it favors biostasis as an approach to the current problem of death. These points well apply to Yuai as well, and indeed Yuai is fully compatible with Venturism, though rather more detailed in its model of reality and in the answers it provides to certain, fundamental questions. (In fact, a still very nascent Order of Universal Immortalism was set up within the Venturist organization in 1990 to advocate the Yuai position.[38]) Those who are uncomfortable with *religion*—often because of a deep-seated association of the term with beliefs in the supernatural and associated practices—may consider Yuai (along with Venturism) simply a philosophical system. Others may find *religion* more appropriate. This matter of terminology I leave to the reader.

Before leaving the subject some further remarks are in order concerning *faith*, which is often closely associated with religious practices and beliefs. Again the term, like *religion*, signifies different things to different people, and for that reason I have used it very sparingly in this work. But I think it does properly apply here, whatever one's feeling about religion. One can rightly place one's faith in Yuai, which can then serve as one's faith—provided the term is suitably understood in its two related senses. For some doubters of the supernatural, faith is simply belief without reason, or a system based on such beliefs, and is thus to be shunned with sincerity, but I think this is a misunderstanding. A much better perspective on the issue was expressed by Beverly Earles: "...the word 'faith' is a perfectly good Humanist expression not to be usurped by any supernatural concepts. Faith refers to a fundamental commitment to that which a person regards as of ultimate value. It is an attitude rather than a belief. It is a commitment of the heart to one's most significant beliefs and is therefore humanity's safeguard against indifference."[39] And so it should be with Yuai, for those who, like myself, feel inspired to a fundamental commitment.

But involved in this is an additional concept, that of belief, which again can take different meanings and which for that reason I have also used sparingly. In matters of religion, belief often signifies an absolute certainty or dogmatic adherence to certain principles, whereas here I have emphasized the undesirability of such an approach since it conflicts with scientific objectivity. Instead our system is based on what I have termed working hypotheses. These in turn, however, reasonably serve as beliefs, if their ultimately provisional and nondogmatic character is accepted. In this way, I think, we can have strong confidence in these principles while retaining a scientific outlook—for I do not think the important principles of Yuai will be easily overturned and may in fact endure forever.

But we are left with the issue of how effective a nondogmatic, empirically based system such as Yuai may be in addressing the important questions of life and providing assurance about its meaning. How realistic, for example, is the prospect of a good, ultimate outcome of things, a happy immortality, without a God? This will be considered at greater length in the next chapter and later, but some preliminaries are worth noting here. In fact the UI assumptions offer most interesting suggestions.

One is simply that we are, of necessity, immortal. This does not mean that a person cannot die—far from it—but that, following our death, we must eventually be resurrected in a form that allows our continuing consciousness, including awareness of our past. This would seem to follow inevitably because a person, as a construct of finite complexity, will surely be duplicated infinitely often in the innumerable possible histories of the multiverse. In some of these domains we can assume that conditions are such that recreations of people are both possible and likely. Some possibilities are intelligent scientists conducting experiments or other projects of one kind or another and purely unconscious processes that will, very rarely, yield similar results.

In effect, a duplication event, in which a person would be recreated, could be likened to a throw of dice, except that the "number of dice," or quantity of information per person, is very large. (Tipler suggests, as a generous upper bound based on quantum considerations, 3×10^{45} bits per person, equivalent to about 10^{45} six-sided dice.[40] Smaller estimates that will be considered later are probably more realistic, though the number is still very large.) More specifically, we assume, in a more intelligent duplication operation at least, that first a complete description of the person, say a computer text file equivalent to a string of bits, would be generated. From this the living individual would be recreated using advanced technology. More primitive mechanisms of duplication would presumably involve other approaches; there are many possibilities. What is important is that given any perishing individual, there is, among the unlimited versions of reality provided under Unboundedness, a nonzero fraction in which an exact duplicate or other continuer of that specific person is restored to life.

We see, then, a basis for optimism about what will happen if we die. Death is not the end. Whatever is even remotely possible is inevitable somewhere. Our continuers will waken. In effect, "we" will resume life and consciousness, though under circumstances that are unknown and could be quite bizarre. Each reviving continuer of George will think of himself, individually, as George and perceive his circumstances as possibly involving some changes from when he was last conscious, that is, before death. For example, a George-continuer revived by a race of giant spiders on a pink planet with a double sun would have to contend with some rather startling changes. (If this scenario seems disturbing, I will offer arguments in the next chapter that crudely frightening resurrections are less likely than benign ones, based on the anticipated character of the advanced beings likely to carry out resurrections. Better yet, however, is to be preserved in biostasis.)

This multiple-continuer idea of resurrection is validated by the concept of pattern-survival that follows from Interchangeability. Each continuer then must be regarded as authentic, and there is no survival of the individual except by such means, that is to say, through continuers. Under Unboundedness there are as many continuers of a person as there are possible futures for that being—very many indeed. So the observer is always splitting into beings that retain memories and other characteristics of the original and that are near-copies of one another but no more. A split happens each time something we would perceive as a random event occurs. Survival through multiple continuers is all we can ever hope for, even when nothing particularly momentous is happening and we are just passing the time of day.

The individual does not perceive the splitting but sees only certain unpredictable events. This we must imagine happening even in the face of death itself. Death could occur more than once; a resurrection must follow each decease, just as inevitably as the first time. The individual becomes the eye of a whirling cosmic storm, a lone traveler for whom the laws of physics must cooperate even if all around is chaos and destruction. This is not to say that nature will deal gently with the resurrected, only that each individual consciousness will know no permanent end. To one who is trapped in a universe whose laws cannot support immortality, yes, death is inevitable, but so is wakening under different circumstances—in another universe entirely. If the universe does not behave like Tipler, Dyson, or one of the other theorists speculate, even then hope is not lost—but we could be in for a rougher ride than we thought. It is reasonable to hold out hope, however, that the universe will prove able to support immortality, though the answer is certainly unknown; some possibilities will be considered in Chapter 14.

The individual observer, then, must be regarded as the defining principle of the world inhabited by that observer. If this observer-world should span more than what we would normally call a universe, the physics could get complicated indeed. It might defy any reduction to a mathematical theory, yet it can be said that some physics must apply. This physics too should rest not on a higher power but on a comprehensible substrate, as seems true of everything else.

Many cultures have beliefs about an afterlife, though generally the mechanism whereby death is to be overcome is a mystical or paranormal one, at variance with the materialism that is advocated here. Often these beliefs relate to persons believed already to have risen from the dead. Christianity, the most widespread religion, is largely founded on the belief that Jesus rose from the dead shortly after his execution by the Romans around 30 C.E. Hindus, Buddhists, Jains, and others widely believe in reincarnation, in which the person somehow survives though (usually) is unable to remember much, if anything, about previous lives.

From a materialist perspective, such mystical beliefs must be discounted. It is unlikely that persons such as Jesus were resurrected in the manner that ancient traditions hold and adherents believe. Extraordinary claims require extraordinary evidence— here it is lacking. For a different reason reincarnation must also be discounted—the necessary psychological connectedness could not survive the loss of awareness of a past life, whether or not a mystical soul could be said to exist. This and other putative, paranormal survival possibilities have yet to be detected in any case.

So we are left with the thought that hopes and beliefs about resurrection, up to now, have lacked material verification and rather belong in the category of wishful thinking. The views expressed here too are not immune to this problem, though at least there is no claim about extraordinary events (resurrections) hap-

pening through paranormal means. Instead the means proposed
are to be prosaically scientific, making allowance for future advances. But in another, I would say larger, sense we should not
discount hopes based on more traditional beliefs in an afterlife,
even if we do take issue with the details. Any successful outcome, an ultimate bringing to life of persons who perished, will
serve to validate what before was only fantasy. So persons of
different beliefs will enjoy an ultimate vindication, even if accompanied, as we may imagine, by great changes in worldview.

We began this chapter with an observation that hopes for immortality once rested on the miraculous. The miraculous was to
be seen everywhere—and still can be seen everywhere—provided
we allow a comprehensible miraculous. Our own capacity to understand is part of the ongoing wonder, hopefully a big part. The
wonder need not be diminished by our ability to understand it,
especially in view of the vistas that now seem to be opening. So
our hopes, even for immortality, are very much alive—something
that in no way is precluded by a materialistic view.

Happily, life's deepest secrets seem finally to show signs of
yielding to rational inquiry, and there are indications it is not at
all dismal, pointless, or meaningless on a large scale. With growing understanding we find increasing means to deal rationally
with our problems. Let us hope this trend can continue so that
our ancient dreams may be fulfilled through the constructive efforts that alone seem capable of furthering our progress.

CHAPTER 11.

Will the Good Prevail?

Up to now we have considered many possibilities for the future, particularly the more distant future. While some of these may be quite astounding—resurrections of the dead and immortality, for instance—there seems to be little assurance of a favorable outcome. Under Unboundedness we have all possible future scenarios in a very large class. What is possible must actually occur in some of the parallel worlds, which means that very bad outcomes must happen along with the good. Can the good prevail if, as might be supposed, it is so closely shadowed by the bad? Any opinions at this point must be highly speculative. However, to arrive at some feel for what I think might be a reasonable answer, we will now focus more on probabilities. These come into play because, while many outcomes are possible, not all are equally likely.

This is easily seen from basic physics: ice melting in the heat, we noted, is far more likely than water freezing. It is connected, in a subtle way, with the Anthropic Principle, as indeed all features of observable reality must be since the observer's existence must be provided for. In particular, this sets the physical laws that are observed. Another important consideration, for the long term, is the prospect of intelligent control: the self-interest of sentient beings will tend to favor certain outcomes over others. As the beings advance, one can expect that this interest will become more enlightened, and this, I think, is a major reason to be optimistic overall. While the bad can happen, and we can never entirely escape its threat, it becomes less likely if enlightened, advanced beings—hopefully including our future selves—are in control. Moreover, we have reason to hope that future society itself will be continually advancing, so that the good will increasingly outweigh the bad.

But it is worthwhile to see how basic considerations of probability and self-interest would lead to such a conclusion. Among the side benefits will be to see how such a difficult issue as what may happen after death can be rationally approached. This is actually more convenient to deal with first. Again, any answers we obtain must be speculative, and much must be considered unknown—yet I think there is reason enough for an optimistic conclusion about our eventual prospects.

Probabilities and not just possibilities become evident as soon as we consider everyday happenings. We go to sleep at night and wake up the next morning in the same room—not in some remote world peopled by strange beings. Things are pretty much as we left them. A few expected changes, such as sunlight filtering in through the window, tell us not that things have gone awry or the Great Unknown is suddenly looming before us but that events are moving in an orderly way and we have no cause to be alarmed. There is some chance, on the contrary, of a very different outcome—people die in their sleep, for instance. What may be the likely next scenarios for someone who dies is an interesting question we will consider shortly. But we live by the thought that we know, generally and within reasonable limits, what to expect. In this way, then, the probabilities of the various outcomes establish an orderly framework in which we can have some degree of confidence.

Of course, with probabilities there is one complication—observer dependence—as we saw in the discussion of the football teams in Chapter 7. This is especially significant in view of the UI assumptions. When we refer to probabilities, it has to be clear which observer we are talking about, at least hypothetically—but this should be clear in the discussion that follows. The possibility, then, of an orderly framework at the level of everyday occurrences can inspire a reasonable hope of order on a larger scale and allay some fears connected with an unthinking multiverse.

Probabilities have been implicitly considered already, as in our discussion of Unboundedness in Chapter 6. Events that are barely possible but unlikely were discounted, but others that are more typical were taken more seriously. On similar grounds, in Chapter 8 we were led to reject the idea that we are in a computerized emulation. Such thinking we need to refine in a reasonable way, if we are going to extend our present discussion to matters outside everyday experience, including the possibility of life after death. With a coin toss, for example, where we expect heads or tails with equal probability, Unboundedness tells us that the alternate histories actually happen. But it is appropriate to go further and attach equal weight or significance to the two alternatives. Similarly, in a more general setting, where some alternatives are more likely than others, the attached weights should conform to the expected probabilities. This at least will be reasonable in some versions of Unboundedness, particularly many-worlds, though it is conceivable that expectations as to what is really likely in the multiverse could be confounded.

Suppose George tosses a coin and observes heads. From the perspective of the UI assumptions, there is a certain population of George-instantiations, before the outcome of the toss is known, that develop into (instantiations of) George-continuers after the outcome is observed. To say that George observes heads means we have focused on one particular class of continuer for whom heads was the outcome seen. Very likely that will be the only kind of continuer *we* can see, but under the UI assumptions we expect that elsewhere in the multiverse are George-continuers who saw tails. By virtue of the equal probability of the two alternatives, we expect an equal measure, or balancing, of the two. As we noted, it is possible this is not so—the multiverse may somehow favor one type of continuer over the other so that it is more likely. This seems highly unnatural, however, and I can think of no good reason why such a bias should be enforced.

I assume, therefore, that probabilities conforming to usual intuition hold; a coin toss gives an equal amount of continuers' instantiations in the multiverse who see one alternative or the other, while improbable events similarly have small significance and the observers who see them are correspondingly rare. With this in mind we are better equipped to approach the more difficult questions that pertain to probabilities.

Among these are questions connected with death. Suppose we should die in a way that precludes preservation. Based on the UI assumptions, as we have noted, we cannot remain in a state of oblivion eternally but can expect eventual resurrection in the form of continuers. This says little about what the relative likelihood of any particular resurrection scenario may be, and, indeed, there is much we cannot realistically say on the subject, yet we can argue that it is a meaningful subject based on the information paradigm and strong AI. The anticipated process, though strange and foreign to our experience so far, in fact has its counterpart in everyday occurrences such as the coin toss. Here the original instantiations of the observer, equivalent under Interchangeability, are replaced by instantiations of continuers, not all of whom are equivalent. This we imagine will carry over to other experiences. In dealing with the question of what to expect, then, we must consider the relative likelihood or frequency of the different varieties of continuers' instantiations.

Some computational properties seem relevant. A person is described over finite time by the behavior of a finite state machine that in turn is described by a finite record (as we noted in Chapter 8). One such record will describe a person-instantiation before an event such as a coin toss, and another the continuer-instantiation of that person after the event. We can suppose, in either case, that the record in question covers enough time that it is clear which person we are dealing with before the event—and after the event, that it is in fact a continuer of that very person. (The finite time intervals, for instance could include the entire person's life before the event, for the original instantiation and, say, up to ten years after the event for the continuer. Actually, this would not be quite adequate either, but we will deal with the more general case shortly.) In reasonable cases we could, in fact, examine such person-records to see if we obtain an original-continuer pair in which the original matches some experiment that was performed, for example, a coin toss. This could extend, of course, to other experiments involving other observed events. Let us now consider one thought experiment.

An Investigation of Awakening

For part one of our experiment, we start with a large group of subjects, all of whom fall asleep under similar conditions, say at night in a bedroom of a standard configuration with a window to the outside. We have advanced technology that enables us to obtain person-records of all subjects at the point of falling asleep. We note that, while most subjects awaken in a normal manner after a few hours, there are other occasional occurrences, including some deaths. A freak explosion, for example, has tragically ended the lives of some subjects in a manner that precluded preservation of their remains. (Our person-records, due to certain powers-that-be, will also not be available anytime soon for use in a reconstruction.)

In part two of the experiment, which will extend over a considerable time in the future and likely include habitats in distant space, we obtain person-records of people, not necessarily limited to our original subjects. We conduct a very thorough and careful survey. This is supplemented by a thorough analysis of likely happenings in whatever other universes than our own may exist in the multiverse, using advanced understanding. In this way we can finally tabulate a catalog of all the possible continuers and their relative weights or frequencies in the multiverse. (Actually, the number of possible continuers arguably ought to be infinite, so that we could never list them all. However, we could list all of them up to a very large, though still finite size. It may be that we will want to consider more than the ten-year post-event time interval we referred to earlier. Properly speaking, this time interval refers to the subject's waking experience only, not any amount of additional time that may have passed of which the subject was unaware. However, we assume that for some, possibly very large but finite, post-event time interval, "almost all" continuers of interest are included, and we can then ignore the rest. This, I think, would reasonably follow on grounds of probability, even if we suppose our continuers are immortal beings; all in particular must have a finite past.)

Again, the property of being a continuer will depend only on the computational behavior of the person-instantiation that was analyzed. It will not depend other features, such as how that body or construct came into existence with the properties it had.

In each case of a continuer, who must have memories of participating in our sleep experiment, we extract a record corresponding to the waking experience, that is, the first hour of consciousness following the onset of sleep. Over a long period of time, then, we can build up statistical tables, giving the frequency of occurrence of different types of waking experiences, according to whatever classification schemes we would like to apply. A simple scheme, for example, might be to consider whether the first perceptions upon awakening were of dark or lighted surroundings (with borderline cases decided according to some rule). Perhaps in some fixed fraction of the cases, say 80 percent, a lighted area would be perceived. This in fact would seem reasonable if most of the time subjects simply awakened the next morning with the light streaming in. More generally, though, our scheme could be applied to any continuer whatever, including cases in which the original subject died before awakening.

We could indeed ask of the subjects who died, whether their awakening was more often in a dark or a lighted area. This, once again, reduces to a question about continuers of such people, wherever, whenever, and however they occur in the multiverse and what the relative frequencies of such continuers might be. It ought to be a meaningful question based on our digital model of person-stages and person-instantiations. This does not tell us what the answer would be or whether there would even be a meaningful answer in the sense of a fixed fraction of "dark" versus "lighted." (It could be that the more we systematically surveyed, the more this fraction varied, without ever settling down to one value.)

But the question, What are the likely features of your next perceptions? is, at heart, a question about your continuers and the relative frequencies (if well defined) of continuers whose perceptions will have one characteristic versus continuers with another. In this way, at least, the *question* is meaningful; we can sensibly ask what the experiences following death will be like. We can ask, in particular, whether they will be pleasant or unpleasant, frightening or reassuring, and so on. The answer will depend on the nature and relative likelihood of the various processes that would produce continuers. This brings us back to those who worry over the possible indifference, overall, of any process within the mindless multiverse. Along with the desirable outcomes are others very much less so, for example, we could awaken to torture by some fiendish advanced intelligence. So how can this inspire confidence that right will prevail?

Let us consider, for a moment, a scenario for a resurrection. Although much cannot be known, I submit that an advanced intelligence would be the likely agent for this complicated act of construction, and, moreover, such a being would likely be benevolent rather than indifferent or sadistic. First we consider alternatives.

An uncontrolled, unconscious process instead is conceivable, and it might be a cause for worry. Suppose, for example, that an improbable accident created a continuer on an airless planet or in the path of an active volcano or exploding star. Such a process would have no way to know or care what it was doing, so beyond the assumed fact of its having successfully staged the resurrection, things could go awry in a hurry. By analogy, if a monkey typing at random were to successfully reproduce Shakespeare's *Hamlet*, after that we would still expect gibberish. (At least, it might be argued, these putative, short-lived resurrections would not be as bad as being in the clutches of a malevolent being who would be interested in long-term horrific effects and able to carry them out.) Yet these scenarios seem less likely than a house being built by an avalanche.

There is a second possibility along roughly these lines but which, I think, must be given more consideration—a more focused uncontrolled process, yet still accidental in essence. It is suggested by the fact that people exist who have vivid recollections of a past life and believe that they are some earlier person. Discounting any paranormal implications we may attribute this to some form of mental abnormality or, just possibly, no abnormality but lucky "throws of dice"—accidents affecting the brain at various moments during life, possibly many of them very early, that add up to a particular effect. And, indeed, a biologically based process like this must be far more probable than the creation of a being on a lifeless planet through such an effect as Brownian motion. It is thus possible that a person could come into existence who just happens to have authentic memories of a past individual, with the appropriate psychological connectedness to qualify as a continuer of that individual. The question must then be raised whether someone, on dying, might expect to awaken as such a continuer or, in other words, how likely, relatively speaking, is this possible form of coming back.

To deal with this question we must consider other possible mechanisms for generating (instantiating) continuers. There is one other mechanism that I think deserves consideration, which is the conscious, purposeful efforts of advanced intelligent beings to create continuers. In fact, I think this is the overwhelmingly likely route whereby a continuer of a specific, deceased individual will come into being. The case of the biological accident (which would land the continuer in a still-mortal world), though far more likely than pure Brownian motion and perhaps other unconscious, nonbiological mechanisms, is still a more-or-less random choice among alternatives, most of which do not involve creation of continuers. Also, in this case, we would depend on a developing life-form (for example, the human race, or conceivably another intelligent species) at a certain stage of its history, before it attains mastery of its own biology—a period we expect to be transient and limited.

I think then that intelligent agents will normally be involved in the creation of continuers of past individuals, who in turn will be formed in a purposeful, deliberate way with a high probability of success. This will avoid the numerous misses and mistakes we would expect with an unconscious resurrection process. Since technology we do not have now must also be required, the intelligence must be advanced beyond our level. To be advanced very much beyond our level, moreover, would almost guarantee that those responsible would be very long-lived, by analogy with what I expect to happen to the human race if things go reasonably well.

An advanced being would, I think, be very likely to adopt a stance of benevolence toward fellow beings because it should be evident that its own long-term interests are best served in this way. Acting cruelly toward others would invite retaliation, while acting well would have the opposite effect, that is, would tend to reap benefits in return. (Acting cruelly toward weaker beings who might be unable to retaliate would be opposed by stronger beings of benevolent nature.) The middle ground of indifference would avoid both the good and the bad consequences of interactions with others and thus be less rewarding than active benevolence. The best policy then would simply be the Golden Rule at a suitable level, carefully and reasonably applied—befriending others with the expectation of benefits in return. All this should be quite clear to an advanced intelligence, who would have long since adopted a generally benevolent stance.

That future, advanced beings would be benevolent is not just idle speculation despite the unavailability of direct confirmation. Robert Axelrod, for example, shows in *The Evolution of Cooperation* that under appropriate conditions a "weak altruism" is the best strategy for maximizing long-term but selfish interests: *A* is friendly to *B* so long as *B* has not been unfriendly to *A*.[1] The advantage of altruism is greater the cheaper the altruism is. And the cost of altruism to an advanced being might be expected to be low because of advanced technology, much as better computers have greatly lowered the cost of computation.

Such a being must have self-interested reasons to become involved in such a project as a resurrection of a much more primitive being, including a mortal human. Just any reason will not do, though clearly the cheaper it became the more easily a sufficient reason could be found. Again, advanced technology should make operations in general cheaper (and in particular make possible, that is, finitely expensive, what is infinitely expensive or impossible today). Still, while resurrections under various conditions might be expected among the many things that should become possible, some approaches will be preferred to others and thus be more probable.

Arguably, it would not be of serious interest merely to see a race of primitive beings proliferate and individually suffer and die the way creatures, including humans, do today. (Would we similarly want to proliferate a vast colony of rats?) It would also be of little interest, relatively speaking, to resurrect a human and keep it at the human level indefinitely as some sort of pet. Sadistic motives should be unlikely, as we have noted.

A different motive and, I will conjecture, one that would be of more interest to an advanced being, would be to see into what other advanced being the human creature would develop, given the opportunity. This advancement to more-than-human status must involve certain concessions on the part of the resurrectee. Procreation, for example, could no longer play the role it does now to the average human. This might seem a difficult adjustment for some, but probably our advanced resurrector could find ways to smooth the path considerably. Thus I would expect no worse an adjustment problem than, for example, is suggested in the remark of Jesus to the Sadducees that is noted in Chapter 3 in which men and women would no longer contract marriages but live instead "like angels."

It is worth remarking, too, that I do not expect procreation—in the sense of creation of brand-new sentient life-forms—ever to end entirely. It can be regarded as a special case of resurrection, "resurrection from a null being"—more will be said later. But surely there will be great changes in the ways in which new life-forms are made, along with the very sorts of life-forms themselves, and in the part that the processes of creation will play in the lives of those already here.

The advanced intelligence, then, would resurrect a human (or still more primitive life-form) with the expectation that the result would, eventually, be another advanced being with whom it could converse and otherwise interact on an equal footing. The latter, however, would remain a continuer of the original, primitive form. The primitive original would, I think, be viewed with continuing interest, and hopefully, at minimum, a reasonable understanding and respect, much as we today are interested in the origins of any historical phenomenon.

The first successful airplane is the Wright Flyer I, a single-passenger craft that first flew in December 1903. It now rests, carefully maintained, in the Smithsonian Institution. It continues to hold our attention today, not despite but largely because of the great advances in aviation that have occurred since its first tentative lift-off. True, in its own day it was a technological marvel too, but part of its importance lies in how greatly it has been superseded by improvements in the very features it prototyped.

It is interesting, in this connection, to speculate briefly about the possibilities for advancement that may one day exist for a newly restored human. It might be thought, for example, that our resurrectee could never "catch up" to the presumably very advanced entity by which he or she was revived since said entity, eternally vigorous too, would also be making progress. (I assume, for simplicity, that the resurrecting entity is a single individual.) One possible remedy would be for the resurrector to recreate, not the human in original form, but an already-made, advanced continuer. But this rather drastic step would, I think (usually), prove unnecessary and also less interesting in the long run. Better, in most cases, would be to let the human develop, more-or-less autonomously, from the human level. As for the catch-up problem, I think this would resolve itself with time. Eventually, the former human would be half as old as the resurrector, then 90 percent as old, and so on. Overall levels of advancement should equalize, and interactions on an equal-for-equal basis should become the norm.

But long before the two beings were, for most purposes, equal, the younger should be able to contribute ideas the older would find interesting. The "tree of knowledge and creativity," as we might call it, is no simple totem-pole with the items linearly stacked but has myriad side branches, each with its own complex specialties. There is far too much of interest, it is reasonable to conjecture, for even an advanced intelligence to explore in a reasonable time. This would leave the door open for other explorers to find further items of interest as well as provide for rewarding interactions based on an exchange of information.

This we certainly find today in mathematics, the sciences, and the arts. It is hard to imagine the trends not continuing and deepening as we become more advanced, even if unifying developments are taken into account. Physics is unlikely to become simpler or uninteresting, for instance, even if the long-sought "theory of everything" is found. And if everything in physics were explained so that it became a dead science (as was feared erroneously in the nineteenth century), there are other disciplines that we do not expect ever to die. We noted how Gödel's results make mathematics in some sense inexhaustible. As might be expected, its close cousin, computer science, contains many riddles too, and it is not difficult to formulate problems there that are mathematically unsolvable. These sources alone should provide ample food for thought and research, quite literally forever, and there is no doubt much more of inexhaustible interest too.

A World Not Perfect but Perfecting

Although we might expect that, overall, the world would become an increasingly better place under the tutelage of more-than-human, developing intelligences, it still would never be perfect. Bad things could and would still happen, and, indeed, by indications, this must always be so. From the observer's point of view, events happen at random, which must always allow the possibility of misfortune along with benefit. In particular we cannot rule out the possibility that a good, advanced being could turn bad and inflict harm upon an unfortunate, lesser being. According to Unboundedness there must always be domains in which this is happening, and it must continue to happen regardless of how advanced and benevolent our own civilization may become. However, we—our future selves—can act to make such possibilities increasingly rare and academic in our universe at least, and I think this is what we shall accomplish for reasons of individual self-interest. We in our crude imaginations today can easily conjure up very bad scenarios, someone tortured horribly for eons, for example. But these occurrences should be so uncommon as to be, for all usual purposes, nonexistent—like air freezing solid in a bonfire. Should a bad scenario ever start, we would expect that either advanced beings or perhaps other, fortuitous events will intervene to halt it, in almost all cases, before it gets very far.

Thus there should be no chance whatever of an infinite period of misery or eternal punishment. Satisfaction or happiness is possible and, I think, indefinitely extensible through rational efforts. Such efforts, moreover, are in general mutually reinforcing—the happiness of one person should normally contribute positively to that of another, and this trend will, hopefully, not diminish but increase as people become more advanced. In view of this, the only outcome that any being will tolerate, long-term, is that individual's personal, eternal happiness and, indeed, every other person's eternal happiness. The unending happiness of all, then, should be the only long-term possibility, though it should be kept in mind that this is a long-term possibility, an eventuality, that could take a long time to materialize.

This may seem to contradict Unboundedness, but remember, Unboundedness applies to *finite* histories. *Infinite* histories are not similarly provided for because probabilities and not just possibilities become increasingly important as the finite size or number of events at the substrate level (changes in the quantum state, for instance) increases. Whole classes of infinite histories could thus be ruled out because their combined probability is zero. Specific types of happenings could be enforced or excluded depending on such properties as the longterm behavior of intelligent beings. The latter, I have claimed, will tend toward increasing benevolence, and thus each entity will be rewarded in the end, not punished. But this reward will not be reached by uniformly pleasant routes. Instead, there can be many wrong turns and much privation for the unwise or unlucky before the higher ground is reached.

Something further should be added here, relating to the possible role of challenges, hardships, and even evil in one form or another in the continuing scheme of things. Some would argue that, without continuing challenges, life would become boring and meaningless—and use this as an argument against the desirability of the sort of outcome I have been advocating, in which evils are to be overcome. But I think we can reconcile the position that evils are to be overcome with the thought that life must pose fresh challenges to be meaningful. A boring world would itself be a problem to deal with, so one way or another problems will come up. I foresee no end to challenges that will make life worthwhile overall. This might encompass even considerable hardships—whose resolution eventually leads to benefit. To say that good will prevail does not mean that evil will not continue to exist—for surely it will—but that certain ultimate negatives such as eternal oblivion or torment are avoided. And life overall, for each individual, should be rewarding and progressing without limit, meeting the challenges that come.

It is worth remarking that despite this largely optimistic assessment, there is certainly much we do not know. We can have confidence that things will turn out right in the end, but that end could be a long time coming, and before it the road could be rocky. A healthy respect for this unknown element tells us that we should make our decisions with care, especially in the matter of coping with the possibility of our own death—a topic we shall return to in later chapters.

Free Will, Determinism, and Progress

Everyday experience tells us that the future is affected by the choices we make today—what we do now makes a difference. This is a good place to consider the issue of free will since its absence, as in a deterministic universe, would seem to preclude our ability to really make choices. But in a practical sense this is not so. Certainly from our point of view, the ability to choose is independent of whether the universe is deterministic or not; effectively there is free will even if events in an overall sense are predetermined.

And in a reasonable sense our behavior *is* predetermined. Determinism prevails, so again, there is no absolute free will even though in a practical sense the will is free. In the course of our existence we are instantiated in finite state machines. The behavior of such machines (the output and state transitions) depends in turn on the inputs and the state transition table—nothing more. A complication, it is true, is introduced because a person is a probabilistic device—we cannot predict the exact behavior, but we could predict the probabilities of the various possible behaviors of the system or characteristics derived from them. Over the long term, if immortality proves possible, we should outgrow any finite construct such as a particular, finite state machine. But even then a person should be no more complicated than a (probabilistic) Turing machine with an infinitely inscribed tape. Again the behavior could be explained through prior, or at any rate, external, causes. Other interesting arguments against the will that is free in a deep sense, based on twin studies and brain experiments, are considered in Chapter 15.

The dependency of the will raises some interesting philosophical issues, including that of responsibility. A criminal may claim that he cannot be held responsible for his actions. He is just a machine, and his behavior results from external causes over which he had no control. He might then argue that there is no basis for penalizing him, and he should be set free. This, however, overlooks practical goals that society should reasonably seek, such as: (1) making restitution, as far as possible, for the harm done; (2) rehabilitating the criminal; and (3) deterring similar crimes by others. These goals are appropriate whether the will should be considered free or not. Coercion of the criminal is justified because his bad action was voluntary, that is, not forced upon him against his intentions or wishes, whatever the ultimate causes of these intentions may have been. He thus can be held morally responsible even if, at a deep level, there are comprehensible, external causes for all his behavior. Measures such as fining or incarceration may be crude from the vantage point of more advanced beings who might have better ways of resolving the problems, but they can still be the best choices we have. This will hold irrespective of the issue of determinism, the important question being whether a greater evil would result from not taking such measures.

The position advocated here, that determinism is consistent with free will in a practical or virtual, if not absolute, sense—and thus with moral responsibility—is known as compatibilism. It has a distinguished following—and also a distinguished opposition.[2] I think compatibilism is fully justified—if nothing else, holding individuals morally responsible should have the effect of promoting good and reducing evil, as we have seen. The benefits, overall, should more than outweigh any negative effects. But I think also that the presence of underlying determinism forces us, in a larger frame of reference, to soften our stance against the wrongdoer. In a deep sense an evil person, whose actions are predetermined, never "deserves" punishment even if coercive measures are called for. Though there is moral responsibility, there are also reasonable limits. An infinite penalty or eternal punishment would never be called for. No justification for it on grounds of practical necessity or offsetting benefit seems possible, and in view of the attribution of behavior to external causes, no one can be said to deserve punishment beyond such considerations. Determinism thus provides one more defense of Universalism.

In general it seems reasonable to conjecture that more-than-human persons of the future, through growing understanding and benevolence, will advance to states of greater overall meaningful happiness. All must realize, at some level, that this course of advancement is in their best interest—so the evil person must inevitably change for the better. Once again, this does not mean that temporary departures from advancing goodness are precluded or that good progress will always be swift. It does not rule out forms of benevolence that would seem not that at all—until we too attain a greater enlightenment and have rethought our position. There are many possibilities for hardships, and the unknown is ever with us. And some hardship, perhaps quite a bit, may be desirable to provide challenges that give life greater meaning. But overall we can have some confidence in the happy outcome. One can argue too that inequities in the happy state of different individuals will tend to be further leveled by the mutual exchange of information, based on the great volume and diversity of ongoing research and overall, constructive effort. For in effect, all will have become scientists, artists, and all-around creative geniuses, though each will have particular gifts and specialties not duplicated by the others.

The progression to individual, eternal happiness must follow even though, overall, the multiverse is a kind of steady-state entity whose features remain fixed. From the individual perspective, things would progress even though from an imaginary outsider's perspective they would stay the same. If this seems contradictory, we might compare the scenario to an escalator in which people are continually ascending while new ones take their place at a lower level. In fact, there is a reasonable point of view in which time does not flow at all but the future is already here. Individually there is progress, while overall conditions are constant. The future is malleable from our point of view, even if fixed from the standpoint of a hypothetical, detached observer. (There is no such observer in reality; all real observers must be in some universe, though not necessarily ours.)

As for happiness itself, we have noted before that prospects seem good based on the relative ease with which, even today, pleasurable mental states can be induced—though this alone will not be enough. Life must have meaning beyond mere pleasure. But an important consideration is that our future control should extend not only to the external world but also into our own psychology. In our quest for meaning, we will be able to adjust both the events that occur in the world at large and our reactions to those events. Pitfalls are to be expected, and some no doubt will be deep, but overall, again I find cause for optimism.

In particular I see no future for intolerable pain, even if brief; we will simply redesign ourselves so it will be impossible (or vanishingly unlikely). Like death, it is another thing to get rid of. But I see a considerable usefulness for variations in the states of pleasure, ranging possibly from painful, but not unbearable, on up. (Arguably there should be pain, in some degree at least. Also, I will grant that states of feeling are far more complex than simple pleasure or pain; however, all should always be bearable.) The alternative of just one state of pleasure (necessarily maximum since improving it would create another state) would leave no incentive for creativity or further development: not the best for the would-be immortal. In general, I would hope that an increasing variety of richly rewarding experiences becomes possible. While negatives (in the sense of less than the best) should not disappear, the good should so overshadow the bad that an overall, growing happiness becomes possible and even inevitable.

I think it would be reasonable to expect more advanced beings, such as we will hopefully become someday, to succeed in the pursuit of happiness in ways we could scarcely imagine. This, we can hope, will accord with some rational notion of enlightened self-interest, though precise details cannot be specified. As for what sort of lifestyle and world this will lead to, in large part we will just have to wait and see. Among other things, we may expect to have far better brains and thus be able to fathom things that far elude us today. Many of the problems that seem intractable now may be found to be trivialities, while others, presently unknown or little regarded, may prove surprisingly important and difficult. Overall though, the possibilities for self-understanding and self-modification should diminish the prospects for avoidable disasters such as wars, and this alone is ground for optimism.

The Doomsday Argument and the Fermi Paradox

Some other issues have been raised in connection with our future prospects that are worth addressing. One simple objection to the idea that humans and our civilization might be very long-lasting comes by considering how long humans have existed already. This is the Doomsday Argument advanced by astrophysicist Brandon Carter and elaborated by Richard Gott and especially philosopher John Leslie.[3] To illustrate the basic idea, it is estimated that about 100 billion (10^{11}) humans have been born on Earth so far.[4] The fact that we find ourselves in this group but not further along, say only in the first 100 trillion (10^{14}), must say something about the likelihood of there ever being 100 trillion humans. For if that number is destined to be born, it is very odd that we should happen to find ourselves only among the first thousandth part. More typically we should expect to fall somewhere in the middle, say between the 10 and 90 trillionth human. On the other hand, if less than another 100 billion humans are to be born, at current world birthrates of over 100 million a year,[5] the last human would enter the world before a thousand years from now.

Even if the birthrate should drop to only a million a year, the end would come within 100,000 years, which is minuscule on the cosmic scale. This says nothing about just how the end would come, only that we must expect it from one cause or another, which could be anything from an exploding supernova to a human-caused nuclear firestorm.

But it seems to me that there are ample grounds for challenging this argument, one being that perhaps infinitely many humans (or other intelligent creatures spawned by our civilization) are destined to appear in our universe over infinite time. In that case, no individual would be typical—all must appear among the first N beings for some finite N, thus much nearer the beginning of the list than the infinitely remote end. A different sort of argument accepts that the number of humans, here taken to mean members of the biological species Homo sapiens, will be finite because we will soon get beyond the human level.[6] Indeed, we ourselves could be among the last humans who will be born, though not the last intelligent life our civilization will bring into being. Newer intelligent beings will presumably be based around artificial constructs, when such have been developed that are clearly superior to flesh and blood. At that point, superhuman enhancements, such as greater intelligence in bodies immune to aging, should become possible to humans as well, so that they (we) can also enter the ranks of higher life-forms.

We know we are doing some unprecedented things now, and still greater accomplishments seem likely. There is no guarantee against a pessimistic outcome, but something that few people want—doomsday—is something we can take rational steps to avoid. Meanwhile, I think there is insufficient evidence to take a pessimistic prognosis too seriously, except as a warning of what could happen if we do not act with our best long-term interest in mind.

Another related problem is seen in the "Fermi paradox," noted by physicist Enrico Fermi some decades ago, that to date we have not detected extraterrestrials.[7] (Here I discount claims of having done so, which, I think, have been uniformly refuted whenever they could be carefully investigated.[8]) On the face of it, this could provide a case against the likelihood that good will prevail with our species through its own self-advancement.

Other civilizations, so the argument runs, must exist in our universe—the conditions for life that occurred on Earth must occur elsewhere as well, and there are many billions of star systems. Yet we do not see these civilizations. Where are they? One ominous possibility is that advancing civilizations are likely to self-destruct relatively quickly (again suggesting the Doomsday Argument)—with the implication that ours too is not likely to survive and prosper. Another is that advanced civilizations exist but they are not particularly benevolent. Certainly we do not see them coming to our aid, curing our diseases, settling disputes, alleviating famines, and so on, as advanced, caring creatures might be expected to do.

There are interesting counterarguments against a pessimistic conclusion, however. The strongest, I think, maintains that life, and especially advanced intelligence, is a rare phenomenon and unlikely to spontaneously develop, as we seem to have done. Advanced extraterrestrials are either nonexistent in our universe or distributed so sparingly that an encounter with one is not likely to have happened. (This of course would not preclude the occurrence of many intelligent species across the multiverse—for in that inconceivably vaster domain we expect a much greater profusion of such things than in our own, more limited theater. But we can only detect and contact those who are part of our universe.)

The rarity of life is suggested by, among other things, the evolutionary process as we have deduced it from the fossil record. There we see several stages, any one of which might have been unlikely to happen, even if environmental conditions were as favorable as possible. These include: (a) the transition from non-life to life itself; (b) the development of photosynthesis; (c) the appearance of the more advanced, eukaryotic cell; (d) the advance from single-celled to multicellular organisms; (e) the emergence of sentient life-forms; and (f) the emergence of human-level intelligence from nonhuman sentience. Several if not all of these difficult-seeming stages appear to have happened only once, and all were necessary for intelligent humans to emerge.

As one case in point, most life-forms other than bacteria, including all animals and plants, are composed mainly of nucleated or eukaryotic cells. Each such cell is an enormously complex mechanism containing a smaller structure, the nucleus (a "cell within the cell"), and an intricate array of organelles and other structures. By a complicated procedure the entire assemblage is able to reproduce itself; the cell divides into two cells which, by ingesting material, grow into nearly exact replicas of the original. In contrast a bacterium—a smaller, simpler, prokaryotic cell—lacks a nucleus and many of the other structures. From traces in the fossil record it appears that life-forms were prokaryotic for several billion years until, relatively recently, the far more complex eukaryotic form emerged by a process that is largely unknown and possibly very unlikely.

If the long evolutionary sequence needed to make beings such as ourselves requires one unlikely step, it could be enough to make intelligent life a rarity or even unique in our universe; or several steps together could form a prohibitive barrier. An additional possibility is that the entire evolutionary sequence is not that unlikely, given the surrounding conditions, but those conditions themselves are very rare. The sun must have burned very steadily for billions of years, while the earth maintained a nearly constant orbit. The planet Jupiter seems also to have been important in deflecting large asteroids that could have struck Earth and extinguished all life. Occasional, smaller objects that did get through, however, may also have been crucial to the evolutionary process, such as the impact, about 65 million years ago, that appears to have killed the dinosaurs and opened the way for mammals to develop.

In 1996 some dramatic findings were announced that seemed to have a bearing on the likelihood of life evolving: traces of ancient organisms, it was said, were seen in rocks from Mars.[9] The rocks themselves had been blasted away from the Red Planet by meteoric impact some 16 million years before. By chance their wanderings in space placed them, a few thousand years ago, on a collision course with Earth; they crashed in Antarctica. Painstaking analysis of the fragments, discovered in the 1980s, established the likely Martian origin and also that the rocks were actually several billion years old. Moreover, they contained traces of what some claimed were biological remains, including tiny, rod-shaped "fossils."[10] This sparked a spirited controversy, but in the end, the case for life looked doubtful, though the proponents continued to press their claims and extended their investigation to other Martian meteorites.[11] It seems safe to conclude that so far we have not found any compelling evidence of life that originated independently of earthly forms. (If, to the contrary, the claims of Martian life are vindicated, there is the intriguing possibility that earthly life still did not originate independently but developed from organisms that survived a journey from Mars, or, conversely, Martian life could have originally come from Earth.)

There is another interesting argument that claims extraterrestrials are very rare or nonexistent. An advanced civilization might be expected to send out probes to other points in the universe for various purposes: to observe, claim territory, or even establish benign contact with other intelligent life. For maximum effectiveness the probes could be made self-reproducing, processing whatever raw materials they encounter in space for this purpose, that is, building copies of themselves. The copies in turn would receive further orders to explore, occupy, and reproduce. Such "von Neumann automata" (John von Neumann pioneered the study of self-reproducing automata in the 1950s) might then be expected to be almost everywhere. This would follow, presumably, if even one small swarm of such devices was ever turned loose—and not relentlessly hunted down. Such a swarm could be launched by a single sufficiently advanced and motivated individual and might occupy many galaxies after a few hundred million years. The fact that alien probes are not seen is one more piece of evidence that we are alone. Such evidence, of course, is not conclusive. Maybe the von Neumann probes are all around us but advanced enough that we do not recognize them. But the absence of evidence, while not the same as evidence of absence, gives us no better choice than to discount this as a serious possibility.

The grim possibility also remains that civilizations are plentiful but self-destruct quickly. But this, I think, can be called into serious question if we keep in mind that such civilizations, composed of many individuals, would not be expected to be uniform. Some would last longer than others, and we might expect them to contain large populations at some point, as our own does now. Some of the many individuals would be lucky and survive longer than average. In some cases the civilization would surely be spread some distance into space before the start of the cataclysm that is to end it. A planet might be rendered lifeless by a nuclear exchange or killer nanites. It would be more difficult and less likely, however, that creatures spread over a sizable volume of space would be uniformly annihilated. So even though, as usual, we do not know the answer, we certainly have reason to doubt an explanation of the Fermi paradox based on inevitable doomsdays.

Another possibility is that advanced civilizations are out there and stable but not particularly benevolent, that is, they know about us and realize we are a struggling, fledgling bunch with many problems they could help with—but they choose not to. (As noted, they may have even sent out a swarm of von Neumann probes, only cleverly disguised so we do not notice them. The probes could be refined in other ways so as not to pose a threat, though, of course, not offering assistance either.) This would be more hopeful for our own future, since doomsday is clearly avoidable. But it would still pose a problem for our philosophical position, that sentient beings tend toward good will as they progress in other ways. This property in turn seems essential if we are to have confidence that, over all, good will prevail.

Yet an alien civilization that could contact and benefit us but chose not to would not necessarily be acting out of malice or indifference. To them, in only an eyeblink we must be immortals too, or perhaps would self-destruct. At present, they could make us immortals instead, and solve the remaining problems, both technological and psychological, that we must otherwise solve ourselves. The outcome, in so doing, would be a kind of hybrid— a race of immortals (ourselves) partly shaped by our own progress, partly created by friendly visitors. Would they wish to create such a hybrid, or wait the eyeblink and let us immortalize if we will? To me it seems entirely possible they would just prefer to let us develop and earn our stripes on our own.

This argument has a weakness, related to our rebuttal of the short-lived civilizations argument, for in a sizable population of individuals there should be a variety of opinions. Some of our putative space creatures could be interested in saying hello and eager to try, even if many others were not.[12] In balance then, I find it less convincing than the hypothesis that we are alone. (It is possible too, however, that more advanced creatures would tend toward uniformity on a matter such as this—see below.) But it does raise an interesting issue, which is what is really "best" for us at our present level, given that we would like to go on to something higher.

We have some significant transitions to go through, psychologically as well as technologically. As an example, it is often said that we are mainly machines to perpetuate our genes, as we have noted, which would seem to provide poor motives for the would-be immortal. Our putative extraterrestrials, again assuming they are out there, could be waiting to see how we deal with this problem, knowing their immediate intervention could produce something more like a rat farm than the wise immortals we need to become. It is possible that they will intervene if we seem about to destroy ourselves—perhaps with severe penalties—out of ultimately benevolent motives, of course.

There are other reasons that advanced life-forms could be able to contact us but are unwilling. One might be a gulf separating the reality they inhabit from what we think of as the world. They could exist as programs in a fast-running, advanced computer, which to them forms a vast cosmos full of wonder and delight. They could be so happy with this mode of existence (which they would have spent considerable effort perfecting) that the idea of setting forth to explore the rest of the universe or even sending out automated probes is uniformly unappealing. Travel to other distant points in space in search of possible lesser life-forms to benefit would not be a priority. The rat farm argument could serve as one justification of such a policy, but in this case interstellar travel itself must have less interest—there would be so much to see and do right at home.

It is entirely possible too that an advanced life-form *is* actively intervening, though in ways that are invisible to us. This could take many forms: von Neumann automata, other sophisticated monitoring devices, or the aliens themselves. They might be disguised as familiar objects, distributed over swarms of intercommunicating nanites or otherwise expressed in ways that escape our notice. Or letting the imagination run wild, we can conjecture that the whole universe we see, ourselves included, is a computer simulation in some vast machine operated by a more-than-human intelligence. Such possibilities we can neither confirm nor deny. But one thing seems clear. There is no intervention of which we are aware. It is most unlikely, then, that anyone "out there" wishes us to be aware of its presence, or is expecting any response from us based on such awareness. Once again, we must fend for ourselves.

In summary, while the absence of extraterrestrials could be a sign of trouble to the idea that an intelligent species will naturally develop into a benevolent race of superbeings, it is no strong indication of this negative possibility. We might well be alone in our universe. Other alternatives consistent with benevolence are plausible too, and there is no reason to abandon a hopeful stance on the prospects for our own species.

Meeting Other Challenges

One other difficulty can be raised, however, based on the notion that we must fend for ourselves. In doing so we would simply be carrying on an already ancient tradition—the evolution of life on Earth—though one hopes on a loftier plane, with more rewards for the individual, including unlimited life span. Some argue, on evolutionary grounds, that our future history might not be so benign, nor would the individual fare so well. The rationale is, in keeping with the evolutionary process, that a species that reproduces best survives best, regardless of other consequences. Nature has not found much survival advantage in extremely long-lived individuals. Most sentient organisms, even if protected from predators, disease, and starvation, do not survive many multiples of the time it takes them to grow to maturity and reproduce.

In particular, the development of superior technology with the ability of an organism to self-modify could lead not to kindly immortals but to rapacious von Neumann automata bent on replicating at maximum rates. Hordes of such devices, reminiscent of giant, swarming insects, could then spread throughout the cosmos, devouring all in their path. There would be a fierce struggle for survival, including much internecine warfare, which would further hone the capabilities of the advancing swarm and make it increasingly difficult to stop. The case for this science-fictional nightmare can be reinforced by the argument that it is favored by the principle of natural selection—in a struggle for survival, the most effective replicators win. This has been true, certainly, of life here on Earth. However, not all life-forms are insects, nor would it be expected, in a technologically advanced future, that mad replicators would hold all the survival advantage.

In fact, the possibility of von Neumann automata would constitute one more hazard, like nuclear weapons, that good immortals must guard against. I think, however, that with reasonable precautions the danger could be kept to a minimum. (Meanwhile, benign versions of such devices might be found useful.) Nothing closely approaching a von Neumann automaton has yet been made. It should not be trivial to create one, which would deter an occasional malicious attempt to do so. A horde of such devices, if they did come into existence, could be opposed by killer devices focused on exterminating or disabling them. (Much later we could consider resurrecting any dangerous, sentient mechanisms that regrettably had to be destroyed—this time in the form of benevolent continuers.) In all, I am confident that our posthuman continuers will find ways to deal with the possible threat of proliferating automata, as with other dangers. But one can also hope that dangerous, sentient devices requiring severe measures will be quite rare, much as was conjectured in the general run of the posthuman population.

An issue is sometimes raised, in connection with Unboundedness itself, that certain courses of action would be beneficial when common sense says otherwise. Consider the suicide lottery. You purchase a state lottery ticket and instruct a confederate to kill you painlessly in your sleep unless you win. (This could be facilitated by having yourself anesthetized before the results of the lottery are announced.) In this way, so the argument goes, you (your continuers) would only wake up in those parallel worlds in which you did win. Our earlier discussion suggests otherwise, however, since continuers should be possible—indeed inevitable—even after death. Assuming that winning the lottery is unlikely, it would seem that most of your continuers, far from being instantly wealthy, would find themselves no better off than other suicides. Most likely, then, you would emerge from this without the intended benefit. A similar rationale would caution against a simple but diabolical solution to the problem of poverty, in which a few lucky poor people are selected at random and made rich while the rest are all euthanized. No, the many victims will not simply wake up in those parallel worlds in which they were among the lucky!

At least it seems likely that the problem of poverty will be enormously alleviated by posthuman civilization—of course, our very notions of wealth and poverty will no doubt change greatly.

But there is reason to think that future life will prove rewarding to all in ways that, once again, escape human imagination.

When we are more-than-human, our sharpened intellects and refined sensibilities will hopefully find many wonders to investigate that are completely beyond comprehension today. One issue is surely to be of concern, however, which we can appreciate now: the fate of the universe. Will it last forever and can it support immortal life? Based on Unboundedness, we have reason to think that not all is lost even if the answer is no—immortality in the face of a collapsing universe is still possible and good can still prevail. But a yes would be reassuring at a level we can grasp. As yet there is no definitive answer—there are some interesting possibilities, however, which will be explored in Chapter 14. The problem of resurrection, which concerns the more immediate future, will be addressed first, then the issue of biostasis.

CHAPTER 12.

Resurrection

The possibility of resurrection is necessary to the whole philosophical position developed here—it is a cornerstone of Yuai. Scientific arguments favoring resurrection have been considered already in preliminary fashion. This chapter will further explore the issue, with emphasis on the philosophically difficult and numerous cases of people who died and were not preserved with any intention of a physical reanimation. Much of the discussion will also apply to the "easier" possibility of resuscitation from biostasis, and a small part will apply more specifically to this case. A general theory is presented, starting with why resurrection is necessary. Our model of resurrection is built on the UI assumptions and the notion of pattern-survival. The necessity of resurrection in turn will follow by appeal to the three principal working hypotheses that were introduced in Chapter 4.

Let us now consider the first of these: Life, fundamentally, is good. To describe life as "fundamentally good" is to make a positive assessment but a careful one, intended to take account of reality as it is. Caution is justified because bad things happen—evil exists. In what sense, then, can life still be "fundamentally" good? I propose, as the beginning of an answer, that life can be fundamentally good despite the presence of evil, if in the end wrongs can be righted. This should apply directly to each individual. For each person, then, the wrongs that occur should be redressed progressively as an ongoing process, with full restitution occurring in the limit of time.

Next, let us consider the second principal hypothesis: Death is an imposition and ought to be alleviated and eradicated. ("Ought to be" is here understood in the sense of indicating a desired effect, irrespective of the feasibility of achieving that effect.) Death is identified as a wrong to be righted. On the individual level, it means that death must not be the end: there must somehow be a resurrection. Otherwise life cannot be fundamentally good, at least for some individuals. A wrong to some individual is, simply, a wrong—meaning a wrong to every individual. This latter position I will argue in more detail in Chapter 16, on grounds of enlightened self-interest. For each of us, then, death is a wrong that must be righted. We are committed, irrevocably, to consideration of the task of resurrecting those who have died.

Finally let us go to the third hypothesis: Rational means, rightly inspired, are the proper tools for understanding all things and solving all problems of interest. A framework of scientific materialism, then, is a necessary tool. (If some other rational approach could be found this might be employed, but in lieu of that, some version of materialism is the only choice we have.) This must apply even to such a problem as resurrection, which by the canons of traditional materialism seems intractable and forever beyond reach. New possibilities have been provided by scientific and conceptual advances, as we have seen. This has made feasible a philosophical approach based on what I have called the UI assumptions. Starting from these, we have tentatively considered a possible mechanism for resurrection in which a continuer of a lost human, who would remember being this earlier person, is to be created (instantiated) through advanced technology. We shall now look more closely at this possibility, which involves such issues as personal identity.

Resurrection is, of course, the sort of problem whose solvability depends on its detailed formulation. Like squaring the circle, it can be impossible in one version but feasible in another. In the approach we have considered, the UI assumptions provide a pathway to the authentic recovery of lost persons. Unboundedness, with its implication of a multiverse, ensures that there will be enough happening overall that such a thing as the creation of replica persons can occur and, indeed, that such creation is unavoidable. Moreover, within broad limits, the creation of a person with a random set of memories will have authentic historical antecedents. Interchangeability establishes the necessary link between a replica and a person of the past. Persons endure, when all else fails, through pattern-survival. There are some interesting precursors to this thinking that are worth examining briefly.

The Afterlife: Doubt and Rational Hope

The possibility of Unboundedness can be seen in the ancient, materialist theory of the Epicureans. The number of atoms was infinite, though the number of kinds of atoms was finite.[1] According to Epicurus himself, "The atoms suited for the creation and maintenance of a world have not been used up in the formation of a single world or of a limited number of them, whether like our world or different from it. There is nothing therefore that will stand in the way of there being an infinite number of worlds."[2] A similar opinion is echoed by Lucretius: "...nothing...is the only one of its kind, unique and solitary in its birth and growth....So you must admit that sky, earth, sun, moon, sea and the rest are not solitary, but rather numberless."[3] In effect, all finite constructs must be repeated infinitely often, which, by a slight extension, should stretch to happenings involving these constructs over finite times. If we also grant a kind of Interchangeability—that constructs composed of the same kinds of atoms arranged the same way are one and the same construct multiply instantiated—we then have the possibility of resurrection.

Yet Lucretius would deny this possibility and instead argues the case for a finite existence followed by eternal oblivion, in the manner of traditional materialism. His reasoning depends on the failure to observe people who can reliably report a past existence, which would require awareness both of a vanished past and a discernible present. The possibility that such beings, though not extant (discounting some claims), might eventually appear, and more particularly be constructed someday, by means yet to be developed, apparently did not enter his mind. (The claims of certain individuals regarding memories of a past life, considered last chapter, will be examined again in this chapter.) Such constructions, however, seem almost certain possibilities if nano-technology can be perfected, as we have noted.

It is interesting that Epicurean-like ideas of recurrence have gained a following in modern times. More seriously than for ancient advocates, they have furnished hopes of an afterlife. This we have seen with Nietzsche (Chapter 2). J. B. S. Haldane (1892–1964) also shared much of this viewpoint and adapted it to harmonize with twentieth-century (quantum and relativistic) physics. In both cases constructs like ourselves—sharing our thought patterns and effectively us—will reappear but without memories of a past life. But clearly this amnesia is not logically required since memories like everything else are contained in the physical structure of the body, so that a suitably formed replica must reproduce them along with other features. If time is infinite as imagined, near-copies of us must be created that have the necessary brain information amounting to psychological connectedness with a past self or, in other words, continuers.[4] So resurrection does become a possibility, even an inevitability. But this sort of resurrection would happen automatically or blindly, without the control of an intelligent agent, though for reasons we have examined it does not seem the most likely or most desirable possibility. (There is another problem too, in that both thinkers imagined that events take place in a single size-bounded universe, which leads to an Eternal Return—more on this to come.)

Fedorov's effort at a scientific theory of resurrection, which was based on Newtonian mechanics, was considered in Chapter 2. Basically, the universe is seen as fully, accessibly deterministic and reverse-deterministic: the past in particular should be deducible in minutest detail so that deceased individuals could eventually be mapped and then reconstructed. History has a single timeline (as with Nietzsche and Haldane), and the single-world ontology supports resurrection in a particularly satisfying way, inasmuch as the information necessary for a resurrection is always part of the historical record and only awaits discovery. (In this case, Interchangeability may not be strictly necessary, though it would still be convenient. We could recover the exact, original atoms of a deceased person and reassemble them—though we would also have to deal with the problem that the same atoms must sometimes be present in different persons at different times.) Unfortunately, the Newtonian-Laplacian view of accessible determinism on which this idea is based has been well-refuted by experiment. It simply does not describe reality except in an approximation that becomes increasingly rough as the scale of distance shrinks. For insight we must look to more recent physics.

Actually, modern quantum-based physics does not strictly deny the possibility of accessible reverse-determinism. A principle known as phase conservation does provide for full recoverability of information under ideal conditions. Roughly, phase conservation means that a complete historical record of any interaction of particles, including any finite happening whatever, is "written" in the photons that emanate from the interaction. If we could collect all these photons and analyze them, even if they had been streaming into space for millions of years, we could determine the history in question to the minutest detail.

Some hint of this principle is given by the thought that, if we had a powerful telescope trained on some distant galactic civilization, we might learn a great deal about that civilization over the course of centuries, even quite a bit about specific individuals. It would have to be a very powerful telescope indeed, however, to penetrate very far into space with the needed resolution. As a wild extrapolation from today's resources, a visible-light, reflecting telescope with a mirror the diameter of Pluto's orbit could peer about 1,000 light years into space—still well within our own galaxy—with enough resolving power to begin to distinguish objects the size of human faces. (Although such a construction seems unlikely, its effect might be achieved someday by distributing many smaller telescopes in space and training them all in the same direction.) In any case, such a strategy would fall far short of the requirements for phase conservation.

Tipler's Omega Point Theory, in which a collapsing universe is to lead to an explosion in information processing (effectively, the Omega Point), does call for all photons eventually to reverse their outward streaming and converge.[5] The photons might then be captured and analyzed by an advanced civilization. The theory (which is also a many-worlds theory) thus calls for the complete reconstruction of the history of the universe as a preliminary to a universal resurrection. But I think this is highly unlikely. Based on present evidence the universe does not seem destined to collapse,[6] but even if it is, it is questionable whether life and civilization could persist under such conditions and be able to carry out the project.

Tipler's theory retains Fedorov's reverse-determinism, but, as noted, it is a many-worlds theory. (Interestingly, then, it supports Unboundedness and thus offers another possibility for resurrection, in this case through the UI assumptions.) Some other theories do not provide for accessible reverse-determinism but do have a single-world ontology. History, they imply, has a unique manifestation; only one possible version of it really happened. But in general, we do not know which version that was—and never can know, beyond the limited information that still survives in our records or what might be deduced from archaeological discoveries yet to be made. (I think it will be clear that these future discoveries, however serendipitous, could never begin to tell us all we would like to know. The literature and lore of the numerous tribes that perished before the invention of writing is lost, for example, to say nothing of details at the level of individuals: memories, brain structure, and so on. Indeed, very many people are not recorded at all, though perhaps much more survives of ancient individuals in certain forms, particularly recoverable DNA, than we are presently aware of.) But whether the worlds are many or single, this lack of knowledge would not absolutely preclude resurrections, since a sufficient description of a past individual could be arrived at by accident.

More generally, through a systematic enumeration process (feasible somewhere, if we accept Unboundedness, though doubtful otherwise) we could arrive at a description of everyone who ever lived, from which the resurrection of everyone could follow. In Chapter 10 we briefly considered the amount of information that would be involved in a description of one individual: an upper bound at the quantum level is 3×10^{45} bits per person though, as noted, smaller estimates will be more realistic. Ralph Merkle, for example, estimates that to adequately describe the brain at the molecular level would take about 10^{25} bits.[7] Even this would be overdoing it; focusing on the really essential structures such as brain synapses might reduce the total below 10^{13} bits, while a more realistic guess may be about 10^{18} bits.[8] In any case we see that some finite number N must suffice—this again being the requirement for just one person. The number of all possible persons then would be at most 2^N, which is a large number indeed,

RESURRECTION 337

even if N is only 10^{10}, yet still finite. The feasibility of creating or recreating all possible humans would then follow from Unboundedness. (It is worth noting that this possibility holds regardless of whether we assume that, in keeping with strong AI, persons in their functioning are digital devices.)

For a single-world ontology, creating all possible humans in this way could pose the problem that only a small subset of the possibles would be actual persons who lived. The rest would be unhistorical fantasies, fully fleshed out but fictional characters; indeed, these must enormously outnumber the "real" people. This difficulty we considered in Chapter 4, where we noted, however, that it is nullified by the assumption of Unboundedness. In the totality of all existence, all possible persons, regarded as finite constructs, must have actually existed and in fact must recur, over and over. More generally, persons do not exist in isolation but in surroundings—whole worlds—that also must have existed as finite constructs and must also recur. Each person must have existed, then, in a historical setting conforming to what that person perceived as "real."

These conclusions gain strength from the arguments we considered in Chapter 8, invoking the information paradigm and the computational view of the historical process. They in turn allow the possibility of multiple instantiations, and, indeed, Unboundedness would seem to provide infinitely many instantiations of all possible finite constructs.

A resurrection would then be achieved if an exact copy of a person (more precisely again, person-stage) prior to death could be created. To fully satisfy the demands of exactness would require creating an object in the same quantum state as the original—then, according to modern physics, the two objects would be literally the "same," as we noted in Chapter 7. (Persons uncomfortable with the idea of surviving in a replica should thus have no difficulty here, though as it appears there would be considerable difficulty in practice with recreating the exact quantum state.[9]) However, our quantum state is constantly changing, yet "we" survive; far less stringent standards must reasonably apply.

Requirements for a Resurrection

Based on Interchangeability, it should be adequate for a resurrection to restore a functioning individual with feelings, awareness, and intentions that are the same as in an earlier person. If the new person feels the same as the original, has the same memories, dispositions, and so on, then a success occurs, even if differences imperceptible to the subject are present. (The problem of deciding when such an identical being would recur is presently beyond our understanding, but I conjecture it will be resolvable in the more advanced future.) In particular, it should make no difference if the new individual's physical body is different from the original so long as there is perceptual identity. It is possible, in fact, that the new physical structure could be very different, for example, a computer emulation.

Here we have been assuming that a resurrection must in some way restore exact conditions that were perceived prior to death. This is clearly unnecessary, however, and would sometimes be undesirable, for example, if the subject died in pain. There is also the philosophical conundrum that we could restore innumerable individuals corresponding to different points in the life of the original—more will be said on this shortly. For now we wish to consider how the conditions of a resurrection might be reasonably varied without disqualifying it. The main possibility, which I expect would be applied, would be to create not an exact replica but a continuer.

We would have to create an individual, that is, who considered herself to be a later version of the past individual we were resurrecting and met reasonable criteria including retention of memories of the earlier individual. (Again it is unclear what full range of criteria should apply here, but presumably this can be worked out in the future.) In the terminology we used in Chapter 4, the continuer would have to exhibit an appropriate kind and degree of psychological connectedness with the earlier person-stage. This should pose no fundamental problem; on waking from sleep, for instance, we do not have identical perceptions to those we had just prior to falling asleep but are only continuers of our previous self.

But there is a potential problem. Interchangeability, strictly interpreted, may seem to provide for resurrection only under a very limited circumstance involving exact duplication. If we consider the example of someone, say, who died in an accident and who, moments before the accident, was in perfect health, we could recreate a perfect replica (instantiation) of this individual (again, a person-stage) moments before death and call that a resurrection. (We might assume this person was dreamlessly sleeping before death, that is, unconscious, to avoid any possible difficulty over losing the last few moments of consciousness.) Our grounds for considering this to be a true resurrection are straightforward: the replica person is an instantiation on an equal footing with the original. As much as the original can be said to "be" the person, so must the replica be the person by Interchangeability. The replica, on the other hand, does not die with the original but lives on, becoming a continuer of what the original had been before. The person, therefore, lives on in this continuer just as would have happened through some other continuer, for example, if the accident had not happened.

We thus enable the person to continue his/her existence through the replica, and we have carried out a true resurrection. We must understand, of course, that this is only one possible continuation of the person and that there can and (by Unboundedness) will be others. But this in turn is what is always happening; by Unboundedness we are constantly splitting into continuers. Our one self is fissioning into many selves.

But Unboundedness can now resolve the potential problem if, rather than creating an exact instantiation or perfect replica of a person, we simply create (instantiate) a continuer. Done properly, this continuer would conform to a real history in which we did create the exact instantiation and the continuer developed from that. In the latter case the continuer would "be" the person in question as we have just established. On the other hand, if we simply created an exact copy of the continuer without going through the developmental process, that (instantiated) continuer would be an instantiation of a real continuer and thus "real" too. Creating a continuer, then, should qualify as a true resurrection as well.

The continuer option would have many advantages, including relief of pain, curing diseases and infirmities, and more radical changes for certain cases such as dangerous criminals, who could be rehabilitated. (With the possibility of modifications, especially radical ones, would come the potential for abuse—a problem that must also be dealt with but presumably could be. It would also be necessary to consider how far a modification could go and still claim to "be" the original person, even in a later version, that is, whether we really had a continuer—again, this would have to be worked out.) In fact, the continuer option opens the prospect that everyone, even the most unsavory and reprobate, could be resurrected in a fully rehabilitated form, which would be valuable and justifiable to others on grounds of enlightened self-interest.

Person-Segments and Person-Stages

A further discussion of some aspects of the resurrection problem will be useful, to tie in ideas we have considered starting in Chapter 4. A person-stage, the person at a particular time, is a limiting case of a person-segment, the person persisting over an interval of time. The person-segment is represented or "implemented" by one or more instantiations, which are processes in the multiverse that "run" the person in question; these processes are treated as equivalent and interchangeable. When the time interval is short, we approach an instantiation of a person-stage in which a momentary mental state is expressed. A person-segment, on the other hand, will embody a succession of person-stages, so that an instantiation of the segment, in the course of its run or execution, will pass through instantiations of the intervening person-stages with the later stages representing continuers of the earlier stages. Later segments similarly are continuers of earlier segments whose time-intervals do not overlap. Here it will be simpler to consider earlier and later stages rather than segments.

An instantiation, we have noted, need not express all that is part of the person during the time in question. Here, however, it will be convenient to assume that the instantiation occurs by activating a "self-contained" construct, a person-replica that does have these elements. So memories and other features must be present in some accessible form that would eventually (at least), in the course of continuing execution, exert an effect on the states of consciousness. If this were not so, these elements would have to be "inserted" from the outside at appropriate times to exert the needed effects, which means they could just as well have been present all along, though hidden from consciousness.

An instantiation of a person-stage P_2, through a replica or construct that is self-contained in this sense, could be considered a resurrection of any other person-stage P_1, of which P_2 could be said to be a continuer on grounds of psychological connectedness. This is our basic notion of resurrection. Again, it is not intended to be the most general notion possible, which would depend only on some mechanism whereby a suitable instantiation could be sustained. But I think that, by a reasonable argument, the extra generality is not essential, that is, would not enlarge the domain of resurrectible beings.

So in particular this means that P_2 would be a more developed version of P_1, someone who, as the instantiation runs, would remember being P_1 at an earlier time. This would cover the case of P_2 being simply a later stage and P_1 an earlier stage of the same, continuously living person, though we do not usually think of this (survival of P_1 in P_2) as involving resurrection since there was no death interval. In this case P_2 arises from P_1 by a gradual process we call "growing older"—normally there is both physical and psychological continuity between P_2 and P_1 as well as a degree of psychological connectedness. However, the requirements of being a continuer, which are to depend only on psychological connectedness, could be met under more general conditions: there is no necessity that P_2 should physically develop from P_1. There is no requirement that P_2 even be at a later time than P_1, though the memories, perceptions, et cetera, of P_2 must be such as to conform, in a reasonable way, to what would be present if P_2 was in fact both later and more developed.

This will, no doubt, seem to pose a great difficulty to some. If P_2 is not really a later version of P_1 but only a replica, albeit an exact one, but still existing at an earlier time, what ground do we have for calling P_2 a continuer? (In practice I do not think such a conundrum is likely to arise very often, even in an eternally advancing future, but let us allow it here for the sake of argument.) On the other hand, if time precedence is important, then some criterion besides pure psychological connectedness must be met, which I have disallowed. The issue of time precedence was considered in Chapter 6; I tentatively suggested a resolution of the problem based on the endless possibilities for exact repeats of finite histories in the multiverse. In this manner the notion of "true" time precedence ultimately becomes fuzzy and not so important. In the case at hand, P_2 would have an exact replica that either *was* truly in P_1's future or at least was not definitely *not* in P_1's future and thus would have a plausible claim, on more usual intuitive grounds, to be a continuer of P_1. By Interchangeability, however, P_2 must share the properties of this replica, thus P_2 must also be a continuer. More will be said later on time precedence and the related problem of causality, mainly in Chapter 15.

Let us now back down from the above thought experiment to consider another issue raised earlier. Strictly speaking, resurrection requires instantiation of a person-stage P_2, which in turn is a continuer of some other person-stage P_1. P_1, we should then say, has been resurrected and lives on or survives in P_2, a property that depends on the fact that P_2 is a continuer. On the other hand, the relation of continuer is transitive: P_2, being a more developed version of P_1, must also be a more developed version of P_0, where P_0 is any earlier stage or predecessor of P_1. In other words, to resurrect P_1 is to resurrect many other person-stages, including all those of which P_1 is a continuer.

In these resurrections we are clearly not limited to the one person-stage P_2; any other person-stage P_3, which is also a continuer of P_1, would do as well. P_3 would also resurrect any predecessor P_0 of P_1. But there is also the possibility of a resurrection of P_0 that is not a resurrection of P_1. An instantiation of P_0 itself would have this property, and, more generally, so would any (instantiation of a) continuer of P_0 that was not a continuer of P_1. (Such a continuer would either be a predecessor of P_1 or have memories diverging from P_1 but agreeing on the subset of memories pertaining to P_0.) So from the one person-stage P_1 we could carry out many resurrections of separate individuals. To say we could (which, once again, ought to become physically feasible in the future) is to raise the issue of whether we should, which will be examined in later chapters.

The Problem of Identity

There is another issue our discussion raises, which has to do with the idea that a continuer is the "same" as the earlier person-stage that is continued, something we first encountered in Chapter 4. Clearly, when we say the continuer is the "same" we do not mean this in the sense of truly (numerically) identical or even, as in the case of different person-instantiations, functionally identical. I am a continuer, for instance, of myself as a preschooler but hardly identical. On the other hand, there is one property of being the same that is usually regarded as holding between different person-stages: transitivity. If P_0 is to be regarded the same person as P_1, even if at an earlier or later stage in life, and P_1 similarly is the same as P_2, then usual intuition would have it that P_0 must be the same as P_2. This accords well with ordinary experience, as can be seen if we consider people at different stages in life. However, it must break down if we consider the possibility of different, initially identical copies of a person-stage, as above. So, for instance, both P_1 and P_2 could have started as exact copies of P_0 but then developed separately. Both then would be continuers of P_0, hence the "same" as P_0, but neither would be a continuer of the other, thus not the "same" as each other. Transitivity of identity must fail.

Some, such as Robert Nozick, have insisted that transitivity of identity must hold and would reject the idea of survival of a person through multiple continuers. Thus in *Philosophical Explanations* Nozick allows that a person may survive in a "closest continuer," but that no survival occurs—only nonexistence—if there are two or more continuers equally close.[10] To this I respond that if there really is a multiverse, as the evidence suggests, then we are simply forced to accept survival through multiple continuers or give up the idea of survival entirely. For then we are constantly fissioning into multiple near-copies (continuers), with no one copy particularly closer than the rest. Of course I am not denying that the actual occurrence, side-by-side in the same universe, of multiple continuers would create problems for existing legal and social institutions—but that is a side issue.

But an objection might now be raised about our semantics. Perhaps we should not speak about personal identity being carried or transmitted through continuers—if so basic a property as transitivity must be given up. (For then "identity" is no longer even an equivalence relation, let alone expressing what we often think in other contexts—namely, that two ostensibly different but "identical" things are one and the same in all respects.) Certainly this objection has substance, but I would propose a different concept of identity to apply here. This I think it important to legitimize because the idea of survival is important to us. We like to think of ourselves being identified with a past person—that in some reasonable sense we are the same person, only now grown older and, we hope, wiser and better in other ways. It is a valuable source of meaning. The "identification" we make need not equate us with the past self in all details nor preclude the possibility of some other present self being identified with the same past self, as in the case of multiple continuers. We thus need to think of identity as a sharable commodity.

So personal identity, as understood here, will refer to a connection that exists between one person-stage and another. P_1, a person-stage, is identified with P_2 and said to be the "same" person in case either P_1 is a continuer of P_2, or vice versa. In either case, P_1 need not be the same in all respects, or identical, to P_2. The relation of being a continuer is transitive, but that of being the same person is not. In principle, many person-stages could arise from one original and identify with that original yet recognize their mutual differences and not identify with each other, beyond the common origin. I see no reason this recognition of differences should interfere with the value each would attach to the ties that existed with the original stage. Put another way, if two different people were one and the same person at some point in the past, each could still value that past in a personal way, with no necessary impediment from the fact that some other different individual also personally valued it.

I hope it is becoming clear, then, how survival is to be effected through continuers, and particularly, how the possibility of resurrection is to be realized under a functionalist version of the concept of personhood. We see then how resurrection must appear from the viewpoint of the resurrectee: a conscious state (pre-resurrection) followed by another conscious state (post-resurrection, after activation of the continuer) with essentially nothing in between. This would hold regardless of how long an interval in time or space might separate the pre-resurrection and post-resurrection states or even if the two were to happen in different universes. A deceased person, prior to resurrection, is in one sense truly gone and not "somewhere" yet also remains latent in the everlasting fabric of reality and is unavoidably involved in a process of coming back.

Onticity

There are some difficulties that still need to be addressed besides the problems of forgetting and false memories (see Chapter 15). We will now consider an issue I will call *onticity*.

This is a concept I apply first to a hypothetical historical record, a purported fact about some occurrence in the past. I distinguish between the surviving historical record—information that has been straightforwardly transmitted from the past or is recoverable through investigation—and other purported historical information. Information that is part of the historical record I will call *enontic.* For example, we know with reasonable certainty that Lucretius (full name, Titus Lucretius Carus) was the author of *De Rerum Natura*, a poetic treatise on Epicurean materialism dating from around 55 B.C.E.—this information then is enontic. There is much we do not know about Lucretius, however, such as what he looked like and whether he was born on May 15. This information then, which does not contradict the historical record but is not contained in it or derivable, so far as we know, from surviving sources, is *hyperontic.* Finally, despite our scarcity of knowledge, we can be sure Lucretius never had a pet pterodactyl—to say he did contradicts the historical record (here understood to include the fossil record, and all other reasonable sources of past information); such details I will call *xenontic.*

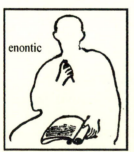

Lucretius demonstrates onticity. *Left:* Lucretius is known from historical records as the author of a treatise, *De Rerum Natura* (enontic information). *Center:* possible image of Lucretius, not derivable from but not contradicted by historical sources (hyperontic information). *Right:* Lucretius with pterodactyl, something that *is* contradicted by historical sources (xenontic information).

We have then three classifications of onticity for purportedly straightforward historical information. The classifications can be extended naturally to the case of a resurrection, as follows.

Suppose the resurrection is made from preserved remains that fully capture the necessary information, as might possibly happen through cryonics. The information, then, is entirely part of the historical record and only awaits a straightforward application of future technology to realize the living person. This then is an enontic resurrection. In the usual sense it can be called fully historical—it is derived entirely from surviving information about the past. In Chapter 4 we briefly considered reasons why the fully historical resurrection is to be preferred, if possible, something we will soon examine at greater length.

The second case is where the resurrection results in someone who fits the historical record, but to reasonably fill out or "complete" a person, some details had to be invented. It may be that only the most minor details must be filled in this way, as in the case, say, of a cryonics patient who was frozen with a slight but definite loss of identity-critical information. Or at the opposite extreme, we may have to reconstruct the whole person from scratch: a prehistoric man, say, no identifiable particle of whom exists, nor any record whatever. This type of resurrection then is hyperontic. Though less desirable (generally) than the enontic, it is a form we must consider, given the importance overall that must be attached to resurrection. All individuals from the more distant past, for instance, can at best only be resurrected hyperontically.

Finally, a xenontic resurrection would use information that contradicts the historical record. A Lucretius who remembered his pet pterodactyl would qualify as xenontic—such memories must diverge substantially from our history, based on what we can conclude from fossil and other evidence. Conventional intuition would describe this as a simple case of fictional memories, but Unboundedness assures us otherwise. *Fictional* instead is only a relative term. Different historical timelines to our own are real too and so must be the persons who took part, whenever present. The xenontic case, though, is arguably of less interest than the other two—at least for now and some distance into the future. We might say that the xenontic person more properly belongs in his own milieu—let him then be resurrected by his own people, where he will fit better (be enontic or hyperontic) and perhaps more readily find fulfillment. However, I forecast that sometimes we will be interested in xenontic resurrections (for example, his own people may not exist)—more about this shortly.

One thing to note before proceeding further: the three categories of onticity are presented as if sharply defined, which we know is far from true. Historical records contain blemishes and complexities that make it difficult to decide, in some cases, what their onticity really should be. This will no doubt continue in the future, even in the face of additional evidence we might uncover (barring complete recovery of the hidden past). Difficulties are increased by differing opinions about the nature of reality, or about the personal experiences of oneself or others, et cetera. Some, perhaps many or most, of these differences may also be resolved in a more advanced future, but clearly onticity is a far more complicated subject than can adequately be treated here. Still, the threefold classification seems a useful beginning.

It should be noted, however, that by using the term *historical record* I include all future discoveries minus any future losses of information. With reasonable care perhaps the future losses will be minor, particularly of information that is well known generally today and that we consider important. (One exception, however, is the memories of living individuals today, many of whom will die without biostasis.) On the other hand, with new discoveries and deductions, the actual record should be more complete in many particulars than it now appears to be, though numerous and large gaps must remain. I think probably that, in view of the likely progress in nanotechnology, we will be able to recover substantially the full, surviving historical record, up to our present era, in a few centuries at most. Most of the information of interest to us will be found, very likely, on and near the surface of the earth. Other valuable information would be captured in the photons streaming outward from Earth at the speed of light, but that is inaccessible to us, by appearances. By Interchangeability, then, this information is not even uniquely defined, being instantiation-dependent. We must confront a past with ambiguities, including different, equally authentic, mutually inconsistent versions of people in our approach to the problem of resurrection.

Ontic Robustness, Dreaming, and Past Lives

There are two interesting properties we have noted about resurrections that appear to be guaranteed by the UI assumptions: on one hand, every sentient being who lived and died will be resurrected; on the other, every resurrection is authentic. Given anything that could reasonably be considered a sentient being, one with coherent memories of plausible, causative events, there is a history that gave rise to that being through those very events. And some allowable histories must produce continuers (resurrections) of that very being. The two properties together—the universality and authenticity of resurrections—I will refer to as *ontic robustness.*

A further comment now seems in order in regard to the claim of authenticity. I have characterized a resurrection as the creation of a continuer of a person who actually lived, someone (at minimum) who was historically part of some parallel time stream. That is really the only requirement for authenticity—and it seems reasonable that it be the only requirement, in view of Interchangeability.

For instance, we cannot tell that we are not, at this very moment, running in some computer simulation in a universe far removed from our own universe. We could, in other words, be xenontic resurrectees, about to be informed by an advanced being of the true state of affairs. Although it seems very unlikely (we have never had such an informative visit before and do not see any evidence that it is about to happen) still, among our instantiations, with which we are identified by Interchangeability, there must be those for which it is true. They are about to learn something very surprising, and, meanwhile, they are identical in thoughts, feelings, and perceptions to us. Our present identity then must somehow encompass them too and, in particular, extend over parallel universes that are not causally connected in the usual sense. (It could also, conceivably, extend to constructs in our own universe that occur at earlier or later times than our own, as we have noted.) It is not necessary, then, for the resurrectee to be causally connected to the original person as we normally understand it, that is, enontically. Acceptance of a resurrection on this basis, however, raises other interesting issues. There is the phenomenon of dreaming, which for our species is normal. Less routine but still not so rare are the cases of people who claim to remember past lives.

Dreams in particular offer a challenge that needs to be resolved if our theory of resurrection is to stand. While dreaming we generally believe that what we seem to experience is really happening. It certainly seems real to us, though afterward we often recognize many absurdities and inconsistencies with reality as we usually perceive it. On awakening, then, we normally revise our opinion about what has transpired and shrug it off with "Oh, I was dreaming." We do not interpret our new circumstances (wakefulness) as amounting to a xenontic resurrection. It is clear, nonetheless, that the dream sequence corresponds to some real happening—the mental events were real enough, it was just our perception of these events that was temporarily off-base.

Our reasons for concluding this seem straightforward—the dream sequence does not fit the rest of our perceptions about ourselves and our remembered past. Additionally, it has precedents—we have had other experiences before that exhibited a similar ephemeral character. These fleeting experiences we also confidently label "dreams" and note that others like ourselves do the same thing for like experiences of theirs. If, on the other hand, a "dream" were the whole or main part of our remembered experience, it would no longer be a dream. So I think the possibilities of resurrection we have considered do have substance, even if there are complications. There is even the possibility that one's main perceptions will be seen eventually as a dream—unlikely though it may seem. By the same token, even a dream personality, if reasonably well-defined, should have actual substance in some parallel universe.

Another interesting problem is posed by persons who claim to remember a past life, prior to being born. In the best cases these claims are offered in all sincerity with no intent of deception or perpetrating a hoax. This is not to imply, of course, that anything of a mystical nature should be attached to these claims. A plausible explanation would be that material from dreams is not always recognized as such but instead is attributed to experiences prior to this life. A similar mechanism could account, in some cases, for other paranormal encounters, such as visits with space-aliens. Another possible cause that some have conjectured is temporal lobe epilepsy.[11] More generally, the brain is a most complex organ. We may imagine it can be affected in numerous unsupernatural ways, depending on circumstances, to produce a variety of "supernatural" experiences in the minds of certain subjects.

In any case, some have vivid tales to tell, which are not necessarily contrary to any of our historical records, though no major, new enontic facts have been brought to light and verified by way of confirming such "remembrances." It is clear then that this extra information is not historical in the usual sense but fictionalized; at best then it would qualify as hyperontic. We considered such cases in the last chapter, in connection with the possibility that a continuer of some specific individual could arise in this way, with the conclusion that it was an unlikely route though not impossible. Here we consider the other half of the ontic picture, which is, given some individual with ostensible memories of a former existence, should we then regard that person as an authentic resurrection?

In view of ontic robustness, it is clear that under appropriate circumstances we would have to consider such a person as authentic, a resurrection at least of the hyperontic or xenontic variety. By Unboundedness, any reasonably consistent set of "memories" must belong to an actual person from some real history. A person who reasonably felt himself to be a continuer of such an individual and had corresponding memories, dispositions, and so on, would qualify as a true continuer. Again there is nothing supernatural or paranormal about this resurrection possibility. Yet I doubt such resurrections will be taken very seriously in the future, at least in the way their proponents now imagine. As we progress beyond the human level, we will increasingly understand such effects and their causes, and especially when, as we may expect, our progress allows us to treat and alleviate these causes, perhaps by various sorts of brain enhancements. No doubt we will then look indulgently on the extraordinary experiences some were subject to in our human "childhood." But I do not see great homage being paid to effects that seemed to fly in the face of science, if explainable in other ways, as they probably will be.

Many have dreamed, and been convinced at the time, that they were past individuals—but in their waking states do not claim or feel themselves to be such persons. In a similar vein we can imagine that becoming more-than-human—or perhaps a simple cure at the human level—will induce a "waking state" for the past-life advocate. Those of today with strangely functioning brains who are convinced thereby of having paranormal experiences will, I think, see matters in a different light. It is worth noting, nevertheless, that in the hopefully infinite future, I expect there will be a place, eventually, even for the ephemeral "beings" of our dreams and our brain pathologies—more on this in Chapter 16. But I think that long before this, though still well in the future, we will focus on more normal creations of past individuals, which will be carefully planned and carried out by the more-than-humans we will have become.

There the prospects are arguably encouraging, if the future is to be truly open-ended, and patience, wisdom, and good will predominate as they should. Ontic robustness means that we could reconstruct an entire population of humans and their ancestors, secure in the thought that all these beings really lived. Moreover, assuming mutually compatible memories and records, they all really lived in the same universe, which really had the history they collectively record. (The earlier life-forms we might want to resurrect, however, not in original form but as more advanced continuers.) In fact, I expect such a resurrection project to happen, but only after our more immediate problems of survival have been solved and we are more or less comfortably settled in an immortal lifestyle. (In particular, the full enontic historical record extending from recent events back to the oldest fossils and beyond should have been recovered using advanced technology. Also, we clearly must have vast resources, both computational and material, before a project of this sort could be seriously attempted.) The project would focus on recreating in minute detail a history that fit our surviving records—it would be no worse than hyperontic, though for obvious reasons it could not be enontic. (Well before this, all enontic resurrections will have occurred, that is, any feasible resuscitations of people from biostasis.)

Along with such a project, Unboundedness tells us that, inevitably, many similar projects would also be in progress in parallel worlds. One version of Thomas Paine, say, would be created in one universe, another in another, and so on. Any specific Paine back in 1809, the year of his death, facing the destruction of important identity information, could still be confident of awakening in a project of this type or in some other setting. He would not have to fear that while someone like him might be created, it would not be him. (His deistic hopes of eventual resurrection, then, would be fulfilled, whatever his expectations may have been as to details.) On the other hand, he would not have to greatly fear awakening in the "wrong" universe—if we assume that the majority of his resurrections were hyperontic. For in this case, through Interchangeability, he must equally fit and be part of many different possible historical timelines. (If he were to be awakened xenontically, on the other hand, and thus indeed in the "wrong" history, we can hope that the benevolent resurrectors would provide some form of reasonable compensation.)

Heaven Despite Hardships

A being, once resurrected, should not want to die again: otherwise, what a futile exercise! Instead, immortality should be sought, and hopefully it can be achieved. Of course, based on the UI assumptions, we are hopeful that some form of immortality can always be achieved. The best kind, however, must involve no further death, or equivalently, all further resurrection must be enontic. (In a sense, then, enontic resurrection is not true resurrection but instead only an awakening from a more or less extended sleep.)

We are thus offered a prospect of Heaven that, in important ways, strikingly parallels the concepts found in various religions. There are interesting differences too, of course, the main one being that this Heaven is to be engineered by ourselves and/or others like us. Another difference with many traditions is that Heaven is yet to be realized, not something that "souls" have departed to already and where they now enjoy a state of consciousness. Indeed, our Heaven as implemented will tend to be "last in, first out": those who die later can expect an earlier resurrection since the technical difficulties should be less.

One property that Unboundedness may seem to guarantee is perpetual enonticity, which would generally be the best form of everlasting survival. Anyone facing the prospect of dying from whatever cause, we could argue, will always escape death in some of the parallel worlds, however unlikely. But these are far from the only scenarios in which they (their continuers) can expect to reappear. In certain circumstances such a favorable outcome would be very unlikely, as with a plane crash or the suicide lottery we have considered. Perpetual enonticity, under conditions of perpetual serious danger, is a myth, an impossible expectation. The only way it might hold is if death is simply not likely, as in a future with advanced technology that successively reduces the probability of dying, a topic we will examine in the chapter on immortality.

At an opposite extreme to this, consider the fate of people in a universe that cannot support eternal life. They and their civilization must perish. If their perceptions clearly included the approaching cosmic doom, it seems very likely that their resurrection, anywhere else, would be xenontic. In their new surroundings it would be most unlikely that the state of the world would also indicate approaching doom, or doom just past, in perfect consistency with the other disaster. On the other hand, such a resurrection would be a wonderful act of more-than-human compassion in rescuing those who would otherwise be lost. We can expect such individuals to appear as replicas in our own universe, if our civilization endures and progresses, as part of our "labor of love." This then is a way that life can survive the self-destruction of the universe that gave it birth. Unlike Tipler, we do not have to assert, of a universe unable to support eternal life, that its entire contents never existed in the first place.[12]

One difficulty that might be raised about this idea of xenontic resurrection is connected with temporal succession, a topic we considered earlier in relation to hypothetical continuers but now need to face again. The resurrectee ought (normally) to awaken in a later time—but in the case of a collapsing universe, time, in a sense, comes to an end (or so it seems, from today's perspectives). The notion of relative time between one universe and another could get very confusing. But clearly, reasonable conditions can be imagined in which the resurrectees would accept their new surroundings as corresponding to a later time as they should—if only because, subjectively, it would seem so to them. In general, in the more distant future there should be many opportunities for carrying out what amount to resurrections, and for the most rewarding interactions with the beings that result. This I would expect to become apparent to advanced civilizations, which would stand to gain from their own resurrection projects.

Indeed, the eternal life of every sentient being whatever is possible even if there is no universe capable of supporting eternal life. How? By having not one everlasting universe but a succession of increasingly long-lived universes in which increasingly advanced beings can develop and, in due course, carry out xenontic recreations of less fortunate beings from other universes. True, it could make for an interesting journey through transcosmic hypertime. We each would eventually face the self-destruction of our own universe, be resurrected into a longer lived one, then a still longer-lived one, and so on. In each transition, perhaps, we would eventually find an honored place among the immortals there and help them carry out further resurrections before their coming catastrophe. With enough love and compassion, perhaps even an endless succession of such cataclysms could be offset by the awakenings that would interleave them so that the highest good will prevail in eternity.

Tipler's retrocreationism, in which only those universes exist that have an Omega Point, is not a requirement for the existence of a sentient being in some particular universe. We could argue, however, that some form of retrocreationism holds because by Unboundedness, any sentient being or history must be brought eventually and repeatedly to the attention of other sentient beings. (In fact, it would appear that every sentient being must become known actively to every other sentient being, where the two are represented by suitable, instantiated continuers.) Nothing has existence, then, that is not perceived over and over in replica form throughout eternity in innumerable settings by innumerable observers.

All this must hold, again, even if no possible single universe can support eternal life. Still it can be hoped that some universes can support eternal life, in particular our own. This and other themes relevant to immortality will be examined later. We continue now with an issue having less cosmic import but more relevance to the present and near future.

CHAPTER 13.

Biostasis As the Better Way

It is a source of satisfaction and comfort when we feel that events are progressing in an orderly way, not threatening but still offering elements of interest. We can then live life as a willing process of helping history happen, with our personal, day-to-day experiences forming a respected part of a larger whole. As such, our life experiences should also be worthy of remembering later and, consequently, retrievable in some form. Life with no surprises would be dull, and we want surprises, maybe even considerable ones, but want them kept within bounds. We seek security and an absence of disruption as well as novelty and the liberty to explore newfound territory. I expect the issue of security to be important in the future, when hopefully our immortality is won. Indeed, it may be rather more important than now, for our expectations are conditioned by what we perceive as possible and rise accordingly as new possibilities are opened by our progress.

Today, of course, there are basic limitations on our security and confidence, particularly since we must face the prospect of a physical demise. This we can try to counter through the biostasis option, and it has interested a handful of us, but so far most remain indifferent. Many or most of these are not disinterested in overcoming mortality but have other plans to do so, generally based on belief in a supernatural deliverance or other paranormal mechanisms. Here we have discounted such prospects but have offered instead a means of eventual resurrection based on scientific principles.

In this way we find grounds for an optimistic stance. Persons who have died have not lived in vain, for they too shall one day return to life through appropriate, material constructs, though certain ties with a historical past must, by appearances, be irretrievably lost. By the same token, though, a possible weakness is exposed in our insistence that the biostasis route is the better alternative when circumstances permit. With eventual resurrection possible through other means, we must ask why preserving the remains is still important. This issue was considered briefly in Chapter 4; it is time to take a closer look now.

It is worth remarking that in addressing such an issue we put ourselves in the difficult position of trying to anticipate distant events and effects beyond our experience. Despite uncertainties though and indeed because of them, I think a good case for biostasis can be made. We do not need to pick the brains of future, inscrutable resurrectors to establish certain basic properties that lend support.

One such property relates to death as it applies to us today: it introduces a strong element of the unknown. We do not really know what will transpire after we are deceased in terms of our next perceptions, good or bad effects, and so on, despite indications we have considered that good will prevail in the end. The surprise element is more than most of us are eager to embrace (this caution being naturally selected), which provides one motive to avoid death when possible. On the other hand, if we see death coming and realize it cannot be forestalled, as has always been the case up to now, we can consider whether one means of coping might be better than another. And, indeed, I think fear or dislike of the unknown (or of a pending calamity or unwanted state) is what motivates most people who choose cryonics or other biostasis options, not to mention others who make other choices to cope with their own death.

Given the element of the unknown, however, there is another feature of biostasis that commends it over these other choices: it keeps options open that otherwise would be irretrievably lost. If someone just deceased is frozen, he could be unfrozen and buried or cremated. If buried or cremated, however, he cannot be converted to "just deceased and frozen"; the effects of decomposition are substantial and, as far as we know, irreversible. Among the unknowns that then confront us is the effect of the loss of identity-bearing structure and the information it encodes. True, the loss itself is not quite an absolute; lost information and consequently structure can be recreated by guesswork, but this will not restore broken ties with the historical record. I will offer arguments that these very ties, if maintained, will prove important in an open-ended, more-than-human future. In any case, we cannot be sure they will not be and do have reason to think otherwise. Similar ties, for example, are most important to the historian of today, who is not impressed with manufactured relics however convincing but seeks original, ancient artifacts or information derived from them. And every survivor becomes a kind of self-historian. We are thus provided a motive for preserving our direct ties or informational continuity with a remembered past.

So now we have two possible connected reasons for choosing biostasis: coping with the unknown and forestalling irreversible loss. I think they are good reasons, and they are not negated by such a possibility as an eventual, universal resurrection and a happy ultimate outcome of all persons' lives. For this still leaves many uncertainties, and the crucial requirement for survival— the presence of identity-critical information—is clearly favored by a preservative process.

But other interesting arguments also favor biostasis, and we will consider these in turn, trying to look, tentatively, beyond the barrier of the unknown to consider how the preservation of identity-critical material now could prove of value in the future life of a presently dying individual, and even more generally. Here there are two perspectives of interest. The more important is the viewpoint of the individual in question, the participant or patient, someone who is to undergo death (the clinical variety at least, the cessation of vital functions) and, we hope, reanimation or resurrection. The second perspective is that of an external observer, as an interested party.

A Problem of Anticipation

We are concerned, then, with the long-term, future effects of carrying out a hypothetical resurrection of our patient, a restoration to a functioning form. Mainly we wish to ascertain, as far as possible, what the patient's settled judgment would be as to the quality and advisability of the course that was followed relative to another procedure that might have been used instead. In the one case we imagine that the patient (at least a critical part including the brain or an adequate portion) was placed in biostasis at death. The remains were then used so that the resurrected patient's memories, et cetera, remain part of the historical record, or, in terminology introduced last chapter, are enontic. In the other scenario, in which there is no preservation, this information is lost and must be restored by guesswork, so it is, at best, only hyperontic. We want to know if there is a significant advantage in the biostasis-based, enontic route, which we imagine is best to be judged by the patient herself.

This judgment in turn will only reach a settled form in an immortal future, when the former patient has attained a more-than-human state. So our task, to anticipate what such a person might think and decide with far more wisdom and understanding than we can expect to muster, is a daunting one. But we must make the effort to arrive at a better judgment on the advisability of an option open today but so far exercised by only a few.

Already there is a difficulty because it is entirely possible that different patients will see the matter differently, with no strong majority either way. As one example, we might imagine that someone who took the biostatic route would be glad she did and prefer that route (though having no experience of the other one). One who had to be resurrected hyperontically could argue, on the contrary, that it made no difference, she was none the worse for it. But I will argue that the latter alternative is unlikely, at least as a settled opinion, based on certain expectations about the way an immortal personality would develop. In short, then, I am claiming that any immortal being eventually must arrive at the position that enontic survival is better than hyperontic (barring certain special circumstances), and, similarly, that hyperontic is better than xenontic.

Again, it is no small matter to try to judge what the state of mind of an immortal, former human might develop to. We need a starting point. There are certain traits, interests, and dispositions we possess as humans; these must furnish our foundation. Among these are a will to survive and an interest in the past. These traits are not uniformly shared, of course; many seem to have little interest in the past, and the lack does not necessarily make one reproductively unfit. Natural and cultural selection will tolerate such a lack of interest—to some degree. But I submit that this will not prevail in an immortal future. People must have a reason to want to be long-lived, and this must particularly apply in the case of more advanced beings in an immortal setting. Given enough time, I think any such being would develop an interest in the past and its conservation, both personal and more general— or be replaced by a continuer who had this orientation.

Let us now consider what can be called a communitarian argument for biostasis. Persons are valued in terms of their association with one or more others and, more generally, a community at large. Death, the loss of a loved or valued individual, is a tragedy to be avoided, forestalled, or, if possible, reversed once it has taken effect. If clinical death must occur, reanimation should happen sooner and more straightforwardly if the remains are well preserved. Indeed, it might be said that the one who is preserved is not really dead at all but in a kind of deep coma, if reanimation from the preserved state will eventually be possible. This should be especially meaningful to someone who wants to further the survival of someone else. If we can assume biostasis will benefit the patient directly, that is, from her point of view—as I will begin arguing momentarily—the other who cares will also benefit from helping and knowing the patient is being cared for in a mission of attempted rescue. Later we shall return to the communitarian argument and, more generally, to problems with acceptance of the biostasis option that seem to come from the social nature of human beings.

One expected form of direct benefit from biostasis relates to the patient after resurrection and her relations or ties with the surrounding world, or what in Chapter 4 was called the Interface. If all goes well, an important feature of the Interface will consist of ties with a community of immortals who will be well-disposed toward the one they have resurrected and who will interact with the expectation of mutual, reciprocal benefit. Though hopefully well-disposed toward all, I conjecture the resurrectors will be better disposed toward those who earlier affirmed their valuing of life and immortality by choosing the option of self-preservation.

Another direct benefit of a more personal nature involves recollection. Think about a memory: "I was there, did that." If the memory was created by guesswork, it must still be considered authentic, provided it met basic criteria such as consistency with other memories, this being guaranteed by Unboundedness. Yet our intuitive response is that this sort of made-up memory is unreal. It would be possible rather than actual history and, of course, manufactured rather than saved and preserved from the time that the events actually happened. Better, we would say, if the memory had been laid down in the usual way in our brain in the course of really experiencing something, then straightforwardly preserved. Otherwise we must in a certain degree suspend disbelief, assuming we understand how the memory was actually acquired. This I think would be the likely reaction of people today, whose sensibilities are tempered by the hard road of selection our ancestors went through to get us where we are now, with some emphasis on survival and what is meaningful to that goal. We have to distinguish our dreams from our reality, even if those very dreams depict some reality somewhere.

The future, of course, has many unknowns. We cannot expect to second-guess the detailed preoccupations of people in a more advanced setting, even where this may include our future selves, as we hope it will. But the issue of survival will not go away, and I think it will actually take on greater urgency when we are no longer mortal and can really make a science of survival. So I do not expect our thoughts to become indifferent to whether our memories possess historical ties in the usual way or were put in by guesswork. We can tentatively assume that our feelings on the matter now will carry over to the future and retain some validity.

Advantages of Historical Ties

What then should be the advantages of the historical ties, of memories possessing enonticity? There should be an increased facility for meaningful interaction with fellow beings, which should translate to a better, more meaningful life overall; again, the Interface will be augmented. In the terminology of Chapter 3, the meaningful interaction amounts to taking part in a cultural drama. This should be furthered if one remains attached to the historical process. If death intervenes, the brain or a portion containing a record of events as they happened should be saved. But the focus on motives of survival has led away from the communitarian argument to what can be called a Darwinian argument, something we will return to later.

Aside from any direct benefits to the patient, preserving the remains as part of the historical record also suggests an archaeological argument. The remains can be seen as a kind of relic that ought to be saved from destruction. In fact, this sort of policy is used today in special cases deemed to have archaeological value, such as Egyptian mummies, but not more generally, as we in cryonics feel it should be. This does not mean, of course, that persons are to be reduced simply to museum specimens. But archaeology is one field that recognizes the importance of history and the physical evidence that delineates it, and this has relevance at the personal level. We can regard the brain as a kind of archival storage center of information about our past life, an object deserving of preservation when, as in clinical death, intervention is required to prevent loss.

Of course, here we are not simply trying to preserve history but even more important, to save and extend a person's life. Nevertheless, historical ties have significance—as in more conventional archaeology—and not just the relic considered in isolation. An ancient manuscript, for instance, has value because it is historical and tells us something about our past. The same text could just as well have been created as some modern exercise, with care to make it appear authentic. It might still have interest but not the same as before. With remains intended for reanimation we have some additional considerations, which we will now examine briefly. In particular, we need to take account of one very substantial departure from the usual focus of archaeology, in that the artifact in question may later become an observer, an archaeologist in her own right.

To deal with that issue first, we see that it brings out a weakness. The archaeological argument is primarily an outsider's argument, oriented to those who find and preserve artifacts and those who study them for what can be learned. We do not normally consider that a preserved "artifact" is to awaken someday and may then have feelings of her own about the whole process. If she too has an archaeological bent, she will perhaps appreciate what was done on general or aesthetic principles and be grateful. Indeed, we have already considered reasons to expect that sort of response. But there are other arguments that better make our case for the preservation option; first we will examine some possible criticism.

One objection to the biostasis option is that if we grant in principle that the preservation would be worth doing, the best techniques may still be inadequate. Would a brain be well enough preserved to recover the desired information concerning the subject's identity, so that a reanimation could occur? Or, taking the most conservative stance, would there even be any significant information at all? The answer to the second question seems clear enough: certainly, significant information would be there, beyond, say, what could be inferred from the genome or isolated cell or tissue samples. As for the possibility of reanimation, I have advocated the controversial position that here too there is a reasonable likelihood that the preservation will prove good enough; more will be said in Chapter 17.

But a second objection can be based on the issue of what is really significant, that is, what are we interested in. A preserved brain clearly contains structural information not deducible from a cell sample (inasmuch as its structure is not exactly defined by the DNA), but that alone does not make it worth saving. There is much information in our world that appears briefly and is lost with no attempt to preserve it, though we could easily do so, in particular cases. But, for example, we do not go out of our way to preserve snowflakes or blades of grass, and the loss is not a matter of concern. True, there is some preservation of this sort too, but mainly for representative sampling only—it would be absurd to try to save all such information and a task beyond our powers.

Rightly or wrongly, this is also the approach used today with the human brain at death. Most of the time it is discarded—committed to burial or cremation with the rest of the remains, though a more comprehensive preservation, in this case, would be within our means. The idea is resisted that preserved remains, at least the brain, would make it possible eventually to reanimate the person. With that possibility discounted, the physical structure becomes expendable. The dead are preserved piecemeal for representative studies, medical instruction, investigation of causes of death, or briefly and cosmetically for funerals—that is about it.

Here we shall assume provisionally, again with more to be said,

that the preservation is good enough to raise the prospect of reanimation, which means that individual, remembered experiences
are captured. Acceptance of this would probably remove the significance objection in most people's minds since a human life is
now at stake. It was worth raising anyway, since many, including
some cryonicists, question the importance of individual experiences and the value of memories. I will contend shortly that such
disinterest is mistaken.

In summary, the archaeological argument suggests that we
ought to be preserving human remains, much as we would save
other historical artifacts or relics. But our argument left more to
be said on how the fact of the preservation would benefit the
persons we hope to reanimate. Other arguments will help clarify
this.

One of these can be called the conservatist argument: that major dislocations in life are to be avoided, and, more generally, a
conservative course is to be charted in an effort to find meaningful happiness. This recalls the remarks at the beginning of the
chapter, in which an orderly, nonthreatening progression of events
is seen as desirable, while disorienting or disrupting occurrences
are to be avoided. The latter would not necessarily be physically
painful, but could be inconvenient or stressful in other ways. Quite
arguably, one form of unwanted experience of this type would be
a long period of diminished or absent awareness, with the expected disorientation and need for adjustments that would follow
on returning to one's senses.

Other factors equal, then, we would not want to spend a large
amount of time unconscious and then return to consciousness,
but skip the long sleep instead. This would be so even if, for
example, we had a curable form of sleeping sickness but all the
more so if a more serious problem developed. We would not want
to be sick in the first place, of course, but if ill we would rather be
cured and remain functional than die and be frozen. If, on the
other hand, clinical death was unavoidable, we would want to
choose the least disruptive course—to be frozen rather than recreated by guesswork. At least this is physically the least disruptive, though whether it would also be so psychologically, that is,
in terms of our life experience, might still be questioned. But,
more generally, a course that is more conserving of life is preferred, with the physical and psychological notions of what is

"conserving" being (usually) more or less in agreement. The more conserving choice, with its orderly features, should lead to greater overall contentment, enjoyment, and meaningful life experience. There is no guarantee, of course, that this must be so, though we have examined possible reasons based on an interest in survival and will consider others.

It is worth noting too that the conservatist argument fits well with the ideas we examined of biostasis as a way of coping with the unknown and avoiding irreversible loss. Actually, it goes a bit further, suggesting that even reversible changes, for example, a long period of curable coma, are to be avoided if possible because of dislocation. It could thus be used as a rationale for biostasis even if we expected that historical ties could be restored through some other more difficult route, as in Tipler's Omega Point resurrection.[1] It could also be used to rationalize other life choices today, for example, exercise and dieting to remain physically healthy, as a way to increase the chance of survival to life-extending breakthroughs and avoid the necessity of biostatic pres-

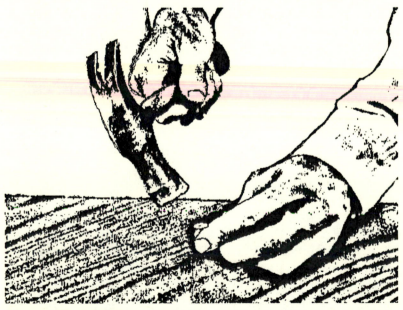

The conservativist argument. "Even though my fingers would recover (and others meanwhile could drive nails), I am going to avoid hitting them if possible."

ervation entirely. Finally, it might be used to favor conservative
choices in a case where some form of eventual doom or disruption is inevitable, as a way of making the best of a bad situation.
This could cover the ultimate calamity of a life-annihilating universe—to live well and prepare as far as possible for what might
follow one's destruction being preferable, say, to a quicker and
more thoughtless suicide or a life ended by carelessness or indifference. But let us return now to the biostasis issue.

Addressing Some Objections

A critic of the conservatist argument might counter that while
day-to-day life might be preferred to clinical death, it is far from
obvious that when the latter is inevitable, biostasis must be the
preferred choice. Biological disruption need not equate to psychological disruption, given the reconstructive process as envisioned. If resurrection through guesswork is the guaranteed alternative to biostasis, who is to say it would not be just as good or
better? In either case we must depend on "our friends of the future" to restore us, and help get us started in a new life that we
will hopefully find worthwhile. If we would trust them in the one
instance, why not in the other too? A person, for example, whose
life is centered on simple pleasures, might especially see little
difference either way. Here it will be instructive to take a closer
look.

Hank, let us say, is a retiree in still-vigorous health, who is
interested in making love, playing golf, and sipping wine with
buddies. Hank finds life worth living and wants more. Knowing
that he may die of one cause or another, even with medical advances, he is considering making cryonics arrangements. He is
persuaded that, indeed, if he is frozen and the proposed, eventual
restoration to health succeeds, he should be able to resume his
chosen lifestyle or something close enough but wonders why that
would not happen if he is only recreated by guesswork. "Why,"
he asks, "would these other resurrectors bring me back a cripple,
or impotent, or with stomach ulcers? I have no reason to expect
such petty cruelty and, especially, no more reason than with cryonics, so I see no real advantage in it, and there is the extra trouble
and expense. I will just be conventionally buried." Questioned
more closely, Hank confirms that yes, he considers memories

and past history important to an extent but only as a means to an end, which is enjoyment. "It is especially not critical," he says, "to maintain the historical ties or what you call 'informational continuity.' I really see no value in it for myself, given your assumptions, since its absence will not interfere in any way with what I do enjoy."

So how do we answer Hank's objections? I propose to do so by carefully considering the idea that seems implicit here, that certain simple pleasures are all Hank desires for eternity, which I submit is highly unlikely, that is, Hank must inevitably reconsider. The course of our discussion will bring in other arguments favoring biostasis. First, though, it is worth remarking that real cryonicists rarely, if ever, have Hank's cast of mind but instead tend to see cryonics as their only hope of life after clinical death and discount resurrection through guesswork altogether. But I think that a sizable fraction do have the orientation toward simple pleasures and consequently take the view that if this other resurrection is there as a backup, there is no substantial advantage, and possibly even a disadvantage, in the biostasis option.

It is also worth noting that unlike Hank, many people consider their friends, loved ones, and associates important enough that they wish to share their fate and would only consider cryonics if these others did also, a topic we will return to shortly. Cryonicists are usually more "stand alone," and I have assumed Hank is too—let us say he would like his friends or loved ones to join him, whatever his choice, but is individualist enough to choose independently.

But let us look more carefully at the idea that simple pleasures might be the important things in one's life and could remain so indefinitely, oblivious of such subtleties as whether one's memories were part of the historical record. To accept this position would be to argue for a kind of confining hedonism in which one is stagnated at a particular level indefinitely. It suggests that, while the repertoire of one's experiences could be large and varied, a finite set would do, leading inevitably to an Eternal Return or repetition of states of consciousness. This subject we will consider next chapter, but the important point is that an Eternal Return must forfeit true immortality. A person like Hank, in a garden of delights but unable to escape or progress, would resemble the Eloi in H. G. Wells's story *The Time Machine*, a diminutive race of human descendants the narrator encounters some 8,000 centuries in the future. "A queer thing I soon discovered about my little hosts, and that was their lack of interest. They would come to me with eager cries of astonishment, like children, but, like children, they would soon stop examining me, and wander away after some other toy."[2]

Unlike the Eloi, however, real children are not stunted at one level but advance over time. And, though Hank might protest that he is far above these simple folk who really are like children, this is not really the issue, but that a limited repertoire of activities would be enough for future life. In practice, perhaps Hank would progress, gradually but willingly, and not be doomed to an Eternal Return. However, in one other way his attitude is disturbingly reminiscent of the Eloi, which is that they are not their own masters but are kept and maintained by another once-human race, the Morlocks—who, it happens, use them as food.

In the future as we have envisioned it, "our friends" the resurrectors will indeed have charge of those they return to consciousness, and we hope and have reason to think that they will take a loftier view than the Morlocks. Still they will, initially at least, be the guardians and masters of those they bring back and must have motives for doing so, which will not necessarily be to gratify every whim of their charges forever. Later we will consider this issue in more detail (Chapter 16), but the upshot will be that Hank had better plan on becoming his own, self-sustaining master. Perhaps Hank himself would protest again that he is already his own master, with savings permitting retirement, for example, but again this is not the real issue. For as a future resurrectee, he must be subjected, at least for a time, to the care of others. Again, he should plan on weaning himself from that subservient state and fending for himself. This in turn has consequences that arguably would enforce attention to one's surroundings, including interest in the past. To approach this topic it will be useful to consider the more general issues of why and how we live our lives.

We live life to satisfy wants. All behavior, then, can be interpreted selfishly as a process of attempting to gain one form of satisfaction or another. Perhaps this will seem inadequate as well as inappropriate. What about altruistic behavior, done not for oneself but for others? But this too can be interpreted selfishly: altruism induces a special satisfaction, much prized by the practitioner, who feels good knowing that others are benefited. So we may imagine that everything we do is done for motives of self-interest and ultimately for some form of personal satisfaction.

The satisfaction of wants, of course, is not a simple process; often in attaining one goal we find additional goals we would like to achieve. In so simple an act as eating food to satisfy hunger, for instance, we further a process (metabolism) that will eventually result in our being hungry again. On a higher level a scientist will, in the course of investigating one problem or phenomenon, find others of interest that were previously unknown. Galileo in 1610 pointed his telescope at the heavens to better observe the celestial objects then known and discovered new objects of wonder—the moons of Jupiter and other things not seen before. This oft-repeated process of discovery has created a cornucopia of knowledge and in the bargain kept hordes of scientists happily engaged for centuries.

A general principle is suggested: life properly lived should generate a succession of new goals. In this way we never run out of things to do. Otherwise we would stagnate, eventually, and the whole enterprise would become pointless. (Arguably, then, it was pointless all along.) And indeed, the inexhaustible nature of some lines of investigation suggests that, with proper orientation, a person would find no end of interesting things to investigate, thus no eventual boredom. Mathematics and subjects based on it are inexhaustible, we have noted, though I think there are other good reasons too that boredom need not be a threat.

A person, though, who is eager to accomplish things, would be interested in more than simply having an unlimited time in which to operate. We live life, normally, on a day-to-day basis and not like some imagined automaton that is turned on rarely, putters around briefly, then is put to rest again.

Instead, living life means, among other things, shaping events ourselves, under our own control. We investigate, we create, we do—hopefully not as part of some experiment or project under someone else's direction but by our own authority and wishes. We thus take part in a cultural drama and play a creative role. This is not arbitrary but involves specific historical events of which we are part and which are affected by our actions. We cause history, or help it happen. And, if rightly disposed, we want to continue in this manner, participating in the historical process under our own control—which means, by inescapable logic, we want to continue indefinitely. We thus do not want to be incapacitated by illness, we do not want to be enfeebled by age, we do not want to die. If death must come—the clinical sort at least—we are interested in overcoming that too, if possible. Having our important elements preserved for eventual reanimation becomes a logical choice.

In this manner we hope to achieve not only a return to life but a better return than might be possible, say, if our remains are destroyed and we must be recreated by educated guesswork in a resurrection project of a more distant future. It is hard to imagine a strong motive for living that is indifferent to such thoughts. Surely, if we have to be formed at random all over again, we must have more trouble getting to our feet and finding a niche from which we can function, in meaningful ways, as independent individuals. I think this would hold, even though I attribute good motives to our hypothesized resurrectors.

Some things could not be undone even by them, such as the fact that our identity-critical information would not all be part of the still-surviving record. Lost memories recreated by guesswork, I will conjecture, will seem less real despite being also authentic because selection pressure would maintain an interest in historical ties. This should follow no matter how advanced our technology becomes. For technology alone will never guarantee our survival, but we must also have the will to survive, and it calls for certain interests, including some concern with our personal history and its preservation. The presence of guesswork (hyperontic) memories in place of historical (enontic) ones would significantly complicate our interactions with others and be less satisfying overall. Put another way, we would find our Interface impaired and would expect greater difficulty establishing meaningful ties with reality and a framework for further interactions in the world. So, to anticipate the beings we will become, the enontic is to be favored over the hyperontic and xenontic.

This, then, somewhat restates the conservatist argument for biostasis but also emphasizes an additional element—a concern with one's own persistence through time. It thus elaborates the Darwinian argument we touched on earlier, which is based on a will to survive. The will to survive carries the imperative that we should be interested in how we survive and, in particular, in favoring the enontic over alternatives. In Darwin's evolutionary theory, it is the fittest who survive, and so it will be, I predict, even after the causes of death have been eliminated. Those lacking the will are destined either to fall by the wayside—to self-destruct in some manner even if they could save themselves—or to make necessary adjustments. I expect that most will be able to adjust in due course. Future immortals, then, will come to agree that enonticity is best. But it is worth emphasizing that this Darwinian principle, with its favoring of the will and survival of the fittest, neither precludes our stance of Universalism nor compromises the prospects of benevolence in future immortals; more about these issues shortly.

On resurrection, Hank might initially be perfectly comfortable, whether his coming back was by the biostasis route or not. The benign resurrectors should see to that—unless they in their superhuman wisdom decide on another course entirely, which for the sake of argument we will discount. So Hank, a resurrectee, is able to enjoy his old lifestyle almost as if nothing had happened. Eternity, though, is a long time, and eventually Hank must face up to the larger issues of an open-ended existence. This must especially follow, I submit, when Hank acquires a more advanced understanding of what he has gone through—death and resurrection—and what this means, scientifically and in other ways. And I submit he will—and should—find this out. The resurrectors are not going to keep him ignorant forever, like the witless, clueless Eloi, for his destiny is a higher one: to help nourish thoughts rather than supply physical nourishment.

Hank, as we have imagined him, thinks that personal information is simply a means to an end that is enjoyment. But this is incorrect; for personal information defines who it is who enjoys. To an extent, then, we must view the maintenance of personal information as an end in itself, complementary but not subordinate to the goal of enjoyment. It is connected with finding meaning in life, which in turn is not simply the attainment of pleasure, as usually understood. So if Hank *himself* is to benefit, he must consider more than just the raw enjoyments and must adjust his thinking to an active participation at a higher level. He must develop a true survivor mentality. If Hank was not preserved in biostasis but had to be recreated by guesswork, he must come to feel that it was not the best course, despite his finding life worthwhile and the problem of onticity manageable. Such are my views at any rate. I will conjecture, more generally, that those who are resurrected through guesswork will not initially experience particular hardships because of it but will come to feel and understand, over a long or short time, that the enontic route would have been better.

Attributes to Aim For

Would-be immortals must be interested in life and living, but proper immortalist orientation, I maintain, additionally involves a proactive rather than a passive or reactive stance. We should be producers more than consumers, self-reliant individuals interested in the control of our own destiny, who actively seek means of life-enhancement. The interest in life and living translates to a wish to be part of the historical process—for indeed, this is what living is all about—which also favors activity and individual responsibility. This suggests another argument for biostasis I will call the libertarian argument, which recognizes that death or incapacitation is a limitation on freedom and seeks the best route around the difficulty, again by avoiding disintegration.

The libertarian argument is clearly related to the Darwinian argument, but the emphasis is different, and, more generally, it does not follow that survival interests coincide with individualism and the exercise of freedom. This is especially true today in our mortal world, where individuals do not survive long but hopefully will in an immortal future. However, today we find that few seem interested in the biostasis option, but that social bonding is substantial. Most people, as noted in Chapter 3, are not stand-alone individuals but think and act according to the expectations of their culture, especially where the forbidding issue of death is concerned. Our earlier communitarian argument suggested a possible reason such people might have for favoring biostasis, namely, to benefit someone else and participate in an effort to save a life. One thus can focus on something that is outside oneself and advantageous to society more generally. Realistically, however, I think this alone will not prove sufficient. A real communitarian—and I imagine this includes most people—is simply too rooted in a surrounding culture and will only change when that culture or some substantial part gives the nod of approval.

Otherwise biostasis is not likely to be the preferred choice, and this especially follows, I think, for a "radical" if comprehensive version such as freezing the head or whole body. (A milder form, such as preserving a cell sample, may be more socially acceptable though offering far less in the way of preservation.) Indeed, the communitarian might invoke our very conservatist argument in retaliation: "There would be a big social price for me to pay, were I to sign up for cryonics, both now, when I would be considered 'weird,' and in a future when I might come back shorn of those who are dear to me (at least for a long time). Unsettling—considerably so. Overall, I expect the problems to be greater with this route, than with your 'other' resurrection and, mainly, because other people I know have not opted for cryonics. True, I think it has a chance of working, but that is not the main issue. Just as now, so in the future, I want to stand with those I specially care about!"

Such an argument, based as it would probably be on a strong gut feeling, is a hard one to counter. And it too perhaps fails to do justice to the "typical" communitarian, who may in addition have strong religious inhibitions or just a simple, pervasive lack of interest. Certainly the question can be raised if, indeed, the dislocation resulting from compromise of social or cultural ties—for the many who especially value and need them—might prove a greater hardship than the more abstract problem we have conjectured over onticity. But such people also seem in a way either joyless, fear-driven, or deficient in a sense of meaning and purpose. A case could, I think, still be made favoring the preservative option, but it would be necessary to convince such people that the future will not merely bring physical health, but a substantial improvement in the mental state as well, with more enlightenment all around.

The thought occurs that mental doldrums could be a price to be paid to impel people to be the "social animals" demanded by the selection process, biological and social, that shaped them. We must bear in mind that the selection process does not necessarily favor the survival, happiness, or well-being of individuals, but in our death-haunted world, what will propagate their genes. Not to be overlooked too is the possible severe dislocation our civilization has inflicted by the many changes it has made in human lifestyles over too short a time for biological evolution to adapt.

As a possible consequence, there are some who wish to reject not one choice of an extended life for another one but any chance of coming back at all. Such people alone seem to far outnumber cryonicists.

One such sufferer, who had been taking antidepressants, finally did sign up when urged by her cryonicist husband but then was guarded. "Only recently have I been able to reverse my own generally pessimistic outlook and to view long life as anything other than an extended prison sentence." To her, feeling good meant "neither depressed nor anxious," nothing more, until finally she felt an uplift while walking on a fitness trail and looking at azaleas in bloom. "I was familiar with the intellectual absorption and excitement of a fierce card game and the physical delight in, say, having my back scratched, but this emotional quality of enjoyment was something completely new to me." Questioning several others, she found that, while most considered that they had experienced some positive feelings, one other person could only offer that "feeling good was when living didn't hurt."[3] It seems that life in a fundamental sense is not all it might be—and should be—to many if not most people. For clearly life ought to offer much more than, at best, an absence of pain or release from burdens and stress, or even positive but limited rewards that are overshadowed by negatives. And of course it can offer more, as those of us who have experienced the right sort of meaningful benefits know, but convincing others has proved to be a tall order.

It should not be assumed, however, that wanting an extended life for oneself precludes interest in the welfare of others who tell you they do not, or do not want it your way. It is possible to care deeply about people who have no intention of escaping the usual demise yet also be driven by a strong wish not share their fate. Indeed, this is the uncomfortable position we cryonicists often find ourselves in. We would certainly like to change the ingrained thinking that inspires behavior that to us seems sadly suicidal and lemming-like. But probably such a change, a very radical one by indications, cannot take major effect soon. Very likely there must more tangible evidence of the workability of any of the biostasis possibilities or, alternatively, antiaging and other breakthroughs to reduce the need of them. Then we can expect a turnaround in social forces that have operated up to now against an immortalist commitment on the part of most people. Meanwhile, some of us are trying to accomplish what we can with words and existing technology while not overlooking the need to support research.

A Moral Argument

Here I will suggest a final, moral argument for the biostasis option, based on Fedorov's ideas of resurrection as a moral project. It is in this vein too that I think we must approach the matter, this being an issue on which, once again, there will be more in later chapters. The moral position stresses that one should strive for the highest good, which involves both overcoming death and attaining proper enlightenment. It is not necessary or desirable to limit one's attention either to oneself as the principal beneficiary (the patient), or to someone else that one might like to help. An enlightened viewpoint recognizes that one's own good and that of others are inseparably linked and treats all on a more-or-less equal footing. Value is placed on life and its continuance, both in oneself and others, and life will be furthered through the biostasis option, for reasons we have considered.

The moral position thus incorporates the other arguments that have been advanced—indeed, requires them—but also adds an additional, normative element. It urges that what is being advocated, an approach to the problem of death and its possible alleviation through careful preservation of the remains, is good, right, and appropriate, but also that failure to consider this option raises an issue of moral accountability. It would be wrong to withhold a medical procedure that might save a life, without peculiar, extenuating circumstances, as most will agree, even those who believe in a resurrection to paradise in the event of death. Similar considerations must apply to the biostasis option, and particularly cryonics, as advocates including myself insist. True, the uncertainties preclude a firm conclusion at present that failure to freeze kills the patient. But the evidence favoring this very hypothesis or, in other words, that the presently frozen "dead" can eventually be awakened is significant and we must take it seriously.

The moral position also recognizes that the good, in general, will not be uniformly attainable at a given stage of our advancement but that compromises must be considered, and a lesser evil may have to be tolerated to avoid a greater one. But human life is valuable, and high priority must be placed on conserving and extending it, even if unusual and novel procedures are involved, including cryonics.

Overall, then, we have explored several arguments favoring biostasis as an approach to the problem of death. First was the idea of coping with the unknown, and the property that biostasis prevents an otherwise irreversible loss. Next came a number of arguments: communitarian, Darwinian, archaeological, conservatist, and libertarian, which suggested that both oneself and others would benefit from the historical ties that could only be maintained by preserving the remains. Finally, a moral argument linked the other arguments together and reminded us that we must bear responsibility for our choices on life and death issues. The upshot: though resurrection could happen without prior preservation, it would place the recipient at a disadvantage that she or he would come to recognize as such.

Much of our discussion, of course, must be considered highly speculative. And we acknowledged that very many people today have a particular impediment, in view of cultural ties, beliefs, or a general lack of interest. At this stage, the problem may be insurmountable. But the arguments do have some plausibility; time alone can tell how well they will hold up. Meanwhile, we are called upon to act, to choose and advocate the biostasis option and what appear to be the best forms of it, particularly cryonics. A few additional matters should now be addressed.

We have noted that the Darwinian principle implies that some future would-be immortals could fall by the wayside and self-destruct. This may seem to contradict Universalism, which would be a difficulty for Yuai, but there is really no difficulty if we remember that survival of individuals is to occur through continuers, which may come in varied forms. Thus, if someone is not well-disposed toward survival, probably a continuer of that very person is possible who *is* well-disposed, and would be able to further that person's immortalization. Such a continuer we may hope will eventually appear, whether enontically or in some other way, due to the efforts of benign resurrectors (this being a major theme of Chapter 16). In terms of the eventual outcome, the result would be similar to the case of a suicidal person who later reconsiders and becomes a survivalist. The non-survivalist is gone, but the person lives on in one of a number of more viable forms.

It is interesting that Yuai's Universalism does not put everyone on an equal footing of salvation immediately after death, as in the religious doctrine of Ultra-Universalism.[4] Nor is full salvation something attained at a definite point in time. Instead, each sentient being attempts progress, sooner or later repeatedly succeeds, and over unlimited time advances to unlimited heights. All are to achieve supreme good in the end, but we have to make a choice among unequal pathways.

Another apparent difficulty we noted with the Darwinian principle is the stress it lays on the will to survive, which may seem to imply a narrow selfishness and lack of concern for others. An advanced immortal, however, should be able to see that narrow selfishness is not consistent with enlightened self-interest. A fierce will to survive need not be incompatible with concern for others, but the two can complement a mentality that seeks the greatest personal reward over endless time. The highest good for oneself, I submit, will require benefiting others and even, in the end, their own highest good as well; this should, moreover, be clear to an advanced being.

Our discussion so far has centered on the rather narrow issue of two alternatives, biostasis versus disintegration, and the choice between them. We need to broaden our scope of inquiry since life will not always offer the clear-cut choice, and, moreover, we must sometimes "pick up the pieces" when a better choice was available but not made.

One difficulty we have already noted is that the preservation of a patient in biostasis may not be adequate to fully accomplish its purpose. The necessary, missing information must then be filled in by the usual backup method of guessing. Though there will be full awareness and retention of memories, some historical ties will not be recoverable. The shortfall will be less extreme than if no biostasis had been attempted. The patient will experience an "ontic deficit" that will be more or less severe depending on the quality of the preservation. This issue is considered in Chapters 16 and 17. Minimizing an anticipated ontic deficit will be an important consideration in our Philosophy of Action. The less-than-perfect state of the preservation art has another consequence too, in that it should motivate us not to abandon this approach but to try to perfect it—through more research.

But I have referred to "picking up the pieces" after a bad choice or other misfortune. This will not always be the fault of the patient or anyone else; a cryonicist may die in a plane crash, reduced to ashes with nothing left to freeze. The resurrection, then, can only be hyperontic at best. Thereafter, however, a similar policy could be followed to what went before; choices on the part of the resurrectee could be based on the conservatist argument. With immortality hopefully at hand, biostasis or anything comparable may never be necessary again. But following a conservatist strategy would tend to minimize further dislocations and thus be the preferred course. Any problems attributable to an existing ontic deficit should then diminish progressively and ultimately lose significance. Similarly, other disadvantages should vanish in the limit of time, this being necessary to our concept of justice.

For we have noted that while evil exists, there are also grounds to defend our working hypothesis that life, fundamentally, is good. Evils must be overcome in the course of unlimited time. Many evils are fortuitous, striking without warning, and, alternatively, many benefits also occur by chance. This applies in particular to biostasis, which, if accepted as a benefit, is one that is fortuitously available in our time. Persons of the more distant past, lacking the preservative options now open, were disadvantaged through chance circumstances. But the prospect of overcoming all evils in time leads to a principle we can state as "the impermanence of fortuitous advantages"—something that will follow if things go as they should and good prevails in the end.

So far in this chapter we have put the emphasis on preservation, but this too must not be seen as an absolute. There are times, many times in fact, when it should be foregone, as in the case we noted of snowflakes and grass. In all cases we must consider such issues as cost and benefit. It takes resources to preserve something, and we need to ask what offsetting benefits to expect from our commitment. Still, the preciousness of human life demands we consider the biostasis option for those now dying. There is no need or warrant to take the callous position that such people are expendable, but we can direct rational efforts toward saving them after conventional medicine gives up.

But there are other circumstances in which information and structure, even including our own, would not be appropriate to save. Swarming, short-lived insects could hardly all be committed to biostasis, given our limited resources, while their loss, ultimately temporary anyway in view of Unboundedness, does not seem so serious. (True, we have to consider the possibility that one of these tiny beings will one day return as a more advanced being, who might then regret the loss of *its* full enonticity. Still I think the problem in this case is minor—but we must always be diligent in giving such issues what seems to be their due.) At the personal level too, by appearances we are constantly losing information that never makes it past short-term memory, and this loss (some of it, certainly) seems a good thing. In extreme situations, moreover, a noble self-sacrifice could be called for on the part of us humans, forfeiting the preservation option. It is also possible that the universe itself cannot support immortality, as we have noted, so that we must resign ourselves to the eventual loss of enontic ties and place hopes in a different sort of reprieve from oblivion. These matters too will be addressed again later.

We have emphasized the contrast between enonticity or preserving the historical record, and hyperonticity, in which information consistent with but not derived from historical sources is to be filled in by guesswork. The enontic, we concluded, is to be preferred over the hyperontic, at least for the important case of resurrecting humans. By the same token though, we can argue that the hyperontic would be preferable to the xenontic, that is, if guesswork must be done, at least the result should not contradict the historical record. A resurrected Lucretius, then, might remember his birthday being May 15 or some other date but would not have recollections of a live pterodactyl. A simple extension of the conservatist argument could supply a rationale here; the xenontic resurrectee is, effectively, in the "wrong" universe, which would in a special way prove unsettling and disorienting. This position too, however, should not be considered absolute; more will be said in Chapter 16.

Another matter to be considered in connection with the idea of a hyperontic resurrection is that it should not happen in isolation, contrary to the enontic case. For the latter, we could restore each person individually, secure in the thought that different persons will have mutually consistent memories and generally show a good fit with other past information we have. Historical data, when expected blemishes are taken into account, are noncontradictory. Physics seems reassuringly adamant on this point, though we might still be able to extract extra information by considering several cases together. A resurrection by guesswork would be more demanding, if we would do what I think is our best. Without a special, coordinated effort, different individuals who knew each other will end up with mutually inconsistent memories, something that again would be unsettling and should generally be avoided. A hyperontic resurrection, then, could be quite a complicated group affair; again, more will be said in Chapter 16.

There too we shall consider in detail why future benevolent immortals would be expected to want to restore other sentient beings to a functioning state and immortalize them. For now we are left with the thought that much good should be possible in the future, including resurrection of the dead by one means or another, with the biostasis route being preferred. After this, we should be in the position of having to make the most of a very long and hopefully infinite lifetime, a subject we shall now explore.

CHAPTER 14.

Immortality

Trrue everlasting life is often held to be an impossibility, even among those materialists who think that the present human life span can be greatly extended. Generally, their reasoning is that the universe as we know it does not seem able to support life indefinitely; for example, the Heat Death of the universe may be inevitable by the Second Law of Thermodynamics.

On the other hand, we have considered rational arguments that favor true immortality, notably the sort, based on the UI assumptions, that seem to provide for the instantiation of continuers of ourselves. Such an outcome could follow (or accompany) any catastrophe whatever that might end our life, even a life-annihilating universe. These resurrection arguments at least provide us with something to go on, but are clearly of the "last resort" variety. For those truly interested in immortality, not dying in the first place, or not dying after once being resurrected, is also of interest. Thus we must consider the enontic possibilities for immortality.

More basic than this, however, is the question of just what do we mean by immortality. It is connected with but not entirely answered by the idea of resurrection we have examined. We must further examine the concept at a basic level before approaching the subject of the possible varieties of immortality and whether one or another of these may be realized in the multiverse or the universe we inhabit.

After considering the "what" of immortality, we will examine the "why"—why immortality is desirable and essential—though this subject is treated additionally elsewhere. We will then be ready to address the "how" of immortality and, in particular, how we might be able in a universe such as ours to postpone death indefinitely, though of course we have no guarantee of this.

Let us begin, then, with what immortality should reasonably involve. Clearly it is some notion of survival that is not limited by time. The issue of survival was dealt with in Chapter 12 as a necessary consequence of resurrection. There it was argued that a person would survive in a more developed version, or continuer (including but not limited to the case of starting the resurrection from an exact copy). But now we must consider what ought to be involved in survival beyond the bare fact of resurrection. Also, it must not be thought that the notion of survival is to be limited to the case of resurrection, but ordinary survival with no death interval is to be included and can in fact be treated similarly.

The case was argued that person-stage P_1, supposed to be living at some particular time, survives in person-stage P_2 where P_2 is a continuer of P_1, meaning a more developed version of P_1 living at a (normally) later time. We are thus comparing P_1, supposed to be carrying out some sort of conscious activity, with the later conscious activity of P_2. By "living" I will assume "living and active," which means, at minimum, "conscious." So a person is an entity that is conscious at least some of the time: there are no persons that are never conscious, though other possible things that are never conscious, such as certain descriptions or chunks of information, might be straightforwardly transformed into persons. When it is said, then, that P_1 was living at some particular time, and P_2 was living at some later time, it means that both P_1 and P_2 were engaged in some conscious activity at the respective times. Moreover, if P_1 is to survive it suggests that the activity of P_2 is not simply arbitrary, but the conscious experiences of P_1 must somehow be reflected or recapitulated in those of P_2.

To make further progress we need to look at several questions more carefully, mainly the following: (1) what are the important features of personhood, for the problem of survival? (2) what do we mean by a "more developed version" of a person? and (3) what activity on the part of a more developed version would reasonably satisfy our notions that survival of the earlier version has occurred?

Personhood

To start, let us consider the issue of personhood, a topic on which much can be said; we must be careful to limit discussion to what is relevant. As a basic intuition, I will think of a person as a digital process, following the treatment of this in Chapter 8. Of course we imagine that the "digital process" may be complicated to any finite level as needed to account for all the subtle and non-machinelike features we find in real persons (the Principle of Large Quantity).

A Turing machine, by hypothesis, can model such digital processes as human beings. In the course of its action over time, a Turing machine goes through a succession of states. In a similar way I will imagine that a person is a kind of process that, in the course of functioning, goes through states of consciousness. The change from one state of consciousness to another we can consider a conscious event. Intuitively, it seems natural to regard the person as being definable in terms of conscious events, as we noted in Chapter 7. It should be clear, however, that a progression of events or state changes (going from one state to another) amounts to a progression of states. Indeed, in a formal sense the two notions can be shown to be equivalent: state changes can be treated as single states. (More generally, an assemblage of a finite number of states describing some progression of events could be treated as a single state. In this way, then, we can obtain many equivalents of our basic computational model that, however, may vary greatly in complexity and suitability to our purpose.) In what follows, then, we shall assume that states of consciousness form the building blocks of personal experience and of what it is that defines a particular person.

In a Turing machine the successive states are sequential or linearly ordered in time, though we might wish to allow that states of consciousness, while forming an overall "progression," are not so strictly ordered. This consideration in particular might be significant if we want to emphasize how states of consciousness and assemblages of states forming events and episodes, are remembered; it is possible to remember events without remembering their order of occurrence. But here we can distinguish between what actually occurred and what is remembered; it is not necessary that all the details of a sequential process be captured in memory. In any case, we have seen (in Chapter 8) that a sequential Turing machine can model nonsequential devices such as cellular spaces and the natural world at the quantum level. So the difference between sequential and nonsequential devices does not seem fundamental, though it certainly could have practical significance; more will be said, however, in Chapter 16.

I do not propose to define precisely what consciousness is—this is too tall an order, and I think simple intuition will suffice. I assume that whatever it is, there are meaningful states of consciousness that are visited more or less sequentially, if not always strictly so. Such traversal, moreover, fully characterizes the phenomenon of consciousness as we know it, and these states are at least roughly analogous to the states a simple computational device might traverse in the course of its operation.

A state of consciousness, however, can be expected to be far more complicated than the state of a simple Turing machine, for which a single letter or numeral may suffice. So I will make another analogy: a state of consciousness can be compared to a meaningful sentence in some chosen language, assumed to be fixed throughout. The language would use letters of some finite alphabet; the number of possible sentences of some given length or less would be finite, and each sentence would then capture a finite amount of information. (Indeed, a universal language as suggested in Chapter 8 should be adequate for this purpose.) In fact, in the case of states of consciousness I will make an assumption connected with Interchangeability. Each state, however we should think of it, can be fully described by some finite body of information. This is an "in principle" assumption; I do not claim such a description has yet been given, but only that it could be given if our knowledge were sufficiently advanced, as ought to happen in the future.

A finite, orderly arrangement of states of consciousness such as a person might traverse in a finite time I will call an experience. An experience, then, is like a body of writing; reading a book, in fact is one type of experience that correlates well with this idea. A succession of sentences is scanned; each might be said to induce a state of consciousness, and the whole then adds up to an experience. In particular, just as states of consciousness are finite in the sense of being finitely describable, so are experiences in general. (The whole of one's life, which is hopefully not finite, might also be called an experience; however, as used here, an experience will refer to a finite interval only, corresponding to a person-segment but not an immortal, diachronic self.)

The idea that such experiences should have finite descriptions accords with our physical theories, in which all finite processes have finite descriptions, as we have noted. Once we have a description of a state of consciousness we should be able in principle to create the conditions under which that particular state would reappear. (The description, naturally, might have to be very lengthy.) In general, an arbitrary experience could be made to reappear if we had the information that characterized it. A person as a whole, then, involves a visiting of states of consciousness that in principle are sharable—more than one person could have a state of consciousness, and experiences more generally, in common. Two distinct persons, however, cannot have all their experiences in common, for then by Interchangeability the two persons would be one and the same.

The above, then, is a simple, suggestive characterization of a person, based roughly around a Turing machine. Many details for a full formal model are unspecified and will remain so, though from the basic digital nature of processes it should be clear that such a specification could be given in principle. Other easier and more crucial details will be introduced as needed.

A Turing machine, in addition to assuming a succession of states, engages in some sort of action in a physical environment—in this case marking squares on a tape and moving left or right. Similarly, a person in the course of an experience is generally engaged in some sort of action in a physical environment—but only the experience is important to the person in a direct sense. Detailed consideration of the physical environment and allowable actions of a person is largely omitted here, though there is one issue relating to this—the necessity for personal growth—that deserves mention and will be considered shortly.

An experience, moreover, has a twofold aspect that needs clarification: what we might call its feeling content, on one hand, and on the other, its information content. The feeling content refers to the meaning of the experience for whoever has it. The feeling content should fully capture the information content; otherwise the entire experience is not really "experienced." The information content, on the other hand, fully characterizes the experience computationally, in the manner suggested above, so that, from the information content the complete feeling content must be reproducible. The information content will in general specify meaningful details such as the time and place of the experience, specific events that occurred, what feelings were had, what actions were done, what was said and heard, what thoughts were thought, and so on. It may thus have to be very detailed and involve matters beyond our current understanding, though as usual, not beyond the laws of physics.

In particular, the information content may include the complete information content of some earlier experience, with the feeling content conforming too, so that the earlier experience is remembered. The information that is recalled in such an act of remembering can take different forms corresponding to past visual or auditory perceptions, emotions, and so on. In this way the past can truly "come alive." (It is not necessary, on the other hand, that the past, including unpleasant events, be experienced exactly as it was originally. In general, the subject will be aware of remembering something that has happened already rather than thinking it is happening now for the first time.) This sort of recall of specific happenings, or episodes, is actually only one of many possible ways that information retained from the past can influence our present conscious state. But I think episodic memory has a special significance and have emphasized it, while trying not to overlook the alternatives. Certainly an experience worth having is one worth remembering, which calls for the ability to recreate the past through recall, and thus I think such recall is or ought to be an important part of one's life experiences.

Requirements for Immortality

In general I imagine that the life of a person is divided between involvement in new experiences and recall or in some manner being influenced by old experiences. It seems clear that both activities—experiencing the new and being affected by the old—would be necessary for the would-be immortal. Without new experiences in some form, the person would be stagnated—forever trapped in the past and effectively dead to the world, contrary to any reasonable notion of immortality. (A mental disorder, Korsakoff's syndrome, leaves the victim unable to form new memories and somewhat approximates this condition.) An old experience that had no effect after some point, on the other hand, effectively would no longer be part of the person. If every experience were eventually to become entirely lost in this manner (a particularly devastating form of progressive amnesia), even with an endless succession of new experiences, then clearly no well-defined person could be said to endure.

For immortality, then, the person must, over infinite time, assimilate infinitely many experiences adding up to an infinite information content. In particular this rules out any true "survival" according to a doctrine of "nonself" in which there is no developing individual. Something definite and growing—a body of information detailing an increasing succession of experiences—must accumulate and be under the control of a specific agent—the person in question. Each of these experiences must be remembered by this one agent and not once or a few times only but infinitely often. This does not mean that no experience can be forgotten or permanently lost, however, but only that some growing body of experiences must not be forgotten. It is this growing body then, that progressively defines the developing immortal, who, after all, is no static entity but, at least in the long run, must progress with time. Endless life requires endless progress.

Properly speaking, the permanently remembered experiences are the only experiences that are part of the immortal being. Such a being had a beginning in time, with the earliest of the remembered experiences, but will have no end. A finite sequence of consecutive experiences together make a larger experience, which also must be of finite duration. More general arrangements of one's past experiences, beyond a simple, consecutive ordering, could also comprise experiences in their own right, which again will be finite. In particular, the whole of one's life up to any point in time constitutes a single experience. Thus it must be remembered in its entirety infinitely often by the developing immortal, insofar as it can be said to constitute part of that immortal. (The remembering could be frequent or rare, however, depending on the subject; "infinitely often" is not necessarily a demanding requirement, though there could also be a problem of infrequent remembering, which we will consider later.)

In the above I have used the term *remembering* mainly in the sense of reliving an experience, as might happen with episodic memory—however, the type of activity I have in mind is really more general than ordinary recall. Basically, an act of remembering may be said to occur whenever a person's past information is used in such a way as to affect the feeling content of a new experience. It is thus possible to involve information beyond what we would usually consider memories, such as dispositions, intentions, or general knowledge. An experience, on the other hand, may incorporate this sort of information, whether implicitly or explicitly, and thus will generally consist of far more than simple impressions of specific past events. Different experiences too may share information, particularly of the nondeclarative sort. Finally, an act of remembering, though normally thought of as something done quickly, could be more complex and even extend over considerable time itself, while different parts or features of a past experience are revisited or in some manner exert their effects at the conscious level.

In summary, then, a person maintains an archive of past information, a fund of experiences that is interacted with and added to from time to time. Although a specific archival record may be lost (forgotten or permanently repressed or destroyed) the archive must contain a growing body of records that are never lost or permanently ignored but are inspected or "revisited" again and again.

I should emphasize, too, that while remembering must be considered important for our information-based notion of survival and immortality, forgetting may also be important for other reasons. A person may wish to discard certain information in the course of life—indeed, this certainly happens in our lives today, although our capacity for forgetting, like that of remembering, is conditioned by biological and psychological features that may not be under much control. In the future our level of control should improve. For a reasonable notion of immortality, however, it is essential to have some constraint on allowable forgetting.

The person, I have said, must in any case build up an infinite archive of experiences that are never forgotten, over infinite time. This is rather lenient, however (and may in fact be too generous—should we require, for example, an infinite archive of epi-sodic memories or would another sort of "memories" suffice, for example, mathematical theorems? This problem I leave to the reader for now.) The accumulation of information could be slow and careful with much winnowing of uninspiring or distasteful material. On the other hand, preserving some of even the least liked memories could be valuable in the long run as an aid to the learning process and a reality check. But the partial forgetting of an experience does not mean that no experience is remembered; a suitable abridgment should qualify as an experience that is full and complete in its own right.

Along with the possibility of forgetting is what we might call dissociation. Information relating to past experiences could be preserved but felt to belong, say, to some other individual. Disso-ciation, in its simplest form, could be treated as a form of forget-ting (enontically reversible however). More generally, though, we would have to consider various forms of partial dissociation in which the simple dichotomy of forgetting versus remember-ing may not apply. The general problem of how past information is to be regarded is complex, and only the more central issues can be treated here. (I hope the foregoing will be enough for a useful start, however.)

We must also consider the problem of the corruption of infor-mation. We have no guarantee that a memory is authentic, and in fact distortions do creep in (or perhaps are deliberately induced). I will have more to say on this subject in the next chapter. As a general rule, however, I will advocate the position that distor-tions beyond simple forgetting or erasure and some forms of dis-sociation are to be avoided even if some advantage seems to fol-low, as in the case of unpleasant memories that are "improved." In any case, guarding against corruption of information must be considered along with protecting against loss.

The need to endlessly accumulate information would ultimately shape the developing immortal in rather profound ways. Barring certain exotic possibilities, there must be endless physical growth since each bit of information requires a nonzero volume of space. (This may not be a problem for some time to come, however; information, it appears, can be far more compactly stored than it is in the brain.) The universe, if survival is to be enontic, must accommodate this growth. A vast, thinking structure could develop out of each person, which would entail some novel logistic problems.

The human brain maintains an illusion of a present, an instant of time in which we are fully conscious, aware of what is going on, and interacting. In fact a nonzero reaction time—at least a fraction of a second—is required to integrate sensory input, consult short-term memory, and so on, to produce our state of awareness and interaction. More time is needed for more involved recollection and deliberation. We think typically that we can attach a specific time of occurrence to a state of consciousness, much as our Turing machine will be in a specific state at a given instant in time. This may call for adjustment, particularly to accommodate our unlimited growth, though not only for that. But if the reaction time were to lengthen considerably, as might happen if we became more complicated beings, a description of ourselves in terms of a sequential device would become more difficult. A person would still be embodied in a physical process and thus be a digital system—so the machine model, which can be based on a sequential device as we have noted, should again be adequate in principle.

Immortality is still a dream of the future, but a human being does at least provide an approximation of the immortal person just outlined. Memories are stored throughout life and can be recalled at will. Some things are forgotten too, but often many things even from early life are remembered throughout. Some other information, such as that in the genome, no doubt continues to have discernible effects. It thus might qualify, in the more general sense, as a component in one or more experiences and be "remembered" insofar as it can be said to exert a continuing effect at the conscious level. It is clear too that human memories are not just of the dry, declarative sort but may have emotional content too. On the other hand, nondeclarative information is also important—mathematics or language skills, for example. In all, a human can serve as a starting point from which to develop a more refined model of the would-be immortal.

This expands to human society as a whole, which in better moments is a prototype of the immortal society that will hopefully arise in the future. Among the functions of today's society is to store information that will have beneficial effects in the lives of individuals, and this can be expected to continue in a more advanced society of the future. This information generally is not to be identified with the past experience of any one person—the historical record, for instance, involves events that extend across many lives, and this too will continue. In general, immortality will not be an individual but a collective enterprise, though, of course, designed to serve the needs and aims of individuals, for whom society rightfully exists.

We have now considered general features that would reasonably apply to all notions of immortality. In addition there is the issue of onticity, which raises the possibility of different varieties of immortality, some of which would be preferred to others. Some useful concepts based on earlier definitions will apply here.

Enontic immortality will refer to the condition that the individual never experiences the loss of information that would make resurrection hyperontic or xenontic. Someone born in the future may be so fortunate—immortality may be possible technologically and be a normal expectation of life, so that people simply will no longer die. Similarly, someone dying today who undergoes an enontic resurrection through biostasis could awaken in such a future and thus be privileged to this form of immortality.

There is also what I will call *almost enontic immortality*, where the person is resurrected, hyperontically or xenontically, but is enontic from then on. (It should be clear that this is logically possible; a person's experiences beyond a certain point could all be contained in the known historical record, even though earlier experiences might not be. The known experiences could even include recollections of the unknown; such recollections would qualify as enontic even though the recalled experiences are not. Similarly, I can read a novel; my experience of reading then is enontic though the book, as fiction, is xenontic or perhaps hyperontic.) This immortality, then, comes in the two varieties of hyperontic and xenontic depending on what sort of resurrection(s) preceded the hypothesized interval of unlimited enonticity.

Finally, hyperontic and xenontic immortality could come in the strong forms of *not* almost enontic. We have seen, for example, how the only possible immortality may be one that is strongly xenontic in this sense, where no universe exists that can support eternal life. We will have to be resurrected again and again, in an endless succession of new universes, and after each resurrection the enonticity of any previous experiences will be lost. On the other hand, once again enonticity is to be preferred if possible, and it might be hoped that almost-enonticity will obtain for all beings. (Each being then would be resurrected non-enontically at most a finite number of times.) This should happen if at least one possible universe can support eternal life and suitable other conditions hold, a topic we will return to in Chapter 16.

Why Immortality Is Important

We have now considered the "what" of immortality; let us go on to the "why." We shall look into the reasons that immortality would be desirable and something we ought to strive for, building on earlier ideas, some of which were considered last chapter.

From one point of view, the issue seems transparently simple. Life ought to be worth living. If life is worth living, it should not come to an end, therefore one ought to be immortal. This, of course, overlooks the details of what one might be doing with one's life as well as such other features as what sort of society would emerge if individuals were immortal. These matters are impossible to second-guess in detail, but some things can be said with reasonable confidence.

Whatever the details of a life may be, they should be such as to produce meaning and fulfillment—including, most importantly, a reason to continue, to find something always new, interesting, exciting, something from which one can learn. This applies to our limited existence today; it should apply all the more to the hoped-for immortal future. Life should be habit forming!

Another aspect of life being worth living is that it should be worth remembering. Pleasure alone thus is not enough. The nature of one's experiences should be such that thinking of them later causes enjoyment too—a requirement that, I think, should not prove too difficult in the sort of future that seems possible, even though people today often do not seem to value the remembered past.

Finally, what is worth remembering is also worth sharing. Life should be something shared with others so that all in the end will mutually benefit. Of course it must be the "right" others, which will follow if individuals are well disposed and develop in reasonable ways.

In short, then, commonsense notions that apply to life today,

even with its present limitations, lead to the conclusion that immortal life, properly conducted, would be good and desirable.
This is also bolstered by considering the opposite viewpoint.
Could we learn to make peace with death? Could we see in it
something other than final ruin and frustration? Could we find
meaning in spite of (or because of) the thought of an eventual,
permanent concluding, a restitution once and for all of all our
striving and cares? But I think all attempts to do so must ring
hollow. Knowledge of one's mortality and its apparent inevitability is not an easy burden for the rational mind to carry. I doubt if
belief in one's impermanence can inspire much real satisfaction,
except perhaps for those who view life, fundamentally, as a burden that ought to end. Certainly life should have more to offer
than that. There is no proper substitute for immortality and the
benefit that springs from a reasonable hope and confidence in its
likelihood.

Bertrand Russell, a leading twentieth-century British philosopher, was firmly convinced of the inevitability of death—based
on a belief in the Heat Death of the universe. Russell was not
happy with this state of affairs but thought it must be accepted,
arguing that "...only on the firm foundation of unyielding despair, can the soul's habitation...be safely built."[1] His solution
was to downplay the issue. The thought that "life will die out...is
not such as to render life miserable. It merely makes you turn
your attention to other things."[2] But again, this rings hollow. In
particular, it invites the question of whether painless, immediate
suicide would not be a better alternative, particularly since in
view of the Heat Death all life in general must eventually die out.

True, there are venerable schools of thought that accept death
as a necessary accompaniment of life. In the early centuries C.E.,
"[t]he Stoics insisted that man must learn to submit himself to
the course of nature; it is not death which is evil but rather our
fear of it."[3] The related, roughly contemporary Epicurean doctrine held that "there are only a limited number of gratifications,
and, once these have been experienced, it is futile to live longer."[4]
Buddhism, more ancient still, considers the "wish for continued
existence" a form of "defilement."[5] Many hold similar attitudes
today, and much has been written and said by way of rationaliz-
ing death as an acceptable transition, a nonburden. Such rational-
izing philosophies deserve at least some respect for their effort to

make the most of a difficult position while adhering, as they generally do, to doctrines based on reason. Happily, however, modern science offers new perspectives and makes feasible a more optimistic but still reason-based outlook. We see increasing prospects, both for the means of eliminating death and for meaningful activity beyond what many have seen as unassailable limits.

Other interesting issues are explored by Frank Tipler in *The Physics of Immortality* that further strengthen the argument for the desirability of immortality. Two possible alternatives to unlimited, developing existence are examined, the Heat Death, and the Eternal Return. The difference between the two is that in the Heat Death life simply ceases to exist after a time, while with the Eternal Return, events are cyclic or approximately so and literally repeat themselves. (Although the second possibility, repetition, may seem improbable given the complexity and apparent randomness of events as we see them, it is implied by certain recurrence theorems that apply to quantum mechanics.) Though each has some arguments in its favor, neither the Heat Death nor the Eternal Return can be considered well-established—more on this later in the chapter.

Both viewpoints deny the possibility of endless progress. Each on the other hand has been endorsed by noted philosophers, which led to a rejection of the idea of immortality (a true, progress-based version at any rate) and an extolling of other, in some cases diabolical, alternatives. For example, the Eternal Return idea led to the thought, expressed by Nietzsche, that "the *goal of humanity* cannot lie in the end," as would happen with endless progress, "but only in *its highest specimens*."[6] Nietzsche himself was no crude racist and especially no anti-Semite, but some of his ideas were taken up in twisted form decades after his death by those who were: the Nazis under Adolf Hitler.

As self-styled high specimens and a "master race" (another misappropriated Nietzschean concept), the Nazis engulfed the world in war and committed horrible atrocities to "purify" it of entire populations rationalized as inferior. Jews in particular, seen as unwelcome intruders and competitors and furnishing a convenient scapegoat, were slaughtered by the millions in the infamous action later known as the Holocaust. (One legacy was the formation of the modern Jewish state of Israel in 1948, three years after the Nazi defeat.) Others in the troubled twentieth century, such as Stalin in Russia and Mao in China, though not so hideous ideologically, had millions more executed for political ends.

All this carnage reflected the general rationale that what is good for the group need not be so for the individual, who is, after all, a transient, mortal creature in any event. Though many would certainly disagree with mass murder, the impermanence of the individual has acted as a damper on the champions of individual rights and freedom, which is one more reason to favor a change.

Achieving Enontic Immortality

Taking the grander view, I think (and many others have agreed) that what is highest and best in humanity can only be adequately supported if immortality proves possible, while the consequences if it is impossible, even apart from a final cataclysm, could be dire indeed. This applies more or less to whatever unknown possibilities may exist for immortality; however, something more can be said regarding the different varieties of immortality that were defined earlier. Indeed, we have reason to think that enontic and almost-enontic immortality would be best of all—assuming of course that they are possible at all.

Groundwork for this position was laid in the last chapter, in connection with the desirability of the biostasis option; the issue will be further addressed in later chapters. But the point was made that as the future unfolds, advanced beings will come to be the type who favor life and shun death. Such persons will likely be the ones who carry out whatever resurrection projects are attempted. They will, I think, feel a moral obligation to see to it that immortalist-leaning resurrectees are favored over others more "deathist" in their orientation, other factors equal. Again, to be immortalist-leaning is, by a reasonable argument, to favor the enontic over alternatives. Let us assume, then, that straightforward enontic immortality is desired and investigate ways that it might be achieved.

To approach the "how" of immortality for this special but important case, we must confront the physics of our own universe. We can no longer take refuge in the possibilities of Unboundedness to overcome any calamity however great. Much is unknown, despite ongoing, exciting research and the efforts of theoreticians such as Dyson and Tipler. The latter, though, offers one insight that I think provides additional hope. As is often true of events on a smaller scale, the universe as a whole seems to be a chaotic system—meaning that small differences in conditions can give rise to large differences over moderate intervals of time. This opens a door to us as an intelligent species: we may, by calculated maneuvers, be able to exercise great control over the developing universe when we are more advanced, and ultimately win our goal of immortality by shaping an appropriate cosmic destiny. As usual this is not a guarantee, but let us look at some of the possibilities. We will start by correcting a simple fallacy.

Many people doubt that immortality can be achieved scientifically. Aside from such problems as the Heat Death, their reasoning is that although aging and diseases might be cured, no technology could make us invulnerable to accidental death, so sooner or later, death must claim us. This conclusion seems to be bolstered by physics. A result known as the fluctuations and dissipations theorem asserts that arbitrarily large catastrophes must occur. Eventually, an exploding star or some other large-scale disaster must catch up to anyone, however well-protected. But this overlooks one possibility: that people might make themselves increasingly hard to kill over time.

How could this be done in a way that would counteract an impacting asteroid or a supernova? Mainly by storing identity-critical information redundantly over an increasing volume of space. A catastrophe that destroyed some of this information would not end or compromise the life of the people affected, so long as enough remained to reassemble them. Although, at any given time, a disaster sufficient to kill could happen, with more copies of vital information in more places, the possibility of it happening would grow increasingly remote. (The extra copies would also serve as a deterrent to corruption of information; a growing supply of copies could be read against one another to see if any contained errors.)

Still, the critic might counter, at all times there would be some chance of dying. Would that not mean, in the end, that death is inevitable? The answer is: not necessarily. In fact, if the likelihood of dying decreases fast enough with time, there is a nonzero chance of surviving, literally forever. This can be illustrated by a simple if artificial example.

Let us say that by the year 2100 aging and diseases are cured and other advances have been made. The chance that you will die in the following century is only 1 percent, meaning you have a 99 percent chance of still being alive (in excellent health of course, which is very likely if you are alive at all) in 2200. Then more advances occur, including more redundant information storage. With that, your chances of dying over the next century, that is, by 2300, are halved to only 0.5 percent. That is, if you are among the 99 percent who make it to 2200, there is an even better chance you will survive to 2300, 99.5 percent. After that, progress continues, halving your chance of dying in each successive century. What, we then ask, is your chance, starting in 2100, of never dying at all, or living forever?

This can be estimated using a calculator or, better yet, a short Basic program. Chances or probabilities of survival multiply—I assume that potentially lethal events in different centuries are independent. In performing the calculation, it is more convenient to express the probabilities as fractions of 1 (99 percent=.99, for example). Thus the chance of surviving from 2100 to 2300 is the chance of surviving from 2100 to 2200 (.99) times that of surviving from 2200 to 2300 (.995), or overall, .98505. (From here on I round the results to five digits.) Multiplying this by the chance of surviving from 2300 to 2400 (.9975) gives the chance of surviving from 2100 to 2400, or .98259. If we continue in this manner we see that after fourteen centuries the chance of survival falls to .98013, but with no further significant change no matter how much further we go. So after a hundred, a thousand, or a billion centuries, the chance of survival is still .98013 or just over 98 percent. The probability, then, has converged with time to a limiting value. And most important, this value is greater than zero, in fact not far from 1 or 100 percent, though slightly smaller. There is some chance then, of dying over an infinite time interval but also some (in this case a much greater) chance of surviving forever. Moreover, the chance of ever dying lessens with passing time; here we see it is virtually zero after fourteen centuries since there is no significant further change in the chance of survival.

Of course this is not intended to be a realistic scenario. The whole idea of "dying," which seems rather simple and straightforward today, will probably be seen rather differently in the light of greater wisdom. Many other things too are unknown at this point, and projections are hazardous. But the example illustrates something about the idea of infinite survival, namely that in the form envisioned it is probabilistic in nature and involves contrary possibilities, each of which has some chance of happening. The chance of one possibility (dying) decreases with time but never falls quite to zero. The decrease is rapid enough, in this case, that the other possibility (infinite survival) dominates, though again, not so totally that its contrary is ever ruled out.

A reminder: we are assuming here that the survival of interest is the enontic variety, which is irreversibly ended by "death" or loss of identity-critical information. Should this occur, other forms of survival are possible, but it seems reasonable that full enonticity, once lost, can never be restored.

Today we are inclined to think of "death" as an all-or-nothing proposition, although we know even now that this is fallacious. One only has to consider the sad case of a stroke victim who is conscious but mentally impaired. Death very often happens partially or a bit at a time rather than all at once. This is a problem that should be greatly alleviated in the future.

Indeed, we noted in Chapter 9 that clinical trials are under way now for repairing and restoring stroke-damaged brain tissue with apparently encouraging results. Such treatment is still in its infancy but certainly shows promise. More distantly we can imagine more radical means of assistance and enhancement.

One crucial development will be the use of artificial devices that can interface directly with the brain. This, an impossible dream today, should follow straightforwardly once we have a mature nanotechnology and possibly well before then. Brain backups—devices that store useful information or capture capabilities—will then become feasible and perhaps make the problem of brain damage almost trivial. A stroke victim whose speech centers were destroyed, for example, could recover full function by "switching in" the appropriate backup device. In more severe cases the revivifying functions might be switched in from the outside by medical technicians.

Backups could be made for all important brain functions including memory, cognition, motor skills, emotions, and sensory processing. In addition to correctly functioning, they must be integrated smoothly into what is already there. The person should feel no intrusion or be aware of anything out of the ordinary, so long as the original, surviving brain tissue was functioning normally. And if the original malfunctioned or ceased to operate, it should be possible to restore what seemed in all respects to be normal function, even if something other than the old gray matter was involved. I think all of this will be possible and straightforward once certain technological hurdles are overcome (and various philosophical and other objections are met, of course). The brain, in fact, already has many backup systems, and it seems reasonable that providing new and better ones, without in any sense "sacrificing" or compromising the person, will prove feasible.

Brain tissue—the natural variety—has its limitations. It is physically very fragile, requires most careful maintenance, and is designed to last a few decades only, marvelous though it is; its quantity is limited too. We are now apparently learning how to augment it with other brain tissue to restore functions that have been lost through prior damage, but that approach too has limitations. (New brain tissue, for instance, would not restore lost memories.) It seems likely that over the course of time the biological brain will be discarded for hardware that better serves the developing immortal. We may conjecture, I think, that this will largely have happened by 2200 if not sooner. Similarly, the body's other hardware will probably be replaced by material found to be more suitable. Persons may wish to have independent bodies, as today, or may spend much of their time as programs in a large computer. Either lifestyle could be possible as well as alternations from one to the other. In any case, the information that characterizes an individual—10^{18} bits or so today, more in the future—should become much more secure with such precautions as redundant storage and frequent backups. In this way, then, virtual immortality should be achievable over a short historical time scale.

We can imagine, I think, that conditions of survival could be maintained for very long periods this way. A million years is a short interval on the cosmic scale. There should be an adequate supply of energy from the sun to support many more-than-human beings in comfort and luxury for such time, plus opportunities for journeying elsewhere in the cosmos and establishing oneself. Hopefully long before one's millionth birthday the value of benevolence will be fully recognized along with the absurdity and inappropriateness of harmful alternatives. Meanwhile, with proper self-development based on self-knowledge and other deep understanding, life will truly be rewarding and full of joy, meaning, and wonder.

Cosmological Perspectives

What would it be like to be a million years old? Such a life we can scarcely imagine, but a few features we can reasonably conjecture. *Old* will not mean what it does today, with its associations of weakness, enfeeblement, rigidity, resistance to new ideas, and loss of zest for living. Our million-year-olds should be more fresh, vibrant, and youthful than anything we can imagine, having had thousands of centuries to perfect themselves in these ways. Beyond this a few other properties should hold. Past experiences, enshrined in memory, should continue to have value, and life should continue to seem worth living for new and wonderful things that are hopefully still to come. Life, rightly lived, should overall improve in value and meaning, without ceasing. Increasingly, death must be an unwanted and hopefully unlikely possibility.

But to go on from there—from long lives to literal immortality—our more-than-human continuers and future beloved friends must confront cosmology directly. Their knowledge we may presume will be vastly greater than ours, and the question of whether (enontic) immortality is possible in our universe may long since have been answered.

Today the answer is unknown, though physicists in recent decades have increasingly addressed it. There are pessimists as well as optimists. Some of their viewpoints are of interest and will be examined starting from our earlier vantage point, where we were considering the fluctuations and dissipations theorem.

The remedy for this, we noted, was to imagine that people could store their identity-critical information with increasing redundancy over a growing volume of space. We can assume that by the time such an issue became important, people will be expressed in forms whose functioning, repair, and interfacing will be fully understood. It should be abundantly clear how people can be considered, essentially, as programs running on hardware. Such operations as readout and electronic or photonic mailing of memory information should be straightforward and routine or there will be other, even better, technologies for doing these things. It should be very easy, then, to carry out storage of memory information, rebuilding damaged hardware, and reinstalling previously erased or corrupted software. A full computerization of what was previously the species Homo sapiens will have occurred. The species will have died—the limited body and brain will no longer be suitable, and there will be no human creatures such as we are today. (Or else real humans may be created rarely and sporadically but only soon to shed their mortal bodies for more durable housing.) But formerly human individuals will live on, in a life more glorious than was possible before.

We hope this wonderful life can continue forever, and not just a "long time" (a relative term). It seems evident that infinite survival will require infinite growth. Over infinite time there must be both an infinite proliferation of information overall in the form of new memories and other records, and an infinite proliferation of copies of particular, already in-place records to guard against loss or alteration. We must store as well as generate an infinite body of information. There must also be a proliferation of linking information so the growing body of records will continue to form a unified whole. Linking information must also be redundantly copied to guard against damage. Certainly, then, the universe must be open-ended in the sense of providing an infinite amount of room in which to grow. Another requirement is that there must be enough energy so that consciousness—a form of information processing—can continue forever. A third requirement is that the open-ended universe must not be too uniform. Otherwise we would run into a problem suggesting the fertile garden in which "flowers" (individuals or entire civilizations) spring up but in such abundance that each has only limited growing room and is choked off and dies.[7]

For immortality, then, the universe has to be open-ended, nonuniform, and with energy adequate for processing always available. There can be no Heat Death and no Eternal Return. These requirements are rather exacting, but at least the universe is very large and old yet does not seem overcrowded with intelligent life already. (Indeed, that the universe appears to be finite and evolving rather than infinite and steady-state is one suggestion that any problems with the "fertile garden" will be manageable.) So some encouragement is offered, though there is certainly no strong argument yet that the universe will provide the everlasting habitation we would like.

If immortality is to be possible in our universe, we must expect to engineer it, which means we must play a significant role on the cosmic scale. This brings up an interesting property we noted earlier: the universe appears to be chaotic, meaning that small effects can quickly mushroom into bigger effects that grow and grow. As one example, if a single butterfly moves a distance of one meter from one flower to another, the cumulative effect in 500 million years, under the right conditions, would be to move the earth from one side of its orbit to the other (300 million kilometers).[8] With this in mind there is much that we might do given a few billion years to constructively affect things on a cosmic scale. The possibility is opened that we can shape the universe of the far future to fit our needs of survival, though there are limits too. Changing a closed universe that eventually collapses into an open universe that does not (should that prove necessary) appears to be impossible.[9] But we will have to see.

In any case, we are just beginning. We have a few future scenarios, which serious physicists have now devised, that may provide for enontic immortality. In considering these we will first examine what seem to be the two biggest potential obstacles to eternal life in our universe, the Heat Death and the Eternal Return.

It is a basic principle of physics that in any closed system the amount of disorder or entropy increases—the system runs down. In the closed systems we can create in the laboratory—by thermally insulating and sealing off a volume of space and considering what happens inside—a uniform temperature is eventually reached (ignoring quantum effects), with no usable energy. This will happen regardless of what may be going on initially—electrical or chemical activity, for instance, or a clock that is ticking or a motor that is running on its own fuel supply. After this, essentially nothing happens. A potential energy difference is required between some point and another point in the space to derive any useful work. Without a temperature difference, or equivalent mechanism providing a source of energy, all energy exists only as unusable heat. The system has then reached the state of Heat Death.

Applying this to the universe as a whole (and the universe, certainly, is thermally insulated from whatever may exist outside it), it seems that everything must eventually run down and reach a uniform temperature. Given the present great size of the universe, which is mostly empty space far from any stars, the available energy (mainly from nuclear fusion in stars) would not be enough to maintain any but a very small uniform temperature. (In fact, if the universe expands indefinitely as it may be destined to do, this temperature must approach absolute zero.) The stars would burn out, and things would freeze and grow very cold. Life too, since it requires energy to function, must cease, never to revive again. This, then, is the cosmic Heat Death, a gloomy future scenario first predicted by physicist Hermann von Helmholtz in 1854.[10] A more recent alternative form of the Heat Death is that the universe collapses into a fireball—the constant temperature then is very high (or not constant at all but zooming up to infinity) because the volume of the universe has become tiny.

Actually, there are effects that make the Heat Death scenario seem unlikely—though they are not a guarantee of what we would like either. But one effect of this sort comes from quantum graininess. Matter is not uniform at small scales but resolves into particles. (This is true even if the particles can be explained as virtual effects of waves, as follows under many-worlds.) Particles are never at rest but vibrate and agitate constantly (Brownian motion), even under the most placid macroscopic conditions. Thus even a closed, thermally isolated system cannot reach a state where nothing is happening but can only approximate a condition of true Heat Death. The residual motion of the particles, in fact, carries the possibility that major rearrangements will occasionally happen. Entropy can diminish and large-scale activity start again.

Nevertheless this is not a guarantee, on the scale of the universe, that intelligent life will survive and enjoy endless progress. Another possibility is the Eternal Return, in which limited progress is inevitably followed by collapse, and this occurs over and over, forever. It is easy to see how this condition too would be compatible with avoidance of the Heat Death—not, however, with avoidance of mortality. One variation, for instance, would be a closed universe that collapses then re-expands, over and over, each cycle involving no more than a fixed complexity of structure and information. In this case, as with the Heat Death, only finitely many different constructs are possible, including persons at particular stages of advancement (person-stages). Though it may take many,

many cycles for exact repetitions, the same structures must recur again and again, precluding the progress necessary for immortality.

It is worth remarking that the Eternal Return is a different condition from Unboundedness, despite some similarities. For the latter too requires that different histories and constructs happen over and over, yet the total number of different realized conditions is infinite, not finite. This leads to the possibility of infinitely many subjective experiences or immortality for an individual through a succession of increasingly advanced constructs or continuers. The individual does not subjectively experience the same history over and over but only once, though through a multiplicity of instantiations. The same considerations would apply in the more limited scenario of the Eternal Return. Histories would not be experienced over and over even if they recurred, but subjectively each individual's life experience would happen only once. Again, the multiple instantiations (in this case stretching over time, if not space) could not be perceived as such by the subject. One's life history, self-perceived, must be finite and terminate at some point, never to be resumed. There would be no detectable difference whether there was an Eternal Return or simply a finite life span followed by oblivion—a point that advocates such as Nietzsche seem to have overlooked.

Coping with the Mysterious Universe

Cosmologists have studied many possible models of the universe. These often give very different predictions about what conditions will be like in the remote future, when one might imagine fantastic projects being carried out by an advanced, intelligent civilization. A small case in point involves the expansion of the universe, which has been amply verified, we think, by the redshift of light indicating the recession of distant galaxies. (Light from a rapidly receding object is noticeably redder, or lower in frequency, much as the sound of a train whistle falls in pitch as the train passes a stationary observer and speeds away into the distance.) Though the universe seems clearly to be expanding now and to have expanded in the past, it is more difficult to forecast what the future may hold, and different theoretical models have proliferated. There are theories where the universe stops expanding, then starts collapsing, ultimately shrinking to nearly zero volume, in a reverse Big Bang. This is the "closed" universe, in which, as it happens, space is positively curved into a closed surface like an orange skin (only it is a three-dimensional surface in four spatial dimensions) and its lifetime is finite. Other theories postulate a "flat" universe that endures forever but expands more and more slowly, speeds of recession and curvature of space both going to zero as time goes to infinity. Finally there are the "open" universe models, where the expansion also goes on forever, though the recessional speeds do not go to zero but approach some limiting, positive value or possibly different positive values in different directions. This type of structure has negative curvature like a potato chip or saddle (only again, a three-dimensional surface in four spatial dimensions); the curvature in this case is maintained at nonzero values, rather than flattening out.

These model universes all have one feature in common: their behavior is gravity-driven or "free-fall": other forces besides gravitation become negligible at large distances. The outward expansion of their constituents (stars, galaxies, and so forth), supposed to have started at the Big Bang, can only slow down over time (gravity being attractive), though it will slow by differing amounts depending on the initial conditions. The fate of such a universe depends on whether there is enough mass that the gravitational attraction will eventually overcome the expansion (closed universe), just balance it out (flat universe), or always lag behind (open universe). Some recent astronomical findings, however, strikingly suggest that rather than slowing down, the expansion of the universe is speeding up—objects are moving faster and faster apart. In other words, there seems to be a repulsive force at large distances. So far the data fits the hypothesis of a "cosmological constant," in which empty space has a nonzero energy content, proportional to volume.[11] (This odd idea was introduced into general relativity by Einstein himself but then abandoned. He called it his "biggest blunder,"[12] but it has now gained a new hearing.) Such a mechanism could yield a different kind of flat universe in which recessional speeds eventually surpass all bounds, even the speed of light, because space itself is expanding at an increasing pace. This in turn could pose a new insuperable barrier to immortality in the universe, though a reprieve may also exist—more on this later in the chapter.

In any cosmological scenario, we have two basic requirements for immortality: (1) an adequate supply of energy to carry out the necessary activities of life indefinitely (expression of identity); and (2) appropriate management of information during all this time (conservation of identity). Thus, for example, information must accumulate without limit, and suitable accessing pathways to archival material must be maintained. The universe, in short, must exhibit an appropriate kind of open-endedness, whether through endless expansion or some other means.

Two main cosmological possibilities have been proposed for allowing immortality, Freeman Dyson's endlessly expanding universe, either open or flat, and Frank Tipler's closed universe.[13] Both scenarios use the older, free-fall assumption and thus stand in need of updating, but still offer useful insights. In both cases the open-endedness required for endless progress is provided by an infinite "phase space." Phase space is a coupling of ordinary three-dimensional space, which gives the physical location of a particle—with a second three-dimensional space that specifies its momentum, or mass times velocity. (Velocity in turn specifies direction as well as speed, so it, and thus momentum, requires three dimensions or coordinates just as location in space.) For a single particle, then, phase space is six-dimensional. For a system of N particles, there are six dimensions for each particle or $6N$ dimensions in all. If N is large, as in the entire universe, there are many possibilities indeed for storing information through arrangements of the particles.

It is also worth noting that a point in phase space corresponds to a distinguishable quantum state, something we encountered in Chapter 8, where we considered the Bekenstein bound on the number of such points that can occupy certain regions of space-time. In a bounded region with finite energy, phase space too is finite—this is why systems confined to such regions behave as finite state machines. But under general relativity this restriction is removed. The universe as a whole, even if spatially finite, has an infinite phase space, something that is necessary if we are to avoid an Eternal Return.[14] Phase space thus provides a cosmic tableau upon which our immortal future might be enacted and archived. Dyson's and Tipler's universes both achieve infinite phase space as needed for immortality but do it in different ways. Dyson's open or flat universe has an infinite configuration space and a finite momentum space, while Tipler's closed universe is just the opposite.

Dyson's endlessly expanding, infinitely extended universe is also cooling and in the end must approach absolute zero temperature. (It exists for infinite proper time, however, so "the end" is a potentiality not an actuality—it never really occurs.) Seemingly, life must freeze up but in fact this is not so. Information processing can proceed however close we might approach absolute zero because computation can be thermodynamically reversible so that very low and diminishing energy is required. (A true Heat Death, in fact, could only occur if some nonzero absolute temperature floor is maintained indefinitely, so that things cannot get any colder than this and, additionally, if the energy supply is finite.[15]) The world of the far future, however, will be very different from ours today. Matter as we know it could disintegrate leaving only rarefied constituents scattered across huge volumes of space. Information would be captured in the positions of these constituents, however, and increasing amounts of information could be encoded as accessible space enlarged.

Among the durable constituents in such an environment, Dyson speculates, would be positronium—a substance whose atoms are electron-positron pairs. (Electrons and their antiparticles, positrons, are permanent, as far as we can tell, though when the two collide, they mutually annihilate. But electron-positron pairs can also reform spontaneously from the vacuum of space.) Our "bodies" may, in fact, ultimately take the form of vast clouds of positronium, spread out in space, within whose swirls and billows information could still be processed and retained. We must not, of course, assume such a scenario would seem at all bleak or unpleasant to ourselves in the remote future. As Dyson says, "immaterial plasma may do as well as flesh and blood as a vehicle for the patterns of our thought."[16] (We should add, not *quite* immaterial and, also, that it should do as well as flesh and blood for such things as emotions too, which, according to the tenets of strong AI, must also reduce to information processing.) With suitable adaptations we could find practically any environment enjoyable—and could also experience, convincingly, any past environment we wished, through the medium of virtual reality. (This should hold too in other possible immortal futures besides the one Dyson imagines.)

Whether or not Dyson's scenario proves correct, it does suggest that great adaptations must accompany our hopefully endless journey through time. The world of our present habitation is not standing still, and we cannot do so either. We will change almost unimaginably, yet if survival occurs, we must retain the earlier experiences captured in our memories. Settings once familiar and valued will disappear, yet their essence will endure even as we discover new and exciting domains that are beyond imagining today. In this way, I think, we can approach the prospect of even the greatest changes with confidence. The more things change, the more we should find of value that stays the same.

Tipler's universe, on the other hand, is not open but closed and collapsing. The collapse concentrates the energy in a smaller and smaller volume, which makes the momenta of particles get larger and larger—things get hotter and hotter. In time the average temperature must exceed that of any blast furnace, or the heart of any star. (It is momentum space that is unbounded, then, not configuration space; the momentum goes to infinity in such a way that it more than offsets the shrinking configuration space, and the overall phase space volume becomes infinite.) Tipler proposes to store growing amounts of information in this fiery inferno. The collapse of the universe will not be uniform in all directions, but the unequal rates, or "gravitational shear," will create temperature differences that can be exploited by intelligent life for usable energy and information storage. The collapse must go to completion in finite proper time, as an outsider would see it (if such a thing were possible, though an outsider to the universe cannot actually "see" inside it). But the subjective time for the beings inside could still be infinite so that a reasonable immortality becomes possible.

It is certainly not clear, however, that the sort of processing necessary to maintain conscious beings could continue in this unlimited manner, even if the phase space goes to infinity. This is not to say it is known to be impossible either, for it is not. But a cold environment, on the face of it, seems a better place to maintain records and live out an endless life than a hot one. Here on Earth we are familiar enough with this principle: deep cold preserves things, high heat destroys them. As Dyson puts it, "The colder the environment, the quieter the background, the more thrifty life can be in its use of energy."[17] Moreover, the astronomical evidence seems to favor an indefinitely expanding, cooling universe.[18]

One possible difficulty with Dyson's scenario, noted by Tipler, is that an endlessly expanding universe might have a growing population of intelligent life-forms (the fertile garden), which would limit the space available to each. The course of events could thus conspire to deny each being the infinite phase space needed for immortality, even if the space is infinite overall. But I do not think this possibility can be assumed to apply to our present universe, based on what we know. In particular we have not yet found any extraterrestrial life-forms though we are, apparently, beginning to find extrasolar planets.[19] (In Chapter 11 we also noted the excitement over possible signs of life in Martian rocks, though the evidence now seems weak.[20])

The universe seems to be finite, though destined to expand forever. Phase space seems correspondingly finite too but possibly also destined to increase without limit, thereby providing hope for immortality. There are some other difficulties with the expanding universe idea, however, such as whether there would be means, with the dwindling temperature, to communicate across increasingly vast regions of space, so that a single organism would remain aware of its own, growing archive of memories.[21] Thus we could still run out of the necessary energy even if less and less is needed at the bit processing level as the universe cools. The resolution of this and other difficulties will depend on properties, it seems safe to say, that are not yet understood and probably unsuspected.

In particular, the findings suggesting an accelerating universe could yield a radically different picture than so far imagined. Tipler's scenario seems all but ruled out, which means we do not have the problems associated with the collapsing fireball. Instead the universe must expand and cool indefinitely, but it now has an extra energy input, which could be enough to provide for our future needs and alleviate any problems with Dyson's scenario. But we must not go overboard in our optimism, and in fact there are serious problems created by the newfound expansion that, if they cannot be solved, appear to doom any hopes of unlimited survival.

Mainly, we seem to be confronted with a runaway inflation of space that will ultimately isolate our galactic cluster from the surrounding universe, pushing this other material beyond our event horizon. Effectively, the rest of the universe will just disappear or become part of the multiverse that is inaccessible to us. Meanwhile, the continuing spatial inflation will provide an effective minimum temperature above absolute zero. This thermal background will jam our information processing when levels of the ever-dwindling reserves of usable energy fall low enough and essentially create the conditions of a Heat Death. At minimum the effect must be to limit the amount of bits we can store and process to finite levels that would doom us to no better than an Eternal Return. This unhappy conclusion has been noted by cosmologists Lawrence Krauss and Glenn Starkman, who, however, remain hopeful that a way will be found around it.[21] It goes without saying that there is much that still awaits our understanding that should have a bearing on the issue—and we do have a long time to find an answer.

One possible way around the problem would be to exploit "basement universes with wormholes." This scenario was developed by science philosopher Michael Price[23] based on work of such physicists as Kip Thorne and Matt Visser, who investigated the possibility of a wormhole—a kind of short bridge between two distant locations in space. In this case, space-time must be imagined as folded over, so that a short channel between otherwise distant points is possible. By analogy, by sticking a pin through the layers of a folded bed sheet we can open a short channel to points that will be far apart if the sheet is straightened out. To an ant unable to wriggle through the hole, the sheet might as well be straightened out; the distances the insect must travel are considerable, on its scale of things, but they shrink to almost nothing if it can squeeze through.

For many years wormholes were a minor curiosity only—predicted by physics, to be sure, but not likely, even in principle, to be of much consequence because they appeared to be very short lived. But further investigation showed a way that a wormhole, normally so transient, might be stabilized, though only with great difficulty. A stable wormhole would then be traversable, though even then with certain restrictions, for example, limits on how much mass a given wormhole can carry, which also restricts its information-transmitting capacity. One of the allowed possibilities, though, is stretching a wormhole between two distant points in space. Apparatus containing one end of a wormhole could be transported to connect Earth and another point outside the solar system. Traversing the wormhole would make it possible to travel to that point and back much faster than by conventional space travel. In fact, travel to other points in space and time would become feasible, though the possibilities are intriguingly limited so that travel into one's own past is impossible and the paradoxes of relativity are avoided.

A network of wormholes could then provide a fast way to visit very distant points in the universe. Access to a faraway region might be retained even as it slipped beyond our event horizon and otherwise became inaccessible. In this way we could establish the unlimited growing room we would need to avoid eventual death. Beyond this benefit—great though it would be—could come others, such as linking up with a wormhole from some civilization besides our own. Once this happened, there would likely be more and more such hookups, and generally a cosmic "Internet" could take shape, which would extend over many independent civilizations. And, indeed, a giant mind might form, thus might exist now, powered by the combined intelligence of innumerable immortal beings who would now have a means of rapid communication. (This then would be something like a God, though once again, the lack of tangible evidence would seem to rule out any contacts already between the human race and such an entity. So this sort of "God," if it exists, is not the Supreme Being of our theological traditions.)

Another intriguing possibility is a structure like a wormhole but closed off on one end—a "basement universe." The closure effectively isolates the structure from everything else, except at the single opening where the structure attaches to the parent universe. Basement universes could branch off our own (or some other) universe, or like successive buds on a branching twig, off each other. In this way another means would be opened for unlimited room in which to grow. Indeed, this could even explain why we have not seen extraterrestrials: when a certain stage is reached, they withdraw to their own basement universes. Whether this is so, basement universes could greatly facilitate information storage and security for would-be immortals. The problems of eternal survival may thus prove not so difficult at all.

Yet traversable wormholes have not been demonstrated and may be impossible, along with basement universes. Or if either is possible, it may be on a scale so limited as to be of negligible help to us in our quest for an endless existence. Many other questions are still open; we really do not know how well the universe of the far future will be able to support life, however much living forms of the future may be able to adapt to changing conditions. There is ongoing, sometimes heated, debate about the various possible futures that have been proposed and whether any of them would be both adequate and feasible.[24] The task before us may be much harder, not easier, than we imagine.

Easy or hard, however, immortality will be attained if it can be attained at all. Here we have considered some ways that life might be extended indefinitely, through a buildup of information that records the past life of each person in a way that is open to later recall. The information is preserved indefinitely, which includes making backup copies to guard against loss and corruption. This then is enontic or almost-enontic immortality—the best alternative for eternal survival, if possible. If not, there are other possibilities, as we have noted.

Any sort of definitive treatment of the "how" of immortality must await future discoveries. We cannot know what these might be or be sure they will work to our advantage. But science has often provided astonishing opportunities and benefits, even when it seemed that such progress was blocked. With the prospect of a livelier universe than we thought, and despite some newly noted difficulties, it may be that doors are now opening.

CHAPTER 15.

The Philosophy of Assurance

W e have now explored some possibilities for the future and our continuing role in the universe or, more properly, the multiverse at large. There is uncertainty, yet also reason to be hopeful. A basis exists for what I shall call a Philosophy of Assurance, starting from the position that life, not death, is the ultimate inevitability. As suggested in Chapter 1, the Philosophy of Assurance is to be the first of the three main pillars of the system developed in this book, the others being the Philosophy of Aspiration and the Philosophy of Action, which will be taken up in the next two chapters. The three parts are not intended to be separate and stand-alone, however, but mutually reinforcing and complementary, and there is no attempt at a strict partitioning of subject matter. Topics treated in this chapter are sometimes given more attention later, and some "later" topics are included here for clarity.

Much of the groundwork for the Philosophy of Assurance has already been laid, particularly in the last four chapters. To round this out I will briefly summarize the main points that have been argued about the nature of personhood and the prospects for eternal life and happiness through a scientific approach. I will then explore some additional issues, with the goals of tying up loose ends and answering possible objections. In general, the object will be to arrive at a resolution of difficulties, or "position of assurance," on problems of importance such as imperfect survival.

The position was established that death is a detriment to life that must be alleviated and eradicated scientifically. This calls, in particular, for the physical resurrection of the dead and for immortality, goals that have seemed scientifically impossible but are now shown in a new light through developments in physics, mathematics, and computer science. A person, basically, is a type of program running on hardware we call the brain. Recreating the conditions of program execution will recreate a lost person in replica form.

Two principles have been defended and adopted, the UI assumptions, that open possibilities for resurrection and immortality through scientific means. Unboundedness provides that the conditions for recreating persons of the past will occur and recur. Interchangeability implies that these recreations—replica processes—will qualify as true resurrections. More generally, a resurrection can occur by recreating a more developed version or continuer of the original person. Unboundedness additionally means that successively advanced continuers of any person must come into existence, whether these are all in one particular universe or distributed over more than one. While there is no consciousness or survival without embodiment, such embodiment is not unique but a recurring effect. Both humans and non-human creatures stand, ultimately, to benefit.

The processes that qualify as continuers and thus as resurrections can be created in the total absence of known information about the originals simply by guesswork. This means that persons of the past who have totally perished could be restored to life, as was conjectured will actually happen at some point in the future, when the erstwhile human race has developed beyond its present limits. Human limitations will be superseded both in the resurrectees and the resurrectors. This, it was argued, will likely involve an increase in benevolence along with various capabilities, based purely on the enlightened self-interest of each being affected. Resurrectees will enjoy a happy immortality along with others and should themselves progress so as to approach a status of equality with their advanced and benign benefactors.

Meanwhile, persons of today have a chance to participate more directly in the process of transition from human to more-than-

human. There is hope that medical advances will bring about biological immortality in the lifetimes of some of us now living.
Clinical death meanwhile may be circumvented through such
means as cryonics. This is a special opportunity and a source of
assurance for those of us who can see the advantages, while not
precluding a future happiness even for those who could not be
preserved.

In fact, it is worth emphasizing that some sort of future existence is provided for all of us, whether we like it or not. How it
goes will depend significantly on the choices we make in this
life. When it comes to our personal encounter with death, we
have considered arguments that arranging for the biostatic preservation of our remains is the better course to follow.

The Problem of Forgetting and the Ideal Self

In addressing the problem of immortality in general, there are
two important issues: the mind-body problem and the problem of
personal identity. The mind-body problem we have treated in
terms of functionalism backed by strong AI. The mind, thus a
person who makes use of it, is a type of computational process or
entity, depending on the functioning of underlying components
but not on any further intrinsic properties of these components.
The treatment, I think, is mostly adequate for our purposes, though
a little more will be said about the functionalist position later in
this chapter in connection with free will. Meanwhile, there are
still some matters deserving attention in regard to the problem of
identity. These include forgetting, false memories, and more generally what can be considered imperfections in survival, in which
a continuer may not truly reflect a more developed version of the
original person.

Of these problems, that of forgetting or loss of information is,
I think, the most central, and calls for a stance on what personal
information is to be considered important. In fact it should not be
so important to survival, I will argue, that a continuer contain all
information whatever that was accessible on one occasion or other
to the numerous versions of the past self. Indeed, the pruning of
information must have importance too, which could even be considerable. But this then raises the question of just what information can be discarded without sacrificing a reasonable notion of

continuer. This in turn depends on the basic question of identity: what shall determine when one person-stage is to be considered "the same" as another one?

The position I will argue for involves the notion of an ideal self, a topic that is developed by Max More in *The Diachronic Self*,[1] though I approach it somewhat differently. I think a sound theory of the ideal self is possible through the computational model that has been adopted here for persons and processes more generally, based on strong AI. Using this approach it will be feasible to postulate the convergence of a developing immortal to a being with certain permanent features. Losses and other informational difficulties need not abort the process of convergence for the permanent features can accumulate in the face of temporary reverses. Steps along the way, or person-stages, will be linked with previous person-stages, as usual, by psychological connectedness so that a particular trajectory of events is not needed to establish the necessary ties.

To develop this point of view it will be helpful to start with a well-known prototype, the memory criterion of personal identity of John Locke presented in *An Essay Concerning Human Understanding*.[2] According to Locke, a person is a "thinking intelligent being, that has reason and reflection, and can consider itself as itself, the same thinking being, at different times and places." Consciousness in some degree always accompanies thinking. It is "what makes everyone to be what he calls self, and thereby distinguishes himself from all other thinking things." Consciousness thus makes personal identity and suggests how we ought to regard a person as persisting over time. "[A]s far as this consciousness can be extended backwards to any past action or thought, so far reaches the identity of that person; it is the same self now it was then; and it is by the same self with the present one that now reflects on it, that that action was done." Memories, then, serve as the link between the present self (person-stage) and a past version of the self. In more modern terminology, the criterion of psychological connectedness determines whether a present person-stage is a continuer or later version of a past person-stage.

This is underscored by Locke's doctrine that personal identity is not the same as identity of substance. "For, it being the same consciousness that makes a man be himself to himself, personal identity depends on that only, whether it be annexed solely to one individual substance, or can be continued in a succession of several substances." So long as ties of consciousness (implying psychological connectedness) exist, neither time nor "change of substance" can split the person-stages into two persons, anymore "than a man be two men by wearing other clothes to-day than he did yesterday." Thus "it will be possible that two thinking substances may make but one person. For the same consciousness being preserved, whether in the same or different substances, the personal identity is preserved." This then is an interesting foreshadowing of our principle of Interchangeability, in which "two thinking substances"—in this case person-instantiations with the same process "running"—would indeed have one and the same consciousness and "make but one person."

This may not be precisely what Locke had in mind. He does not seem to have been thinking of two identical copies of a person running simultaneously or in parallel but apparently a temporal succession of what amount to continuers, with at most one existing at any one time. However, by linking personality with expressed consciousness he finds an ingenious way of upholding what amounts to a materialist conception of personal identity. Locke did not deny the possibility of an immaterial soul. Indeed, he was a dualist who thought that a thinking process could never arise out of "bare incogitative matter," as we noted in Chapter 8, but needed something more, in this case, an "immaterial substance"—a form of "further fact." But the soul, however remarkable, still was only a substance. It might inhabit the body, and the same soul might inhabit a succession of bodies. But the same soul would not make the same person, unless the criteria of consciousness were met, including awareness of past actions, and, on the other hand, the criteria might be met by different souls entirely. "For as to this point of being the same self, it matters not whether this present self be made up of the same or other substances...."

In Locke's view too, the same person is not the same "man"—which in turn Locke identified with "nothing but a participation of the same continued life, by constantly fleeting particles of matter, in succession vitally united to the same organized body." Locke, in effect, here invoked the criterion of physical continuity we considered in Chapter 4. Physical continuity would make the same human being. The latter could thus be considered a unique individual process similar to a fire or a storm, a system of interacting particles in which matter is constantly taken in and expelled so that the whole persists through a change of substance. Yet the identity of the whole is not the same as the identity of persons, since it (the whole) does not depend on consciousness but simply on the ongoing process. It is this idea that Locke uses to answer a possible serious objection to his theory of personal identity: the problem of forgetting.

If someone forgets something he did, and we assume this forgetting is permanent and not later reversed, then his consciousness no longer extends to that act. By Locke's criterion, he cannot be the same person who did the act, though common sense finds this position untenable. We consider it reasonable, in appropriate circumstances, to say "yes, I must have done that, though I cannot remember." The notion that a person can forget something he did and still be the person who did it is deeply ingrained in our way of looking at things and extends to our social institutions. The legal system holds a drunk driver responsible for an accident he caused, even if afterward he has no recollection of it. Locke, however, would not attribute the accident to the same person who later cannot recall it, but only to the same human being. Our legal system can only penalize people as human beings. It can pass sentence and carry out measures against a physical body, but it has no direct access to persons as persons. In this way, then, it might be possible for an entirely innocent person to be punished. Locke was aware of this problem and, interestingly, believed in a God who would set matters right: ultimately, when all were to be judged for their actions in this worldly life, no person would be held responsible for anything he or she had entirely forgotten.

I propose, however, to give a nontheological resolution of this difficulty but one that will draw on the idea of an immortal, ideal self. First, however, we will explore some other issues connected with forgetting, including reasons it may be desirable—if suitably limited. I will start with a basic problem: how, with psychological connectedness as the sole criterion to establish personal identity, that is, essentially Locke's memory criterion, we can establish a robust enough theory to overcome the problem of forgetting. For, strictly speaking, we are forced to the extreme conclusion that forgetting even one past act or state of which we were aware precludes our being a continuer of the person-stage who had this awareness—that person-stage does not survive in us. By the same logic, if I am aware of something happening now, however minor, and later forget it, I "die."

But certainly this is absurd. I am not worried about "dying," for example, if tomorrow I can no longer remember an exact configuration of dust particles that I vacuumed up today or the shapes of the leaves on the trees I happened to see, in all their numerous perspectives, while out running for exercise. Indeed, for most of us there are countless details we are briefly aware of but are then lost from consciousness and can best only be reconstructed approximately. Sometimes these details are important momentarily—I will have to know something about where the dust is to vacuum it up. Once that is done, though, I do not normally feel a compelling reason to retain the detailed information.

As one interesting variation of this, I remember some years ago living in a certain city and sometimes visiting a barber shop for a haircut. The barber, a dignified gent with an ample, silvery shock himself, went quietly about his work, which offered some time for reflection. Looking down at the floor from the swivel chair showed an interesting pattern—bits of hair strewn over lighter squares of asphalt tile and other finer details that increasingly became apparent: scratches, dust, and so on. Searching verified that the patterns were stable—a bit of material over here would be in the same position when I looked again. In effect, the floor with its contents had momentarily become part of my memory—part of the conscious experience of getting that haircut.

These thoughts were interesting, but overall I did not think the experience at all memorable. Certainly it was nothing out of the ordinary and, apart from the philosophical angle, might have been quite boring. After I had paid and left, it did not disturb me that I could no longer remember the exact patterns on that floor—a general impression seemed enough. This sort of thing would be repeated every few weeks. Now it is years later, I live in a different city, and other circumstances have changed. One is that, with due respects to the barber, I now cut my own hair, so that the barbershop memories enjoy a privileged position as part of an unrepeated past. The experiences are not remembered so much individually, but I do have general impressions as related, which seems adequate and appropriate. This information seems stable, and I want to retain it. Yet I am not bothered by what was lost, in particular, the rather large amount that must have been lost right at the beginning, by the time I had left the shop. It is interesting that even though so much specific information has been lost, I still remember the visits episodically, that is, I am sitting in the swivel chair, looking at the patterns on the floor. So I have an impression of an actual experience and not just abstracted data, even though my memory is far from a videotape and must in fact be highly compressed.

For many purposes that seems enough, even desirable—certainly too much information, of a certain, monotonous sort, could be much more a burden than a benefit. I am privileged, in this case, to retain an appropriate amount, neither more (as far as I know) nor less. This, of course, is an idiosyncratic view. Different persons will have their own preferences as to which of their memories are worth retaining, and in how much detail, even as the mechanisms and powers of memory will vary. And in the future I may think differently about the issue. It remains to be seen what the options for mind enhancement will be and what attitudes and practices will then be thought appropriate by those involved, hopefully including myself. But I offer it as a starting point.

Also, it is an unsettled question how much past information is really retained by our brains. Much information may be in there that we do not and cannot usually access—yet surely there are limits. Exactly how much is truly lost that was truly present, however briefly, is unknown—but that some loss occurs seems indisputable. Much that we see is lost in the early stages of short-term memory, by appearances, and there is a further, major winnowing before something of our experience may finally wind up in long-term memory. But, I think, we can rationalize quite a substantial loss of the initially available information as still consistent with "our" survival.

It is a rationalization, of course—in effect, a reformulation of the problem of survival—but is surely justified on grounds of what is really important. To complete the reformulation I will invoke the idea of convergence to an ideal, immortal self, which we may hope the fabric of reality will support in one way or another. Such convergence, like the more usual course of living we are familiar with, would involve a succession of person-stages occurring at different times. Information present in one person-stage may be lost to later stages. However, some information must be retained, however rarely, and transmitted indefinitely from one stage to another to form part of a permanent archive. Over the course of time this archive must not only persist but grow without limit, to prevent an Eternal Return. With this in mind, then, we can arrive at a position of assurance. What is truly important will endure, and in the process we can even benefit, by the loss of what is inessential and tedious.

The process of convergence in fact provides for something quite close to the original idea of a strict continuer-based notion of survival. Later person-stages can still be more developed versions of earlier approximations of the ideal self, even if these earlier approximations are not coextensive with the earlier person-stages to which they were associated. To illustrate, let us consider the barbershop scenario again.

The person-stage that I was, momentarily, when looking at the floor, becomes unrecoverable as soon as I go away and can no longer recall the exact patterns. And even later there is further consolidation and loss, when I can no longer remember the exact occasion but may have only a generic memory of these visits. However, if I assume that the information still remaining persists, that information, and similar information relating to earlier times, in effect defines a person-stage, a "quasi-stage" or q-stage, for the period to which it applies, and that person-stage endures in the ideal self.

On the other hand, if I imagine myself actually in the barber chair once again and seeing the detailed information I am soon to forget, it does not seem unsettling that this loss will occur, that "I" will not fully survive in a more advanced continuer. My anticipated q-stage is me enough—and that will survive. Thus I can feel confident that an appropriate amount of what is momentarily present will endure, not too little or too much but enough to reconstruct what is important about the episode then happening. There will then be an appropriate amount of psychological connectedness between the earlier and later person-stages, both of which will really be q-stages. For the later stage in turn will ultimately be replaced by a q-stage too, in the further process of consolidation of memories.

In this overall process, then, we have subdivisions that pertain to particular times or stages in one's life. For each of these times a succession of temporary, "working" q-stages may be formed and edited or modified, but some final, stable, representative version must eventually emerge, whether a small or great amount of processing, modifying, and consolidating is involved. This final, permanent residual—what is to endure in the ideal self—will then serve to delineate what that self was at that point. A sequence of these final stages covering an extended time interval will also form a q-segment, with the information, much of which will be redundant from one q-stage to the next, telescoped and otherwise arranged and distributed for convenience in memory. More generally, the whole diachronic self will, in effect, be formed of q-stages.

It is worth remarking that this is a sort of rationalization that fits the circumstances applying in this particular case. To me it seems quite reasonable—perhaps the reader will agree. Different persons, we noted, will have different ideas as to what and to what extent memories ought to survive and play a part in later conscious experience. Perhaps some will not feel it is particularly important to remember what they were like at an earlier stage, though again I feel that such remembering is an important part of personal survival. For me, today, to survive to the future means my future self must remember something of what it was like, as I sit here typing this—I simply cannot see it any other way. In the future, to be sure, one's values about memories could change dramatically, depending on what options become available and the choices one makes. But there will be more options, not less. If it should be possible, as it should, to store considerably more detailed information about present events, interest in storing this information could grow in step. I expect that the ability to develop an interest itself will be more under individual control, so that quite surprising and diverse effects could result.

But there is an important point to make in regard to the above notion of survival through an ideal self, which is that this notion again depends only on psychological connectedness. The information content of the later q-stages determines whether they are continuers of earlier q-stages; how these q-stages came into existence is really a secondary issue, whatever its significance may otherwise be. We noted in Chapter 4 how some philosophers, such as Parfit and More, have held to the contrary that both psychological connectedness and psychological continuity are important in establishing when a later person-stage is to be considered the "same" person as an earlier stage.

The necessity of some degree of psychological connectedness is rightly recognized, for example, in the thought experiment where Derek Parfit is gradually changed to a copy (thus a continuer) of Greta Garbo—the new Greta is clearly not the same person as the old Derek. But it would be infeasible to require perfect psychological connectedness. If the earlier person-stage must be perfectly captured in and reconstructible from the later stage then the smallest forgetting would "kill" that earlier stage— we could be forced into a worse straitjacket than in the day-person hypothesis.

Continuity and Causality Issues

Since we cannot rely solely on psychological connectedness in its pristine form, the critics of pure connectedness add a continuity requirement. This is one way of managing things so that our usual intuitions about personal identity are not violated—but it is too heavy a price to pay from the standpoint of what is most important here, the possibilities of resurrection and immortality. In particular More insists on informational continuity. The later person-stage must be causally derived from the earlier stage, as we usually understand causality. Thus, only enontic resurrections could be permitted—with limited allowance for loss or alteration of information, to be compensated by the continuity requirement. This would invalidate a resurrection by pure guesswork, even if a perfect replica of the original was constructed. It would mean, barring unexpected abilities to recover a hidden past, that no deceased person who was not well preserved in biostasis would ever again see the light of day. All lives previous to ours would be so much wasted effort, as far as the participants who are the principal beneficiaries were concerned. This is a completely untenable conclusion, I strongly feel, and would unacceptably mar any moral philosophy based around the idea of overcoming death scientifically.

But this gloomy consequence can be countered through the idea of pattern-survival, in which a person survives in a replica, or more generally, a continuer, as we have seen. Through Interchangeability personal identity is distributed over multiple instantiations of the person-stage. This would extend, unavoidably, to instantiations in domains not causally connected to our own, that is, other universes. This position was justified by a variant of the principle known as the Identity of Indiscernibles. We cannot by definition know at any time which of these instantiations "we" may be or distinguish one from the other, therefore it is unreasonable to identify ourselves with any one and not the others, and we must treat them all on an equal footing.

In this simple way then, if we accept Interchangeability, personal identity must transcend our usual notions of causality, though in another way causality must still have its usual significance. A later person-stage, that is, must at least feel a causal connection to an "earlier," less-developed stage (which may in fact not be earlier in time). But this should be no insurmountable obstacle—such a feeling and comprehension, that I am now here (later stage) and was there (earlier stage), would depend on the functioning of a construct that could be made and programmed in numerous, functionally equivalent ways.

An interesting viewpoint on the issue of causality and the flow of time in general is advocated by (among others) David Deutsch in *The Fabric of Reality*. It relies, as here, on the position that our universe is embedded in a multiverse. The point is made that time does not flow at all—there is no need to assume that our usual notion of time exists at the fundamental, physical level, the level of underlying reality. Instead, existence as a whole—the multiverse—consists of simply an unordered family of "snapshots," each of which in turn defines the way things are under special conditions, for example, at a particular moment.[3] All pasts, presents, and futures are always present and unchanging. We have a perception of time, it is true. But at the underlying level this means simply that a set of snapshots can be selected, out of the many possible, that forms an appropriate sequence indicating a temporal progression. Moreover, at one particular moment corresponding to one snapshot, we—as represented in that snapshot—have memories of a past that conforms, in certain essential ways, to what is found in certain of these other snapshots.

In the same way we could imagine reaching into a very large box of still photos, arranged however you wish, and selecting a small subset that forms an ordered time sequence, a movie. The multiverse in turn, a "large box" indeed, is like the Babel Picture Gallery of Chapter 6, only larger still. The pictures inside, individual snapshots of possible histories, are also unordered, but if we like we can arrange some of the snapshots so that they form a movie. Certainly very many movies could be made in this way. By choosing the right snapshots, just the right events will happen, to enforce particular laws of physics and, moreover, the existence of physicists who understand these laws for what they are, or more generally, observers whose perceptions and recollections mirror what is happening in their surroundings. This then seems to be the sort of reality an observer inhabits, what I have called observer reality, as long as we keep in mind that certain types of movies, or event sequences, will be much more likely or easier to assemble than others. This likelihood, which seems to depend on the presence of embedded observers in the reality that is assembled, in turn conforms to probabilities at the quantum level and in particular the following of phase paths.

But a basic property emerges that is at least consistent with our observations. It is that causality itself has no particular ontological significance beyond the perceptions of observers. This is not to say that difficulties connected with causality are unimportant. But I maintain that they are not so important as to preclude the possibility of resurrecting persons who lack the more usual causal ties, such as informational continuity, with their past selves.

There is an interesting difficulty along these lines considered in *The Diachronic Self*. More is worried that the absence of causality as we usually understand it would destroy a claim that a later person-stage could be the same person as an earlier stage. "Our notion of persons," he writes, "involves enduring entities with certain properties such as (a capacity for) rationality, responsibility, the ability to make choices, foresight, and (a capacity for) self-restraint." Without causality these properties would, it seems, lose their meaning, as in the case of a later person-stage, an "I" created by chance. "If I form an intention to do X at one moment, it can have no effect whatsoever on whether I (or the appearance of a continuing 'I') later do X."[4] However, this must be seen differently if we accept Deutsch's snapshot model of the multiverse.

A person-stage in one snapshot will be matched by similar but more-developed person-stages in other snapshots. The presence of an intention in the less-developed, or earlier, stage will correspond to effects of the intention in the more-developed, later stages. (More will be said shortly, however, about this notion of "earlier" and "later," which, as a remote possibility, could involve time reversal.) Nonstandard causality will come into effect in the case where the sequence of snapshots leading from the earlier to a later stage is peculiar and, in particular, does not allow inferring the earlier stage at each successive step.

Even then there is still a reasonable tie between the less and the more developed stage, I maintain, based solely on internal characteristics, that is, psychological connectedness. If the earlier stage had had a different, contrary intention, for example, then we could simply choose a different sequence of snapshots leading to a different continuer, one that also reflected this different intention but which could also show the lack of informational continuity. With a superabundance of snapshots to choose from, this would be no problem: Unboundedness enforces counterfactual indefiniteness. We never have the worry that the later continuer is that by a lucky, unrelated accident only, in the sense that most of the time such a continuer would not come into being at all. Instead, the continuer is going to be present no matter what. So in this way, I think, we can justify the position that we have a true and not just accidental continuer who, we may presume, would also have a reasonable feeling of being a continuer.

This line of argument can be used to meet the difficulty we raised in noting that the original person-stage could not be inferred at every step in the transition to the later stage. From this alone it might be argued that the later stage is clearly severed from the earlier despite any ties that became reestablished fortuitously through guesswork. As an extreme example, the person could be vaporized then recreated by a random event. Once the links are broken, the critic might argue, they cannot really be reestablished in this accidental manner, only imitated, so the later stage is not a continuer.

But based on the multiverse perspective, we could say that the links are never broken, though perhaps strangely pushed around.

This is because the destructive event (vaporization) would not just happen to one construct in isolation but to many similar though different constructs in various universes of the multiverse. Again, loss of information makes the past ambiguous. All would then participate in the same reality. It would not be possible to say, from an observer's standpoint, that one particular construct belonged in one particular universe rather than another—this information is unavailable and nonexistent. Similarly, the random recreation would not happen in isolation but would restore all the constructs to different universes again—neither the wrong nor the uniquely right universe in each case, but a universe nonetheless. The reconstruction of the vaporized victim by guesswork would be unlikely only in terms of its relative frequency in some larger totality. It would not be unlikely to happen at all but, in view of the plurality of processes in the multiverse, actually inevitable. So we could plausibly argue that a genuine tie must exist between the earlier and the later construct and that a true continuer has been obtained.

Perhaps the biggest challenge to this position would come from the possibility, however remote, of time reversal. The "later" stage could in fact be in the same universe and earlier in time than the "earlier" stage. The creation, at an earlier time, of a construct that possesses just the right features to be a continuer of a person from a later time is possible through a random process. But it would have to involve so many correct guesses in a pattern of 10^{18} bits or so, for an ordinary human, that it must be rare indeed, if inevitable somewhere. It is far more likely that Shakespeare's collected works would be typed at random by an australopithecine who has accidentally assembled a typewriter from rock chips and rubber tree sap, millions of years before Shakespeare.

I see no reason for such time-reversed continuers to occur as the result of conscious planning either, barring the possibility of backward time travel. It would be like someone of a thousand years ago making a detailed prediction of events in our own time, only harder. The difficulty would not be so much in creating a real person who resides in some actual history as in the fact that our history must then unfold correctly to match that history. In other words, we must predict our own future, so far as it may be known to the entity we are making. No amount of intelligence could be expected to master such a task because intelligence itself, with its strong unpredictability, must play an important, continuing part in future history. As Tipler says, "whatever happens, happens,"[5] and much of what is coming will be known only as it arrives.

Still, however unlikely a time reversal scenario may be, we cannot absolutely rule it out. "Our" present, right now, may really be earlier than "our" past. We can take this in stride, recognizing that reality may surprise us in numerous ways, subtle or otherwise, as we get to know it better, though what is to all appearances fantastically improbable need not be taken too seriously. As long as we are on the subject, I should note that backward time travel itself would be another form of time reversal. Here the later self is transported to an earlier time, though a causal link along more usual lines is maintained somehow.

It is interesting that this would not necessarily involve any paradox: the later self might want to change the earlier history but would not have to be so inclined. But if a change was made—contradicting the observer's own knowledge—a paradox could be avoided if we simply assume our traveler is thrust by this very act into a parallel universe (and thus becomes xenontic). There is no change then in the "original" universe, thus no possibility of interfering with your own birth. This, however, would not be true backward time travel since the universe one wound up in would not simply be one's original universe at an earlier time. But backward time travel, even in this approximate form, though not yet completely ruled out remains to be demonstrated, with little sign so far that it will be. If it could be achieved, it might make possible the recovery of far more past information than we now possess and even the rescue, enontically, of persons who are now long deceased. But I think it unwise to rely on such mechanisms. (In particular, the data-erasing experiment described in Chapter 5 is an argument against the possibility for otherwise we might determine which path the photon took even after the information is "lost.") If resurrection or immortality are, in fact, easier goals than I have imagined, so much the better, but let us be prepared for what seems more likely.

In any case, we have considered how a person could survive in a continuer defined by the sole criterion of psychological connectedness. Survival does not require the more usual causal ties between the earlier and later person-stages but only appropriate functional similarities between two physical constructs. Once again though, I do not see the causal connections as unimportant, just not essential.

More on Memory Problems

Something more should be said about forgetting, however. It is sometimes argued that Locke's criterion would lead to absurdities in everyday life. If I cannot remember putting on my shirt this morning, as will happen,[6] must I conclude that no one put on my shirt? I would say no—because there is other information than what is stored in my brain that tells me what I must have done. I see I am wearing a particular shirt, and no one else put it on for me. (Or else I must have remembered so unusual an occurrence, or some other strange thing must be going on of which I see no evidence.) So I conclude, reasonably, that I must have put it on.

At this point I may even construct, in my mind, a little q-episode showing where I probably was at the time, the approximate motions I must have made, what I must have seen and felt, and the like. Thus I must have noted, if fleetingly, the appearance of the shirt, colors or patterns it may have, the feel of putting my arms in the sleeves (right arm first as I normally do), the actions of buttoning up, and so on. I would also probably incorporate some information about the surroundings such as the window with blinds in the room where my shirts are kept and the thin carpet underfoot. In effect, the available information about my past actions could—and does—extend outside my brain proper, just as in the barber shop example, and can be legitimately employed to reconstruct past events and even refurbish my memory. To be sure, such a q-episode probably will not long survive individually but, as in the barber shop, will blend with other information so that I have only a general impression of the activity in question.

It is not true, of course, that all events one has forgotten can be reconstructed, even in an approximate, generic form, by examining the effects afterward, or certainly it does not seem so. Some real, irreversible loss does occur. We are justified, I think, in regarding that which is truly lost as not part of ourselves. But many commonplace events will not fall in this category even if they are completely erased from what we usually think of as memory.

This principle we might use in resolving the practical problem of someone who commits a crime but claims innocence based on forgetting the incident. In the case of a drunk driver who cannot remember the accident he caused, the evidence could furnish the basis for reconstructing enough of what happened to establish "his" culpability. On the other hand, we cannot rule out the possibility that he—or the person that resides in what used to be his body—should be considered innocent after all. If enough mental changes have occurred since the incident in question, we might by reasonable, reductionist standards be dealing with a truly different person, one that should be considered innocent. A third possibility is a Jekyll and Hyde case of a dual personality resident in one brain, with one of the personalities aware and guilty of wrongdoing and the other ignorant and innocent. A fourth alternative, which might especially apply, again, to the drunk driver, is to accept that he has truly forgotten, thus is "innocent," yet still has a demonstrated tendency to commit acts of this sort. As a practical matter, then, and an attempt to avoid the greater evil, penalties may be imposed with such justifiable aims as reducing the likelihood of similar incidents and compensating for damages. Clearly, though, the legal system can be baffled by such conundrums and no doubt sometimes penalizes persons wrongly.

These problems I do not expect to be rectified by a God—unlike Locke; however, something along these lines ought to happen as we develop beyond the human level. As our understanding deepens and we progress in other ways, we will both know better how to deal with such cases and, we may hope, be able to reduce their likelihood through our overall progress. These trends should continue as we develop to ever higher levels and converge, hopefully, to infinite immortals. In the limit of time, then, such problems should vanish completely through our diligent, enlightened efforts.

A problem related to forgetting, however, is infrequent remembering, something that could plague the would-be immortal and jeopardize the claim that a given version of the self develops into later and later versions and overall is immortalized. The ideal self, we have noted, must never (permanently) forget an experience—all past memories must instead be recalled to conscious-

ness infinitely often over infinite time. This is a minimal requirement, however; it says nothing about how frequently or seldom a
given item, including one's whole life up to some point, may be
recalled. If the recalling is infrequent enough, it arguably must
have little effect on conscious existence. An advanced being thus
might be so dissociated from an earlier stage as to constitute, for
practical purposes, a different person entirely, even if, very rarely,
the earlier material is recalled. At best then, the earlier stages
would not give rise to later versions of themselves but only participate in successive, limited revivals—a form of the Eternal
Return.

Austin Duncan-Jones considered this problem.[7] One's early
life might be completely overwhelmed by the volume of memories that might accumulate over time. "As time passes, the number of happenings available to be remembered increases. It follows that if all that is memorable gets remembered equally often,
any given memorable event must be remembered more and more
rarely as time passes." A million-year-old individual, for example,
would have to remember 20,000 fifty-year time periods, so the
whole first fifty years of one's life could shrink to utter insignificance and be, for practical purposes, not at all part of the continuing person. On this ground John Hick, writing in *Death and Eternal Life*, is doubtful about the idea of an endlessly surviving person, or immortal ego. "If we conceive of people as continuing to
develop during an endless future, as we each have throughout
our past, we encounter a limit to the individual's capacity to identify with earlier states in which he was very different."[8]

This issue is a serious one but, in a certain sense, less a problem than simple forgetting in which information is lost and unavailable. Basically I see it as an attitude problem, and I think it
can be resolved as such, without sacrificing the idea of an immortal ego or infinitely persisting self. To persist, though, we
must have a feeling of respect and reverence for our past selves
whatever their imperfections; this will help in maintaining a bond
of identity. Such reverence in turn, I think, would be one reasonable outcome of a love of all sentient beings, each and every one
of which we should wish to help develop into an immortal ego.
This position, along with the problem of infrequent remembering and related issues, will be considered more fully in the next
chapter.

One further problem that arises with psychological connectedness is false memories. This is actually a common feature of human psychology and sometimes a serious problem in our culture today. Ulric Neisser, a psychology professor at Emory University, notes that "[m]isremembering and retrospective reworking of the past are a part of human nature; they go with the territory and they happen all the time."[9] False memories become a serious issue, for example, when a woman claims and believes, though incorrectly, that she was sexually abused as a child by her father. (It appears that notwithstanding the real and tragic cases of abuse that do occur and are authentically remembered, false memories can be implanted by an overzealous therapist in trying to induce recovery of repressed memories.)

The memory is a tricky thing and is often unreliable. But the problems with it, though not trivial, do appear in a different light from a perspective that incorporates the idea of a multiverse and other ideas such as that the loss of information makes the past ambiguous. Unboundedness in particular makes it hard, I would say almost impossible, to have genuinely false memories. Within large limits, anything we remember must have really happened, though it may not have happened in the universe where we presently reside. It is also worth noting that whether a memory is to be considered "false" (xenontic) or hyperontic or enontic must depend on a careful assessment of all relevant evidence. In what follows I assume that indeed reliable evidence exists to establish the falseness in question—for without such evidence, no such conclusion is possible.

In the case above then, it does not follow that the remembered perpetrator of the abuse—the woman's father—is guilty. The guilt, we would have to conclude (at the risk of sounding facetious and shallow, but with validity), must reside in someone in a parallel universe, not in our reality. Or to be more accurate, the instantiations of the perpetrator occupy universes other than our own, though in this case an instantiation of the victim has managed to appear in our reality. But, insofar as she wishes to remain the victim and uphold the memories of abuse as authentic, she does not originate in our reality but instead must also be said to come from the same alien domain as the perpetrator. This, then, is one example of xenonticity, where a person is clearly out of place in our universe and best identified only with some other one. With the evidence presumed in this case, a natural response for the woman would be to happily relinquish the victim role, accept her memories as faulty, and think better of her father.

In this as well as more usual cases of what we normally consider false memories, we can make a choice. Probably the most likely choice, when we find discrepancies between what we remember about our reality and what we have reason to think actually happened, is simply to adjust our memories accordingly.

I have noticed this on returning to a place I have not seen for many years. Maybe I seem to remember a highway nearby that I can now see is not just where I thought it was (and have good reason to think has not been altered). "Oh yes," I am likely to think, "that is how it really was"—and the minor adjustment is made. Such small changes probably will not affect my memories much, even if carried out to the full extent that opportunity may allow. Thus it is likely I did not have too distinct a memory of the highway not being the way I really found it, so it is not much problem to correct what I do remember. Memories can also carry implied uncertainties, which is useful if an adjustment later is called for.

It is worth noting that a process of adjustment, revising memories in the light of later discoveries about what is likely to have happened, is not inconsistent with our notion of convergence to an ideal self. Such adjustments, I imagine, will be limited and not negate the possibility of an eventual settled consensus that will not be further altered with time but instead form part of a permanent archive.

The possibility must also be noted, however, of memories that do not square with the "known" facts but one might like to keep anyway. Perhaps for reasons of self-esteem we would like to think better of our past than it really was. Or a victim of a crime, say a true case of child abuse, may wish to believe better of the perpetrator than the evidence warrants. But I think in these cases it is better simply to face the truth. The future will, I think, eventually be such as to redeem the past, with all our human pains, misdeeds, and sorrows swallowed up in something greater and more glorious. Our past history, including personal history however horrific, should then be something we can approach with full objectivity and value more because it is what happened than because it is something we wanted to happen or would like to believe happened.

But still we must consider, as a more radical possibility, cases where a person to survive in a reasonable sense must maintain "false" memories. This would occur with the xenontic resurrection, something that, again, may be inevitable for all of us, if we are to survive at all. But here again we can invoke Unboundedness: our memories must conform to real events in some universe, even if it is not where we may eventually find ourselves.

So in one way or another I think the problem of false memories can be resolved, and with this in mind we can sustain a reasonable position of assurance. Again, the pure criterion of psychological connectedness is adequate to establish the continuer property, and on this foundation we can base our case for the ultimate feasibility of resurrecting those who have died.

The future, we noted, should be glorious enough to redeem the past. This I see as an important part of the Philosophy of Assurance. Persons who were disadvantaged in one way or another should have eternity to make up for it—surely that ought to count for something. In the limit of time, we may conjecture, our immortals will approach infinite beings all of whom are on an equal footing of happiness and meaningful existence, though maintaining a distinguishing diversity. Some such outcome as this seems necessary to a reasonable Philosophy of Assurance. A persistent state of misery or other irremediable disadvantages for some is conceivable, yet I do not think it will happen. Our future progress should make remedies of increasing effectiveness available to all who may need them.

This is not a guarantee that the problems that come up will prove solvable, and it is important to put some restraints on our optimism. But I do remain optimistic for reasons we have considered, ranging from near-term possibilities to cosmological arguments favoring immortality in one form or another.

Avenues for Advancement

Something more is worth saying here about the avenues for advancement that should open, if we imagine our biological limitations overcome—though more will be said in the next chapter and Chapter 18. Generally, I imagine the developing immortal

will acquire information of various kinds and become knowledgeable on many subjects. I will even conjecture that essentially any piece of available knowledge will eventually be examined and reexamined—simple curiosity should see to that. In this
way one person could acquire considerable knowledge of other
persons, enough, say, to make continuers of them, at least in the
form of a growing collection of their person-stages. More generally, one person-stage P could contain in memory a complete
description of some other person-stage Q. This, however, would
not automatically make P a continuer of Q; though the latter is
possible, clearly the Q-information must be contained in a special way to produce a Q-continuer.

On the other hand, it does not seem ruled out that P might not
only be a continuer of Q but also of some other entirely different
person Q', provided the requisite information was there so that
two or more people could fuse. Still this could involve serious
difficulties. How would we harmonize two or more independent
sets of past memories and still maintain a sense of being a "single"
person? Would such a union ever seem desirable, in a posthuman
future? Would two lovers, for instance, want eventually to join,
literally, into one being? My feeling is that while such joinings
would probably be possible, they are not likely to predominate
for certain reasons we will consider next chapter. Generally I
would expect immortals to remain, in a reasonable sense, separate individuals, whatever their ties with others.

Along with the possibility of acquiring information about others is that of acquiring it about oneself—that is, it seems reasonable that arbitrary chunks of information will eventually become
available, through one path or another, including simple random
generation. Eventually, then, a developing immortal might find a
chunk describing an episode that fit perfectly into his/her own
life but was not already in memory and possibly was not contained in the historical record. A choice could then be made, with
several interesting options.

As one straightforward possibility, the information would simply be incorporated and become part of the past experience of the
individual. It thus would be treated as lost memory information
that has now been recovered. It would be possible in this way to
append an entire "forelife" to one's memory—or more than one
forelife. But to me the more modest idea of a recovery of lost

memories, not adding up to entire "other" lives but enhancing the life one already remembers, has more appeal and, I think, more practical significance for the relatively near future. Indeed, this option suggests one possible, eventual resolution to a real and tragic problem today.

Suppose Anna, the victim of a debilitating stroke, has lost substantial amounts of her memories and other personality traits, which are not recorded elsewhere. By conventional wisdom, she is hardly "the same" anymore and can, at best, look forward only to a twilight existence. Yet overturning this dismal prospect is possible in principle. We could still restore our victim to the same state of alertness that once existed, with the same memories and other details exactly as before—though it would require advanced technology of the future. The missing details must be filled in by guesswork, of course, and will not retain their original enontic ties with the historical record—this is the price that must be paid. But with this in mind, we are in the same position as in the scenario in Chapter 12 involving Tom Paine (a more difficult one since Mr. Paine was fully deceased, not just partially so, as we could reasonably say of Anna). By the UI assumptions we do not have just one Anna but many, and by ontic robustness not only will they all be restored, but all restorations of "Anna"—fitting broad criteria—will be authentic. In this way then we can reach a position of assurance regarding persons whose identity, by reasonable standards, has been severely compromised in a way that conventional wisdom would tell us is irreversible and hopeless. They can be restored and their injuries undone, though, again, there is a price to pay.

This I think is most heartening, yet there is room for other approaches to what we might loosely consider lost personality information. Some information, for instance, is reasonably regarded as unimportant and not worth reinstating, as in the example of the barbershop. Certainly I could recreate some of this information by guesswork and incorporate it as part of my experience—but I have no wish to do so nor do I feel compromised by not doing so, but unburdened instead.

It is even possible that some of this lost information *is* recoverable, that is, actually enontic. Some businesses use videotaping for surveillance; a hidden camera might have recorded some of the floor details when I was there, and those pictures might one day come to light. Suppose this happened two hundred years from now, when it was valuable simply because of its antiquity. (By the same token, trash dumps from centuries past are valued today by archaeologists.) I would not advocate destruction of the information (assuming my outlook would be roughly what it is today, as I anticipate it would be, assuming also, of course, that I would be alive and well). Yet I would not feel compelled to incorporate it at the personal level either. In effect the information would be saved and available but I would remain dissociated from it—another possibility that could be applied more generally. Remember that forgetting too could be important in shaping the developing immortal—kept within certain bounds. And of course, the information may be simply discarded after all, though arguably it must be encountered again and again, possibly without enontic ties. Over infinite time, all finite patterns must recur.

Generally, I expect that developing immortals will particularly value information that *is* historically derivable, that is, enontic. This issue could be more important than may seem possible today. Some may not want to incorporate information created by guesswork, while others may find it desirable. It is possible too (actually unavoidable in view of Unboundedness) that multiple versions of a person will come into being that differ in that some have accepted the filling out of memories by guesswork to a greater or lesser degree than others. (This possibility will be explored next chapter, in further making a case for Universalism.)

In any case, I expect the future to offer many options of which we can have only the barest inkling, if that. Serious mistakes are not ruled out, and some will be made, but glorious advances seem likely too. Efforts for constructive changes should become more serious and diligent as our understanding improves. Overall, I find this alone very reassuring and exciting. We can train our resources and talents toward making the future what it ought to be, with a realistic hope of success.

It will have to be our initiative, however, as I have argued throughout: we do not have reason to expect outside assistance. In particular, we cannot rely on divine help. We have considered why our reality does not seem ruled by a God in the traditional mold who will ultimately solve the hard problems for us. But this too can be seen in a positive light, as we have noted. Some additional remarks seem appropriate here, in connection with the issue of free will and the problem of evil.

The two are connected: why is it, asks the believer, that a God who is supposedly good allows wrongdoing and suffering? An explanation is that even though God is benevolent, he/she is also a respecter of free will—persons are free to choose right or wrong. Inevitably, some choose wrong and this is held to account, in some manner, for the evils that are prevalent in this world. But I (along with many others) do not find this explanation adequate— it hardly seems to justify the great suffering of the innocent, for example, if we suppose there is a God who could have prevented such suffering. (Often this suffering does not seem to follow from the willful acts of others anyway—there is no obvious "free will" that would be compromised if, for example, a cancer patient in great pain and disability were miraculously cured.) The absence of a benevolent Overseer in turn raises the possibility that our future prospects are not so good, but it is far from clear that this must be so or that one would be better off under the sway of a Deity.

Free Will, the Multiverse, and the Brain

As for free will, it is contradicted by the idea of determinism, in which a person's behavior is not intrinsic in some deep sense but is explained by outside causes. It is interesting that Tipler and Deutsch, who are scientific materialists, both address the problem of determinism and appear to reach opposite conclusions on free will, though the difference can be explained by a differing viewpoint on what the concept should mean. It will be worthwhile to examine both of these arguments briefly, and then consider an entirely different argument that is closer to home. The upshot will be to support the compatibilist position we have considered before; the will is "free" enough for ordinary purposes, including holding persons morally responsible. But it is not free in a more fundamental sense; a reductionist explanation of persons and the absence of a Deity are advantages.

Tipler claims there is "ontological free will," this being part of his theological argument—that there is a God who has (retroactively) created humankind "in his own image."[10] The Creator, in so doing, endowed us with free will in a deep sense, so that we have at least a shadow or image of the divine will. True to form, Tipler's argument is not mystical but primarily computational. The argument starts with a consideration of what determinism should mean. Basically it means that we can infer events in a certain domain or region of space-time by knowing events outside that domain.

Tipler notes how, under relativity, there are or seem to be rather deep limitations on this inference process, if we push far enough. Remove a chunk of space-time—represented by a record of events or, more precisely, of probabilities of events—and you cannot calculate that portion of the record (the probabilities) from all the surrounding data and particularly from what happened prior to the events in question. The missing events, that is, will not be Turing computable from what is left—or this is what seems to be true, though the question is still open. (The events might be computable in any case by a more general device such as a Turing machine with an infinitely inscribed tape. To me this would still qualify as a causal and deterministic explanation, though it would also add up, in practical terms, to unpredictability or "whatever happens, happens.") The uncomputable effects, if they exist, are also very subtle and do not appear able to affect perceptions at our present level to a significant degree. For most purposes, at least, the universe remains quite computable and its properties can be accounted for by the (deterministic and computable) application of quantum mechanics and classical relativity, with unpredictability—apparent randomness—explained, say, by many-worlds. (It is worth keeping in mind, though, that if genuine chance events do play a part, this does not demonstrate an exercise of will, whether free or not.)

Deutsch takes a somewhat different view, emphasizing that in a sense, time does not flow at all and the future is already present—though not accessible to us just "yet." But on this basis things are predetermined and there is no deep free will. Deutsch does, however, uphold a simple notion of free will that is a form of compatibilism. The will is free if, when I do something, I could have done something else—that is, if, in the multiverse, there are versions of me that did do the something else. (I take a somewhat different view, in which the will is free if it subjectively seems to be free, which would in extreme cases allow for predictable controls—see below.) Deutsch also advocates determinism in another sense: that slices, or snapshots, of reality, such as our present, form an orderly collection with any one snapshot inferable from surrounding snapshots.[11] The inference does not always fit such a simple notion as deducing a "future" from a "present" or "past" because a universe like ours in which these concepts are meaningful is something of a special case. Still, there are no surprises that would lead us to suspect either a controlling Mind or a mystical "free will" that is not accounted for in our materialist theories.

A most interesting further insight into the issue of free will is provided, however, not by remote cosmological or computational properties, but features much closer to home—in fact, right inside our heads. Nobody would suggest that the brain is a predictable device, yet there are clear indications that underlying, unwilled causes account for the things we imagine occur by choice.

Evidence of this comes from studies of identical (monozygotic) twins separated at birth. Two people with nearly the same physical body and brain, who are completely unacquainted and sometimes unaware of each other's existence, show remarkable similarities in personality and behavior, even when raised in rather different circumstances. One example is of twin brothers, separated when only a few weeks old and unacquainted until they finally met at age thirty-nine. They found they had married (and divorced) women with the same names, had had children and pets with almost the same names, both enjoyed carpentry and mechanical drawing, and had worked part-time in law enforcement. They also liked the same brand of beer and chain-smoked the same brand of cigarettes.[12]

Nobody is claiming that this or any other pair of "identical" twins is one individual having an identical life experience in two bodies at once—the very exacting standards of Interchangeability do not apply. But it does seem that a similarity in brain structure yields the same sorts of "free" choices in two different individuals. At minimum it casts further doubt on whether there is free will in any deep sense. But it also raises another interesting issue, which is whether this very brain structure could be willing these choices in ways not perceived at the conscious level. Controlled experiments involving brain function appear to confirm this.

Electrical stimulation of the brain is a therapeutic and research tool that finds application in some brain disorders such as epilepsy. Different parts of the brain, when stimulated by implanted electrodes, induce very different effects, one of the many being "willful" behavior such as turning one's head and looking for things. (More complicated effects and controls might also be possible, but techniques have not been developed.) In experimental studies of José Delgado, a patient who repeatedly showed this one effect, turning the head and looking, when stimulated in a particular brain area, offered different explanations. On one occasion, it was "I was looking for my slippers," another time, "I am restless," or "I was looking under the bed," "I heard a noise," and so on. But there was never anything like "your electricity is stronger than my will," which another patient reported when, under stimulation of a different part of the brain, his hand balled up into a fist.[13]

This suggests that not only behavior itself but the subjective feeling of voluntarily choosing it is subject to outside control and manipulation. Such a conclusion is further supported by the work of Benjamin Libet and others showing that willed intentions precede our awareness of them.[14] Subjects were asked to perform a voluntary act, such as bending a finger, and also to note the position of a fast-moving spot on a TV screen when they first "made the decision" to act. In this way the time of the decision could be accurately compared with a concurrent record of electrical brain activity. It was shown that the brain triggered the event about a third of a second before the subject was aware of having decided to act.

The impression is clear that truly free will is an illusion, even in the weaker sense that demands only that our actions be uncontrolled from the outside. Brain events of which we have no conscious awareness move us to act and provide the convincing impression that we acted by a free and voluntary choice. In principle such events could be controlled by an outside agent, as seems to have been approximated, if crudely, in the Delgado experiments. More usually, a part of our brain is involved that is not really "us" or part of us but instead would seem to play the role of puppeteer. This part will normally act independently of outside controls, so that the compatibilist view of free will should still have force, though this is not guaranteed.

An interesting conundrum then arises. Perhaps we could be entirely controlled from the outside, using advanced future technology, without feeling we were being manipulated at all. We would think we were acting by free choice yet would not be. We would truly be animated puppets with awareness, feeling, and volition that seemed perfectly free and natural but still was not our own and might instead, within close limits, be perfectly predictable.

This recalls the discussion of the movie characters in our thought experiment in Chapter 8, which, it appeared, could not be conscious because they would have no way to interact with the outside world and vary their predetermined behavior. But under brain control, it seems a person would both have predetermined behavior, that is, lack the capacity to interact, yet also be conscious. (This consciousness too would find its expression in our time and not some other universe's.) True, the controls could be removed at any time and the behavior might revert to normal, with the usual unpredictable causes and effects. There would, moreover, be no reason one could not also remember the experiences one had had while under outside control, and these would seem part of one's "real" past.

There are ways too in which controls could be removed for the movie characters (by instantiating them in the flesh with future technology, say), and they could converse with us about their movie experiences. This would not necessarily mean we must regard these very experiences as conscious and "real" in our universe, albeit predetermined, but the possibility is there. (Remember too that this was no ordinary movie but something on a grander scale for which common intuition may not apply; again we must take account of the Principle of Large Quantity.) But in the absence of evidence, I think we are safe in discounting the likelihood that we are either controlled like puppets by a cosmic intelligence or parts of a sentiently designed movie. (True, in a cosmic sense we are unavoidably a family of snapshots, but this need not involve additional extraordinary possibilities.) Let us continue now with that part of the observable world that is right beneath our skulls.

In the new field of brain imaging, experimental tools are beginning to reveal just how the brain's internal activity correlates with external behavior. Brain imaging allows watching the brain function in real time, while the subject may be talking, thinking, or performing some task. Functional magnetic resonance imaging (fMRI) and positron emission tomography (PET) show brain blood flow patterns, and magnetic resonance spectroscopy (MRS) measures biochemical changes. Results are shown on a TV monitor, making it possible to look right inside the subject's head: when a given part of the brain is activated it lights up. We can see, then, which parts become active when someone is answering a question about apple juice, or thinking of that music concert the other night, or getting ready to strike a nail with a hammer. It is even possible to follow the activity of specific genes in your gray matter.[15] Much more sophisticated refinements, which might be able to show the functioning of individual neurons in large clumps, are also being pursued.[16]

The brain, clearly, is a mechanism like any other, only very complicated. We—our conscious selves—do not exercise some deep control over our actions or thoughts. If such control is exercised by some agent outside our consciousness, it is outside ourselves and not part of us. (This position differs from Tipler's, who would attribute a special significance to unpredictable, controlling events,[17] yet it is essential to the philosophical viewpoint here. It is our conscious experience alone that makes us the persons we are—as is demanded by Interchangeability.) Our choices of whatever nature have an intelligible, nonvolitional explanation, even when subjective impressions tell us otherwise.

Once again, though, the will seems free to us, and that should be good enough for practical purposes. In particular we may and should assign moral responsibility to behavior because that is the best practical way to achieve desired results, though it is not because we believe in a transcendent notion of "responsibility." (Still, with no evidence that persons are consciously controlled from the outside—despite the preceding discussion—we feel justified in assigning responsibility to those persons themselves.) The absence of deep free will, moreover, can be seen in a positive light, as we saw in Chapter 11; we will return to this issue in the next chapter. More generally, we find ground to uphold a reductionist position, based on functionalism, which we have considered at length. As a type of computational process, not only are we lacking in mystical souls but even our matter is not our own. We could exchange it, as indeed we do, without sacrificing

our real essence, our continuing or once and future consciousness. This is no despairing conclusion but opens incredible possibilities as we have seen.

The Problem of Evil

There still remains the problem of evil, however. It is especially important to the theist, for the reasons we have considered,
but we cannot ignore it either because of our principal working
hypothesis that life, fundamentally, is good. To uphold this position we must argue that evils and suffering, though extant, at least
are somehow compensated or requited by the good that also happens—and most important—the good that will happen. Our approach, we have seen, is to look toward the future as the means
of obtaining final compensation for the wrongs of life. This future will be of our own choosing and making; it is up to us to
determine both what should be done and how to go about doing
it.

Thus we are saddled with an immense responsibility: we must
develop into more-than-humans, in part simply to requite the evils
of our present existence and of the long, often unhappy past history of life on our planet. But this position has advantages too.
We can acknowledge the evils of this life for what they are, without fear of offending a higher power, on one hand, or despair at
never finding a remedy on the other. The aging process is a good
case in point.

Aging is natural, but it is also an abomination. Any thoughtful,
objective person who has any doubt should visit a nursing home.
Much wrong has been done by willful, human misconduct. But
blind nature—the same principle that gave us life—is surely the
greater culprit (so far at least). The majority of deaths today are
aging related, which adds up to billions of lives extinguished in
the short span of a few decades. Aging destroys everybody, in
fact, who is not felled by some other cause (often also "natural").
In so doing it is often most cruel, robbing people slowly of both
mental and physical vigor before they are finally sacrificed. Some
of its complications, such as cancer, can also cause horrible and
prolonged pain.

Apologists of the "natural order" sometimes try to argue that
our problems with aging are also really our fault. In the "natural

state," humans had no need of nursing homes. Crowds of the feeble elderly, such as we must provide for today, were unknown. Cancer and heart disease were uncommon. Yes, indeed: because our hunter-gatherer forebears were not that numerous to begin with and, moreover, did not live long enough, being picked off by predators, starvation, warfare, or disease before or as their bodies started to weaken from aging. Those who did live into old age would find additional hardships. In a hunter-gather society, with its nomadic lifestyle, surplus food and energy are in short supply, making care of the elderly problematical. "Only 8 percent of Yanomama Indians, a primitive South American tribe, survive to the age of 65, compared to 85 percent of modern Americans," one source reports. "In true neolithic cultures, as little as 2 percent of the population may have survived to the age of 50."[18] But if the shortening of life and picking off of people are reasonable remedies to the aging problem, one wonders why they are not more widely advocated and used.

In fact, of course, it is not in shortening life but in lengthening it—beyond any point where biology makes a difference or has any meaning—that the true solution to the aging problem must be found. The complete abolition of aging as we know it—along with other causes of death—is the only viable approach. Our human nature demands this, and human nature is part of nature seen as it ought to be seen, which takes into account our intelligence, feelings, and aspirations as well as the nonhuman ecology. It will not be easy to remake ourselves, but it ought to be feasible, and we must try.

Meanwhile, however, we need not, must not, rail unduly at unconscious forces, including the evolutionary process that gave rise to us. Instead we can be positive, even in our recognition of great and pervasive shortcomings. Life as a whole is beautiful and fundamentally good. But good though it is, it is also just a beginning, and it is up to us to continue, to take up and go on from where blind nature has left off. We can accept this as an

 Aging is a major cause of misery and death in the world today, but it ought to be curable in the future.

important part of our Philosophy of Assurance, and it can be a valuable inspiration. There is no one to blame for much of our present predicament—certainly not ourselves and not some other, extrahuman intelligence—and there is hope.

By *present predicament* I refer, of course, not merely to such details as political institutions that *are* of our own making but to more fundamental features such as our biological limitations. We must acknowledge the wrongs we are done for what they are, including the great wrongs inflicted by nature, yet once again, we must not waste energy in hatred and rage. Instead, after recognizing the problems that are there, we must proceed with courage, good will, and care toward their resolution. Once again, the problems are there and are serious and hard, but we can and must work diligently to overcome these towering obstacles. In adopting this stance and acting accordingly, we can be comforted by the thought that much ought to be feasible through a scientific approach, much that has never been attempted or even imagined.

Assurance in the Face of Uncertainty

We have now considered how some challenging difficulties can be met in formulating our Philosophy of Assurance. When we focus on the immortal beings we will hopefully develop into, problems such as forgetting and false memories do not pose insurmountable obstacles to the functionalist viewpoint and the memory-based criterion of personal identity. More generally, we must confront an ever-present uncertainty and the thought that matters may not turn out as we wish. At the same time we have reason to be positive about life and hopeful about our future prospects.

The Philosophy of Assurance, then, can be briefly summarized as follows. First, something is in control, something that overall can be accepted as good. The "something" is not a sentient God or other conscious being, yet it is real, and it expresses itself to us through laws of physics and other principles or facts we can discover through rational inquiry. In particular, good, bad, right, and wrong all have meaning that extends across cultural and species boundaries and are not simply relative concepts. Second, even though the controlling "something" is not sentient, it opens the way to us to take control of our own destiny. This does not mean that we will control the whole of reality—far from it—but that, nonetheless, the extent of our powers should increase dramatically, and this should have an important bearing on our future. Third, we have reason to hope that our ancient dreams will be fulfilled, including resurrection of the dead and immortality. This of course must happen through scientific means and our own efforts, possibly assisted by other finite beings like ourselves. The means and opportunities that seem open to us can encompass even such apparent impossibilities as these.

This brings up one more issue, which involves what I will call a *moral platform*—in this case, a stance on what ought to be, with an associated call to commitment. Life ought to be worthwhile—thus it ought to come to no permanent end. If a person's life does end, there ought to be a way back, that is, the possibility of resurrection. We see then that there ought to be a valid Philosophy of Assurance along the lines we have considered. This thought can motivate us in our search for ways of refining and validating such a philosophy. The search will involve an assessment of reality as it appears to be but, in addition, a careful formulation of the problems that most need resolution.

In particular, to provide for the necessary possibilities of resurrection and immortality, the moral platform demands that we consider most carefully what it *should* mean for a person to survive and live again. There are various competing ideas about this, as we have seen. Often they are more or less equivalent in everyday affairs but lead to very different conclusions for the larger issues we are considering. We have examined reasons why pattern-survival was the best of the possible choices, in terms of allowing for the individual with original memories to survive the death and disintegration of the body, albeit by a somewhat difficult route. Here the moral platform guides our choice. Our idea of survival must not be too superficial, as would happen if we omitted the necessity of having authentic information pertaining to a past life. On the other hand, we must not choose too stringent a requirement, such as informational continuity, which would imply that lives lost in the past cannot be resurrected and thus were lived in vain.

The best position, then, is to allow for some adjustments in our own intuitions about survival, so that a satisfying philosophical stance can be found and justified. Kept within reasonable bounds, such adjustments can be of great benefit. We can give up what are inappropriate attachments to less essential details and thereby successfully stand our ground on the more important issues. The moral platform, then, can help refine our worldview so that life will become more meaningful as important goals are made feasible.

The moral platform, however, is no arid theoretical doctrine divorced from action but calls us to commit ourselves to a task, namely, our physical immortalization. This commitment seems all the more urgent in view of such possibilities as preservation through biostasis and, more generally, the new capabilities for both good and bad that our progress is bringing. By directing our efforts toward immortalization and the myriad related goals and issues it fosters, we find that life takes on new meaning and contributes to the very state of assurance we are seeking. The moral platform should also be helpful in bringing the world around to our position that human immortalization is at hand and a goal to be won through our own efforts.

Needless to say, there is much that needs to be done. We are seeking what no humans have ever remotely achieved, a physical transformation that will make us higher than human and even extend to other life-forms. The Philosophy of Assurance thus calls for action, which in turn requires motivation. In approaching the issue of what actions are called for, we must first ask what sort of motivation is appropriate to the would-be immortal, or, in other words, what sorts of aspirations ought to guide us. To this we now turn.

CHAPTER 16.

The Philosophy of Aspiration

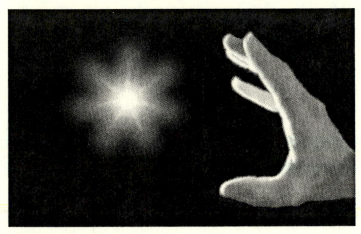

Many people seriously doubt if immortality is worth striving for and wonder why a finite, mortal existence would not be "enough." These matters have been addressed before, but some issues need clarification. We need to consider further why a person should seek an endless life, and what sorts of activities might occupy one's time during such a long interval, which is mostly to be spent, if things go as they should, at levels far beyond the human. So we have another daunting task and cannot expect the perfect completion, yet an effort must be made. It is necessary, then, to return to the issues of why we live life in the first place and whether and how our motives ought to be adjusted to approach the prospect of an unlimited existence.

Building on the discussion in Chapter 11, we shall extend our investigation of why, if a hopefully eternal future is taken into account, motives of simple self-interest will also lead to a beneficial stance toward others. Acts of reciprocal kindness can be expected, empowered by the superior technology that will by then have been developed. We can be hopeful that whatever may be good and worthy that can happen will eventually happen, in some fashion—which, however, leaves room for personal choices to make a difference. Such thoughts will lead to a Philosophy of Aspiration that is a necessary component of the whole system offered here. But, lacking other models, we will have to base our thinking about more distant, future life on what is closer to home.

Here, at least, there is something to go on. Numerous religious and philosophical traditions have addressed the issues of life and its meaning over the centuries. Among them, Hinduism, in its philosophical core, has insights I find particularly relevant. A reference is Huston Smith's *World's Religions*, which also contains useful thoughts from other religious traditions.

Different people pursue different goals. Some live mainly for pleasure. This in fact is the kind of goal likely to be pursued at first—a baby is very pleasure oriented—but with more sophistication it may be realized that pleasure alone (in the simple way that we usually understand it) is not enough. Another goal then is sought, one of the possibilities being worldly success, which takes such forms as wealth, fame, and power. Ultimately, though, this too may be found wanting. A third goal, community service or devotion to a social or political cause, may then be tried and found to give additional meaning. But in the end, as some firmly conclude, this goal too is not satisfying. Something beyond this, and outside of all the usual worldly pursuits, is needed.[1] This fourth goal we can call transcendence. Interest in transcendence is certainly not confined to Hinduism but is universal and makes its appearance in different cultures and traditions under various guises and names. At root I see it as the goal of becoming more-than-human.

In Chapter 1 the question was raised of whether the would-be immortal should have an overall goal or mission and, if so, what should it be. The answer, then, is transcendence. It is what people really want, even today. It is, of course, a short answer only and must be filled out with details pertaining to particular circumstances and conditions. For us here and now, it means becoming more-than-human, but, assuming we succeed in our endeavor, the goal can also be scaled up accordingly, to apply at any level we may reach. In this way we may hope that life will always have an unfulfilled element, to provide us with a reason to go on even as we endlessly progress.

To accept the goal of transcendence does not mean that we no longer care about day-to-day affairs—far from it—but that we acknowledge an overall trend of advancement, a deeper meaning in what might otherwise lose any meaning it has. Our lives must rightfully be open-ended, with no final consummating state but one level leading to the next in endless succession. Again, this principle should apply however far we may advance, whatever the future may hold in store, and particularly after we have attained a sought-for status of more-than-human. But first, of course, we must deal with our human existence; this alone, and especially in our time, offers many challenges.

The differing traditions offer various approaches to the goal of transcendence. For some there is a transcendent domain or mystical world beyond death, generally with a superhuman agency or power whose assistance in attaining the desired state is critical. Buddhism advocates a kind of transcendence founded on a simple extinguishing of worldly cravings and attachments. Hinduism similarly urges detachment from worldly pursuits, which in this case is to make it possible to grasp an "ocean of truth" within oneself. There are numerous other variations. Sometimes ascetic practices are used as a means of detachment and approaching a more-than-human condition.

Here I have advocated treating the problem as a scientific one: we can elevate ourselves to more-than-human status by our own design. I think that this is the only viable approach in the end: we cannot become more-than-human while remaining merely human, and the progress we make must be our own. Yet I would not disparage all that has gone before—far from it—though I do think it is time to bring science more fully into the picture and start thinking, additionally, of what future capabilities to aim for.

What should we be aiming for? Hinduism itself proposes what I think is an excellent starting answer: what people really want, the kind of transcendence they seek, is (1) existence, (2) knowledge, and (3) joy—all in unlimited abundance. This we can surely support, with reasonable allowance for how the terms should be understood. Unlimited existence—immortality—is a necessary part, but we also want our lives to be rewarding and meaningful. Joy and knowledge too must grow without limit. One point to emphasize: these objectives are viewed by Hindus—and others the world over—as worthy aims of a life well lived. And so they are. Properly understood and pursued, they are in no sense hubristic, excessive, or even unnatural—for it is human nature to want to rise above itself. Accordingly, we must seek these aims of transcendence as best we can.

Thankfully, our means are growing. We must use our capabilities to the fullest, with the full expectation and intention of making changes at deep levels that affect us, including our biology. We must proceed with due caution, not overlooking the pitfalls but proceeding nonetheless. To do otherwise, when we can do so much, and so much good thereby, would be unconscionable and, I think, probably dangerous to the survival of ourselves and life as a whole on this planet. For life, and especially human life, will not stand still. If we do not seize the initiative and make the advances we can to better our lot, frustration will follow. To be trapped at the merely human level, with a rising population on a limited globe, will invite all the disasters we have feared now for decades, including mutual annihilation through nuclear and other terrible weapons. We must do better than this.

Of course we ought to become immortal! We ought to find joy and meaning in a life that has no end. We ought to strive for the abolition of the sentence of death that has been our lot here on Earth but which we now may hope physically to overcome. Properly handled, our aspirations to more-than-human status can ennoble as well as empower us and make possible our deliverance. In our striving we will make use of whatever means our technology can provide. But individually we must have the will to succeed and must act accordingly. Immortalization must be self-immortalization, an effort of each person separately, though hopefully a happy one, enriched and enlivened by contact with others.

Wants, Survival, and Healing

Let us now take a closer look at the issue of what it is that people really want. There is a twofold aspect to this, whose second half is usually overlooked. People have wants of various sorts. That is usually the focus when, after all, we are considering what we want. The object then becomes to satisfy the want. But the other side of the coin is that wants themselves are malleable. Interests can be displaced by other interests or perhaps simply extinguished, as has been emphasized in Buddhism. In the future our understanding of our wants and how to modify them will deepen, I think incredibly. We will be able to change our basic drives, should we desire, to make old attractions fade and newer ones take their place or possibly do the opposite and revitalize old, faded enthusiasms. It should be possible, in particular, to so structure oneself that great pleasures could be had by simple, even trivial, means.

Here there seems a clear danger in going too far. Would we want to exist in a rapturous but mindless state? This recalls certain ideas in science fiction, such as the "wirehead" scenarios of Larry Niven in which future thrill-seekers undergo electrical brain stimulation and are chronically ecstatic but also incapacitated.[2] Future technology, we might argue, could arrange for brain stimulation and thereby satisfy our various appetites more thoroughly than is possible today.

But this I think must be firmly discounted, if it went so far as "hedonic stasis"—an unending, pleasurable paralysis. One argument against this idea would be that unless there is mental activity, including storage and eventual recall of memories, there is no continuing awareness of time—subjectively, one's time is finite even if pleasant. There is no true immortality but at best only an Eternal Return. And, with time effectively limited, there would also be a limit to enjoyment, however intense it might be. In addition there would be the practical problem that such a state would be incapacitating, so the participant would need outside help maintaining it. Others in turn would not be enthusiastic—what interest would they have in sustaining such a mental vegetable? Automation might seem to offer a possibility, but an automated support system, I should think, would have limited adaptability, resourcefulness, and dedication—unless you made it sentient too, thus eventually again prone to disinterest and frustration. So the best future life would, I think, involve both continuing mental development and self-sufficiency. Such a life could still contain a great deal of satisfaction, but it would also have more meaning. The problem would be how best to structure it, both in terms of one's basic drives and interests, which again should be malleable, and in terms of what activities one participated in as a consequence to bring fulfillment.

The prospect of modifying one's drives raises the issue of whether, in so doing, the original person could survive in a reasonable sense. This is a vital issue, of course; if we do not survive then we do not benefit, no matter who does or how much. But at least it is clear that drives can be altered without "killing" us. For instance, just before mealtime I am hungry, but after it I am not, yet in a reasonable sense "I" am still the same person. Though hunger is a recurring effect, it is possible that a drive or interest may be permanently altered without thereby eradicating the old person. The learning process offers examples of this.

I remember the excitement when the first closeup photos of Mars were returned by a spacecraft in 1965, about two dozen low-definition images. By later standards they were quite crude. But picture 11 showed, unmistakably, a large crater—something never before seen beyond the moon. Up to then we did not really know what Mars was like. That it might, in an important way, be moonlike was a possibility only and as I recall had not gained much currency. By now, of course, the face of Mars has been far more finely mapped, and these first pictures do not have the interest they once did, nor is it likely they will. More generally, as we learn, our interests adapt and are otherwise modified, yet "our" existence continues. Indeed, without some such learning process, involving a progressive modification of interests as understanding deepens, "we" could not really survive, as we have noted, but must be doomed, once again, to no better than an Eternal Return.

Yet a difficulty can still be raised. If we allowed an arbitrary change in drives, dispositions, et cetera, might it not be possible, after all, to change any one person into any other person? But there is one crucial property in the examples we have considered that argues against the position that the original person is lost, which is that a memory of the earlier state is presumed. From this it should be possible to reconstruct the earlier state. Thus I can remember my own excitement about the Mars pictures, even if that is not just how I would react today. Of course, the memory may well not be perfect; in general we must call upon ideas of the last chapter, including q-stages that, we hypothesize, will retain information incorruptibly, to argue that a true survival based on psychological connectedness could occur. With this in mind, though, the problem seems less serious. For example, another person would not be expected to have memories of the state in question, lessening the prospects for a confusion of persons.

Still we must exercise caution. It is possible, as noted last chapter, that person P may know so much about Q that some of Q's earlier stages can be reconstructed from P's memories. (This could particularly hold in the future if the brain is augmented or replaced with electronic devices so that exchange of the deepest levels of personal information becomes possible.) In such a case, though, there should still be a clear distinction between what *P* remembers as *her* personal experiences, versus what she has learned about *Q*. Nevertheless, the issue, we may imagine, will not always be clear-cut. There seems to be a strange border between an experience we might have a clear impression of but nevertheless think of as another person's and what we choose to regard as part of our own past—more on this later.

For now we shall assume that our own experiences, including modifications of desires and other traits, are clearly distinguished from another's experiences of which we have knowledge. While there must be some limits, a considerable modification of dispositions might take place with the feeling that one is still the same person, only grown older and wiser. This in fact can give great meaning and overall satisfaction. Thinking back on what one has learned, how one has coped and progressed, mistakes one has made, bad times as well as good—even terrible wrongs one may have once done and sorrowful, searching repentance—and what future plans all this may suggest, can go far in making life more worthwhile.

One case in point that has considerable interest is the evil person who changes for the better. With the right change of heart, the vilest villain could become the noblest saint—not an easy transformation, but one we must not dismiss as impossible.

Viktor Frankl, a Jewish psychiatrist and philosopher, survived four Nazi concentration camps in World War II. In *Man's Search for Meaning* he recounts the case of Dr. J., the "mass murderer of Steinhof," Vienna's well-known mental hospital. "He was the only man I ever encountered whom I would dare to call a Mephistophelean being, a satanic figure....When the Nazis started their euthanasia program he held all the strings in his hands and was so fanatic in the job assigned to him that he tried not to let one single psychotic individual escape the gas chamber." Dr. J. was later captured by the Russians and ended up in Moscow's Lubianka prison, where he eventually died of natural causes (cancer). But while there, an inmate reported, "he showed himself to be the best comrade you can imagine! He gave consolation to everybody. He lived up to the highest conceivable moral standard. He was the best friend I ever met during my long years in prison!"[3]

Although this brief account leaves some questions unanswered, it does suggest how a strong change of heart is possible. Persons are not simply bad or good as part of their identity or nature but can reform. In one sense they become different. But in another, important, sense they are the same individuals as before, except that they have now undergone a process of growth and change for the better. This I submit should be extendable even to the most reviled figures of history. Such despised villains as Hitler and Stalin must not become objects of permanent hate—we must ask how even persons like these might be healed and redeemed.

John Hick, British Christian philosopher and advocate of Universalism, writes in *Death and Eternal Life* about the sort of redemptive change that must occur if someone is to be cured of evil. "His perfecting will have involved his utter revulsion against his own cruelty and a deep shame and sorrow at the memory of it. At the end of this hard creative process he will be the same person in the sense that he will remember [his wrongdoing], and will feel ashamed and sorry and in desperate need of forgiveness. But in another sense he will no longer be the same person; for he will have changed in character into someone who is now morally incapable of behaving in such a way...."[4]

The forgiveness sought will not be won lightly, of course. A person may change for the better, but in no sense must we condone the wrongs that were done. But maintaining an attitude of permanent hostility and hatred, when a true reform has occurred and bad has turned to good, would be inappropriate and even inconsistent with our own long-term self-interest.

Such thoughts lead to a working hypothesis that can serve as a principal underpinning for our Philosophy of Aspiration: all sentient life is precious. Fundamentally, each and every being is good, and its life, considered as a whole, is good too, both for itself and for others. True, this often does not seem so at our level. The good in some may not be realized until a future time when they are present in more advanced form. But overall we can value each sentient creature, even as we anticipate that being's eventual immortalization. Echoing Kant, sentient beings thus are never, primarily, "means to an end" but "ends in themselves."[5] This will apply to human beings, both good and bad, and even other lifeforms, a topic we will investigate shortly.

The Search for Meaning

For now let us backtrack a little. We are seeking survival, knowledge, and joy in unlimited amounts. While we have reason to hope that physical means of extending our lives will be possible, we must think about what we will do with ourselves in our expanded setting. While, as a general rule, we are interested in satisfying "wants," we have to face the issue, not merely of what we want, but what we ought to want, to ensure that life will be meaningful and rewarding on the scale that we hope will open.[6]

Frankl argues, rightly I think, that what is most important in one's life is to find meaning—making due allowance for the imprecision of the term and how it should be understood. Meaning in particular transcends mere pleasure (or we might instead call it a higher form of "pleasure," taking precedence over others) and such goals as success or even the respect others may tender for services one performs in the public interest. Though all of these could contribute to a meaningful existence, meaning can also be found in the most trying circumstances—as in a concentration camp. And there is no guarantee that life in happier circumstances will prove so meaningful either. In any case, meaning can be found if diligently sought.

Our options to find meaning should expand along with our future capabilities—though again there will be pitfalls to be navigated with care. But, among other things, understanding of our mental and psychological characteristics should be greatly enhanced as well as of how to make constructive changes. One obvious change, of course, will be that we will no longer suffer progressive physical deterioration with age, and we may hope that the death rate will drop, essentially, to zero. It does not take much reflection to see that that event itself must inaugurate profound changes.

Today we are products of natural selection, which has not acted with any plan in shaping those that make up our species beyond the obvious property that individuals must be so disposed that the species continues. Since they are mortal, this means they must make others like themselves and, moreover, must be interested in doing so. It is fairly difficult to make a person, requiring several years minimum for a creature able to survive on its own where necessary. This interest, then, is not a casual one but, with most people, a powerful obsession to which they willingly devote a large portion of their lives and energy. It is a major source of meaning.

Yet it is doomed, at least in anything like its present form. The elimination of death will not only eliminate the need to reproduce, it will make any idea of devoting a large part of one's life to the task an absurdity. Couples could, at most, average two children between them without fostering exponential population growth. Most of one's very long life thus could not be spent in the making and raising of offspring, at least for most people. Exponential growth must end, one way or another—the available resources cannot support it. If we do not curb our own production of people by an orderly process, nature will do it for us by less pleasant routes.

Yet I find much reason for optimism on the issue of overpopulation—it is not likely to happen, at least on the global scale that many have feared. Thomas Malthus in the early 1800s predicted that living standards could not rise among the poor, who with more income would just have more children. The net effect would be more poor people, not better-off people. But that did not happen. Industrialization did lead to more income per family and fewer, not more, offspring. Today's living standards, worldwide, are far higher than they were in Malthus's time—it is hard to make a direct comparison. So many things are now available: medical procedures, means of transportation and communication, computers, and so on, that could not be had at any price, and these are becoming increasingly common in all parts of the world, along with a growing abundance of simple necessities. True, there are also many more people now, and the population "bomb" is still ticking. Poverty and starvation have not been eliminated but still are all too common. Matters could get out of hand, but increasingly, I think, people realize that it is in their best interests, individually, not to overdo it and raise this threat.

"Not overdoing it" is far easier now, with contraceptives becoming more widespread, effective, and convenient. People can have the sex they want and avoid the babies they do not want. This solution seems to be working, as decreasing worldwide birthrates attest, but of course it is a crude one. There are other options too, and in the future there will be more. People are not simply reproductive machines, whose necessary rituals of copulation must now be increasingly sterilized so as not to threaten the limited resources, but otherwise maintained as in days of yore—or intensified. In our hopefully immortal future, such rituals themselves, and the attendant desires demanding fulfillment, must come under close scrutiny along with everything else.

No doubt there will be many options for adaptation. If things go as they should and aging and physical deterioration are reversed and eliminated, people could keep the bodies and desires of teenagers indefinitely. Some immortalists indeed have expressed a wish to live as healthy teenagers, and this may be tried and enjoyed for a time. But I predict that sooner or later such a lifestyle must be found wanting—greater fulfillment will be possible through other means, which in turn will be sought voluntarily. This is not to argue that there is anything inherently sinful about sex—I do not see it that way—but to suggest that, in view of our future prospects, we will have both reason and means to outgrow it.

The willing abandonment of sex has a long and venerable history already, as monasteries, nunneries, and priestly and other religious vocations in numerous world traditions demonstrate, and it is not entirely confined to religious institutions. Adherents of a celibate lifestyle are not simply trying to exclude unwanted gratifications but are seeking a new mode of existence, wonderful and pleasing in its own right. Their thinking is generally motivated by a strong wish to escape this mortal coil for something higher. Such renunciation is not without its problems, of course, but it can also produce states of exaltation, serenity, and overall meaningful contentment, as joyful accounts bear witness.[7]

So far, of course, only a relative few seek this renunciation with its attendant rewards—natural selection sees to that, favoring the sorts of individuals who tend to procreate while they have the chance. But in the future that should change, with the elimination of death, the means to make people artificially, and increased opportunities and knowledge all around. The future is unlikely to resemble some great, solemn cloister—instead there should be a plurality and proliferation of many individual orientations and lifestyles, all determined by voluntary choice. But I foresee, in general, a defocusing of the specialized interests that are involved in human reproduction. People will, I think, so adjust as to become rather like "angels in heaven," when our know-how is greater and the old mortal verities lose force.

Once again we must keep in mind that along with greater means to satisfy perceived wants will come ways of adapting our desires—in effect, refining these very wants to better address the important issues we will be confronting. Although the refinement process must make many changes, it must not be seen as invalidating what went before, for there is much of value about present and past life that should carry over to an immortal future. As a principal example, the preoccupation with furthering our species has taught us to be concerned about human lives. We do not just make babies, but they have to be nurtured—their survival and prosperity, and that of others as well, becomes important. In better moments we extend this caring to humanity as a whole and even to other species. We recognize a universal theme: the struggling sentient being, striving to become something more than it is, striving for perfection and, however dimly it may fathom, its own eternal divinity.

Shaping Our Own Future

At this point it is worthwhile to remind ourselves that while an immortal world of the future should happen and hopefully will, it must rest on today's world, with all its struggles and limitations, and on previous events. Sentient beings for eons have given their all so that we might have the chance to make and experience whatever sort of Heaven we—or whoever is around in the future—decide is appropriate and can create. Even bad events, we might say, had good consequences, as when evolution honed our intellects and sensibilities through the deaths of others of inferior capacities that our ancestors out-competed, out-fought, or otherwise eliminated from the scene. This is not to condone the many abuses of sentient life that have occurred throughout history and prehistory, but we must not condemn the entire enterprise either. Instead I think we must ask what we can do to produce the best outcome, something that will redeem and justify it all. We must try to correct and compensate for all the tragic shortcomings in seeking what is good and right.

Once again, though, this involves an interplay. We must consider not merely the means we may have to achieve certain desirable aims but our very notions of what *desirable* should mean or, again, what we ought to want as well as do want. This, of course, introduces an indeterminacy. In the future, a man on a bed of nails may have the option of so modifying his desires that the sharp points produce pleasure. Should he seek to remove himself from the nails, as someone of today might singlemindedly pursue, or just make it feel good?

I think, however, that this dilemma will have a reasonable resolution, at least when it comes to the larger issues. We have already considered the idea of hedonic stasis, which, it might be said, would solve all problems for the individual but not solve them well or, at any rate, not well enough. So this idea must be rejected, along with anything else that leads to an Eternal Return or something short of active participation and immortal self-sufficiency. Though it is hazardous, at our level, to try to imagine how developing immortals of the future might structure their lives, there are simple features that ought to have a bearing: a selection process, the necessity for survival of the individual, and self-interest. When we consider these, we can arrive at a clearer idea of what might be important to our future selves, which in turn can inform our aspirations today.

We have already had several occasions to consider selection processes, which shape the kinds of dispositions and behavior we find in people. Unfortunately, a selection process sometimes has serious shortcomings, especially if viewed in immortalist terms. Mortality, after all, is the principal device "used" by natural selection to strengthen a species (or more properly, perpetuate certain genes) by pruning the less fit. We seek to end mortality, but this will not end the importance of a selection process in our lives. Indeed we might ask, before proceeding further, whether ending mortality would in fact improve our fitness as a population. If the answer is no, then potential immortals could find themselves out-competed by more transient forms and ultimately extinguished.

But here, I will conjecture, we have reason to be hopeful and, in fact, much to fear if we do not succeed in immortalizing ourselves. Mortal individuals must necessarily be limited in their capacity for advancement and enlightenment. Though species in the wild may struggle and the fittest survive, our struggles, with the terrible weapons our developing technology is providing, threaten the entire human population and all other life on Earth. Indeed, there is no small threat right now from isolated terrorists and tiny fringe groups bent on violence—will one of these, someday soon, blow us up or poison us all? Certainly we cannot rule this out, especially if we keep in mind the increasing availability and effectiveness of technologies that bright but unbalanced individuals can put to nefarious uses.

Increasingly we are in the position of infants in a small room playing with hand grenades. The small room—now our globe— is not likely to get much bigger, at least as long as we remain "infants." And the "grenades" are not getting less powerful, but if anything, more so, and more obtainable all the time. So we must elevate ourselves out of infancy somehow, become more than what we have been, more-than-human, to diminish the risk. If we do not succeed in immortalizing ourselves, it may well seal our doom. If we self-destruct there is still the hope, based on the philosophical position that has been argued, of our being recreated again, somewhere, by another intelligent species. But this would be under conditions not of our choosing and not necessarily to our liking. Our would-be resurrectors, advanced beings we may conjecture, could be wise and benevolent but in a superhuman sense we would not immediately appreciate. Concerned with correcting our deficiencies, they could impose a Purgatory we would long find indistinguishable from Hell. Perhaps such severity would not really be the chosen course, but I think some penalties and privation could be expected, so that we would long regret our failure to have successfully survived on our own— more on this later.

On the other hand, successes in the direction of our own, self-directed immortalization and on other problems we face should have more immediate, beneficial effects. People will surely be less bent on crude warfare if the quality of their lives and the number of years are increased—they will simply have that much more to lose. And, with our growing understanding of mental problems, the disorders that seem to dispose some toward acts of violence will come increasingly under control, as will other problems we do not recognize today as "illnesses" but likely will in the future, when the functioning of the brain is better understood. (Such a newly recognized illness might be an unimaginative nature predisposing one toward boredom, frustration, and a general feeling that life is not so good and eventual death is acceptable or even desirable.) In any case, I think that if a means of controlling and reversing the aging process is found, as seems very likely, few will willfully resist it. The entire human race then living will develop into immortals, and it is hard to imagine a group not adopting immortality, let alone being able to "out-compete" those who do. This I would imagine to follow, even if we consider a species that is mortal but reproduces fast. A kind of super-insect could pose a threat. But immortality, I will wager, will make possible a level of technical skill as well as overall organization, understanding, and motivation that would prove decisive in any struggle with such a life-form.

With immortality (or more properly, indefinite life span and the end of biological aging, hopefully but a short step from true immortality) we will at least be better able to deal with the sort of threats we face today, including violence on a grand scale. A selection process will arguably, in fact, favor those who are disposed toward personal survival, as we noted in Chapter 13. Those who are not, if serious enough, may be expected to end their lives or, more hopefully, try various remedies and adaptations, which should be available. I will conjecture that anyone who persists will be able to find life worth living. Again, basically we are computer programs running on hardware. The problem at root is an informational one.

Arguably, though many things must change with the coming of immortality, some form of selection process must still be important. In the first place, such a process should tend to produce individuals with a commitment to indefinite, personal survival, for reasons just considered. Such a commitment must profoundly affect the way things are valued and the very thoughts that are thought. This should lead to a new sort of proving ground for an evolutionary process, one that is foreshadowed in our own civilization today, with its lively exchange of ideas. Since individuals, we hope, will no longer die, their manufacture must be limited too, and they will not, collectively speaking, furnish any sort of evolutionary laboratory in the manner of a biological species today. Instead, each individual will be a fountainhead of ideas of interest or memes. The memes, in effect, will furnish the evolutionary laboratory of each individual who in turn will play somewhat the role of a "species"—that is, an enduring backdrop and originator. Each "laboratory" (individual) will confer with others and "compare notes" on different memes to further enhance the selection process. Memetic evolution, we may imagine, will continue at a most vigorous pace, with the "fittest" memes being preserved, replicated, and, in short, granted survival status.

The fitness of a meme will be a matter of how much the developing immortals consider it useful or interesting. Since that must depend on what individuals value, those memes that have a bearing on survival, such as various forms of scientific knowledge, will tend to be favored. Individuals will also seek enjoyment, so memes will tend to be a form of entertainment—art will be important too, and we can expect a rich interplay and hybridization of art and science. Individuals will also evolve developmentally, and this evolution in turn will be shaped by what each person considers advantageous. All, of course, will be as smart and accomplished as they wish to be. All can be physicists, philosophers, and artists on levels beyond what is possible today, however great the powers of some humans.

One possibility in fact will be brain speedups. Perhaps we will be able to think many times faster than today as well as more deeply and with better recall, with artificial devices replacing our gray matter. Such a possibility boggles the mind—and, I suspect, is harder for us to really fathom than for a baby to imagine being an adult. But I conjecture that even with such superhuman intellectual might, we need not lose our sense of identification with a past, merely human self nor come to devalue our past. Increased attainments need not signal such an abandonment of interest; even quite the opposite could occur. Unintelligent, nonhuman species are not interested in their prehistoric forebears, but we are interested in ours—and theirs too. As both our understanding and our capacity to understand develop, such interest could grow in step.

At this point I think it worth remarking that even in an immortal future we must continually struggle to survive. The sun will burn out eventually and before that will swell into a red giant and vaporize the earth—if we do not do something beforehand. More generally, disasters must happen, as we noted with the fluctuations and dissipations theorem in Chapter 14. We will have to be on guard and act over time to make ourselves progressively harder to kill or damage, while procuring such necessities as the energy needed to continue our functioning. (Hunger—the desire for a source of energy—thus must continue, though like many other things it will no doubt undergo great modifications, along with changes in "eating" habits. In particular, it should no longer be considered desirable to kill sentient life-forms and consume their physical housing to satisfy one's energy needs.) We will, I think, give priority to such strategies as backing up important information about ourselves and storing copies from which we could be reconstructed after a "wipeout." In any case, how to further our immortalization should be a topic of unending concern and, given reasonable adaptations, enjoyment. For matters such as this that are of ongoing concern ought to be pleasurable, rewarding, or interesting in some way (the selection principle demands it). We can probably adjust ourselves accordingly so they will be, in proportion to how much we in our wisdom decide they should be.

This sort of thing we carry out today, though imperfectly. I think with future advances we will be able to interact more effectively with our surroundings, to find our expanded horizons fascinating. This brings us to the subject of self-interest, the rational foundation for why we live life or do anything whatever, especially in a more enlightened form that takes the future into account. In a hopefully immortal future, enlightened self-interest should dictate a stance of benevolence toward other beings, as we have noted. But it will be useful now to explore this subject in more detail.

Joy and Benevolent Self-Perpetuation

A future immortal, we may imagine, will have three principal interests: contemplation, creativity, and community. I think the three can encompass essentially all that life has to offer, whether past, present, or future. (*Community*, for instance, refers to our relations with others, which today might emphasize family members, friends, employment, and so on, but in a more distant future could expand to a much larger sphere of interest.) But the subdivision seems especially appropriate in view of how an immortal existence might be expected to unfold.

Today I think most people are more focused on community than the other two—humankind is a social animal, and most individuals are not terribly creative or great at contemplation. In the future that should change. Again, we are basically computational processes, which should be amenable to a wide variety of improvements, not the least being in the areas of intelligence and creativity. Geniuses exist—thus it should be possible for all to become geniuses. Some geniuses are also joyful, so we should be able to become joyful geniuses. Clearly, we ought to become this way as a desired accompaniment of immortality.

Our future development will be a sort of feedback process. We will pursue the interests we have, while also keeping in mind the interests we ought to have and adapting accordingly. This adaptation, I conjecture, will focus much attention on the very survival process itself and what sort of world we ought to shape for ourselves. Our wish to have a meaningful, happy, immortal existence will logically dictate that we put our efforts in that direction. It is reasonable, then, that contemplating the problem of immortality and making progress on it in one form or another will become part of our self-interest and largely an end in itself. This would not be an unwarranted prioritization—unless it should finally become too easy. (I will assume for now that it will not—more on this later.)

By analogy, today the human species is largely focused on survival for a limited life span and biological reproduction. Eliminating the life-span limit will also effectively terminate the need for concern over reproduction, as we have noted, but we will still be concerned with keeping the species we will develop into going. Shifting our interests, even at a basic instinctual level, will probably make eminent sense. Again I think that while there are limits, a liberal amount of shifting is possible without becoming different to the point of "killing" our former selves. We can expect to change a lot of our interests and preoccupations carefully and perhaps rather gradually while still respecting and even identifying with our former selves, who by comparison will have had a less cheerful, more limited existence.

Enjoyment, in fact, should be a great unifying force at the level of the individual, that is, for "pulling oneself together." I have noticed that when I am happier I feel more in tune with past stages of myself that I can conjure up from memory, even when bad or not particularly interesting memories are involved (though certainly not only then). The joy tends to extend to acts of remembrance—I am happy to be thinking about what happened in the past. A pure, unrestrained joy thus can have a redemptive effect and make even the worst failings, agonies, or sheer boredom seem worthy of occasional recall. This will assist in the problem of infrequent remembering that we noted in the last chapter and will consider again shortly. A deep and meaningful happiness, then, can be a great inducement to a reasonable notion of survival and considerate self-perpetuation. Immortality, happiness, and knowledge, including remembrance of things past, are inseparably linked.

Joy will also further relations with others, especially when we keep in mind the benefits to ourselves that should follow. An important part of the world of the future, one may hope, will consist of a marketplace of ideas. The memes we generate and like we will naturally want to share with others for the self-interested reason that these others will be more disposed to share theirs in return. In this way, then, we can expect to acquire much more of interest to us, in a given time, than would be possible working in isolation. So we will benefit from interactions with others, whatever rewards future technology may offer, including complete self-sufficiency at the more basic levels. Thus, if each person had an empire of (willing) nanite slaves, and every material need was satisfied, there would still be an essential need for information, one that could best be met only by interactions with fellow beings. In fact, this sort of information exchange has been going on since time immemorial already, but we can see it intensifying before our eyes, through such means as the Internet; we can certainly expect this trend to continue.

So to best further our own selfish interests we must also focus on others. Their interests too become important to us because we know our own wants, whatever they may be, will tend to be satisfied more if we can interact with others and, particularly, if these others are also looking out for our interests. All this would follow if our only motive was to get something from others, but surely our joy and reward will be greater if we also want to give something in return. So, to maximize our rewards, individually, the well-being of others must become important to us. We will then have a second source of benefit—the perception that others have benefited, though of course this extra privilege will carry a responsibility in that we must now become concerned for these others in a way that was not necessary before. But such concern does not seem unreasonable. Indeed, this love of others—for empathic concern is the basis of love—will add meaning that life lived in indifference or hostility could never offer. More generally, a valuing of all by all seems likely to reap the greatest benefits overall and to each person individually, once again taking into account that we will hopefully be approaching this issue as more-than-human immortals.

There is no reason the love of others should end with beings on our level. I think that the further we can reasonably extend our caring for sentient life, the more we will benefit, particularly, once again, if a hopefully immortal future is taken into account. We can extend our love to embrace all creatures with awareness, and we should, if reasonable considerations are kept in mind.

The valuing of all by all could fully reconcile altruism and egoism. Fedorov foresaw and advocated such an outcome, which he called "all-unity."[8] I think this is what we must strive for, a condition in which oneself and others are highly and basically equally valued. In this way others are awarded the Kantian ideal of being ends in themselves without relinquishing our rational self-interest. No doubt this will not be easy given our present limitations, but we should find ample means as the future unfolds and also, I think, more advantage in adhering to and widening such a policy as we progress. Problems such as the threat of starvation should disappear when we have attained sufficient wisdom and mastery of technology, though new life-threatening problems can be expected to arise when the indefinite extension of life span is taken seriously. But these too I am confident we can handle in an equitable way; indeed, the conviction that each person ought to survive indefinitely could itself serve as a unifying force.

An Illustration

Let us now take a flying leap. In our mind's eye, we will journey to the moderately distant future—perhaps a few hundred years from now. Biological aging and diseases have long since been conquered; indeed, we have carefully modified our housing and the processes that support our thoughts. We are not Homo sapiens anymore but something better, smarter, more knowing, with near-perfect memories, provision for backups, and so on. Perhaps we spend a lot of time as programs in a large computer but also have the freedom to upload into individual computerized bodies when called for. (Though there were many misgivings and problems at first, by now our artificial constructs are so perfected that no one seriously doubts they are rather better for us than the original stuff we were made of.) We are well oriented toward our immortal existence, which means we care about both ourselves and all others in our civilization and want to further what is best for us all, without end.

Among other things, we recognize the value of our fellow beings, all of whom are "like ourselves" in some ways but fascinatingly different too. Most of us by now are superhumanly old and wise and have had lots of time to develop along our individual pathways, something no one else is likely to have trodden for very long for there are too many branching possibilities. We are quite well versed in our respective fields. Indeed, each of us is a world expert at something, a superstar unmatched by anyone else—though we do not spend time gloating over it. We have lots of exciting information to give others, in return, of course, for a reasonable exchange, which the others are also able and willing to give.

Yet despite our venerable antiquity, in another way we are ever fresh and youthful too, for again we have learned to manage quite well the technical problems of advancing years, the accumulation and backup of valued information, maintaining our sense of wonder. We know what we have to do to keep ourselves going indefinitely and we do it, along with ever expanding our capabilities and knowledge. We are eternal, developing children. (Naturally we hope the expanding or otherwise developing universe can at least minimally accommodate our growing needs.) Sometimes we get a chance to put our skills to use. There are information-threatening disasters now and then that require coping, and psychological problems come up, some of them quite puzzling, but in all such matters we proceed as best we can with good will and perseverance.

In addition to our peers we are interested in sentient beings more generally, including younger ones who are not so accomplished or venerable. Such "schoolkids" (some of them less than a century old) can be entertaining just as they are but will develop in time in their own interesting and unique, advanced ways and be "part of the gang" like the rest of us. Just recently, in fact, an ancient spacecraft was located in the cold interstellar depths that contained that greatest of treasures—a load of well-preserved cryonics patients! Now they are resuscitated, all but a few who were too badly damaged. Though babies by our standards, they each have most interesting experiences to relate of the long-ago times that spawned them, plus they are developing into "adults" who can be expected, as usual, to be still more interesting. They in turn are much surprised by many things in our world but being cryonicists are glad they made it to this the future and are eager to go on from here.

As for those who were too badly damaged to resuscitate in the usual way, whose remains are missing crucial identity information, we are not giving up on them, of course. We are going to reanimate each and every one of them too, in appropriate settings. The information they are missing will be reinvented. We have long since recovered most of the relevant historical information from the earth and surroundings. (The spacecraft itself, in fact, was probably the last major information-bearing relic we had not discovered, though we want to be sure.) We know how to create and place information that will be needed to fill out a complete person in each case and to make the knowledge base consistent with the historical record.

Some time ago, of course, there was much skepticism about such an approach, but by now the multiverse is such a well-established part of our scientific worldview that few give the matter much thought. Our resuscitees, as usual, will be authentic people who really lived, even if lacking some historical ties that better preservation would have maintained. Our love of sentient beings in general, based on rational, enlightened self-interest, demands that we do our part to recover these people and nurture them with wisdom and kindness so they can take their rightful places among us.

Living, Loving, and Developing As Immortal Egos

Let us end the flight of fancy here and return to the present, though with an eye toward a still more distant future. The love of sentient beings, I maintain, will have continuing importance however far we manage to go, once again for reasons of rational self-interest. It is good to have such love, which also means we wish, as far as possible, to do good to the beings themselves. If a person we thought highly of were in a predicament, we would want to help. Such a predicament is being dead. Here our help would, I maintain, rightly consist of resurrecting the person in question and assisting that being's immortalization.

In short, we should want to see that all sentient life-forms are resurrected and should want to contribute in meaningful ways to their everlasting happiness. A starting point in this is ourselves, and particularly, the past person-stages we will have gone through in reaching any point in our lives. In the last chapter we brought up the problem that to maintain touch with these past selves and thus realize any reasonable notion of individual immortality would require the recall of an ever-growing family of memories.

Suppose we assume that memorable experiences are given equal weight and continue indefinitely and burgeon our memory archives without limit—as we might demand for a reasonable notion of immortality. Then it seems we must, at least in most cases, devote an ever-shrinking fraction of our time to any given past experience. This could well include our entire first fifty years of life. The mathematical difficulty seems unavoidable in one form or other, and it may have something to do with the problems we actually see in the way people view their past.

Last chapter we noted the misgivings Hick had on this issue. There must be a limit, he said, to how much we can identify with earlier states in which we were very different. Hick considers the diary he composed as a fifteen-year-old (emphasis original): "...I know that it is *my* diary, and with its aid I remember some of the events recorded in it; but nevertheless I look back upon that fifteen-year-old as someone whose career I follow with interest and sympathy but whom I do not *feel* to be myself."[9] This sort of dissociation is, I think, very common and perhaps a majority viewpoint among people today, though not universal. (I for one feel able to identify with my earlier stages, even going back to early childhood despite the many changes.) It is noteworthy that Hick says he does not *feel* he can identify with his earlier self. It is not likely that any arguments I offer here would soon change such a viewpoint. But I will say that we both ought to be able to make an identification with our past selves and in the future, I think, will be able to do so, if our general advancement continues.

I see no insurmountable obstacle to such identification, even though there is the issue we just noted, that, generally, only a decreasing fraction of our time can be devoted to recalling any given experience. If we must continually change so that, in time, our earlier experiences were of someone very different this might indeed prove a fatal impediment, but I do not think it must or will be so. Beings of good will who are seeking what is right and best and to develop in wonderful and rewarding ways over unlimited time, always with love, respect, and consideration for others, can be hopeful of not becoming "very different" in this sense—such is my view. If we are good enough, then our everlasting survival, as separate though interacting and considerate selves, becomes morally mandatory. It is this high calling we must aspire to; it may well be necessary to our survival. And, I submit, being virtuous and considerate will also make us more accepting of our earlier selves, even if they were less enlightened and rather "different."

In the future there should be wonders aplenty for the searcher and many paths to pursue in a vast architecture of possibilities. So each of us should be able develop in interesting and unique ways, all the while maintaining a commitment to virtuous principles that goes far in helping us identify with who we were in the past. Such identification should be no burden but itself a joy: considering where you have been and how far you have come can both comfort and inspire. More generally, once again, joy will help us maintain a reasonable sense of our identity as time goes by. If this course of development can be pursued, the rich diversity of individuals will, I submit, produce greater benefits overall than if all were subsumed in a vast collective enterprise, with individuality devalued or obliterated. As a possible precedent, we may consider how collective enterprises in our own history, and particularly totalitarian governments with centrally planned economies, have been unable to compete with more decentralized, democratic systems. The separate, developing, considerate, immortal ego, then, should have more to offer all around than some form of "nonself" or a fused consciousness.

In our advancement, of course, we should make use of whatever discoveries and technologies may be applicable. Inevitably this will involve risk but "nothing ventured, nothing gained." In fact I think our deepening understanding will make adaptations

possible that would otherwise be out of the question. The elimination of aging and biological death should be accompanied by
increased understanding of the psychological difficulties connected with immortalization, with a proliferation of possible remedies. People should have numerous means to deal with various
"illnesses" they may have inherited from the mortal past.

As long as we are considering the problem of self-unity and
the hopefully immortal ego, it is worthwhile to briefly mention a
more technical argument that the earlier self need not be overwhelmed and reduced to insignificance. We hope to accumulate
infinitely many memorable experiences over infinite time. By
our information paradigm, these experiences themselves will
appear as chunks of information in our knowledge base—each
then is expressible as a finite string of bits. The number of possible memorable experiences of given length or less, while generally very large, is only finite. It is easier to review shorter chunks
of information than longer. Thus, as a long-term trend, the earlier
memories will be more readily scannable than the later ones, one
more counterargument to the possibility of earlier memories being overwhelmed.

As still another argument for the immortal ego, there is the
idea offered in the last chapter of converging to an ideal self. We
noted that it is not necessary either to preserve or identify with
every chunk of information that might briefly appear along the
way. Large parts can be discarded and left behind, this being true
even if they are not really lost but remain in the historical record.
Hick could decide, after all, that the fifteen-year-old diarist was
not him or was not entirely him and still go on to his own immortalization. He would not be a continuer of the fifteen-year-old
but would be a continuer of various other Hick-stages, or q-stages,
infinitely many of them. On the other hand, it is not ruled out that
some other construct would both be a continuer of the fifteen-
year-old and *would* care to pursue immortalization on that basis.
More generally, a way seems open to the immortalization of every being, including every person-stage whatever.

In summary, we have considered four main arguments for the
feasibility of an immortal ego, in which one identifies with past
versions of oneself as preserved in personal archives or memory.
They are: (1) the future, with all the anticipated advances, will
lead to states of joy, which will include joy in remembering, thus

greater unity with past versions of the self; (2) the practice of virtue, for reasons of enlightened self-interest, will reduce the sense of alienation with past versions of the self, particularly if these past versions also understood and engaged in such practice; (3) a technical argument, based on the finiteness and relative ease of reviewing of earlier memories; and (4) easier requirements allowed by the notion of convergence to an ideal self.

Resurrection As a Community Endeavor

The developing, eternal self will be motivated by self-interest in one form or another, but in fact there should be much reason for dealing with the world beyond oneself. Benefiting other sentient beings should be quite important and fully justifiable on grounds of rational self-interest. It should extend to such acts as whatever resuscitations of cryonics patients may prove feasible in the future. Even if the resuscitators have advanced by then beyond the human level, they will arguably benefit from interactions with the humans they befriend, who in time will also advance beyond the human level. More generally, an advanced being can expect to benefit by acts of kindness shown to less developed, less fortunate beings. One possibility along these lines would involve the creation, in replica form, of persons who died. Handled rightly, such a resurrection would be a most fascinating project that would reap rewards all around.

Such a project would be vast, to put it mildly, and probably done in many stages. The starting point would be the easy cases in which the person was perfectly preserved, information-wise, and only needed awakening in one technological form or another. We in cryonics hope to be in that category—if we are not lucky enough to survive directly to the elimination of aging. Next, perhaps, would come the "near-misses," such as cryonics patients who were not as well preserved. Then others might reasonably be considered, such as the long dead who have some of their information captured in DNA, written records, and the like. Later still, the project might encompass those who left no recorded traces at all and, more generally, all possible sentient beings whatever.

Something should be said here about the physical form that resurrections may take. Most cryonicists today, in my experience, imagine being reanimated much as they were before death only healthier, that is, in biological bodies. Such an approach may be applied for the easier, earlier cases of reanimation—or even then it may be decided that a purely computational bringing to life is better. In other words, people may be returned to consciousness as computer emulations, programs running on advanced data processing systems of the future. In fact I think this will turn out to be the preferred course, based on the power and tractability I expect such systems to have. At any rate, some sort of information-processing medium, or model of computation, will be needed to support the activities that make up a functioning being. Future science will have to decide what is best. Let us consider some consequences we can reasonably hope for.

In view of the information paradigm, the possible sentient beings, as being-stages, all have a finite description. They thus form a denumerable set in one-to-one correspondence with the positive integers 1, 2, 3,.... This includes all person-stages or, speaking generally, each sentient being at each point in its life. Over infinite time, our universal "labor of love" could reasonably include the recreation, in continuer form, of all these being-stages and their subsequent nurture to immortal self-sufficiency. Description-wise, we could enumerate every one of these entities and then, through advanced technology, recreate them in functioning form as suitable continuers. In this way, then, we can rescue countless beings from oblivion and be enriched by the contributions they can be expected to make in our lives.

The discussion on the creation of beings has largely focused on reviving people from well-preserved remains or making pre-existing beings in replica form. Another possibility that must not be overlooked is entirely new sentient beings, something that is familiar to us today through the reproductive process. In the future new creations will continue to have significance, if not in the same manner and to the same extent as now. But we can expect, in our great endeavor to immortalize all beings, that life will be enriched by an interspersion of those who do not have a pre-immortal past to remember.

Many fascinating problems must arise in such an undertaking, and our work on these should provide life-enhancing meaning. A few of the difficulties can be anticipated even now and make an interesting proving ground of ideas.

One difficulty concerns the very idea of "rescue" and, more generally, of "helping" someone by benefiting a replica, as is implicit in our idea of resurrection. An objector might say that if someone is sick, we cannot benefit that person by making and curing a replica. Indeed, curing a replica now does not benefit a person-stage that may also exist now who continues to be sick. On the other hand, curing a sick person, however done, amounts to a form of replacement. We are replacing a certain person-stage that is ill with a later stage, a continuer, that is healthy. In effect, then, we have benefited that earlier, sick stage. If, meanwhile, another continuer of the earlier stage is made or retained, who is still sick, of course we do not benefit that ill individual, but we can say, nonetheless, that someone was benefited.

The notion of pattern-survival, we recall, allows multiple continuers of one original, which pursue separate paths and have different histories, though sharing a past up to some point. Some continuers may benefit more or sooner than others. But all should benefit eventually, a topic we considered in Chapter 11. Once again, the enlightened self-interest of advanced sentient beings should see to it that good is done to other less-fortunate beings, starting with resurrections.

Let us now consider another very different problem relating to the characteristics of the beings we propose to resurrect. Some will be good, some bad, and some just stupid, at least in their original form. Some also will have died in great agony or in other circumstances it would be cruel to replicate. In our resurrections we do not want to recreate all the evils that may have attended those we are trying to help. And we do not have to—because in creating continuers we do not have to reproduce exact replicas, just person-stages that remember appropriately. In this way the sick could be healed, for example, before seeing the light of day.

In the same way, an evil person might be enlightened and made repentant and benevolent at the outset, though there could be complications. In the case of a physical ailment, the basic approach would be simple: eliminate the ailment first, then awaken the continuer. But with wrong-headedness, which is basically misprogramming, eliminating the defect could kill the patient. Instead we must consider retaining the misprogramming but with additional overrides and modifiers. In this way we should be able to create a suitable continuer of our misguided original, who still identifies with the earlier stage in the sense of "I was there but am now here" but now is morally incapable of the sort of behavior that once was so dominant.

This could possibly be quite an ordeal for the subject in question. We find today that the behavior of complicated software, particularly that designed to behave "intelligently," cannot be predicted in advance, but we must run the program to see what it will do. So in effect the subject we wish to reform might have to be a conscious participant in numerous experiments both lengthy and unpleasant. Or perhaps our offender must simply endure incarceration, his every thought monitored, until the appropriate, self-willed changes could be verified, showing that a voluntary choice of the right path had been made. Such a purgatorial experience, however protracted, would hopefully produce a desirable outcome.

I am not claiming, however, that some form of "Purgatory" would necessarily be the best treatment to cure a resurrected offender. We would, I strongly feel, have to reject any crude motive of revenge and focus on what was really best from an enlightened perspective. Still it is interesting that certain options could be enforced by those in control of the resurrection process. As one example, there are suicidal terrorists who feel that by sacrificing themselves in the course of killing others they will awaken immediately in paradise. Sooner or later, a comprehensive resurrection project must consider such cases and would rightly withhold the expected rewards, at least until a considerable change of attitude (and worldview) occurred. But with a sufficient change in heart we would have good reason to act leniently and benevolently.

I think there would be something valuable to gain from a former great offender who experienced a true conversion. Such a person arguably would have rare insights on good, evil, and right conduct. With the motive, keenly felt, of atoning for past wrongdoing, much good could follow. In any case, I submit, there is good reason today to take a Universalist stand. Our orientation must be toward objects of enduring love—our fellow beings—and not of enduring hate. We do not wish to condone wrongdoing. Corrective measures, where called for, could even be quite severe. But I think there are limits to what can be "deserved," particularly, as we have noted, in view of determinism. People behave as they do for comprehensible reasons, amounting to the way they are programmed—or misprogrammed—and we must shape our attitudes accordingly.

Fedorov held that all evil is caused by blindness. This, along with the computational argument we have just considered, is another reason to advocate the salvation rather than damnation of even the worst sorts of misguided individuals that history could have produced. And, as Fedorov also maintained, when our bodies become the products not of blind nature but our own labor, we will be able to eliminate our vices.[10] So the immortalization and benefiting of all beings whatever should be an ultimately feasible project and one that ought to be pursued.

Along with the bad, there are other types of beings that would offer their own special problems, though maybe not so challenging to present sensibilities. Retarded persons, for example, might be made smarter at the outset or allowed to develop more gradually but in any case would no longer be bound by their handicap. People who simply did not care much about living could be given new vitality. Pets and other nonhuman life-forms would offer another challenge.

Certainly dogs and cats have personalities. Would we recreate them in original form, or try to make more advanced continuers? In fact several cryonicists have had their pets frozen, intending that they be brought back to life as they were (with the owners)—only healthier, of course. But this is unlikely to be their ultimate fate—to stay at the same level would amount to an Eternal Return. Eventually, then, every dog and cat must advance into something more than what it was, more than a dog, cat, or human, to join the community of immortals at the highest level.

Moreover, I see no fundamental obstacles to advanced continuers built from even the most primitive, nonhuman starting points. I thus reject the argument of Tipler that only humans ought to be resurrected (along with their pets, but no others) inasmuch as humans alone are "self-programming universal Turing machines," and thus, he contends, formed in the "image of God."[11] Intelligent constructs equipped with appropriate memories, I conjecture, would find it natural to identify with much simpler "starting" beings, including nonhumans. The possibility of thus or otherwise elevating even simple sentient life to immortal, transcendent status is, to me, an exciting one.

Various less-than-human creatures then would be recreated in continuer form and allowed or assisted to advance in appropriate settings. In some cases the continuers might be similar to the originals, in other cases, more advanced at the start. Again, every sentient creature that ever existed could ultimately be rescued and immortalized. We could undo all the shortcomings of prehistory as well as our own history and thereby take part in a supreme act of redemption and healing. Across the universes of the multiverse, of course, others like ourselves would also be doing the same sorts of things, even as new life spawned from primitive conditions in still other universes, issuing its own cries for help and struggling with its problems. Overall then, we can glimpse an ordering principle that will glorify all in the end. But to the individual, the steps along the way are important too. Exactly what we do could greatly affect our happiness for a long time, even if we are all assured, ultimately, of a secure footing in paradise.

Mishaps along the way are a possibility, of course. A resurrectee may decide that the future with all its glamour was not worth it after all and opt for suicide. This would not preclude that person's eventual rescue and healing. Our commitment to benefiting all sentient life should extend to such cases. We would need to ask what could be done to make things go better when the person was resurrected again. In what would hopefully be the rarest of cases we might have to make several tries to obtain a continuer who would be happy to remain in the world and join the general advance.

Another possibility along these lines—though also slight, I think—is a being who exists in a long-lasting state of self-imposed misery due to a self-blindness when a happier course is possible. We could imagine someone in a self-reinforcing state of pain afraid to try to alleviate the problem or make any inquiries lest it somehow lead to a worse state of affairs. While there are no doubt people like this today who could be helped but refuse any treatment, such a morbid condition should be unlikely in our more advanced future. But I mention it because an analogous scenario has been proposed in theological arguments to justify the possibility of Hell.[12] God, so the argument goes, is so great a respecter of free will that he would never interfere with a person's choice in the matter, even if it led to unnecessary, everlasting suffering. The divine decision not to interfere would not be made lightly, but if the person were sufficiently set in his determination toward a wrong alternative, eternal damnation might follow.

But our perspective is different, as we saw last chapter. There is no ultimate free will and no moral requirement for us to withhold healing enlightenment, even in a case where someone was very determined in an unfortunate choice. Moreover, and even more important, in view of the infinite future, the finite life lived to that point could never be adequate to inform such a misguided choice, no matter how convinced the chooser might be. So we ourselves should simply choose the lesser evil, which could involve some friendly forcing or overriding the misguided will. In this way the self-imposed misery could be defeated, after which the victim, and, importantly, others too, would be better off.

At this point it will be useful to consider some further details of how a resurrection project might be carried out. There could be easier cases at the beginning, such as cryonics patients, as we have noted. But for the most part we would be dealing with individuals—humans and other life-forms—whose remains were poorly preserved or nonexistent, and I will refer to this more difficult part of the operation as the resurrection *project*. In fact these resurrections will be in some degree hyperontic, highly so in the more difficult cases.

By today's standards the technical requirements would certainly be forbidding and quite out of reach. I think, however, that we could start such a project relatively soon, within a few centuries at any rate, though whether we would go this route or wait much longer is another matter. But in any case, before launching it we should have a mature nanotechnology whose capabilities approach the limits allowed by physics so that stable structures could be made and disassembled at will, with atomic precision. We should also have advanced computational devices capable of emulating large colonies of sentient creatures, who may be advanced to the present human level, or even well beyond. We should also have extracted all obtainable information about our history and prehistory from the earth and its surroundings. Much useful information might be deduced, for instance, by studying DNA in existing organisms and organic remains, with other useful clues coming from older fossils and archaeological sites.

Assuming this is all in place, what beings should we make

first? One reasonable approach, I think, would be to build on the scenario we considered above. After those are restored who can be reanimated directly from biostasis, we start on the project proper. It is not necessary to have such recoverable people to begin with, of course. But the next line of patients, whose remains are partly preserved but not well enough for straightforward reanimation, will be with us in some form. If not as cryonics patients, they will be found in other settings. A body in a grave, for instance, should retain recoverable DNA. Records of this person will normally exist too, at least for more recent cases, and those, along with the physical remains, could be expected to furnish useful information.

Such remnants would allow us to compile a partial description of the person in question. This could then be filled out by educated guesswork to a complete specification of a person who fit the surviving historical record. Repeating this process we would obtain completed descriptions of many people, all of whom fit our surviving history. In addition to making their information fit our history, we would want to make all the information mutually consistent, for reasons we will consider momentarily. Working our way back over time, we could incorporate prehistoric earthly beings and include nonhuman creatures along the way. This, then, would be a hyperontic resurrection project. Ultimately we would obtain a created history far more detailed than what we will have been able to infer from earthly and astronomical artifacts yet always consistent with that recovered history and also self-consistent.

We would then have, in latent form, a large colony of beings, every sentient entity that ever lived, in at least one of our possible pasts. These beings we would first have obtained as descriptions. Each description would specify the being in question at some age or stage of development in life, generally near or at the end, but with health restored. (In a more distant future, we would want to consider other stages in life too, a topic we will examine.) From there we could proceed over time to reanimate them as continuers and otherwise further their immortalization. To carry this out might involve a cosmologically significant amount of time even if we could start "early," that is, in a few centuries. No doubt the computational requirements would be staggering by today's standards. But our future capabilities, and ultimately the expanding universe, would assist as needed so that the project would place no onerous burden on the society that existed at the time. In any case, if the universe can support immortality as we hope, it should be possible; the requirement of resources, however large, must be finite.

I have emphasized that the resurrection would be hyperontic (not xenontic), and this I think would be a good policy for our first effort of this sort. It is also worth remarking that making the recreated information of past individuals mutually consistent should, overall, produce a good effect for those very beings in this important phase of their immortalization. In this way the resurrection would not simply be of individuals in isolation but, again, of an entire history and prehistory back to the dawn of sentient life-forms. How we would treat the more primitive creatures, what form their continuers should take, and so on, would be matters to be decided. But many humans, we might imagine, could be emulated in virtual reality settings that gave them back, as a starting point, approximately their original form and familiar surroundings.

Resurrectees would then have the joy of realizing not merely that they were alive again somehow but that friends and family were also alive and part of the project. This would extend in due course to those they remembered who died before they did, such as parents or grandparents. These in turn would find others they valued alive again, or scheduled to be, and so on. (Here I am imagining the resurrection would be "last in first out," that is, most recently deceased first, though there is no logical necessity for this and possibly some other order would be preferred.) Life in virtual reality might at first differ but little from the earlier life they remembered, except that major sources of pain or degradation would be absent. But other changes would start as they progressed in immortalization, so that in time they would graduate from the "nursery" to more advanced settings, and ultimately take their place at the "adult" level in the community of immortals.

This, then, could be a reasonable course to follow for a first resurrection project, which would recreate persons from one of our many authentic pasts. It would not, of course, be the last such project for surely others must ultimately fall within the reasonable compass of our enlightened self-interest and love of fellow beings. Many, maybe the vast majority of these later resurrections too would be of the hyperontic, mutually consistent variety, that is, recreations of persons based on whole natural histories that fit our records. But not all would fit this category, as I envision it—more on this later.

But we must also not lose sight of happenings at the "top level," which is not simply virtual reality but involves the external world. For the latter, at least, we must acknowledge that the historical record is important. We have considered reasons why, mainly in Chapter 13. Some of the reasons involved one's remembered experiences and their role in personal survival. Something is worth adding now.

If we are to survive and create the immortal community, we must be concerned about preserving our individual histories, as we have noted, along with more general historical information. Thus I expect an unending interest in historical records: despite the multiverse, we will continue to distinguish between actual and possible history and to value the actual more than the merely possible. People, of course, capture a part of the historical record in their identity-critical information, which is another reason for preserving them after death, aside from the issue of their own reanimation.

Those who are resurrected, then, while they must be in full possession of their identity-critical information by definition, will nevertheless have an *ontic deficit*—unless they can be recovered entirely from surviving historical information such as that contained in preserved remains. The deficit, I conjecture, will have the expected effect of marring their Interface—life will not seem as meaningful or "real" to such a person. Indeed, from that person's point of view, there arguably must be a reciprocal effect—some of the outside world, extending down to the Interface, must be "unreal." For it too, we could say, is a consequence of the very guesswork, the extra information that had to be created for their own resurrection.

Over time we could expect the ontic deficit to diminish in importance, as someone from the point of resurrection onward takes part in life as a historical process and cultural drama, accumulating, storing, and retrieving information the same as everyone else. That person's survival, then, if unlimited, would be almost enontic, as defined in Chapter 14, and with time should approach the condition of being just as good as if fully enontic. But the starting point from guesswork must rank as a deficit. Perhaps this will seem a too-subtle point to many. An ontic deficit is not something we normally worry about. But I think it will be seen differently in the future: when long-term survival is the rule, needs and attitudes will develop accordingly—for they too will be necessary to this very survival.

The ontic deficit will reasonably be less in proportion to the extent to which the resurrection *was* based on actual historical information. On this ground we can argue that one's future prospects depend on how one's remains are treated after death. The best preservation is preferred, of course, but lesser preservation is better than none. Cryonic suspension, then, is better than conventional burial, which in turn is better than cremation. Cryonic suspension is to be preferred over burial, even if the preservation is not perfect, so long as we can be assured that significantly less guessing will be necessary in an eventual reanimation. If this is the case, we can also discern another advantage.

A person, we noted, will capture part of the historical record in his/her identity-critical information. Some of this information is undoubtedly unique: the experiences of an eyewitness are not likely to be duplicated exactly in another person, nor can they now be exactly described or otherwise recorded for posterity, given the limitations of language, et cetera. In particular, a person may remember certain details about others now deceased who were not preserved, such as how they talked and behaved, which will be lost to history if that person is not preserved at death. The biostasis option thus could lead to a better (more enontic) resurrection of others as well as a better preservation of more general historical information, all in addition to benefiting the original subject.

At present we cannot be sure how much important information is preserved in the freezing process, though there is reason to think it is far more than in burial or cremation. This we will explore in the next chapter, where cryonics will play a role in the proposed Philosophy of Action.

Some loose ends should now be tied. The "more later" issues noted in this chapter and earlier need to be addressed and a few other points made to round out the discussion.

Fusion and Fissioning of Individuals

In the future, immortal world, we hope to interact amicably with a large "family" of other beings. I imagine an ever-present interplay and tension between unity and diversity—both the similarities and the differences among different beings will contribute, overall, to a most interesting and exciting world scene. Given time, our world must surely extend far beyond the confines of Earth; however, it will also extend in another way perhaps more significant, with the superior devices we use to sustain our cognitive processes.

But, in particular, I would imagine that each of us will gradually come to understand more and more about each other, even as we pursue our own individual courses of advancement. This could create its own perplexing issues. People could acquire enough information and could so modify their dispositions as to become continuers of more than one individual, as we have noted. Another possibility, as part of a resurrection project, is that continuers could be created from scratch who combined several individuals. These in turn may have existed at one time or even at historically different periods or in other very different settings. Presumably if such a project were carried out, or if already extant individuals decided to "join forces" on their own, the resulting being would feel integrated, whole, and happy to be alive— or otherwise might exercise the option of splitting once again.

That some fusion of individuals might occur is, in fact, suggested by comparison with ourselves today. The brain is a complex entity, and its different components function, to a degree, as separate agents that nevertheless are bound together in one "organization." (This idea is explored in Marvin Minsky's book, *Society of Mind.*) On the other hand, we have noted that people usually come in pairs. The bonding between male and female is well ingrained as part of today's reproductive process. I would certainly not rule out the possibility of couples in a transhuman future deciding to form a closer, more intimate association than is possible now—in short to fuse into one, with shared memories and experiences. Nonetheless people could be very close, closer than is possible now, with much information in common but in a reasonable sense remain separate selves. I am not sure how far the tendency toward coalescence would go. For myself, I do not find the idea appealing—I see more value in the diversity and separateness of individuals who are well disposed and, in fact, do form a harmonious whole but one that recognizes personal boundaries. (Indeed, I can see a trend toward less focused bonding between two individuals and a more general valuing of others, as I think will further our interests better when death is eliminated.) A collective entity, it would seem, would also be less efficient in pursuing the several lines of interest we would normally associate with separate individuals.

So overall I would not expect any widespread trend toward the fusion of sentient beings or, more generally, toward the appearance of collective beings, though it must happen, at least to a minor extent, in view of Unboundedness. But we can conjecture that future would-be resurrectors, recognizing the difficulties, would not often create such composites. Instead a resurrectee would likely start life again as a separate individual. The opposite of fusion, fissioning, might not be uncommon, however. Indeed, it could be argued that much fissioning must take place so that continuers of all possible beings can occur over time and enrich all of life as much as possible.

The problem of fissioning, which is no deep problem at all with our notion of pattern-survival, seems to be a stumbling block to many in accepting the possibility of resurrection. Of course in everyday life we do not observe persons fissioning, though something rather like it occurs in the clinical case of "split-brain" patients (see below). Still it is natural to think that personal identity cannot be transferred simultaneously to separate, coexisting individuals.

This point of view is carried into our major religions, which, for example, postulate that a person has a soul, a typical opinion being that the soul of one person cannot be transferred to someone else or be divided into two or more souls that could be implanted in different people. (Locke's viewpoint of one soul in more than one person at different times was somewhat exceptional, though he did not seem to envision the splitting of one soul into two or more.[13]) But under pattern-survival we could get more than one incompatible continuer, thus more than one resurrectee of the same original.

The splitting identity is not a purely academic issue today. Cerebral commissurotomy, surgically separating the two hemispheres of the brain down to the brain stem, has been used with some success to treat crippling epilepsy. Patients afterward may appear normal, their former debilitating seizures absent or much reduced. Careful tests show, however, that one person has now become essentially two, different parts of the divided brain controlling different parts of the mind as well as the body and generally behaving independently though usually with reasonable coordination. Usually only the left hemisphere has the power of speech, but the right hemisphere is capable of complex understanding of verbal and nonverbal material and sometimes surpasses its opposite.[14] More or less the left hemisphere seems to retain the personality of the former individual, including memories, and might be considered a continuer. Whether this would be true of the right hemisphere too would depend on how well earlier experiences were recalled and is presently difficult to test, owing to the absence of speech. In any case we can imagine various options opening to such cases in the future, the most obvious being to join the separated parts again into one individual, with epilepsy eliminated some other way. Other possibilities would not be ruled out however, including the two separate halves remaining separate, perhaps transplanted to different bodies with any deficiencies in either (for example, the absence of speech) corrected. This could be carried out along with creating replica brain parts that would be joined to reconstruct the original (again minus epilepsy).

More generally, any single individual could give rise to many in a resurrection and arguably must, over sufficient time. One possibility would be to resurrect a person at many stages in life. Such multiple recreations, suitably spaced over possibly long intervals of time, would, I think, enrich the overall experience of everyone and thus should be carried out. In any case, in a randomizing multiverse we can be sure that all stages of all people must be created in replica or continuer form, over and over, however rarely. By playing an active role, we could help ensure that most of these constructions would happen under controlled conditions and have happy consequences.

Thus we can see the basis for a resolution of what has been called the "age-regression" problem.[15] If we wanted to resurrect people, it seems we must consider at what age they should be brought back. Should a baby who died be resurrected as an adult?

or an old, senile person as a younger person? The ultimate answer, with our notion of universal resurrection, is "all of the above," though this would likely extend far beyond any first efforts in which only one of our possible pasts was considered and one continuer per individual was created. But with our notion of pattern-survival, the principal focus is really on person-stages rather than the total individual (or long segments). We are mainly concerned, in the first instance, with whether a given construct would reasonably amount to a continuer of some other construct (or more precisely, would instantiate a continuer of a person-stage that is instantiated in turn by the other construct). The two constructs would then represent different stages of one individual, the resurrectee being simply the more developed of the two.

The resurrection of an individual as a whole, in turn, is accomplished through the appropriate treatment of continuers, using the notion of convergence to an ideal self. As one possible scenario, then, we could imagine two advanced beings, both very intelligent and accomplished. One, however, happens to be a continuer of a person who himself had suffered a brain trauma and did not remember much before a certain age, while the other is a continuer of that same person before the disaster struck. The one, then, would be a continuer of the later person-stage but not of the earlier stage. This should not seem surprising, since, by hypothesis, the later amnesiac stage would not itself be a continuer of the earlier stage.

In the infinite, hopefully immortal future, I see no limits on the sort of resurrections of the above type we will carry out, always in the name of rational, individual self-interest and with due consideration to all beings affected. Continuers of every sentient being at every stage of life produced over possibly great stretches of time should create a most interesting mix of interacting persons. This brings up another interesting problem, however.

The amnesiac, above, may want very much to have back his missing memories. We could make of him or assist in his becoming a continuer that possessed those memories or a set of memories that seemed right and that would thus be authentic for some being in the multiverse. But there is another possibility. A continuer, perhaps much more advanced, might be created that would not have those missing memories after all and would not care to possess this information, at least not in memory form. (There would be enough information still, we assume, to qualify the construct as a continuer of the memory-deficient original.) So in all, there seem to be many possibilities indeed.

We could argue that a person survives as long as some continuer of that person comes into being. Here I mean "continuer" strictly interpreted; the new construct must possess the full identity information, including memories, of the earlier person-stage. But if the earlier stage was not happy with itself, we might have to go to extra lengths to create a continuer that was satisfied with this earlier, less-than-happy creature. Yet I think we probably could, and this should open many possibilities for resurrections, in some form, even for miserable people who were sure they would never want to come back in any form. I will boldly conjecture that a happy continuer of any being-stage whatever is always possible. In addition to "happy" I will even add "also suited to life in an immortal society," to rule out the individual who is jolly but dangerous. I have no proof, yet I think it unlikely this would not be so—the space of possibilities seems too large to rule it out or close off any possible being as someone we should never attempt to resurrect in any form. So we could focus on those continuers who, we would have reason to think, would be grateful they were restored to life, and in this way perhaps resurrect, in some worthy form, all beings whatever.

There is one issue connected with the fissioning of individuals that deserves at least brief consideration here. In our world, true total fissioning has not been observed (unless we count the rudimentary case of single-egg twins resulting from fission shortly after conception), and this has profound consequences. Persons possess property, contract marriages, are held responsible for wrongdoing, et cetera, all of which would be called into question if individuals could be duplicated. (Yet the ability to carry out such duplication seems a likely possibility relatively soon, when we develop a mature nanotechnology and not just in a more distant future.) If someone owned a house, a close enough copy would also feel fully the owner of the same house. We can also ask whether a duplicated criminal would be guilty of the same crime.

These are tractable problems for our notion of pattern-survival and the possibility of resurrection. Yes, a duplicate criminal would be guilty too, but by the time that becomes an issue, we should have very different methods of dealing with crime. On the other hand, we must not become too attached to possessions we "own," and I do not think we will need to be. If a person could be duplicated, then so could a house or even a spouse. But the world of the future will be different in many ways, and I think this sort of problem will not be among the hardest.

We considered the idea that a person P could possess so much knowledge of some other person Q that a continuer of Q could be constructed from P's memories, yet P himself is not a continuer of Q. Actually this issue, in an even more general form, is with us today. We may acquire a vivid impression of someone else's experience—a quasi-memory, or q-memory. The other party need not even be "real" but could be a character in a novel or movie (but real, as usual, somewhere in the multiverse). We may be able to identify with this character and visualize the experience as if it were our own, yet on some level we make a distinction between this and what "really" happened to us. The same applies to what is going on around us, which we may learn about from news reports or the many books written on such subjects.

It is important that we can make this distinction—otherwise we might, for example, have to assume responsibility for a crime we so much as acquire q-memories of having committed. In a similar way, in the future I suspect we will learn much more about different individuals and acquire even more vivid q-memories extending to whole q-stages and beyond to complete continuers of other persons. Yet we will find good reason (and means) to maintain our own individuality as a separate entity from the others we know so well. So again, as we progress as immortals, we expect certain unifying trends. Among them will be the increasing knowledge any one being might acquire of any other being. Over infinite time, any such being will, I conjecture, acquire total knowledge of any other as part of an open-ended development that encompasses, ultimately, all possible things one can know. Yet at the same time there will be continuing diversity and separate, developing selves to enrich the experience of all.

Extending the Resurrection

Turning now to another issue, we considered a resurrection scenario that emphasized consistency with the historical record. Such a resurrection of all the sentient beings in one of the many possible versions of our past, could never be enontic—far too much information must have been lost. We can hardly hope to reconstruct, for example, the detailed identity information of persons 1,000 generations ago (about 25,000 years). It must be reinvented. So, doing this once and extending the effort appropriately will give us one hyperontic resurrection. Having done this once, however long it may take to complete, would raise the issue of doing it again—and again. Once more I submit that to receive maximum benefit over infinite time we would indeed carry out resurrection projects over and over. We would be running through all possible histories consistent with ours and even all other histories as well, not to mention all possible, finite beings at all points in their lives. The relative emphasis might vary greatly from one possibility to another, however, so that some types of events and projects would happen much less frequently than others. But we would repeatedly construct the same beings, which, however, would then develop further and diverge from previous creations, so that each would establish a distinguishing uniqueness.

A xenontic resurrectee who remembered things contrary to our surviving history would no doubt pose special problems, but I think a happy continuer of such a being would be possible too and would enrich the totality of our experience, at some suitable point. Someday, then, we could expect to meet Sherlock Holmes, H. G. Wells's Martians, or whatever other fictional characters have been imagined or could be.

Another topic to consider is how far could we go and still have sentient beings we might reasonably consider as subjects for immortalization. We mentioned pets, for example. What about the fleas that bite them? What about even simpler creatures and constructs, worms, say, or certain computer programs? What about "beings" we encounter in dreams? What about parts of our brains that may function independently as conscious agents but of which we are not consciously aware? What about multiple personalities, that some apparently have? What about beings people sometimes think they are or have been, when objective evidence is lacking? What about governments and other organizations, which may be said to plan, decide, perceive, react, and remember, and thus exhibit a kind of sentience? What about patterns of sentience that might be expressed, however ephemerally and transiently, in the particle interactions occurring in such inanimate things as rocks, clouds, and stars? In general, the boundaries, quality, and moral imperatives of sentience pose many fascinating problems.

I do not have good answers to all these puzzles, but the idea of resurrection through creation of a continuer seems to open very many possibilities here too. Thus there would be no requirement to recreate the physical form or housing of any of these and other such entities, just the functional or computational elements in equivalent or enhanced form. Similarly, there would be no requirement for a continuer to "continue" in the same lifestyle as before, with the same functions and purposes, so long as requisite informational ties existed with the past "self"—however that might be appropriately defined. A predator or parasite, then, would not have to remain such but could become the friend of those it once victimized. More generally, each sentient being could advance to a higher purpose than originally designed for. I do not know what it would mean to be an intelligent continuer of a flea, but we have already noted that in a sense we are all continuers of the "empty being" that has no consciousness whatever. Such a being, we might say, cannot receive benefit, but anything higher up the scale might. So I see many opportunities for ultimately benefiting even what we would consider very limited life-forms and other entities of many sorts.

All these things will follow, I think, if the universe is able to support our immortality. Let us hope so. And if so, we can consider the possible rescue of beings, by the usual means of creating replicas and continuers, from other universes not so favorable as ours. Among other things, a universe able to support immortality must have unlimited elbow room. If it is finite, as ours seems to be, it must expand indefinitely, if not in spatial volume at least in information storage capacity. This should allow us to carry out resurrections without imposing unreasonable burdens on others already present, as we have noted. Over infinite time, infinitely many beings could be brought into reexistence with no population glut, assuming the process was well managed. On the other hand, if our own universe cannot support immortality, our best hopes must rest on benevolent immortals in other universes that can support it, as we noted in Chapter 14, or possibly on a succession of mortal but increasingly long-lived beings.

This raises one issue that should be dealt with, once more concerning onticity. If some universe allows immortality, though not our own, we can hope for an almost-enontic survival, if we are created as continuers in that universe. But if no universe whatever allows this possibility, then our best hope for immortalization would seem to be through a succession of increasingly advanced continuers in different universes. We would survive only xenontically—ultimately our historical records must be trashed, even contradicted, and this must happen over and over without ceasing. Yet even here I can see a possible advantage in an attachment to actual history. It would certainly make sense to be so attached, while a given universe was favorable to our survival, and we could prosper at least as long-lived beings. And perhaps, in the advances we could make, we would find the basis for some sort of orderly transition from one universe to the next, so the "trashing"—including our remediable deaths—might lose its sting and even be viewed constructively.

In any case, the transition to long-lived life-forms is surely awaiting us, barring some catastrophe. It will not be too long, historically, before the biology of aging is understood and we can live at least for hundreds, thousands, and probably millions of years or more, if we choose. We will be able to set our sights on the still grander goal of true immortality and see how far we can go in realizing it. Compared to such a prospect, there are many "minor" accomplishments that would be quite astonishing in their own right, though they could also raise interesting conundrums. To take one example, in Chapter 9 we considered the possibility of recreating extinct organisms through nanotechnology. Recently extinct species such as the passenger pigeon should at least be feasible to reinstate, starting with genomic information recovered from preserved remains. A species is not sentient even if its individual members are. What do we do about all the sentient organisms? Ultimately we are bent on immortalizing every single one of them, as we have noted. But, we could ask, what should be our policy more near-term?

Cautions and Restrictions

I do not advocate a massive campaign, here and now, to freeze every dying insect or other moving creature, despite the appeal I have made to regard all sentient life as precious. True, overall we want to gear up to the great labor of love, the universal immortal-ization. But this, if we can carry it through, will happen in an unknown future. There are things we can be doing now, such as making arrangements for our biostatic preservation, which we will consider next chapter. But it goes without saying that in na-ture at large, the birth-death cycle will continue for awhile—we do not have the resources to make a serious dent, constructively, if we wanted to. We should not be dismayed, in fact, at much of the massive loss of information that is going on around us, de-spite the emphasis I have put on the historical record. Eventually all creatures, and all else too, will come back in appropriate ways if all goes well, even if much is now lost. Meanwhile we must consider priorities.

In fact, we must consider killing individual organisms, on oc-casion, as the lesser evil: killing parasites to reduce the spread of disease, say, or a predator to save a threatened human. For the same reason, war was justifiable under such circumstances as resisting Nazi Germany and would no doubt still be justifiable sometimes—though it is becoming increasingly untenable and dangerous. I think too that use of animals in research, including sacrificing them, can be justified in suitable cases as the lesser evil. But what to do about sentient nonhuman creatures is some-thing we must face at some point in our advancing future. Should we use advanced technology to eliminate animal predation, for instance? We shall examine this and other environmental issues in Chapter 18.

Something more is worth saying here about the idea of sacri-ficing nonhuman creatures. The issue then is not one of losing some tedious or uninteresting memory information, as above, but the whole creature—however, this creature is less than human. So we are led to consider such issues as how a future continuer of that very creature might react to the loss of *its* historical ties. This would certainly depend on the creature or, more properly, the continuer, and I will conjecture, be in rough proportion to how sentient the original creature was. An insect-continuer brought to a high level of intelligence would feel less disadvantaged than an equally enhanced dog-continuer, say—supposing, of course, that we could carry out both sorts of enhancements appropriately. Perhaps both resulting persons would feel the issue too minor to think about—or perhaps not. But in any case we see that our concerns for nonhuman creatures should be proportioned, more or less, to the level of sentience involved. A mosquito is not a mouse, and a mouse is not a human. Nonhuman creatures in particular are not simply reincarnations of former humans, as some ancient traditions have held, though potentially they could develop, as I have conjectured, to levels equal to a human or beyond.

Proceeding to the human level, in the last chapter I described how I willingly discarded some of my inessential memory information and would not want to recover it as part of "me," even if I could. Someday, I will speculate, there will be a happy continuer who does remember and does value every bit of that lost detail, all the detritus on the barbershop floor and much more besides. Its reasons may be very advanced and strange by my standards yet perfectly logical and compelling by its own. But that, I think, will be in a very remote future. I do not think I—the person-stage writing this today—am likely to become such a being but, in most of my continuers, will develop into someone else. (This will hold, even though I would also hope eventually to understand such a being and thus to contain that being's extra information that I gave up, though not as part of *my* personal experience.) More generally, not all personal information is worth saving, though again, some certainly is.

But the emphasis I have placed on enontic survival is called into question by some who still hope for an afterlife. This subject we covered in Chapter 13, but some additional remarks are appropriate. The devil's advocate may focus on our friends of the future who, if truly benevolent, will see that we are resurrected in a happy setting—how could it be otherwise? It might even be argued that we have more to gain the more remotely in the future we *are* resurrected, for then our friends will be that much more advanced, thus better able to make our coming back wonderful in every way. Indeed, with this reasoning, it would be advantageous to make it as hard as possible to be resurrected. So perhaps the less well preserved we are, the better.

But such reasoning, I think, ignores one crucial issue, which is that our friends will not simply live up to every notion we can imagine about benevolence. Instead, I have argued, we can expect them to be driven by a selection process just as we are and to be looking out for their own selfish interests. True, there are reasons to think such beings will show an enlightened benevolence, but these are not arbitrary. Instead, every act of benevolence will be done with some expectation of reciprocal benefit, as reason must dictate. In the case of resurrections, the resurrectees should be able to make interesting contributions to the lives of the resurrectors and relatively soon, or be more interesting than usual or in some other way offer an attractive choice among alternatives. So we can ask if it seems likely that future advanced beings would benignly shower happiness on resurrections of ourselves, in proportion to how much we tried to postpone our reappearance. I for one am not confident they would.

Here we see one way that death confronts us with a major unknown. For that we should keep our options open. A person revived from biostasis could always elect later to self-destruct without preservation, should that somehow be established as the better course. The reverse, we have noted, seems impossible, at least in the sense of restoring lost historical ties. I do think future beings will have reason to resurrect all others—eventually. By analogy, mathematicians will investigate every question that comes up in their many domains of interest—eventually. But there, certain interests take precedence over others, and I would expect this to be true in that other setting, the world yet to come.

There is an interesting parallel here to our earlier observations about putative beings who might resurrect humankind if our species cannot solve its problems on its own but ends up self-destructing. Again, if such a backup possibility is in some degree reassuring, still it is not what we want to have to rely on if we can avoid it. Advantage is to be gained by working to solve our problems ourselves, as far as our growing abilities allow, with the aim of eventual, complete success. Placing one's hopes in other beings or powers who may exist and assist at some future time but are presently unknown, unless it is the only choice, must never be the first choice.

Earlier I conjectured there would be definite penalties to be suffered by our continuers if we fail to survive as a species and must be recreated from the outside. While it is not clear exactly what form these might take, it seems evident that there would be a diminution or loss of a meaningful Interface with whatever reality must serve as our new habitat. This would follow simply because of the loss of informational continuity with our past, plus the likely strangeness of the new setting, even if we take into account possible "smoothing of the path" by future, basically benevolent, alien resurrectors. So there is a close parallel here with the case of a single individual.

The future, I think, will belong to immortalists, those who want to survive, to take part as far as possible in an ongoing, enduring, historical process. Self-sufficiency and interactions with others on an equal, reciprocal footing will be the rule. Those who already have this orientation today and in particular have gone so far as to seek preservation of their remains for eventual reanimation, are in a stronger position than others. They should have fewer difficult adjustments if the future unfolds as it should, with immortality for all. They will even benefit, I will wager, if their attempted biostasis fails and they too are lost, only to be resurrected by guesswork like others who did not care or could not bring themselves to try. The reexpressed intentions of the immortality seekers will smooth the path when they, as continuers, are restored again to consciousness and can then get on with the wonders of living. They will not be so well off as if they had succeeded in their own preservative endeavor but better off than if they had lacked the will and intent to succeed in the first place. But others too must eventually fall in line and, I conjecture, will willingly do so. In time all should become good immortalists, Yuaians or post-Yuaians, at a superhuman level. Differences in status, honor, or privilege should approach the vanishing point as all are exalted, though some important, other differences will remain and even greatly increase over time to enrich all existence.

But in particular I think we can rule out such cases as the being who persists in a state of complete withdrawal from actual events. A mathematically focused entity, for example, who cared only for abstract "truths" and spent all its time accumulating them would, it seems, be unable to fend for itself in other ways. Some interest must be shown in what is actually happening, and information about the ongoing affairs of the world, and oneself, must accumulate. If this must happen, then once again it ought to be made pleasant. Again, enonticity is likely to be valued. On the other hand I would expect considerable latitude for one to develop as one wishes. There surely must be many ways of "making a living" with the advanced means that will become available, and thus a great diversity of viable lifestyles, attitudes, and practices can be expected to appear.

I have emphasized the value of enonticity, a tying-in with the historical process that we can further in our own lives today through the biostasis option. But it is also necessary to note that I do not think this value is absolute. There are indeed circumstances today that call for risking one's life and even one's chances of preservation, if one has chosen that option. It is conceivable for instance that an assailant armed with explosives could only be diverted from killing others by putting oneself at risk. This does not mean one should save one's life at any cost. It may not be an easy matter to decide when a noble self-sacrifice is called for, and hopefully the issue will not occur often, yet clearly there are circumstances that would call for such action.

As one example, suppose a diabolical terrorist has trapped you and two other equally "good" people. You must choose whether you or the two others will be vaporized, anyone who is spared being released unharmed. The choice, then, is whether one's enonticity (or the chance of it) is worth the pains of conscience and other difficulties that could follow if one chooses escape through sacrificing the others. Here I maintain that proper orientation would call for the self-sacrifice. At least the prospect of eventual resurrection would be a consolation, and the clarity of conscience and knowledge that one had bravely done the right thing would more than offset the onticity issue, whatever significance it may have. This would follow clearly if one has proper orientation, including appropriate concern for the welfare of others.

Someone with improper orientation and less concern for the others may feel like sacrificing them and saving himself. Such a person could then make the claim that he acted in his own best interest. But I would counter that in the end he will be less happy, even if his onticity is preserved, and realizing it he will feel impelled to a painful change of views, assuming the projected future turns out as it should. One important issue, again, is the sort of individuals and conditions one would likely encounter in an immortal future. A noble character arguably would have value enough to more than compensate the tribulations that must be endured to sustain such a character.

It is easy to imagine other scenarios that would raise the issue of self-sacrifice, some with the answer less clear-cut. Again, hopefully such predicaments will be rare, and you or I will not have to make such choices. But on principle we should be prepared. Milder versions of the diabolical choice are more common. A great deal of risk taking, for example, probably involves some slight risk to life through increased stress. We should not shrink back but, in appropriate circumstances and even when the risk is great, take it to further the greater good, which we can have confidence is ultimately best for us, too. Otherwise however, we can and should pursue our better survival without the fear of thereby making a moral mistake.

But perhaps it will be objected that if the self-sacrifice is *ever* called for, this contradicts the principle we began with in the Introduction, that a life rightly lived is never rightly ended. But really there is no contradiction. A life that ends in a noble self-sacrifice—temporarily in any case—is still wrongly ended. Its termination is a bad thing, though a lesser evil under the circumstance. In any case we can hope that in the future such outcomes and the need for them will be vanishingly rare, as we act with diligence and wisdom to build a world free of mortal constraints.

Summary

To summarize the Philosophy of Aspiration: we should aspire to survival, joy, and knowledge in unlimited amounts and act as best we can to further these aims, through seeking to become more-than-human. Each one of us must work out our own salvation individually, though interactions with others will be important too. Science, reason, and technology, we expect, will play a vital part in our actual transition to more-than-human status, and in what we do thereafter. We must always consider what scientific avenues are open to further our cause in eternity. Today we can promote our long-term survival through the biostasis option, and soon perhaps will be able to further it more directly through aging intervention. Individual happiness, on the other hand, is an individual matter but is not best pursued in isolation, and we expect this principle to hold even in a future in which we have advanced far beyond the human level. Concern for others will lead to greater personal benefit through reciprocal interactions. On grounds of rational self-interest, then, we should love one another. We should seek to immortalize ourselves and assist others to immortalization. We should aspire to a condition of all being highly and, I would say, equally valued by all.

Following and adapting Fedorov, we see that the highest happiness can only be enjoyed by all beings together.[16] The attainment of the highest happiness—and a meaningful, endless existence—must then be conceived as a moral project. Moral perfection must go hand in hand with the sort of future world we would like to create—one is really not possible without the other.

The Philosophy of Aspiration should form an important part of our moral platform—to add to what we considered in the last chapter. In it, and the book more generally, I have emphasized the ideas of resurrection and immortality and their associated problems. Immortalization will be an unending task for us, one we can complete only in the limit of time. The unfinished, ever-present task will always furnish "something to do," something of vital concern. Yet it cannot be ruled out that providing for our immortality, including resurrections, will in the end prove an increasingly minor chore that will occupy a vanishingly small fraction of our time.

If so, then we will surely find other things with which to busy ourselves, and these will, no doubt, be most fascinating too. There is no way, as I see it, that an immortal existence would have to be boring. There is an inexhaustible family of problems to consider and reconsider, and we can adapt our drives and desires as necessary to make life worthwhile, whatever it is we end up spending our time doing. For now, though, the problem of death poses no small challenge. In our own time there are suggestions of actual physical steps we can take to address this problem directly.

CHAPTER 17.

The Philosophy of Action

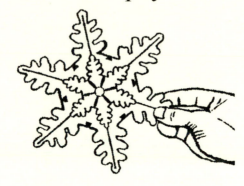

I n the past, death was firmly fixed among the things we could
not change. Cessation of the life processes, followed by the
disintegration of our physical remains, especially the brain,
were as inevitable as our earlier birth. Some of this is true no
longer. It is possible to have one's remains placed in biostasis
after death and thus halt the disintegration that otherwise must
follow. The outlook is hopeful on other fronts too, though one
must be cautious and not expect too much just yet. But, as one
reason for optimism, our science has given many clues that our
demise comes from physical causes, causes we can understand
and master. We are gradually learning about these causes and
how we might alleviate them. Thus the problem of human aging—the progressive physical deterioration that sets in around
age thirty and continues to the end of one's life some decades
later—is a matter of biology, which reduces to chemistry, which
reduces to quantum physics. Purposeful efforts can now be directed toward eliminating biological death and all physical ailments, and tentative efforts of this sort are in progress.

The new prospects call us to a proactive stance that was not
possible in earlier times. We can approach death with neither resigned acceptance nor fearful denial nor mysticism but with the
resolve to physically do something about it, to act toward eliminating it from our lives through a rational strategy. This approach
is geared not to a distant future in which others may resurrect us
by guessing replicas but to a nearer time when we can benefit

more directly from developing technology. We are led to a Philosophy of Action with a strong element of participation, including making arrangements in advance for our own biostasis.

Most, to be sure, are still quite unprepared for such a possibility and cling to the more traditional approaches to death that inhibit any attempt at overcoming it physically. This attitude may be hard to change, for reasons we have considered (Chapter 3), though such a change is called for; more will be said as we go along. For now it will be convenient simply to grant that pursuit of immortality through physical means is desirable and to consider how best to go about it. Wesley M. DuCharme's book, *Becoming Immortal*, is a reference I have used that can be recommended for further reading. (Some philosophical differences with the present work will also challenge the reader.) For those who are further interested, some useful information is listed in the back matter under Organizations, but a better means of finding up-to-date information and getting more involved is through the Internet. (Access through a local public library and "cyber cafes" is becoming increasingly feasible for those who lack a computer connection.) A Web search under such topics as "aging research," "cryonics," "nanotechnology," "skepticism," and "transhumanism" will furnish much useful data and leads.

Basically, there are three issues involved in our becoming immortal in the relatively near future. The first is the means whereby it will be accomplished, through such advances as aging control and nanotechnology. The second is the problem of staying alive until the means become available. The third is what to do if staying alive is not possible—the best strategy being a personal plan of biostasis. These we will consider in turn, both from the standpoint of ongoing research and of what you and I can be doing ourselves to promote progress and maximize our probable benefit.

Nanotechnology, which we have often considered, is now pursued in numerous laboratories throughout the world. Eric Drexler's Foresight Institute has the mission of keeping abreast of this work and informing the public. Joining the Foresight Institute, keeping up with progress, and exchanging views with others, are ways of furthering a positive trend. Be warned—there is controversy between enthusiasts like Drexler who proclaim a brave new world of nanotech to arrive perhaps within a few decades (and who also tend to favor such strategies as cryonics) and mainstream researchers more concerned with immediate problems and solutions. Those with appropriate interests and backgrounds can go further and consider a research career in nanotechnology. A few groups are trying to bridge the gap between the two cultures of nanotech that have grown up. As examples, Zyvex and its rival, Nanotechnology Development Corporation, both have as a goal the still unrealized general purpose assembler, about which many on the mainstream side have expressed doubts.[1]

Controversy is also no stranger in aging and longevity research, which raises high hopes among those eager to reverse the effects of growing old. One must be especially careful here, for there are some in the field who promise too much.[2] Advanced Cell Technology and Geron are reputable organizations that have had some success with understanding and delaying the course of senescence at the cellular level. Some interesting developments in this area deserve mention.

Progress against Aging

One line of aging research that looks promising concerns a property cells exhibit as an organism ages: they lose the ability to divide and replicate. Such activity—one cell splitting into two smaller daughter cells that soon grow up to the size of the original—is normal and necessary for the maintenance of most parts of the body. In this way older cells killed by other aging mechanisms, injuries, or disease are replaced by newer, neighboring cells, so the organism as a whole remains nearly unchanged. (One exception is in the brain; neurons do not divide but have simply become very long lived, though some creation of new neurons does occur by other means.[3]) It is clear, however, that daughter cells cannot be identical in all respects to their parents, inasmuch as ability to divide declines with the number of cell divisions. (Human fetal cells in fact lose the ability to replicate after about sixty divisions, a bound known as the Hayflick limit named after Leonard Hayflick, who confirmed it around 1960.[4])

Some light on this mysterious decline has been shed by examining cell chromosomes. The tiny, spiraling strands of DNA are found in most cells of the body, mainly in cell nuclei, where they direct many activities including replication. All the chromosomes in a cell together define the cell's genome, from which a twin cell can be made. During natural cell replication, the chromosomes themselves are copied, which is essential if the two daughter cells are to function as their parent did. This suggests a possible target for aging research: since we know that, in general, daughter cells are not the same, we should look for changes in the chromosomes.

Some changes have been found. At the tips of chromosomes are structures called telomeres. Telomeres hold the chromosomes together like the plastic ends of shoestrings. The telomeres, it turns out, are shaved down slightly on each cell division. When a telomere is trimmed down too much, the cell changes character and no longer divides. Interestingly, it has been found that telomeres in normal (nonsenescent) cells form a loop at either end of each chromosome; the short, stubby telomeres of the older cells do not.[5] Such senescent cells will eventually die leaving no progeny. The accumulation and attrition of senescent cells seems to cause much of the changes we associate with aging, though some details are unclear.[6] Or, if the cell is still able to replicate, its daughters will inherit the telomere deficiency, enhanced by another cell division. Each cell thus contains a ticking time bomb. Each time the cell divides, the bomb is faithfully replicated but is one tick closer to detonation.[7] Telomere shortening, then, is a prime suspect in aging, though how important it is, relative to all other causes, is still unknown.

It is interesting that telomere lengthening can also occur, through an enzyme called telomerase. Telomerase expression occurs in germ cells, and the consequent lengthening of the telomeres has the effect of resetting the biological clock of offspring so that they start life with as much life expectancy as their parents. Not many other cells are capable of this, however, so that the body in general slides into senescence.

A remedy to this ages-old process of decline could soon be at hand. Starting in 1998 results were announced in which the aging of cells in culture was delayed indefinitely through treatment with telomerase.[8] Human cells modified to produce the enzyme could divide many times without showing the usual, progressive changes that signal the approaching Hayflick limit—it no longer applied. This is an exciting development, hinting at a possible means of controlling the aging process. But telomerase has its downside too. Many malignancies get their sinister powers through their own production of the enzyme—otherwise their rapidly proliferating cell lines might quickly and harmlessly die out. So the shortening of telomeres, though eventually lethal to the organism, seems to be a major defense against cancer too, something a telomerase-based rejuvenation treatment would have to take into account. It is interesting, though, that cell cultures immortalized through telomerase showed no signs of cancer and appeared normal in all respects.[9]

But telomere shortening is not the only important mechanism of aging at the molecular level. For example, accumulating damage in the body occurs from highly reactive, electrically charged molecules known as free radicals; oxygen plays an important part. Though necessary for life, it is also a corrosive substance that can tear apart the molecules within cells. Oxygen-bearing free radicals contribute to such ailments as cancer, arthritis, and cataracts and also impair the function of mitochondria, the tiny structures within cells that are responsible for energy production. Damage to the mitochondria in turn can lead to increased production of oxygen-bearing free radicals, a vicious cycle. Mitochondrial damage from free radicals accumulates throughout life and is a prime suspect in the progressive enfeeblement of aging. Oxygen radicals are also thought to damage the DNA in cells. In this case, the body also has repair mechanisms, but a residual amount of damage is not repaired and slowly accumulates.[10]

Glucose is a simple sugar that, like oxygen, is also vital to life but also seems implicated in aging. Glucose plays a role in converting newly produced cellular proteins into forms the body can use, a process known as glycosylation. But glucose also yields harmful end products, which accumulate over time with detrimental effects. Collagen is a protein found in joints, tendons, blood vessels, and lung tissue and also serves as a structural foundation for skin. Springy and flexible in youth, it hardens as, over the years, glucose end products bind to and cross-link its molecules. Such cross-linking is a major contributor to the stiffening of joints, hardening of arteries, and similar deleterious changes as we grow older.[11]

Another activity that seems to have a role in aging is apoptosis, or programmed cell death. Cells and parts of cells regularly commit suicide through a complicated process that is still not fully understood. This self-destruction is not an unmitigated disaster but actually has many beneficial effects that are essential to the organism throughout life. In the developing human fetus, for example, the treelike, electrically conducting structures known as dendrites that branch out from neurons will self-destruct unless they find proper connections with muscle or other cells. In this way useless, extra neural structure is discarded early in life, and other unwanted tissue is similarly pruned away by apoptosis. In the adult, skin cells migrate over two or three weeks from the interior of the body to the surface. Along the way the cells die through apoptosis and turn into waterproof, tough little lumps that form a protective layer on the surface. In this manner the skin is constantly replaced as it is worn away in use. There are many other processes in the body that also rely on apoptosis. The problem is that all or most of our cells seem prone to eventual apoptosis. When other changes of aging have gone far enough, this mechanism seems important in finally finishing us off.[12]

Further insight into aging has been gained in work that traces an abnormally rapid aging disorder, Werner's syndrome, to a certain defective gene. Werner's syndrome causes roughly a doubling in the human aging rate; a victim in her forties may look in her eighties. (By comparison there is a more serious rapid aging disorder, Hutchinson-Gilford syndrome, in which victims show marked symptoms and typically die around age thirteen, and which seems to be caused by congenitally shortened telomeres.[13]) The problem in Werner's apparently traces to the gene WRN, which when defective causes fragmentation of the nucleolus, a small, spherical body within the nucleus of a cell. Interestingly, the WRN gene was identified by studying SGS1, a structurally similar gene in yeast cells that has been found to have the same effect of inhibiting fragmentation of the nucleolus and consequently of extending cell life. There are suggestions that the fragmentation in turn is caused by circular loops of DNA that accumulate over the course of successive cell divisions until the nucleolus quite literally fills up and bursts.[14] So possibly an important additional aging mechanism has been found.

Such tentative findings are encouraging, but it is clear that much remains to be done before aging can be arrested or reversed. A cure could come soon or take prohibitively long on the scale of your life and mine—or both. People, meanwhile, can try to stay as healthy as possible, exercising, eating frugally but with adequate nutrition, and not smoking or indulging in other deleterious habits. Regular medical checkups are advisable. One can then hope to minimize the effects of aging and increase the number of years and quality of one's life. Progress in more conventional medicine is another encouraging development. As one example, heart bypass operations, first performed only a few decades ago, are now commonplace among the elderly. Such strategies are gradually extending the human life span. Some think there is still a "maximum life span" of around 120 years beyond which we cannot go. But there is no decisive evidence of this and much reason to think otherwise.

As yet, though, there is no escape from senescence, even though certain "longevity gurus who make money by preying on a common fear of death" make over-optimistic claims.[15] The claims involve a confusion between "senescence accelerators," such as poor exercise, bad nutrition and smoking, and "senescence decelerators" such as (possibly) telomerase treatments—if and when developed—that would retard or reverse aging at a basic level. As one illustration, vitamins A, C, and E are able to protect the body to a certain extent against free radicals.[16] Conversely and more generally, inadequate nutrition will tend to accelerate the aging process. Proper nutrition thus should be viewed as an anti-accelerator of senescence, not a decelerator.

Barring certain drugs or treatments that may have marginal validity or whose claims need better verification, the only senescence decelerator now known is calorie restriction. It has had dramatic success in extending the lives of laboratory animals, though as expected it is the shorter-lived species that are the most studied and furnish the best-attested cases. In one representative study of laboratory mice, a diet with only 40 percent as many calories but otherwise meeting nutritional needs increased the average life span from 27 months to 45 months, with a jump in maximum longevity from 35½ to 55 months.[17] It is noted that calorie restriction has some rather profound side effects, including "a decrease in many reproductive capabilities."[18] That alone, however, lends credibility to the claim that this is a true aging decelerator and not simply a feature of a normal lifestyle in the wild, as some have thought.[19] Nature would not be expected to favor a strategy in which reproductive capacities are diminished without a compensating advantage, which so far has not been found.

A new experimental methodology, using DNA chips to detect changes in gene expression in aging animals, shows that calorie restriction does, in fact, delay numerous age-related changes at the molecular level, at least in mice. And in the bargain we now have a much more quantitative way of studying aging changes than was available before. Perhaps this will translate to rapid progress in understanding aging and developing treatments, but for now much is still unknown. We do not know in particular how effective calorie restriction will be for humans, though when effects of disease are accounted for, thinner people with adequate nutrition are longer-lived.[20]

Calorie restriction, in any event, is not a cure for aging. Subjects may live longer, but senescence takes its toll in the end. Other currently available human treatments such as hormone and vitamin supplementation may lengthen life and improve health. But again they appear to do it by counteracting senescence accelerators and not (primarily) by decelerating senescence or reversing it at a fundamental level.[21] Barring a breakthrough, aging or other lethal problems must eventually catch up with us. It is worth noting too that even with a breakthrough, death could claim us at any time, and we want to be as well prepared as possible. We must consider biostasis to make the best stand against physical destruction and, quite possibly, to even have a reasonable chance of defeating it at all. With biostasis we do at least gain a chance of survival to a time when our immortalization can be pursued more directly. We can also benefit even if the preservation is imperfect, as I have argued. Thus, though cryonics seems the best course for optimum preservation, alternative methods of biostasis will also be considered.

Cryonics and Other Biostasis Procedures

Cryonics is attractive because of the high quality of preservation, relatively speaking, that is seen in frozen tissue specimens. Many frozen cells can be restored to functioning through simple thawing, though whole, large organisms and most organs cannot be recovered with current techniques. In particular, brain tissue, crucial for identity-critical information, can be well preserved,[22] though a deep-frozen brain will also show significant, presently lethal damage.[23] Cryonicists are generally somewhat hopeful, if not certain, about the prospects of their eventual reanimation, and highly doubtful about other possibilities such as a supernatural Heaven. In fact, the conventional cryonics wisdom is that while your prospects are uncertain *if* you are frozen after death, they are certain if you are not: you simply are never coming back. This, coupled with a strong wish to survive, provides the motive for choosing cryonics.

The conclusion, of course, is a brutal one, implying that lives were lived in vain up to now, that certain major wrongs can never be righted. One is moved to ask if the problem of survival could be reasonably formulated to sustain a more optimistic outlook. We have considered this issue and found reason to be more optimistic. Historical links that would be preserved through biostasis are not essential but are still important and worth maintaining, if possible.

So again we are brought to consider biostasis. We must not overlook the differing perspectives on the subject, even among immortalists who all take it seriously. The position advocated here is not the majority view, though I think it is a better view, in which imperfect preservation is valued in a way not possible to the more conventional outlook. People instead are never finally lost but will suffer a greater dislocation or ontic deficit if their preservation is poorer, and we want to minimize this shortfall.

We shall, accordingly, consider cryonics and other biostasis possibilities according to two distinct standards of efficacy, or likelihood of working. The more stringent standard I will call the *medical criterion*. It requires that the person be recoverable entirely from preserved remains, substantially whole and intact, with no large gaps or need for inventing or recreating information to complete the person being reconstructed. This then will satisfy the demands of conventional wisdom about survival. The more lenient, *ontic criterion* will be met, on the other hand, if some significant, personal information survives through biostasis that would otherwise be lost, though recreation of information will generally be necessary in reconstructing the person. For the ontic criterion, then, we must invoke such ideas as the UI assumptions and ontic robustness to justify the position that a true resurrection could occur. The subject must experience an ontic deficit that is not present if the medical criterion is met. A resurrection or resuscitation under the medical criterion, then, is fully enontic or historical in the usual sense, while a resurrection that does no better than satisfy the ontic criterion is at best only hyperontic, though the ontic deficit, in the better cases, may not be serious. It will be my contention that (1) even very limited forms of biostasis, such as saving a cell sample, are justified based on the ontic criterion; and (2) with cryonic suspension there is a reasonable likelihood that the medical criterion is satisfied too, despite some challenging difficulties.

It is worth keeping in mind that though we are imagining a resurrection being started from actual remains in a good or bad state of preservation, it is really information that counts. A fully enontic resurrection—the medical grade—could happen with not a shred of original tissue, if all the necessary information is present. However, it seems likely that in a real future attempt of this sort, the starting information will mainly come from actual remains. Technology capable of extracting this information (after which the remains could be discarded, having served their purpose) is now unknown, though its eventual availability seems very likely based on the prospects of nanotechnology. But it will probably not be developed much before that needed to recreate a functioning person from a description. (This, I expect, will reassure those cryonicists who are uneasy about the idea that the remains do not count if the information is recorded elsewhere, though of course they do not, from such a standpoint as pattern-survival or even the more restrictive notion of enontic survival.) In any case, though, structure encoding information is the crucial item—if you have enough of it, the person in question should be considered still here even if quite dead by conventional criteria.

It is encouraging, at least, that current criteria of death are beginning to be questioned. The accepted definitions will probably change considerably and, I think, must come to reflect information-based criteria. Quite simply, it is not reasonable to consider someone "dead" unless there is insufficient information—in the physical remains or other historical sources—to permit restoration of that individual (or a copy or a continuer) to a functioning state. This way of thinking reflects the reductionist view that a person is dependent on or derives from a physical process of an information-processing sort and does not embody a mystical soul or other "further fact." The person need not be "dead" when the process is put on hold, though I will continue with conventional usage for practical reasons; *death* will refer to clinical death as understood today, a (presumed) irreversible cessation of vital functions. But we must keep in mind that a person, frozen solid in liquid nitrogen and dead by conventional criteria, could still be "alive" and recoverable someday through such means as nanotechnology.

Arguably, when such recovery is possible, other advances will have been made, and hopefully among them, the elimination of biological aging and death from now-terminal conditions such as cancer and heart disease. The resuscitee can then begin on the next step—becoming more-than-human. All this, of course, is still in the future, and we cannot guarantee even that any of it will happen. As we have seen, there are exciting things going on that seem to promise a coming era of immortality, maybe within a generation or so. But we may find death unavoidable meanwhile, so that biostasis becomes our backup.

Strategies for biostasis can be divided into two main camps. The more modest version is based around genomic preservation, while the more complete and serious version has brain preservation as the main goal. The brain preservation approach, which includes cryonics, offers realistic hopes of achieving the medical criterion of near-perfect recovery from the preserved structure (or information). But the genomic version is also worth examining, geared though it is to the more modest ontic criterion. We will consider it first.

Genomic Preservation

Actually, a surprising amount ought to be achievable through the genomic route alone. This would require nothing more than a cell sample of someone who dies, coupled with the usual information we might expect to extract from records. Through cloning-related techniques, we should be able to make a functioning twin of the original person. So in the first place, this near-replica would look the same and also might feel and act much the same. That there would be far more than merely a surface resemblance between the two is suggested by the studies we considered in

Chapter 15 involving twins separated in infancy and raised separately. Future technology should allow a still greater fidelity; more will be said shortly.

The genomic route could be well suited to cases of an organism that was not a fully developed human. An aborted fetus, for example, might be salvaged this way, a cell sample later being induced to develop into the baby that could not be born the first time around. Another possibility is pets. We noted last chapter that dogs and cats have personalities, though not at the human level. It is not clear that our pets remember past episodes of their lives as we do. They may be almost day persons (or less), living the same day over and over rather than accumulating experiences and remembering. And they would hardly understand what minimizing an ontic deficit may mean, or be able, in their present state, to value or desire such an outcome. More than people, their personalities seem genetically determined. A loved pet, then, might be well recovered by cloning from a cell sample, if we allowed for reprogramming as well to recapture the endearing behavior and recognition we remember. This is not to deny that objections could be raised. Even a dog or cat may remember things others would value at a later time. (The "others" could even include those very pets, when later they developed into advanced beings.) But using a cell sample plus nonbiological information would at least seem to be more acceptable the lower one goes on the scale of sentience.

But to return to our point about future technology: we should be able to do better than simply create an identical twin baby. We would not have to raise a clone from an infant nor end up with an adult who only remembered events that are now in the future. Instead, using the full powers of the technology that ought to exist, we should be able to create a fully formed and *in*formed adult, right at the start. Arguably, in fact, this would be easier, with advanced technology, than raising an infant to adulthood (no small chore) though we cannot be sure. (Recall our "Purgatory" discussion in the last chapter. But I am inclined to think that a suitable person "program" would not require enormously more resources for its creation, by a process of calculation beforehand, than nature currently invests in the making of personalities—a few decades of work, say. This too could probably be shortened considerably by future computational and procedural speedups.) But our reconstructed adult could be given memories of a childhood in the twentieth century that "felt" absolutely authentic and perfectly fit the surviving records.

George, reconstructed in this manner from a cell sample, would know his full name and the names, appearances and something about the personalities of his parents, any siblings, children, spouses, best friends, or others of particular significance in his life. He would remember something of his high school and college classes, be fluent in his native language, and be able to read, write, and calculate. In the usual cases we should be able to infer, with reasonable certainty, that he possessed these skills originally and could reinstate them. George would know as much or as little as you would expect about any advanced topics he may have studied. If he got an "A" in a course he should know that subject rather better than if he got a "D." He would recall a reasonable stock of personal episodes, good times and not-so-good, et cetera. A large part of this information, in its broad outlines, would come from such sources as school records and reasonable deductions based on his known origin and places of residence. Some might be filled in from recollections of living people or from old photographs, letters, tapes, or diaries. The extent to which his personality would have to be reinvented, or in the more conventional view, fabricated or fictionalized, could be much less than one might think. There could certainly be inner thoughts and emotional states that would not have been recorded but would likely have been remembered. But even this might be partly indicated by our basic biological knowledge, deducible from George's DNA.

Of course, this idea of a resurrection would not satisfy everybody, particularly most cryonicists. The new George, as they would view it, might be closer in some sense than an identical twin but, however similar, must be subtly different from the original. There are simply too many fine details to reconstruct by indirect methods; you must surely end up with a "different" person. The medical criterion, in short, must be violated; only the ontic criterion would be met. But even then, we might claim we still had the "same" person, on much the ground argued for head-injured Ned in Chapter 3. True, George must have undergone changes, but no more, we could claim, than some people do today, who recover from severe brain trauma and who are more or less accepted and accept themselves as the same person who lived before. Other changes of life now occur normally that affect the extent to which an earlier version of ourselves could be said to "survive," including the aging process.

A different and stronger authenticity argument, of course, is provided by the notion of ontic robustness we considered in Chapter 12—for those who accept the Yuai position. We do not have just one original. Many different versions of George acquired an equally "original" status with the loss information that occurred when only the cell sample was preserved. The version we have brought back is fully authentic but is not the only possible "real" version we can make and start functioning in our world. The ambiguity in George's status, in fact, translates to an ontic deficit he must adjust to. We can then ask how serious that problem will be. My hunch is that there will be reasons to take it seriously, but they will differ from the worries usually heard today, which involve a fear that the "real" person is lost forever. The deficit, in any case, must be less the more information there is to start with in reconstructing the person. The genomic sample, then, could be strengthened with other personal information such as, again, photos, tapes, or diaries. The ontic deficit may not prove so serious after all.

This we have no way of knowing at present. We can, however, imagine several interesting distinctions based on the degree of preservation of the remains or information that must be used. At the upper end, presumably unattainable here, the medical criterion would be met and the prospects good enough not to raise an issue of onticity or missing or recreated information. Moving down the scale, it may be that some significant information must be reinvented but only of a "private" sort. This could include subtle, remembered shades of feeling, details of visual impressions, or other personal information that others would have had little way of confirming or contesting. Or third, some information may be missing that would have been known by some others who are also lost. In the first two cases the resurrection could happen largely in isolation. But in the third case, when lost information that would have been known to more than one individual is involved, we would want to ensure a reasonable consistency in the memories of all the individuals recreated. For all, of course, will be candidates for eventual resurrection. In each case, in keeping with the aims of a hyperontic resurrection, our second-best choice, we would want to achieve consistency with the surviving historical record. And, in parallel with this principal aim, we would also want mutual consistency among the resurrectees, as discussed in the last chapter, to form a harmonious whole and increase the level of meaning for all involved.

While the details cannot be specified, it seems generally that the more difficult cases of resurrection involving scant amounts of surviving information and large amounts of reinventing would be larger-scale, group efforts that might be postponed to a more advanced future as part of a large project. Many people would be resurrected at one time: entire societies with mutual consistencies in recreated remembrances. The better cases of biostatic preservation, in contrast, could be expected to return sooner, with less fanfare, greater ease in getting on with life, and surer contact with the historical process that living, we might say, is meant to track. This follows because, among other things, we do not have to worry so much over how to "fit" such people into a more general resurrection scenario. The critical identity information that is already there will not have to be tailored to match some other created information.

The genomic option, in any case, is certainly not all one could ask for in the way of preservation. But though it has defects, it also has the advantages of low cost and unobtrusiveness. In fact, it may be argued that anyone who is buried is de facto committed to genomic preservation. DNA can certainly be recovered from buried remains and probably a complete genome in most cases. In fact, I imagine that an important part of a resurrection project, at some point in the future, will be devoted to the reconstruction of people from ground burials, which stretch back many centuries.

Some people find this idea unappealing and would go so far as to advocate no genomic reconstruction—unless the person in question left a specific request for it. But this we can rebut as follows. In our reconstruction we are producing a new person-stage, who ought to have authority to decide the propriety of the act of creating him or her. If the reconstruction is done properly, the necessary approval should follow. In the future it will hopefully not be too difficult, with all our advanced understanding, to make it likely that a resurrectee would find the new circumstances, if not perfect, at least acceptable and desirable.

Thus we can go so far as to advocate a resurrection, even in cases where there was a specific directive that it *not* be carried out. The question to ask in each case is what would the resulting person-stage want, not what did an earlier stage want. For, while a continuer in one sense is the "same" person, in another sense it is a different person whose rights are not to be compromised by the wishes of someone else, even one of its own earlier stages. We are not morally obligated to withhold the bringing to life of a being that would want to be brought to life, even if a closely related, now vanished someone thought it a bad idea. Such an act, in a suitable setting, must be seen as a good and noble endeavor, one that is worthy of pursuit and indeed ought to be done.

An interesting moral conundrum would then arise in the case of people who insist on their tissues and DNA not being preserved in the event of death. To shorten a possibly long argument, I think such people have a right to arrange for cremation at death and/or other destruction of effects, possibly including all copies of the genome. (By the same token, a person who so wishes has the right not to be frozen or preserved in some other manner.) Though I do not think self-destruction is the best course, the right-respecting stance must be considered carefully. I think it can be justified on the principle of there being at least some significant uncertainty that the denial of rights would be better, while the person in question is still alive and considers the exercise of those rights important. Such denial is, in particular, a slippery slope that can easily lead to a worse situation if not very carefully limited.

People should instead have a right to believe or think as they wish and practice accordingly, respecting the rights of others in turn. This tells us, though, that even the respect of rights has rightful limits. Arbitrary "rights" would include the right to limit the rights of others—something has to give. More to the point here, persons of today cannot expect that their wishes will be faithfully respected for all time, particularly if those persons are not present in a functioning form as advocates. Someday our wisdom should be much greater than that of anyone or any group now living. Someday we may reasonably decide to create a continuer of someone even if the person in question was on record as strongly opposed. Presumably, like the caring and understanding parents of a small and confused child, we will know what is best and act accordingly.

Cryonics and Brain Preservation

In any case, our problems with missing information will disappear if the preservation of the remains is good enough. Toward this end, in cryonics the head or entire body is first treated then frozen and stored at low temperature. The treatment involves: (1) chilling the body as quickly as possible to near the freezing point (0°C, 32°F) to minimize high-temperature deterioration; (2) replacing the body fluid with a cryoprotective solution to reduce freezing damage; and (3) cooling the body or head to liquid nitrogen temperature (-196°C, -320°F).[24] Arrangements for the procedure, moreover, are not made by accident. Generally there is signed documentation that the participant did want to return in the future and has chosen cryonics in hopes it will accomplish that goal.

As yet, of course, we do not know how well it will. It mainly depends on how well identity-critical information is preserved in frozen brain tissue. One problem we have in assessing this preservation is that there is still uncertainty as to how memories and other information is stored in the brain and how the brain works more generally, though a significant amount has been learned, and our knowledge is growing. Any evidence of the workability of cryonics must still, in large part, be indirect—though there is some interesting indirect evidence, as we will see. But we must also give fair hearing to the criticism. When this is done, I think we have reason for cautious optimism, which may also extend to some other forms of preservation.

Unfortunately, an impartial meeting of minds on cryonics in which the difficulties would be addressed scientifically in a broad forum is probably not yet possible. Among the outspoken critics have been cryobiologists, who study the effects of low temperature on biological systems, but their criticism has gone beyond the usual bounds of rational skepticism, suggesting instead the difficulties we noted in Chapter 3 with clashing worldviews. Another, possibly even stronger reason for antagonism may be fear of bad publicity for associating with a fringe element such as the cryonics movement. The negativism is reflected in the by-laws of the Society for Cryobiology. Membership may be refused or revoked for, among other things, "any practice or application of freezing of deceased persons in anticipation of their reanimation…" (Section 2.04). Known cryonicists have been excluded from the society and forbidden to publish in its journal. Society members who openly associate with cryonicists have been threatened with expulsion and loss of funding and jobs.[25] In recent years these exclusionary policies have not been enforced, and there is hope for a further improvement in relations, but a cautious approach is still needed.

One problem with cryonics for many, including scientists, is that under current legal requirements, persons can only be frozen after death is pronounced. This in turn follows because a frozen person is "dead" according to legal criteria that do not recognize the potential of future developments such as nanotechnology (or allow others to make decisions for themselves based on their own ideas on these matters). A procedure (freezing) that would render persons "dead" cannot be allowed unless they are already dead. Once "dead," however, they cannot be brought to life—or so runs the ingrained thinking. In fact many noncryonicists are hard-pressed when asked to give a definition of death.

Criteria for death used to be simple. When heartbeat and respiration had ceased there was no known way of restoring function and consciousness, hence the patient was "dead." That, however, was before the advent of cardiopulmonary resuscitation and other techniques that now are able to restore function after what used to be regarded as a point of no return. Clearly, then, there was a flaw in the definition of death. Again, this definition must be changed to reflect information-based criteria. Death, by a reasonable if unrecognized standard, does not really occur until sufficient information-bearing structure is lost. Until this loss occurs, people could be restored to life by suitable procedures applied to their remains. This, I submit, is very likely to hold even when such procedures have not been perfected and are still a dream of the future—so long as we have reason to think that the information is present. This principle, which we can call the Sufficiency of Information Content, seems a difficult one to grasp, even for many educated people.

To satisfy our intuition and traditional associations, "death" should refer to the irreversible cessation of function of an organism. Ordinarily it poses no difficulty if we assume that *irreversible* means irreversible by means presently available. Any patient that cannot be resuscitated by presently known means will, without special preservation, have long since decomposed by the time, if ever, that means of resuscitation become available. The situation is not so simple, however, for an individual kept frozen at low temperature, since decomposition is halted. The tissues will remain essentially unchanged, almost indefinitely.

To decide what "death" would mean in such a case we must confront the question of what the future holds in store, not merely in the next few years but in decades, centuries, and beyond. This is a very tall order. One has only to reflect on the stunning accomplishments of the last few decades and centuries and how unexpected they were to see how risky putting limits to such things can be. A small part of the possible wonders to come has been considered in the discussion of nanotechnology in Chapter 9.

Still it seems safe to say that technology, based on the world as we know it, has certain basic limits. Some of these involve thermodynamically irreversible processes such as burning or chemical decomposition in which information is lost. (Here I am discounting the possibility of recovering this information at something like Tipler's Omega Point[26] or using other exotic means such as backward time travel.) Even with the best of future technology, the only way we could "unburn" a piece of paper and get back the exact structure of the intertwined cellulose fibers, et cetera, would be through lucky guesswork, a thought that has some philosophical consequences, as we have seen. But in usual terms we are justified in considering burning irreversible, along with melting, decay, and other changes that erase information. Other technological limits will probably depend on the impossibility of doing certain computational tasks. There will always be practical limits of many sorts too, though we can often expect them to relax with time.

Of these constraints, the information loss seems the most serious from a cryonics standpoint, inasmuch as we want to avoid guesswork as far as possible in any proposed reanimation. To get a better idea of how "death" and informational issues affect cryonics, let us consider an illustration.

Suppose you get up in the morning to go to work and the car

will not start. Certainly this does not prove it can never be started again. Instead the problem, say, is traced to a faulty battery. You replace the battery, and everything works. The car was not "dead," only "unconscious." It is clear that much more serious car problems are correctable too, if one is willing to undertake the necessary labor and expense. Say your car is flattened in an avalanche. If you are willing to take the trouble you can excavate it and, over time, repair the crumpled body and parts, ultimately restoring the machine to running order. (This might be justified if you are a wealthy collector and the car is a one-of-a-kind antique.) Again, it was not "dead," only in this case, in addition to "unconscious," it was "very ill." It is clear such a reconstruction could be done under more difficult circumstances, though there are limits. If the car is melted to an ingot, for example (and assuming no blueprints or plans exist) we can only ask, what was it? and give up (or start guessing). Here the problem is that it is not possible to infer the functioning state from the damaged state. There has been too much damage, and the necessary information is lost.

In general, with a repair task, we must infer what ought to be there from what still is there. As long as it is possible to do this, it is a reasonable bet that a technology can be developed to actually carry out the process of repair, whatever that task may turn out to be. So if you can tell what your car would look like, externally and internally, if it were fixed, you can be confident that a means is possible (or can be devised) to fix it, even if no such means is now known. This, then, shows the Sufficiency of Information Content. The same principle applies, of course, to mechanisms other than the automobile and, in particular, to frozen humans.[27]

Here the problems are more complicated. A human being is much more intricate than a car; much finer detail must be preserved to offer a reasonable chance at repair. The nature of the principal repair is very different, too. Since the brain contains the important elements of personality and identity, it above all else must be restored to a functioning state. Memories and means of accessing them must be reactivated. The brain is fundamentally an information processing system, and somehow its "state of computation" must be adequately recaptured. Still, there are basic similarities to the repair of simpler devices.

All devices, simple or complicated, are made of atoms. Atoms themselves do not age or wear out, but only become misplaced.

Repair and restoration is, ultimately, a process of putting atoms into their proper places. (In some cases, as with magnetization, it would also require restoring certain states of the correctly positioned atoms; this probably would not be an issue with the task of restoring frozen tissue, however.) The main problem then is to determine where the atoms should be placed, not the physical operations of placement, whatever these may turn out to be. If the proper places can be determined, then in principle there should exist a physical process for producing the desired, repaired state. In the case of a frozen patient, we should be able to obtain a fully functioning, healthy human who retains the critical identity information that has been present all along and, in short, is the original person.

Resuscitations are now performed, we noted, that were once considered impossible. Death, we must conclude, is a process, not an event. There is no definite point at which the individual simply "departs." Sufficiency of Information Content allows the restoration of vital functions. Similar considerations should apply in the case of cryonics, and we can wait a long time if necessary.

How Good Is Cryopreservation?

We are then left with the problem of what condition a cryonics patient may be in: whether the information content really is sufficient to allow eventual resuscitation. A frozen human, needless to say, is far more "deathlike" than someone whose heartbeat and breathing have only just stopped. When applicable, cardiopulmonary resuscitation works because, among other things, the brain is still viable and can be restored to function if oxygenation and circulation of blood are resumed immediately. The information-bearing structure is clearly still intact. If the circulation is halted long enough without other protection, however, irreversible damage will occur, though the extent of this damage may be overestimated. It is widely believed, for example, that the brain is irreparably damaged after four to six minutes of lack of blood flow at body temperature and that no procedure can ever be developed that will restore it to function. The brain does cease its activity, an instance of what is known more generally as brain death.

Though death has to be pronounced before cryopreservation

can begin, it can still be pronounced under the criteria of cessation of respiration and heartbeat rather than brain death. So the freezing process can be started when the patient, by more recent and reasonable criteria, is still alive. Except under unusually favorable circumstances, however, the ischemic insult (deprivation of oxygen needed by the cells to function) is likely to be at least equal to the four to six minutes of normothermic (body-temperature) circulatory arrest that is believed to cause irreversible loss of function. Cryonically suspended patients thus were probably brain-dead before freezing. Since, as we have noted, belief in the irreversibility of this condition is so firmly entrenched (particularly among the medical and forensic professions), it might be thought that there must be massive obliteration of the brain structure, at least at the cellular level. But such is not the case.

In fact the changes that result in brain death are relatively trivial. Waste products accumulate, neurotransmitters are released in toxic amounts, and levels of calcium and other ions in the cells are upset. Cells swell and blood vessels spasm and constrict. Blood circulation is impeded to the point that it cannot be restored by simple means. Brain cells, however, remain able to resume most functions long after the onset of brain death. Work with monkeys and especially dogs, moreover, has succeeded in pushing back the limits of "irreversible" circulatory arrest to fifteen minutes or more.[28] Again there seems to be a flaw in what is commonly regarded as "death."

A cryonics patient is in worse shape than a barely brain-dead patient. Certainly no one has yet been revived from a solidly frozen condition. (To be truly solidly frozen requires a temperature far below the freezing point of water—depending on conditions, around -110° to -130°C. Tissue, however, will be hard and seem quite thoroughly frozen at a much warmer temperature, say -20°C.) Nothing, in fact, has been revived after complete freezing or solidification but single cells, small multicellular organisms such as early-stage human embryos, small tissue samples, and a few body parts such as heart valves and corneas.[29] (It is worth noting that claims of rat hearts being revived to beating condition after solid freezing remain unverified at this writing and seem doubtful in view of later unsuccessful attempts to repeat the experiments.[30]) Many cells suffer extensive damage from the freezing process that, together with damage on rewarming, renders them unable to resume their functions.

But in some respects freezing is less damaging than is commonly supposed. It is a misconception, for instance, that cells are nearly all ruptured by the expansion of water within the cell as it turns to ice. What usually happens is that water freezes outside the cells, causing them to shrink and even lose material from the membranes, though these generally remain unbroken. Intracellular ice creates its own problems for a resuscitation, particularly for a complicated structure such as the brain. However, interesting partial successes in resuscitating brains have been obtained. Both human brain cells and synaptic tissue (suspected of storing memory information) have shown a high rate of recovery of function after storage in liquid nitrogen.[31]

Some remarkable evidence supporting cryonics came from experiments carried out by Dr. Isamu Suda and colleagues at Kobe University in Japan in the 1960s and 1970s. Cat brains were perfused with a glycerol solution and cooled to subfreezing temperatures for varying amounts of time then rewarmed and supplied with blood. Brain-wave activity (electrical discharge) was observed that in some cases was virtually indistinguishable from that of a live cat. (In all cases the brains had been anesthetized beforehand and were completely unconscious, though electrical activity continued, as is normal under conditions of anesthesia.) In particular, brains could be stored at -20°C for five days then rewarmed, with normal-looking brain waves. This alone is a powerful argument favoring cryonics—certainly it seems that the brains were still viable after cooling. Some detectable, albeit diminished brain-wave activity was observed even after more than seven years' storage at this temperature.[32]

More recent experiments using lower temperatures and higher concentrations of glycerol seem to confirm these findings. In 1995 Ukrainian cryobiologist Yuri Pichugin and colleagues reported recovery of coordinated bioelectrical activity in rabbit brain slices after perfusion with up to 35 percent glycerol by volume in water (versus 15 percent for Suda) followed by cooling to liquid nitrogen temperature and rewarming.[33] This recovery is significant, both in view of the much lower temperature and also the higher concentration of cryoprotectant (glycerol) that was used. Higher concentrations are found to yield better structural preservation but may also be toxic to the cells. Here at least the toxicity problem is apparently shown to be a manageable one.

For good, long-term preservation low temperatures are needed—the tissue must be fully solidified. (The temperature of liquid nitrogen, -196°C, is favored since it is easy to maintain, though probably somewhat warmer temperatures would be satisfactory.) The extra cooling causes significant additional damage, especially in large tissue masses such as a mammalian organ or whole organism. In balance, however, it seems unlikely to be a massive obliteration of information. The tissue does become massively cracked on a fine scale, and cells are squeezed to a smaller volume as cell fluid is lost. Close inspection of the cracking suggests, however, not an unmitigated disaster but reason for optimism. The breaks are very clean, with little appearance of cellular debris. Such debris could be expected if damage of the information-obliterating sort occurred, either from mechanical or chemical disruption. Its absence is no guarantee that all is going well enough, of course, but it does suggest preservation, in an inferable form, of identity-critical structure.[34]

Indeed, the main danger zone may well be not the colder but the warmer temperatures, particularly above freezing where deterioration under ischemia would be far more rapid. But again, the Suda experiments suggest that this problem too is manageable. Other evidence of this sort comes from hypothermic experiments with dogs, monkeys, and other mammals. A dog, as one example, can undergo the preliminary stages of a cryonic suspension, be chilled to near the freezing point of water (not frozen however), and rewarmed after several "lifeless" hours with full recovery.[35] Some additional favorable evidence is furnished by cold-water drowning victims who have recovered with no lasting damage after more than an hour under water.[36] This is not to deny the seriousness of the problem. Despite the use of cardiopulmonary resuscitation, for example, "fewer than 1 percent of cardiac patients survive without any brain damage if they suffer four to six minutes of cardiac arrest."[37] This damage, however, is a long-term effect that does not necessarily imply that brain information was lost initially.

In balance, then, it seems that much information-bearing brain structure does survive cryopreservation, at least under reasonably good conditions. The preservation is almost certainly considerably better than what is achieved through a non-neural cell sample. The ontic criterion, then, is probably far better realized than in the case of genomic preservation only. It is less certain whether the medical criterion is also met, but I see grounds for optimism here too.

More research is needed, of course. We cannot be satisfied with a freezing technique that cannot presently be reversed, even if there is reason to think the damage is repairable in principle. More assurance can only come from improvements in our methods, as demonstrated experimentally. The most straightforward and convincing demonstration of this sort, reversible suspended animation, is now being pursued in earnest. "Twenty-first Century Medicine now has a well-funded research program that is generating the kind of results necessary to improve cryonic procedures, gain greater credibility for cryonics, and achieve suspended animation," writes CEO Saul Kent.[38] New types of solutions and protocols have achieved a substantial reduction in the formation of damaging ice crystals as tissue is chilled and also rewarmed.[39] The methods must still be perfected for use in cryonic suspensions, and, in particular, the problem of toxicity must be fully addressed. The outlook, then, should be better for those cryopreserved in the future. But I remain cautiously optimistic that even today's cryonics patients—the majority at least—can be reanimated mentally intact using just the information in their remains. It will probably require sophisticated nanotechnology that is not likely to exist for decades. But the point should be emphasized, once again, that it is better to freeze than not to freeze. Cryonics, for all its present uncertainty, is at least a better choice for the dying patient than the usual options of disintegration.

One other and I think substantial ground for optimism about cryonics concerns the nature of memories in the brain. I include here as memories any learned or acquired information. Memories, then, are the critical element that must be recovered if reanimation from suspension is to occur since other details, including even missing body parts, should be reconstructible from genetic information that is likely to survive in multiple copies. Memories in the brain are stored redundantly, so that some and possibly much structural obliteration could occur without substantial loss. Though there is much mystery about the details, it appears that storage of long-term memory—the important kind for a reanimation—is a process of strengthening the synaptic connections among the neurons of the cerebral cortex or outer layer of the brain. Memories are "locked in" by the neurons sprouting new connections.[40] The abundance of the neural connections, it is reasonable to conjecture, enhances the likelihood that these very memories would persist in the preserved tissue. Though tiny, the encoding structures are considerably larger than the nanoscale of DNA base-pairs and other such molecular features, a further insurance against easy obliteration. Memories can last for a century in life under body temperature conditions, suggesting they are, in fact, relatively durable and hard to erase. So it is likely, I submit, that memories would at least remain decipherable after a careful attempt to preserve them through freezing, even if present methods leave much to be desired. Cryonics seems worth pursuing for what it can accomplish now as well as with future improvement.

This brings up another ground for objection, however: a cryonics patient must be constantly maintained in liquid nitrogen. The frigid, water-clear substance is constantly boiling off and has to be replenished. (Cryonics patients are generally stored in large, double-walled containers or "dewars" that are filled with liquid nitrogen. Contrary to often-expressed opinion, the cold storage does not require electrically powered refrigeration and is not vulnerable to power failures, but it does require replacement of liquid nitrogen from time to time; typically this is done at intervals of a week or so.) In the past some frozen patients thawed and were lost when their organization went bankrupt, as noted in Chapter 2. Cryopreservation is expensive, costs ranging from around $30,000 to $130,000 depending on one's location, the organization's fiscal policies, and the type of option chosen (head-only versus whole body, for instance). Much of this funding is invested after the freezing is complete and the interest income used to purchase liquid nitrogen on an ongoing basis. One way to reduce the cost is to use a preservative method that does not require such maintenance, which will also eliminate the danger of thawing.

The Chemical Alternative

High quality chemical fixation has been used for many years in preserving biological specimens, and this method may offer promise or even be better than freezing.[41] Once again, its efficacy will depend, primarily, on how well brain structure is preserved in an inferable form. It is not necessary, as usual, that the cells be restorable to a functioning state by today's methods (in this case they usually are not) so long as enough information is captured. Unfortunately, the use of chemical fixatives as a possible route to eventual reanimation is still in its infancy and has not been well researched. More effort is needed to assess how well the critical structures are preserved. (Unlike low temperature, fixative may preserve some structures but bypass others due to impediments in the circulatory system.) Presently such preservation is difficult to arrange, and long-term storage is problematical. Cryonics remains the preferred choice for most people desiring reanimation. There is no guarantee that cryonics organizations will survive or be able to transfer their patients to other organizations if they do not. But at least there are several such organizations that have been in business for decades now, with a good record for keeping people frozen. More are signing up for cryonics all the time, and ongoing research offers the possibility of substantial improvements in techniques, as we have seen.

The advent of such improvements, to the extent of demonstrating reversible suspended animation, would brighten the picture in numerous ways. The scientific community and people at large, including any skeptical cryobiologists, would be confronted with more tangible evidence of our coming immortality. It would be hard evidence to ignore and should lead to much better approaches to the problem of getting suspended for those who need it. Today's suspension is impeded by the legal system. The patient, we noted, must be pronounced dead before freezing can occur. With a reversible process, a cryopreserved patient would have to be considered still alive. Cryopreservation would become simply another medical procedure. It might be used when the patient was in good health but facing a terminal condition, as in the early stages of Alzheimer's disease or even simple old age. The widespread acceptance of such a procedure should translate to many more lives being saved with debilitation circumvented.

But there could also be a great moral dilemma because one likely problem would be cost. Cryonics today is not cheap compared to more conventional means of disposal such as burial or cremation, though there are approaches, such as funding through life insurance, that make the cost bearable for many who are not wealthy. (It might be cheaper if the practice were more widespread, but it still would probably be expensive due to the complexity of the procedure and the necessity and difficulty of maintaining those in suspension.) Great technical improvements will probably make cryonics more expensive and possibly prohibitive to all but the wealthy. The moral dilemma will then arise that many lives could be saved but only through massive subsidies and cutbacks on other expenditures, some of which will be worthy in their own right. Alternative preservation methods will then be sought. Possibly the cruder freezing procedures of today will be retained, or a high-temperature, chemical method may be developed, or a combination, say, of chemical fixation or tissue stabilization and storage in permafrost. (One organization, the Cryonics Society of Canada, has offered fixation coupled with permafrost storage already, though few so far have been interested.[42])

Coming Back: a Possible Repair Scenario

We have now examined biostasis techniques with an eye to how well the critical information-bearing structures in the brain may be preserved. It is assumed that technology of the future, particularly nanotechnology, will make it possible to restore any sufficiently well-preserved remains to the functioning human they once were. But it will be instructive to take a closer, if still speculative, look at this anticipated repair process. We will consider the case of persons preserved cryonically, assuming the goal is to restore them to a biologically functioning state with good recovery of mental functions—in short, achieving the medical criterion.

Repairing a frozen human, if it is to be possible, will require a long wait until the needed technology can be developed and possibly another substantial wait while it is applied. Implicit in the notion of "repair," of course, is the idea of curing any ailments that may be present. All disorders—including the enfeeblements of aging—must be eliminated, and the frozen tissue must be rendered to a condition in which it can be rewarmed and become viable. Perhaps repair and rewarming will occur concurrently, or some rewarming could be done first.

Assuming the preservation was good enough, an issue to face is whether the necessary inference of information, and the repair and resuscitation of the functioning individual, could be done in a practical enough way that society of the future would be likely to carry it out. If not, it is a real possibility that a frozen though recoverable patient could still be thawed and lost rather than further maintained until more dedicated and enlightened individuals could take on the needed responsibilities. This, like many other things, cannot be ruled out in our present ignorance. But I will conjecture it is not likely, based on the thought that persons will probably become more enlightened relatively soon, as the prospects for great lengthening of life and improvements in its quality become apparent.

Frozen people, then, will be seen as assets in the manner we considered before, being expected to make interesting contributions in the lives of their benefactors and others. Reasonable efforts will be made to "bring them around," and self-repairing, largely self-directed, intelligent devices should make it inexpensive. Moreover, there is reason to think that a reanimation process, despite its complexity, could be done relatively quickly, in a matter of years at most (see below). Each case could then be approached with all the care and attention it deserved. Damaged tissue would be repaired or rebuilt, perhaps at low temperature by tiny, motorized components that did not require a warm environment, and then rewarmed to a functioning state.

The imaginative repair scenario below was devised by computer scientist and encryption expert Ralph Merkle,[43] following Drexler's suggestions in *Engines of Creation*.[44] Merkle's is a streamlined approach that focuses on repair of the brain. Rebuilding a body and enervating it to respond properly to the demands of the brain are regarded as of secondary difficulty, easier to carry out than brain repair itself (a view that is widely shared by cryonicists, including myself, though not universal). Merkle concludes, "Restoration of the brain down to the molecular level should eventually prove technically feasible." To speed the almost unimaginably complex repair process, he envisions a "divide and conquer" strategy in which the frozen brain tissue would be parceled into very small pieces, without significant loss of structural information, and each piece analyzed in detail by molecular-scale devices.

Actually two types of repair scenario are projected. The "onboard" scenario requires that all repairs be done in place without excising and transferring bits of tissue to remote locations. The "offboard" scenario relaxes this restriction, allowing greater flexibility in the repair process and other advantages such as a larger mass of repair devices working in parallel. It is the offboard scenario that Merkle gives the greatest attention to and that will be considered here. It should be emphasized that this is, in many ways, a worst-case scenario, intended to make a strong case that at least some form of satisfactory repair process is possible and will one day be realized. (An effort at a more realistic repair scenario has been made by Gregory Fahy;[45] however, Merkle's approach is conceptually simpler and thus seems more suitable from the standpoint of proof of principle.)

The offboard repair process splits into three subtasks. The first has the goal of simply extracting all pertinent information from the given tissue sample. If necessary, a complete description at the molecular level could be obtained. This would probably require "disassembly," or tearing down the frozen tissue into molecular components, but in a controlled way that would allow for reassembly, much as an ancient building may be disassembled brick-by-brick by archaeologists and the parts carefully labeled for later reassembly at another site. (Molecules themselves might be trapped and stored in individual, designated locations to effectively label them.) The second task would be to infer the healthy state of the tissue from the frozen state, something requiring a massive computing effort but feasible (arguably) with the powerful devices we will have in the future. The third and final operation would be to reassemble the frozen tissue in a repaired state, that is, to carry out actual repair. In its later stages, it would lead to integrating the fragments of tissue into an intact brain and integrating that brain into a repaired or rebuilt body.

At some point a rewarming operation would be necessary to return the repaired tissue to a functioning state. One possibility would be first to render the tissue in a vitrified condition in which chemical and mechanical damage have been minimized by the elimination of ice crystals and other optimizations have been performed at the molecular level. The tissue might then be rapidly warmed using microwave irradiation. (Microwave rewarming has in fact been used in cryobiological applications.) Blanket microwaving is just one possible approach, of course, and a crude one, a better one being the use of rapid but highly controlled heating, applied selectively and differentially at different points within the cold tissue. This in turn ought to become feasible, along with other advances, if nanotechnology can be perfected.[46]

One device important to the projected repair process is the general-purpose assembler considered in Chapter 9. Such a machine will not work nonscientific miracles, but it should allow us to approach the limits of what is allowed by physics as currently understood. Conceptually, much of the needed repairs should be simple and straightforward, even if advanced devices we do not yet possess will be needed. Many cells and parts of the body ought to be simply replaceable, as we have noted, from genomic information, and the redundancy of brain information will help. However, even in the case of crucial memory-specific structures, it seems a safe bet that much damage could occur without obliterating the essential information, much as a book can be heavily damaged by tearing or even charring the pages while still allowing recovery of the text.

Basing his computations on the known speed of biological synthesis Merkle is able to arrive at an estimate of the total time requirement of the repair process: 3.2×10^{23} machine-seconds. This (which is intended as an upper limit, not a tight bound) would occupy many trillions of years if performed in sequential fashion, one operation at a time. It becomes much more feasible with the divide and conquer strategy that is suggested, however, which uses many ultraminiaturized components working together. Such devices, suitably programmed, ought to be able to proliferate in vast numbers, much as small organisms do today. Merkle estimates that a device with sufficient complexity to enable it to carry out adequate repairs could be built with a weight of no more than 10 billion (10^{10}) hydrogen atoms. 3.2×10^{15} (3.2 quadrillion) such machines would require a total of about three years to carry out disassembly and repair of the brain, which should be the most difficult, time-consuming step.

Each machine would operate on a tissue mass equal in weight

to about 3 trillion hydrogen atoms, or 300 times its own weight. It would process this tissue during the three-year interval, at the end of which the different fragments (all 3.2 quadrillion) would be reunited and otherwise integrated into a fully repaired or reconstituted brain and body. (Again, repair or recreation of the body would be a minor operation compared to the brain work, taking substantially less time.) The total mass of the machines would be about 530 grams, or 40 percent of the mass of the brain. The major processing could be done in the solid state at low subfreezing temperature. This would not limit the capabilities of the largely mechanical repair devices as envisioned. Since the machines would largely be self-programmed, self-directed, and self-repairing, the cost of the repair could be very low, like growing a field of clover, which is a very complex process that biological devices now perform without human input at all. Moreover, a great deal of variability in these parameters is possible without precluding such an operation. For example, a requirement of 530 kilograms of repair devices, 1,000 times more than just estimated, "would have little impact on feasibility."[47]

This, then, is one possible scenario for the repair and resuscitation of a deep-frozen human. It is certainly not the only possible one. Proof-of-principle concepts have been stressed, and the approaches that are actually used could be quite different. (One possibility in particular is some form of uploading or expression of the person in an artificial, computational device, bypassing the necessity of biological tissue altogether.) Other details have been overlooked, such as the level of understanding of how the brain works that would be needed—much more will have to be understood, beyond our current level. But it shows how, with adequate structural information in the frozen remains, a return to conscious life should be possible. It would, of course, not involve any guesswork or metaphysical assumptions about alternate worlds, et cetera, which we would have to invoke in the more compromised cases such as genomic preservation. Not only would the repair process be feasible in principle, but it could be carried out with reasonable efficiency once the technology became available.

Choosing Physical Preservation

Cryonics, then, or some other method of high-quality brain preservation, seems a preferable course to follow in our efforts to attain immortality. Despite uncertainties the evidence suggests that cryonics may succeed and thus save the lives of those who make the arrangements. Ongoing research should offer both improved techniques and better knowledge, so the cryonicist of today may benefit from a considerably improved procedure when it is finally needed. We will also be in a better position to judge the efficacy of other preservative methods.

Because of its promise, I feel that cryonics is an important strategy to consider for a Philosophy of Action. It—along with any other, comparable brain-preserving procedures to combat the onset of death—should form a major "plank" in our moral platform. In this way we can best support progress to our proper destiny. This raises one more criticism that is sometimes urged against cryonics, that it is "selfish." I reply that, of course it is, but not unduly so—instead, rightly so! This is based on the premise that attaining immortality and a more-than-human status is the rightful destiny of each individual—which of course it is. All sentient life is precious, as I have argued, and this is all the more so for human life—including oneself.

Connected with the problem of selfishness is the problem of resources, which some like to raise. How can we justify committing resources to a project like biostasis "with so many poor people in the world to feed," and the like? Many people who raise this question wear jewelry or nice clothes, drive their own car, send their children to good schools, and otherwise enjoy the fruits of affluence rather more than the ones they are ostensibly concerned about. These fair-weather soldiers we can easily enough dismiss, but it will not resolve the underlying issue, which is certainly a real one. The right starting point for an answer, I think, is to recognize that there are a number of worthy goals we must try to meet, and our resources are not unlimited—but still we can reasonably pursue more than one good thing at once. Ridding the world of its evils, such as poverty, is not a simple matter in any case. Arguably more progress in such matters has come from technology created for self-interested reasons than from humanitarian efforts such as donations of food and material, however well intended, which is not to deny that such efforts are worthy and to be encouraged. But I think we can reasonably pursue many goals concurrently that build toward the greater goals of immortalization and abundance for all—with self-interest as one reasonable motivating factor.

"Looking out for number one" can certainly be mishandled— but a healthy commitment to one's own future, mentally, physically, and morally, is still a right and worthy cause. With the immortalist perspective the future becomes open-ended, and one is no longer bound by old and tragic limits. A new challenge is issued, and one should rise to it boldly. Make your arrangements, and also, make your wishes clear.

This brings up an issue, the problem of imperfect preservation, which we addressed for the case of genomic preservation. Something more should be said now, with the emphasis toward those of us, mainly cryonicists, who are committed to the more serious biostasis option that we hope will fully capture our identity-critical information. The problem, of course, is that it also might not.

Imperfect preservation is something that might be very common, or even universal, for those in cryonics dying today and for some time to come. Certainly we do not know, at the level we would like, how well we are preserving our cryonics patients and probably will not know for some time. This problem is of great concern in the cryonics community, and efforts to address it through research are under way, as we have noted, notwithstanding the grounds cited for optimism. For now, we are stuck with the possibility, at least, that our preservation is inadequate. We must then consider what avenues if any are open to counter the prospect that a full resuscitation from our preserved remains will not prove feasible.

As it turns out, there is something you can do to assist with your reanimation, however your preservation turns out, something we have already considered for the case of genomic preservation. This is to make a record of things that are important to you, and have it preserved for your reanimation. It is something you can start on today, using such means as paper and ink, photographs, and audio or video tape. The information you record might include your fondest memories, your preferences, your hopes, goals, and so on. (To give a rounded, authentic picture, it is also advisable to add your worst experiences, greatest dislikes, et cetera.) This could be of great aid in reconstructing your personality if your physical preservation is inadequate. The record you make could be updated in the course of your life too. Some cryonics organizations encourage their members to make and keep such a record, and probably any will assist with the preservation, if you show enough interest. This, of course, is no guaranteed panacea but a start in forestalling the problem, as it applies to you.

More generally, you should think about what you would like done, in case insufficient information is available from all sources for a straightforward reanimation. Do you want the missing information left blank, in other words, or "reinvented," that is, filled out by reasonable guesswork? Do you want to come back amnesiac, or with full memories but memories lacking the traditional historical ties or context? Or is there still another option you would prefer? We have considered arguments, such as the case for ontic robustness, that favor "reinventing" to fill out a reasonably complete individual—all information, of course, to be consistent with the historical record and assembled by the best educated guesswork. (This, the hyperontic resurrection, is what I would strongly prefer in my own case, if the preservation turns out to be inadequate. And of course I wish to be frozen in the event of death for possible eventual reanimation. So now I have stated my preference and you, reader, can similarly state yours.) But this is a matter for the individual to decide. Once you have made up your mind, though, once again, record your wishes!

In any case, furthering the aim of one's immortalization is very important. Preservation options could save many lives. But to do this they must be effective and affordably available. Involvement in cryonics, to the extent of making arrangements for one's own freezing, will not only maximize one's chances of benefit, but send a message to the world at large. And, indeed, all the world should be making use of the biostasis option right now. This, of course, is a tall order—it is unlikely that any mass conversion of attitudes will take place overnight. It will take time, and, it seems, losses of life will occur on a massive scale that could have been avoided.

As it turns out though, even with the current high cost cryonics would be affordable worldwide. Roughly 50 million people die each year,[48] most of them in ways that leave the brain reasonably intact—for a short time—during which it could be preserved by freezing. Multiplied by $50,000, a typical 1990s cost for a head-only suspension,[49] this works out to $2.5 trillion, about 10 percent of the 1995 world gross national product.[50] So it would be costly to save nearly everybody who dies, but not impossible if, say, there was a massive effort that would charitably bear expenses for those unable to meet the cost themselves. If such an effort were undertaken, and cryonics became a "common task," then economies of scale would probably drive down the price considerably, plus the level of interest in this option would generate much research to improve, diversify, and further reduce the cost of techniques. This, of course, is another dream at this stage. What has been accomplished so far in cryonics is but a small beginning, affecting a handful of "aficionados" while leaving most of the world the way it was. But interest is growing, a trend we expect to continue so long as research progresses both in and outside the field and people continue to think about what they want out of life and might be able to attain.

Summary and Conclusions

In summary, the Philosophy of Action demands we take a pro-active stand in furthering our own prospects for immortality. This, while directed toward self-benefit, need not be selfish in a narrow sense. To eliminate death and bring about a proper immortality is a noble and worthy cause, one with implications for humanity as a whole and its future. It is a cause we should commit ourselves to, here and now, as far as we are able, even though the world has many woes that need addressing.

Conditions now are still primitive—we cannot control aging and senescence, for example, though we are making progress and can at least take some steps to better our health and marginally extend our lives. But because of our still-mortal status, an important part of our commitment must involve the steps to be taken at the time of clinical death. (And we will have to worry about clinical death even after the advent of radical life extension, as we have noted.) Taking these steps for ourselves—making arrangements in advance for our own preservation in hopes of eventual reanimation—should inspire us to a more optimistic attitude about life in general, and we can then try to make that feeling conta-

gious. The world, we may hope, will waken to a stronger feeling
that immortality is a worthy aim—one, moreover, that can be
realistically pursued even in our present, death-dominated existence. Through our personal commitment, then, we inspire the
outsider to join and assist our cause, and hasten the day when all
may enjoy what none has known before.

Commitment to a personal strategy of biostasis is only one
rather limited feature of a Philosophy of Action. I think it has
overriding importance, however, given the state of things today
and the consequences that logically follow if one accepts biostasis for the reasons we have considered. Because of this and the
resistance with which such commitment is often met—for what I
think are insufficient and tragically shortsighted reasons—I have
emphasized it strongly. Second to this (once one has settled on
such commitment) is to support research and development as
much as possible. This can be pursued by keeping up with progress
in the relevant fields (cryonics itself, of course, but other areas
too, such as aging research and nanotechnology), investing or
donating funds, or even, in appropriate cases, becoming a researcher yourself. We should also, of course, be attentive to new
therapies and treatments and, in appropriate cases, consider their
usage to improve our health and further our immortalization. The
issue of what attitudes more generally we should cultivate was
addressed in the last chapter; a few remarks are worth adding.

In general, once again, a stance of benevolence toward others
is called for: we should be kind, compassionate, and loving. We
should, with due care and consideration, practice the Golden Rule
in both of its forms: Do not do to others what you would not want
done to yourself; do for others what you would want done for
yourself.[51] Prejudice based on such divisions as race, gender, national origin, or sexual orientation we must shun, as immortalists
generally do. Besides the all-important value of love, other values worth upholding are courage, reason, creativity, hope, truth-
fulness, fairness, freedom, unity, tolerance, responsibility, and
respect for life.[52] If we can take these seriously and convince
others to do the same, the world will be a better place, with a
greater likelihood of becoming what we would really like it to
be.

Among other things, this will involve a reasoned and considerate effort at promoting our ideas. Certainly an immortalist has a

unique perspective on "respect for life." We hope our particular respect can become contagious—we would like, if we could, to bring the world around to an immortalist stance—as a prelude to securing it for eternity. A world of considerate immortalists would be a better world all around—which of course would work to our individual benefit. But we must be realistic and not expect too much too soon, nor fall into too strident a promotional effort among the unready. Such "arm-twisting" can easily backfire and do more harm than good. A decent show of respect and willingness to consider other positions will probably accomplish more, overall, even if tragic and avoidable losses must occur.

More generally, we can cultivate respect for sentient life, not overlooking its prospects for a higher destiny but also respecting the realities of today. Every such life-form, I maintain, has some worth and can expect an ultimate immortalization. As a gesture of respect toward fellow creatures, and for reasons connected with health, some immortalists, myself included, have become vegetarians. The issue of vegetarianism is a complex one, however, and I do not feel the moral imperative in this case is clear-cut. More generally still, there are many matters relating to attitudes, practices, and policies that have no obvious or easy answers and seem, at least for now, best left to individual judgment.

But we are left with immortalization as a moral project, as we noted in the last chapter. This is the way we must approach this great task, the realization of our destiny. For it is only in this way that I think three important objectives can be met: (1) to fully justify our aspiration to an immortal existence; (2) to realize maximum benefit, both overall and individually; and (3) to optimize our chances of success. As we approach the task, our dedication must grow, nurtured with courage and hope. From a project, then, our immortalization must advance to a crusade, albeit a careful, kindly crusade, in which we seek to interact constructively with others, even our bitter opponents, to best further our aims and win them over in the bargain. But we see that our position, to work for immortalization through reason, science, and technology, inspired by love and guided by knowledge,[53] becomes our moral imperative. Let it be so.

CHAPTER 18.

The World at Large and the Future

An old adage claims that "the more things change, the more they stay the same." This is interestingly confirmed, on the grandest possible scale, if we accept the multiverse. We have noted how the multiverse is timeless and unchanging overall, regardless of happenings however hectic, at the level of observer reality. But I think the adage applies even at the observer level, and from it we can draw comfort in the face of a strange and unprecedented future.

In today's world things are changing fast, much faster than they did in former times. Many are frightened and wish the pace would slow down. To us immortalists, by way of contrast, certain changes are not happening fast enough. We have no use for things such as aging and terminal diseases and are hoping for a time, the sooner the better, when we will not have to put up with them. But we too have to confront a future where many things will change. It raises the questions of what sort of world we can expect and whether it will be a suitable place to live out a very long and maybe endless existence. Here I think we can take heart in the likelihood of certain, positive things remaining the same through all the anticipated changes, which in turn should mainly be changes for the better. But it will be worthwhile to briefly address the concerns of those who do not share this optimism before considering more directly the sorts of changes and constancies that might occur in our transition from mortal to immortal.

In fact, many of the worries are twofold. There is concern over change—the collapse and disappearance of the familiar as alterations take effect and a possibly worse situation develops. But it is also feared that certain unwanted things will stay the same—bad effects such as social injustice, poverty, and terrorism, along with such problems as difficulty in finding work. The changes, in fact, are seen as prolonging such problems or making them worse. Life extension could overburden the job market, for instance, as older people remain productive and fail to die "on schedule." Generally though, the worriers do not consider more radical changes such as modifications to the human organism, which we can now foresee. Such changes are inevitable and, indeed, have started already on a modest scale, with such advances as tooth and corneal implants, bone and skin grafting, artificial hip replacement, coronary bypass surgery, gene therapy, tissue engineering, and the use of chemical "strength builders" in sports. Another class of advances is neural implants. Electrically active components are surgically inserted into the brain or at other points in the body to control seizures and motion disorders, provide the deaf with hearing, maintain the rhythm of the heart, or, more experimentally, assist in seeing and motor control of artificial limbs.[1] Overall we are living longer in better health, a first step toward becoming more-than-human.

This suggests a more optimistic outlook, in which changes for the better, such as improvements in our very physical makeup, will lead to ways of overcoming once and for all certain traditional limitations. Such "innate" traits as basic intelligence, health status, and other strengths or weaknesses should no longer depend on accidents of our genes or upbringing. Education, including reeducation, has long been available to impart new skills or knowledge and facilitate changes in location and lifestyle. Today it is helping overcome limits based on cultural and other divisions, and the world is becoming more unified as living standards improve. But the more venturesome can now go further, in a limited way. Such "basics" as race and gender can be altered through surgical and other techniques, for example; the future should open many more such doors. It is hard to imagine any nonsuicidal person who will not eventually desire substantial changes, reversal of aging, for instance, then—why not?—enhanced intelligence, and so on.

Meanwhile, automation on unprecedented scales should free us of drudgery. The necessity to "make a living" in some sense will probably always be with us, but it will not seem at all what it is now. Today we distinguish business from pleasure, as in "business before pleasure." People spend much of their lives working at things they would not do if they did not have to, "to make ends meet." Some of this mismatch seems traceable to the fact that, despite our advances, including fledgling successes with improving our physiology, we are still basically the creations of unthinking nature. We are biological throwaways, jerry-built by natural selection, and we evolved for lifestyles very different from what most practice today. Our past and present deserves a respectful remembrance, yet by themselves are limited and limiting. Our basic and, in my view, unlimited worth lies not so much in what we are or have been but in what we can become. Toward this end, in the future we will be able to adapt and develop in ways not possible before. I think, then, we will come to feel that whatever sort of world we find for ourselves, it is "right" in a deep sense that is probably beyond our experience now. For life can never be satisfactory or complete—its fundamental, ineffable goodness cannot be realized—until the sentence of death is lifted, aging is cured, and we have options to develop as we wish not bound by old limits.

I see three main stages in this anticipated advance, which we will consider in turn. These I will call *human*—our present level—then *transhuman*—where we may be in a little while, as our upward climb progresses—then finally, *posthuman*—the "high ground" we are really striving for, though not a consummated state either. Needless to say, it will not be easy to imagine what the later features of this process will be like; our speculative survey will be limited to a few main points. But overall we can take comfort in the prospects, which should not frustrate but fulfill our finest aspirations and lead to a new and stable order based on the permanence of the individual.

Coping with Resistance

We noted how there is widespread fear about some of the things we are now doing. One case in point is the cloning of mammals. Humans are mammals. We have cloned livestock and can probably clone a person too, using substantially the same methods—indeed, the preliminary step of creating an embryo has already been announced, as noted in Chapter 9. Many have found this disturbing and feel we are probing into areas we should not. Sometimes reasonable objections are raised. A human cloned from an adult could have shorter telomeres and thus age faster than a natural child. All sensible people agree that this is one reason to hold off for awhile, until we know better what to expect. But I think the objection to human cloning runs deeper than can be accounted for on such reasonable grounds. (The telomere problem might be easily avoided by using a cell from an infant or fetus or one treated with telomerase.) Instead there seems to be a general fear of entrusting our fate to our own devising, which extends to any efforts we might make to substantially change the human condition.

People, in short, fear that bad must follow if we try to tamper with things as they are. Some of this fear I think is attributable to simple alienation. People tend to be repelled by new things in general. Such aversion can be understood as a survival trait since many new things are a threat or are otherwise inferior to the "tried and true." The case of new, advanced knowledge probably throws up additional roadblocks. Scientific subjects are not easy to master and get increasingly difficult as more discoveries are made requiring additional knowledge and understanding.

Certainly too there is tangible evidence of the horrors that can follow when human effort and ingenuity are bent to destructive ends, as in the terrible history of modern warfare. Such bad effects, however, are offset by many good ones: everything from medical advances to improvements in communication, transportation, data processing, and even (sometimes) the food we eat. Not even many doomsayers would advocate a return to the horse-and-buggy era that preceded our present, automated world with so many comforts, however short of perfection it may still be. And things are not standing still. We are caught up in ongoing technological progress, something that should benefit us more and more. Yet there is not much enthusiasm for the thought that this could be our deliverance.

The apathy and even hostility to the idea of salvation through science probably runs deeper than a simple dislike of unfamiliar, complicated subjects or even the fear of a future world war or

other cataclysm. Instead it appears to involve a worldview confrontation, a calling into question that many find difficult to face
and would rather not think about. Consider again human cloning,
in which a person is to be made through a laboratory procedure.
That such a thing should be possible brings home the fact that,
just like every other functioning device, a human is a construct
made of atoms. There is no mystical, "spiritual" essence. It is
easy to see how mystically inclined people will be unsettled. But
others too, who are not strongly attached to such views, are still
reluctant to endorse "technology as deliverance"—though I think
they will be convinced as progress continues.

This could still take considerable convincing, for people do
not change worldviews lightly. Such coping mechanisms are
important for life and death issues and powerfully influence reactions to innovations that may impact such issues. Generally,
worldviews hold that death is unavoidable and irreversible or that
a superhuman agent is needed to overcome death. Typical views
based on science, reason, and materialism hold that death and
eternal oblivion are eventual certainties and must be accepted
with no hope of escape. People who hold such views are, I think,
especially resistant to hoping for something better. Such hopes
might be dashed. It is better to have no hope, to simply have no
interest than to entertain a hope that seems to rest on too flimsy a
foundation. But another viewpoint is possible, as we have seen,
that is neither mystical nor death-accepting, though at the same
time placing the burden on ourselves to solve some tough problems.

The "truths" we have considered in this work are presented as
working hypotheses only, to be tested as far as possible by evidence. It is possible that one or more of them can be overturned,
but we can be inspired by the very fact that they *are* open to
question; we are not committing ourselves to dogmas. It is not
always easy to test claims, especially claims about what is possible in the future but has not happened yet. Some testing can be
done through such means as logical extrapolation based on what
has been reasonably established already. But again there is uncertainty. Uncertainty, however, need not be a cause of despair
but can inspire us: life would be dull indeed if all interesting
questions had been answered already. Instead, it seems that we
can never exhaust the supply of interesting unanswered ques-

tions, and this is one reason to have confidence that life will always have meaning.

Today I think it is often questioned whether life has real meaning, and that brings us back to the first of our three postulated divisions of the future, the human phase. This we can expect will continue for at least a while, though it may end sooner than we think. A reasonable termination point, I offer, is when life spans have been significantly lengthened, including the "maximum" life span. Before that time, we are still essentially human as today, but after aging is no longer able to retire successive generations in the customary manner, we begin our transhuman phase.

Immortalism and Human Problems

Let us now look at some of the problems confronting us today and ask whether and how a philosophical outlook along the immortalist lines developed here might help address these problems. This is a deep subject, of course, and it is only possible to suggest some major themes and what seem appropriate responses.

At a basic level, again, is the issue of meaning. We have come a long way, scientifically and technologically, but uncertainties seem to plague us more than ever, in particular, confusion about the future and what our role in the scheme of things ought to be. Yet some good answers can be arrived at by considering some of our deepest wishes, such as the desire for a nonterminating, better-than-human existence. This we have done, with a cautiously reassuring conclusion. We will have to put forth no small effort to realize the happy immortality that seems to be possible, but the reward will be great. We can then approach the future with confidence: life *will* have meaning for those who seek diligently and will offer benefits that justify the effort—such at least, can be our working hypothesis.

Human history has seen its fair share of violence, something that became particularly horrible in the twentieth century, as institutions of death became more mechanized and new means of destruction were perfected. This, of course, we hope to decisively put behind us as we approach a more-than-human future. We must certainly abolish war—before it abolishes us. There is no guarantee that we can, but the prospect of our self-immortalization at least supplies some strong new incentives. In addition there is the issue of resource management. In former times much conflict resulted over competition for limited resources. Groups with differing cultural backgrounds and worldviews found it especially tempting to fight it out, demonizing each other in the process and fostering hatreds that have festered in some places around our globe for millennia. Something of this sorry "struggle for survival" is seen today in the Middle East, the Balkans, and some cities in the United States.

Here, though, we have reasons for optimism: our new prospects offer a two-pronged attack on such dreary reruns from a mortal past. On one hand, there is our developing capability to satisfy basic wants, which is accentuated by the trends we see toward smaller family sizes and more responsible addressing, overall, of the problem of human needs. On the other, the prospect of our own immortalization calls for a new worldview in which old dogmas, hatreds, and other sources of division are put aside. In our new quest for Heaven, we can hopefully work together more than was possible before.

Though there is this ground for optimism, there is also increasing danger, much of it not from large organized groups such as countries but small fringe groups and isolated individuals. Our population is still growing, with its inevitable retinue of marginal, unhappy elements. Destructive devices can be acquired or manufactured by those with enough ability and/or dedication. There are plenty of smart but alienated people, some of whom are inclined to take matters into their own hands, and terrorism is now inflicted on a private scale not seen before. While general, positive trends may do much in calming and revitalizing the vast majority, the isolated, disgruntled elements may not be persuaded so easily.

Some of the dangers terrorists pose and the intricate, fuzzy boundaries that exist more generally between genius and madness, good and evil, are brutally illustrated in the case of Theodore Kaczynski, the notorious "Unabomber." Born in 1942, a Harvard graduate at age twenty, by the late 1960s Kaczynski had become an assistant math professor at the University of California at Berkeley, with an apparently secure future. But the troubled young instructor had other thoughts.

By the early 1970s he had withdrawn to the Montana wilderness, where he hand-built a small cabin with no running water or electricity to serve as his principal residence and base of operations. There he spent many years in solitary seclusion, perfecting package bombs and mailing them to unsuspecting victims. His targets were generally in computer-related or other high-technology professions. (The "Una" in Unabomber came from "universities" and "airlines," two sources of his targets.) By the time he was apprehended in 1996, more than twenty people had been injured by his explosives, three fatally, and he now serves a life sentence. His 1995 "manifesto" entitled *Industrial Society and Its Future*, published in the *Washington Post* and the *New York Times*, and a letter earlier that year to the *Times*, allow a glimpse into his thinking. (The publication of these and other of his writings also helped generate leads used in tracking him down.)[2]

"The Industrial Revolution and its consequences," he writes, "have been a disaster for the human race. They have greatly increased the life-expectancy of those of us who live in 'advanced' countries, but they have destabilized society, have made life unfulfilling, have subjected human beings to indignities, have led to widespread psychological suffering (in the Third World to physical suffering as well) and have inflicted severe damage on the natural world." Increased life expectancy, for Kaczynski, is seen in negative, not positive terms and does not mitigate the "disaster for the human race" that is imputed to the process of industrialization. In general, the author, while professing concern over humanity and societally imposed limitations to freedom, shows little regard for persons as individuals.

"The continued development of technology," he continues, "will worsen the situation....Whatever else may be the case, it is certain that technology is creating for human beings a new physical and social environment radically different from the spectrum of environments to which natural selection has adapted the human race physically and psychologically." The human race, he offers, will have to be "artificially re-engineered" to adapt; natural selection is too slow. The deduction is a reasonable one, of course— but the author sees it only as a threat. The possibility that re-engineering could result in improvement of human beings and elevation to a better life than could be had before never enters his thinking. Instead there is blindness, hatred, contempt, and destructiveness.

"It would be better," rages Kaczynski, "to dump the whole stinking system and take the consequences." He offers two main courses of action: "to promote social stress and instability in industrial society" and "to develop and propagate an ideology that opposes technology and the industrial system." His ideology calls for deindustrialization and a return to "wild nature." His promotional tactics are violent, infantile, and pathological.

"In order to get our message before the public with some chance of making a lasting impression," he insists, "we've had to kill people....The people we are out to get are the scientists and engineers, especially in critical fields like computers and genetics." Others too were marked for death. "We blew up Thomas Mosser last December because he was a Burston-Marsteller executive....But we attacked Burston-Marsteller less for its specific misdeeds than on general principles. Burston-Marsteller is about the biggest organization in the public relations field....its business is the development of techniques for manipulating people's attitudes....The people who are pushing all this growth and progress garbage deserve to be severely punished. But our goal is less to punish them than to propagate ideas."

This, then, is one dangerous individual, who in his career of serial killing was able to articulate his obsessions and even, as we might expect, gain sympathizers. For there is no shortage of people disaffected by modern society and its technological intrusions who long for a return to "nature." (The nature-loving immortalist replies, "I want to return to the wild too—after my aging is cured—and in the bargain I will make a better steward of the environment than any here today, gone tomorrow mortal.") It is appropriate to emphasize that, of course, it is not Kaczynski's ideas or the articulation of them that is the problem here, whether one agrees with him or not, but the violence that was resorted to and justified as a necessary accompaniment. So his crusade, whatever its merits, was nullified by its tactics and could only backfire against any individual or group that might be associated in the public mind through a similarity of views.

The threat of terrorism continues, and it may not even begin to subside until we are into our transhuman phase—or even later. Sometime before then it could be our undoing. Terrorists with a nuclear stockpile or some new weapon based on nanotechnology could be terrible indeed, if other more currently available weapons such as nerve gas, package bombs, and the anthrax bacillus are not enough. This is not the only kind of threat either. Another one is computer viruses, programs, often self-replicating, that can enter a data processing system through electronic mail and disrupt its functions. Viruses can be created by knowledgeable hackers without involving a weapon as usually understood or any sort of controlled substance or apparatus. They can be launched incognito to remote locations at the touch of a button. They pose their own kind of threat, which becomes more acute as our dependence on computers grows. In a hospital or airport, for instance, a virus-induced malfunction in computer software could end the lives of patients or passengers.

One support of terrorism, though not the only one, is harsh economic conditions in certain countries or cultures that impoverish a substantial number of the well educated, who may then feel bitter toward others in more fortunate societies. Antagonisms at the cultural, national, or racial level can be especially virulent and dangerous. Other persons with long-standing, smoldering grudges may be willing to dedicate major parts of their lives to a disruptive cause, as we see with Kaczynski. Another danger comes from unbalanced or irresponsible pranksters possessing enough knowledge to do major damage, as in the creators of computer viruses, who may be juveniles. Clearly there are many possible causes of harmful behavior. But I see reasons for hope that none of these will prove overwhelming.

Overall trends should diminish privation in living standards and thus set guidelines even for people of destructive bent. Other possible approaches to improving safety range from better detection and defenses against both hardware and software devices to more focused efforts to reach and discourage all those inclined to maliciousness. I expect that, as progress continues and the potential for both good and evil grows in step, curbing destructive behavior will be seen as an increasingly urgent matter. We can then expect concerted efforts to do so by individuals and public institutions. These prospects are no guarantee, of course, either that evil will be checked as desired or that abuses of power will not emerge as an unpleasant side-effect. Shortcomings are to be expected, here as elsewhere. Yet we may hope that by the time we have reached our posthuman phase, assuming we are so fortunate, we will have acquired sufficient maturity, wisdom, and overall satisfaction that the threat of disruption will be a small one. Or—somehow failing that, though I think it unlikely if we progress to this level—we will have safeguards in place that make it difficult even for advanced malcontents to seriously hurt us. The faster we progress meanwhile, the sooner this era of safety will come, and the less chance that matters will go awry before-hand.

Starting from the philosophical perspective of this book, then, we find good reason to deplore violence and harmful acts and advocate another course instead. Few, I think, will contest this basic stance or side with the small minority who do oppose it, including active terrorists. To this we can add that concern with the environment ought to be a priority: our earthly home must become a suitable habitat for immortals—and for now we must preserve and protect our home as best we can—but within rea-sonable limits. Sentience is served by insentience, not the other way around, and more advanced sentience—humanity—has pre-cedence over less advanced, though appropriate respect should be tendered to all.

Today there is much concern over environmental depletion and destruction, with some foundation. For example, tropical forests, important to the global ecology, are now being leveled at a rate that would eliminate them altogether in fifty to eighty years, if not sooner. Other threatening consequences of present civiliza-tion include topsoil erosion, toxic wastes, depletion of water tables, species extinctions, and global warming. These problems are exacerbated in areas where poverty and rapid population growth are especially acute, such as the tropics.[3] Many have de-spaired, fearing that technological progress can only make mat-ters worse and possibly doom the human species along with many or most other earthly life-forms. Needless to say, this would also doom any attempt of our species to rise to something higher.

But a more optimistic assessment of this predicament seems more realistic. Much of the current environmental problem is caused by wasteful, ill-planned practices. Far better resource management is possible. For this we do not have to invoke ad-vanced technology of the future or, as some reactionaries includ-ing terrorists have advocated, the regression of our species to a preindustrial past. Instead what is called for is a more careful approach with the means of today, emphasizing sustainable de-velopment, an important part of which is sustainable design. Waste must be eliminated; materials must be recyclable, reusable, or biodegradable; energy must be conserved. Nonrenewable resources such as fossil fuels must be used less and eventually supplanted by sustainable ones such as solar power. Consumption of renewables such as forests must not exceed the earthly rate of replacement and must also respect an often delicate balance of interacting life-forms.

These considerations apply at our present, still human level, and I think they will continue to have importance in the future, even if great changes in our own characteristics should occur along with other unprecedented advances. For our present and future home is not in some mystical realm but here, in this universe and probably, for a long time to come, this earth and neighboring space. Advancing technology, as it does become available, can and must be used in harmonizing our presence to the environment that sustains us.

Some Controversial Issues

Perspectives developed in this work also apply to more controversial issues. We must, of course, pursue such things as the radical extension of the human life span, even if the effect is to replace the human species with life-forms never seen before, as we surely will do if we succeed. We must not be deterred by the thought that up to now, death after a few decades has been a basic part of our existence. We must accept the unacceptability of our demise. We must boldly rise to the challenge and create a new kind of living creature—ourselves immortalized.

Some other controversial issues of a more mundane nature deserve mention. In the last chapter we briefly considered the unpleasant problem of abortion. Aborted fetuses, we noted, might be salvaged by preserving a cell sample, from which an infant could later be cloned. It is worth adding that this possibility, to some extent, is feasible today—cells isolated from very young embryos can develop directly into whole organisms. Such possibilities, moreover, could probably be extended easily, in view of the successes with cloning mammals and the preliminary stages of cloning humans. On the other hand, abortions are generally performed not with the aim of ultimately producing an offspring but with preventing this from happening—the fetus is discarded and destroyed. Opponents of the practice generally argue that any human fetus, however young, is a human being and destroying (killing) it an act of murder. This consideration extends even to the level of a single-celled organism, a human zygote or fertilized egg, created when a sperm and an unfertilized egg unite—or now, by other possible means. (Here I will focus on the more usual union of sperm and egg.)

To some extent this point of view—that a zygote, even though only a cell, is human—might be justified on informational grounds, for a zygote does contain a human genome. A human could be made from it, though extra information must be supplied from the outside to furnish a personality of any sort—the brain must grow and be "programmed." (The growth of neurons, in particular, is not merely genetically determined but depends somewhat on external influences as a child matures, despite the influence of genes in the makeup of the personality.) But if we classify the genome, on informational grounds, as a human, we would have to do so for an ununited sperm and egg, which will generally combine in only one way to produce a completed zygote. If the destruction of a zygote is murder, then, we could argue, the failure to see to it that any given sperm and egg unite is also "murder"—though I think few would go so far. And I do not think we are justified in calling zygote destruction murder either. Abortion could thus be permitted under certain circumstances, even if no cell sample is saved.

We may hope, however, that this issue will decline in importance, as seems likely if our progress continues, and eventually vanish altogether. Indeed, technology already presents us with the prospect of decoupling the sex act from the reproductive process, through such options as cloning. In the future we can imagine that babies will be started—when wanted—by methods other than the time-honored but emotion-biased procedure of today because new and all-around better methods will have been developed.

But it illustrates how a policy can depend on a worldview. In this case I do not attach a mystical soul to a human fetus as some do but judge the issue on reductionist, informational grounds. It is well to add that based on any particular viewpoint including this one, it is not always clear how to proceed. At what point should a fetus—or infant—be considered fully human, so that its

destruction would be murder? I think there should be a requirement of sentience: before the brain is activated and awareness is
possible, there is no question that a human is not present. But
beyond this I do not think there is an easy answer—and will not
try to give an answer. At least, though, we can understand the
grounds on which an answer must rest: the human seen as having
a material basis and not a mystical essence.

This in no sense justifies any maltreatment—rights of an entity capable of sensing and feeling must be respected. This I would
extend to cases where the entity is not conscious or biologically
viable but could become so by a process not involving substantial creation of information. A frozen cryonics patient would still
be human in this sense, so long as a straightforward reanimation
without guesswork could occur, that is, if the preservation was
good enough. (And it would not have to be good enough to bring
back the "original," only good enough that in a reasonable sense
a person was recoverable.) Even a description of a human—detailed enough to specify a functioning person—would qualify.
To destroy such a record—or, more properly, every copy of the
record—would reasonably amount to homicide. But we need not
worry in a case where clearly no such information-bearing entity
exists, as certainly seems true with the genome only.

Persons arguing otherwise and also denying mysticism would,
it seems, be forced to the position that the personality *is* primarily genomic—but that would raise the problem of the separate
sperm and egg. They would have to conclude that, effectively,
some amount of homicide does and must occur. It is estimated
that a man in the normal course of life produces about 400 billion
viable sperm cells (4×10^{11}) and a woman about 400 mature egg
cells (4×10^2).[4] (Egg cells are much larger than sperm cells and
correspondingly harder for nature to make.) Multiplying the two
together will give us, roughly, the total number of genomic combinations possible for just one couple alone, more than 10^{14}, more
than 10,000 times the entire population of the earth. Nearly all of
these, of course, are never realized, but most by appearances could
be realized. Once again, a sperm plus an egg equals a genome,
whether physically united or not.

Either genomic disruption is not murder or we have to accept,
based on the information paradigm, that a fair amount of what
amounts to human sacrifice is going on and find guidelines for

what is reasonable sacrifice and what is not. As a still more out-landish but real possibility, most cells in the body could, by appearances, be made into whole babies through cloning. Is the killing of even one of these cells to be considered murder? In any case, I have focused on this issue of abortion not to definitively solve it but to illustrate how some difficult choices confront us, which will be affected by our worldview and, in particular, whether this view is materialistic.

It is worth noting, moreover, that the abortion issue has repercussions beyond the simple question of whether to have a child or not. Grafts of tissue obtained from aborted fetuses have shown promise in treating brain disorders and might be used to replace the depleted cells of any other organ as well. But fears of "playing God" and the like have created a hostile political climate to this sort of work, which as a consequence has been greatly slowed or halted in the United States and elsewhere.[5] One may hope this situation will rectify itself with time. (Private funding is one alternative that has already made a significant contribution, for example, in work with embryonic stem cells.[6]) But we see that progress is not guaranteed and instead is often impeded by old worldviews and fear. One should not condemn this conservatism out of hand, for certainly not all progress is constructive or beneficial. Change is not guaranteed to produce improvement—far from it. However, clearly our present time offers unprecedented possibilities of great, constructive changes, and we need to move forward with wisdom and diligence rather than succumb to a paralysis of aversion and indecision.

Another controversial issue, whose resolution depends somewhat on a worldview, is capital punishment. Putting convicted criminals to death used to be much more common than it is now (and more painful). The more developed countries have particularly restricted or, in many cases, now abolished the practice. But some people are still being executed, generally for heinous crimes that themselves involve taking human life. Some advocate institutional killing on grounds that murderers deserve to die. Others, however, would have all institutional executions stopped. As could be expected from the discussion in Chapter 16, I favor the latter view (except that prisoners might be granted privileges of elective, assisted suicide, to match similar rights for citizens in good standing, though I think to choose simple suicide is mistaken too). One reason to favor abolition of the death penalty is simply that persons sometimes are wrongly put to death for offenses they did not commit, but there are other good reasons as well.

As we progress, probably we will increasingly understand why some people do horrible things and how best to ensure that they become morally incapable of repeating these acts. Once again, a repentant wrongdoer could have great value. Moreover, I think a commitment to killing certain people, however repulsive and hateful they may have become, is a corrosive influence that must impede our progress to the happy immortal state we would like to attain. It is natural to feel that the bad deserve to die and to want vengeance, but I feel that simple revenge is an unworthy motive and out of place in the world we would like to create. We can treat even the worst offenders as malfunctional and open to healing rather than depraved in an absolute sense.

As one possibility, our position can be based on determinism and the absence at a deep level of free will, as we have noted. There must be comprehensible causes for any behavior, however inappropriate—and hopefully remedies short of killing the perpetrator. (In fact many death-row inmates were severely abused as children and have major brain abnormalities, which, however, have not spared them from execution, something that must rank as a severe blot on the justice system.[7]) I will say too that the conditions we all live under, in our "normal" world of death and tragedy, are harrowing even in good times and while far from justifying bad conduct, do make it more understandable. The particularly bad players, moreover, are relatively few in number, and their indefinite, secure incarceration—until such time as they can be confidently released as cured—would place no large burden on existing institutions. (Our prisons are generally supported by taxes, and some argue strongly against this on the ground that taxation is theft. But the correctional institution, rightly a kind of hospital rather than a place of retribution, could also be supported by charitable contributions or in other ways.) I do not think this would lead, as some would argue, to encouragement of violent acts. Terrorists, we noted, may feel they will benefit through dying by being inducted into paradise; in general the case seems weak that the death penalty is a deterrent to murder.[8]

As we progress, we hopefully will find the means of reversing aging, and it will become part of standard medical practice. Today there is a feeling, particularly in more developed countries, that persons are entitled to medical treatment regardless of status. It even extends to prison populations. Rejuvenation treatments, when perfected and accepted as part of the medical repertoire, should also be in this class. Ultimately, prisoners—all who are not put to death—will receive them, regardless of their crimes. (Any who are put to death, on the other hand, will perhaps have biostasis as an option, as I feel they should if executions must continue.) We can hope, meanwhile, that our understanding of all human behavior, good, bad, or indifferent will advance considerably. Our means to deal constructively with the tougher cases should advance in step. Meanwhile, our policies can be influenced by the future prospects that seem achievable and even likely, if still unrealized.

Legal issues will, no doubt, offer many challenges as we approach our hopeful immortality. One more concern, for example, is the war on drugs. Drug abuse is real, and users can certainly harm themselves, yet there is argument that each individual has the right to freedom of choice—drugs should be legalized; the "war" should end. As John Stuart Mill summed it up in 1859: "the only purpose for which power can be rightfully exercised over any member of a civilized community, against his will, is to prevent harm to others. His own good, either physical or moral, is not a sufficient warrant."[9]

Over time we have seen an increasing acceptance of Mill's position (which I, like many immortalists, also accept). The authority of governments to limit the freedom of individuals has been questioned and has eroded. This trend I expect to continue, despite complications such as terrorism that could force a reversal in some areas. One very strong motivator is economics. Thriving business tends to produce a wealthier, more educated class of people demanding more freedom and removal of prohibitions. Today prosperity for many is growing, with such advances as the continuing information revolution and the weakening of totalitarianism. So I think we will probably see an increasing legalization of practices now often forbidden: use of drugs, gambling, prostitution, and so on. The effects will not always be beneficial—every privilege carries a responsibility, and many will only learn this the hard way—if at all—and some may lose their lives. The effects of one's behavior on others must be considered too, which will justify some curbs on freedom and some exercise of power over the individual. But responsible choices will at least be possible that are precluded today.

One choice that ought to become possible is of immediate interest to immortalists. This is the right to have a biostasis procedure started before legal death. In Chapter 2 we examined the case of Thomas Donaldson, a brain tumor victim who was denied the right to a premortem cryonic suspension in 1992. Hopefully this will not be so in the future. Assisted suicide laws are making tentative progress, though still desperately contested by conservatives. This could be a difficult route for someone wanting a premortem suspension, however. The laws may be nullified, as happened in Australia's Northern Territory, and otherwise there are restrictions that would make it very difficult for someone to be frozen under such a law. (Indeed this had not happened as of this writing.) But cryonics is not about suicide, despite the fact that current laws treat cryonics patients as "dead" and a premortem suspension, should it be carried out, as "homicide." That will only change with more research, which, among other things, should result in a better case that suspended patients are still "living." More generally, nothing succeeds like success. With more scientific progress to bolster our case, we can hope for more freedom of choice in matters that affect our own survival.

Immortalism and the Outside World

Increasingly I expect a reexamination of the whole issue of death and of what course to follow when death is imminent or has just occurred. The position here, of course, is that persons should not be "disposed of" in the traditional ways but committed to biostasis for the possibility of future revival—assuming they themselves are not opposed to such a course. Once this position is accepted, we are impelled to regard biostasis itself as a medical option. In particular, dying children and institutionalized persons, along with others, must be considered candidates for biostasis. This raises some difficult questions. If cryonics "probably" will work, then not freezing people is "probably" killing them. If the people in question are not able to give informed consent (as with young children or the mentally incompetent) then responsibility for possibly sacrificing them must rest with caregivers.

As yet it is uncertain whether cryonics or other biostasis techniques will work as intended. There is no moral imperative, the many doubters will argue, for enforcing a preservative option in the case of those not competent to decline it. Instead, and despite any counterarguments from advocates, the biostasis option will continue to be overlooked and ignored. This rejection will probably be the norm for most people, whether competent or not, until the as-yet unattained goal of reversible suspended animation is demonstrated. When it is, though, biostasis will have to be taken much more seriously among the legal and medical professions, including many who will probably be ill-prepared.

One wonders if it must be so—or if there could be a way to encourage more preparedness, both for the major changes that seem on the way and in view of the beneficial effects that would follow, even before that, simply from a change in attitudes. This we have considered, but some additional remarks are called for.

If today's experience is any guide, people are unprepared because the new possibilities clash so sharply with their worldviews, expectations, and values. A worldview has been advocated here that is scientific, atheistic, and materialistic but nonetheless opens possibilities for eternal life and happiness. Guidelines have been developed for reasonable expectations and values consistent with this worldview. We may hope that some, at least, will be inspired and persuaded to become good immortalists and cryonicists. But it seems that many alive today will remain thorough skeptics and die without making any arrangements for preservation. We must ask if there are alternative approaches to inspire more interest in the scientific possibilities for life extension.

What comes to mind is to seek to persuade the doubtful through harmonization with their own worldviews rather than laying stress on something new and foreign. This, properly handled, would be no betrayal of the Yuai position, which, we remember, is Universalist and values all sentient beings, including those who disagree with us. Deeds in any case are more important than creeds. We want people to consider the biostasis option now or soon, whatever their beliefs or worldviews. So it is worthwhile to look into ways that certain worldviews could be adapted to an immor-

talist outlook while still retaining their basic character, notwithstanding that this too has difficulties.

Many people have a religious perspective: they believe in God
and an immortal soul. The existence of God was examined in
Chapter 10. The possibility seemed small, and we were led to a
position of atheism, though with a concept of divinity that is to
be realized scientifically. But we hope more traditionally oriented
theists will consider the scientific prospects for overcoming death
and, particularly for now, the biostasis option. In our efforts to
try to convince them we can also try to see things from their
perspective. Theistic religions generally hold human life precious
and agree that improving its quality is good and desirable. The
possibility of human life extension, or even saving lives through
cryonics, can thus be seen in a way that can serve as a selling
point to theists—though clearly there are pitfalls. The theist, we
noted in Chapter 3, may be indignant at our efforts to attain immortality through science rather than trusting in God. But the
point can be made that a loving God should not want to forbid a
possible means of saving lives that humans can master.

It is worth noting here that progressive thinking is no stranger
to theistic movements. Pakistani Islamic philosopher Muhammad
Iqbal, for example, had some interesting thoughts to offer in the
1930s on what is clearly a scientific teleology. "It is the lot of
man to share in the deeper aspirations of the universe around him
and to shape his own destiny as well as that of the universe, now
by adjusting himself to its forces, now by putting the whole of
his energy to mould its forces to his own ends and purposes."[10]
The position of Yuai is that the "deeper aspirations" of all sentient beings—thus, metaphorically, of reality as a whole—are parts
of a harmonious whole and interdependent. All must participate
and contribute with their separate, growing powers so that all can
best find fulfillment.

Another possible common ground with traditional religion, not
without difficulties of its own but worth considering, concerns
the soul. We have firmly discounted the mystical soul or "further
fact" that would invalidate psychological reductionism, but the
door remains open for a "nonmystical" soul, and indeed, the concept of Interchangeability would seem to require it. A person in
effect is a computer program, a chunk of information that could
be running on more than one physical device or piece of hard-

ware. So the program becomes the soul.[11] With this interpretation, the soul is certainly not a material object, and, while it can
be disrupted and destroyed, it can also be recreated so in effect is
capable of surviving death. Cryonics in particular does not deny
the existence of the soul in this sense but seeks to capture it in the
frozen remains that are preserved, so that in due course it can be
restored to a functioning form. True, this informational viewpoint
could be unacceptable to many theists, who may cling to a strictly
mystical concept in keeping with their traditions. But the informational notion of soul does offer at least one way of reconciling
an ancient perspective with modern science, and ought to appeal
to some who might then be persuaded to take immortalist ideas
more seriously.

One more ground for constructive interaction is Universalism.
All Universalists are already united in believing in, or entertaining serious hopes of, immortality and salvation for (at least) all
human beings, including one another. The strong Universalist
stance of Yuai thus puts it in harmony, if not total agreement,
with such traditions as Christian Universalism and Zoroastrianism, and one may hope on this basis for a fruitful interaction.

These then are some thoughts on how we might interest religious people in cryonics and life extension, while respecting their
point of view. But we can ask, too, whether those without strong
religious beliefs might, for that very reason, make even better
prospects. Sometimes clearly the answer is yes, as with those
who have already chosen cryonics, who usually are not strongly
religious. Often though it seems, paradoxically, the answer is no—
people who lack religious beliefs have not, as a rule, been enthusiastic about the idea of being preserved in biostasis but seem
dominated instead by a determined fatalism. Apparently they can
only be convinced by "greater miracles" such as demonstrated,
reversible suspended animation or, even better, successful aging
reversal. Such tangible advances will probably be necessary, when
all is said and done, for most of the theists too. But we can still
hope to gain at least some additional following and increased
credibility and appreciation through a careful approach that respects differing worldviews without compromising our own.

Our Coming Transhumanity

In any case, we probably will not have long to worry over such problems as how to convince the unready. I think the day of suspended animation at some demonstrated, substantial level is coming soon, perhaps within a decade or two, and along with it, or maybe sooner, significant inroads into basic aging mechanisms. There must then be profound changes in medical practices: the newly deceased in particular must be preserved in biostasis to avoid a murder charge. Happily, our deliverance will be at hand—something that especially must follow from aging intervention. For once that has seriously gotten under way, life will never be the same. People will get older without weakening and dying as now and must soon outlive any "normal" human life span. Our transhuman phase will have begun. This, I think, will be of short duration, a few present-day generations at most. But this brief period will have momentous impact and indeed constitute an Apocalypse by reasonable standards, an "uncovering" and awakening of a sort that, if all goes well, could only occur once in our history. Many variations of lifestyles and body modifications will no doubt be tried, and spectacular mishaps can be expected. There is some danger too that a small number of malcontents will upset the apple-cart for the rest—but again I am optimistic that rising hopes and satisfaction will counter this threat.

Among other things, we will increasingly understand the sources of our discontent that are not traceable to simple external causes, such as hunger, and find ways to better our mental states in responsible ways. David Pearce, anticipating the future in *The Hedonistic Imperative*, offers that "The neurochemistry of pain and malaise evolved only because it served the fitness of our genes in the ancestral environment. Its metabolic pathways will be replaced by a different sort of neural architecture....nanotechnology and genetic engineering will eliminate aversive experience from the living world. 'Physical' and 'mental' pain alike are destined to disappear into evolutionary history....all [people] will share at least one common feature: a sublime and all-pervasive happiness."[12] Joy could supplant our various discontents and probably will in most cases, though again I foresee dangers if pleasure is pursued too recklessly, as we see on a smaller scale now with such problems as drug abuse. Nevertheless, "a sublime and all-pervasive happiness" should be compatible with our survival as immortals—and not merely result in replacement of ourselves by "better" but different individuals. Joy—our joy—should be the prevailing state, even if some modest restrictions apply.

The transhuman phase, as I imagine it, will begin with aging reversal and end perhaps with uploading. During this time we can expect capabilities to develop rapidly in many directions—and expectations to grow in step. Increasingly, people must face the issues of what to do with themselves for an open-ended, more-than-human existence. In addition to death, that other "certainty," taxes, and more general demands on the resources of individuals, must increasingly come under scrutiny and attack. Some fabulous possibilities should be realized. Factories should increasingly be staffed by automated, self-repairing devices so that the cost of goods will plummet. Among the "goods" that our future production plants could turn out will be—why not?—the self-sustaining domicile, a household that itself is automated and self-repairing. It would not only provide shelter but produce our food as well, all soberly based not on some exorbitant sacrifice of our time and energy in return but on such fundamentals as the availability of resources in the world at large.

Properly managed, these resources should be adequate to the needs at hand for a long time. In our history and prehistory, different species competed for resources, which were always in short supply due basically to a Malthusian imperative. More abundant resources led to proliferating offspring, which quickly erased any surplus and pitted the organisms against each other in an unhappy struggle. But we will no longer be oriented toward producing, in a short life, all the competing offspring the environment can bear. Instead we may hope to reap benefits as our lives unfold over centuries and longer that provide ample motives to live within reasonable bounds, whatever these bounds turn out to be.

At first, as our knowledge and capabilities grow, we will be occupied with such basics as how to eliminate death and secure our survival in humanlike but more durable form. During this time also, I expect we will restore the easier, straightforward cases of biostatic preservation—assuming as always that there are such cases. Increasingly difficult revivals should occur as we progress. But as advances are made against aging and diseases and indefinite life spans become the rule, other limits are likely increasingly to require attention. In many ways we are not designed for the immortal existence we are seeking, and we will have to consider carefully how to redesign ourselves for a better fit.

One concern must be the reproductive process, which has been so important historically but will lose its principal utility as lives lengthen and other options multiply, including the possibility of babies made to order through nanotechnology. I expect that as death rates fall, so will birth (or creation) rates, even as we see already happening. (Indeed, it should be noted that falling birth rates are now being seen as a problem in such demographic areas as Japan and Europe.[13] And this could indeed create difficulties—if such advances as the elimination of aging are too long in coming. Clearly, our progress in the medical fields must continue.) In an immortal future, I see nothing to compare with biological reproduction—this we will simply abandon in due course, as we advance. When we are more-than-human, we will certainly not be obsessed with creating more humans, precious though today's children are—and we will similarly be less urgent about making new posthuman immortals.

This is not to say that no new persons will be made, but it should happen at a much reduced pace accompanied by such eventual exotica as the resurrection of past individuals through the creation of replicas. Probably the means we use will have little to do with our physical bodies or housing but instead invoke specialized nanites, software, and/or other apparatus created for the purpose. With such great changes as the abandonment of the reproductive process will come changes at the mental level—which, however, we will be able to approach gradually and carefully, with ample time and accumulated wisdom. Overall I see us becoming more caring and close-knit, not less, as we define and adapt to our roles as immortals, driven by rational self-interest at ever higher levels.

Another concern is the brain, the seat of consciousness and survival, which, for all its marvels, is limited in capacity and durability. Even with a rollback of aging, there must be limits, for example, on the storage capacity of our memory, which can only be overcome by modifying the brain in some way or supplementing it with artificial devices. Today we are exploring the possibilities of "gray matter on a chip."[14] Neurons can be induced to grow in tiny wells interconnected by tunnels on a silicon rect-

angle. Miniaturized wiring detects electrical transmissions between the developing cells, opening the possibility of direct interaction between organic and inorganic information processors.
Some simple neural implants are already in use too, as we have
noted. As further progress is made, possibilities will develop for
devices that could help rescue what is really "us"—our functioning minds—from their eventually limiting, biological medium.

Artificial computational devices, miniaturized for workability
and convenience, might be implanted in our heads or bodies and
connected electrically to our gray matter to enhance our mental
functioning, a topic we considered in Chapter 14 and elsewhere.
A suitable implant, such as future technology should be able to
provide, ought to be able to listen in on the neural chatter, make
appropriate deductions, and learn to duplicate the functions of a
part of the brain. By further keeping in touch with events, such
components would "know" when and how to assume an active
role if the original, functioning brain elements became impaired.
In this way it seems ultimately feasible that the entirety of our
minds could be expressed in the interactions of artificial components. We have examined this issue and, based on functionalism
and Interchangeability, concluded that what is "really" us could
indeed be activated this way, provided the functioning of the artificial parts was equivalent to the originals at a suitable level.

This, then, is one possible path to uploading—in which we
become expressed in the behavior of artificial, information-processing devices, or directly as computer programs that could then
be transmitted to other devices. In this way our essence might be
transferred to another physical housing or body, or many people
might inhabit one device, such as a large computer. Another, cry-
onics-oriented approach would involve the recovery of information from a frozen brain. The information could then be "run" on
suitable hardware to reactivate the person[15] while the brain tissue, no longer needed, could be discarded. A very sophisticated
form of brain imaging might even be used to obtain the required
data, rather than manipulating the tissue directly.[16]

Such possibilities boggle the mind. Among the many consequences, for instance, should be the ability to communicate
thoughts to others by direct signaling: electronic telepathy.[17] The
complexity of a program able to carry out such tasks and sustain
the functioning of even one human being, let alone a large popu-

lation, is far beyond the powers of any computer we now have. But we are still a long way from the limits allowed by physics, as nanotechnologists like to remind us. And there are exciting possibilities such as the quantum computer that may even make this easy.

Many today are repelled by the idea of uploading—a machine no matter how complex seems incapable of emotion or conscious states. This issue we have considered, with the conclusion that despite the apparent lack of feeling in systems that obey knowable laws, we must allow that such systems could be conscious and emotional. After all, we have these traits, and we are just interacting swarms of the same sort of particles: electrons, protons, neutrons, and photons, that make up other material things. And though it may seem farfetched, I will offer that ultimately our artificial devices will prove superior to our natural housing as emotional habitats. We will have better and truer feelings, deeper and more meaningful experiences, in equipment designed for the purpose than we do now in the creations of unthinking nature. This of course is still a long way off (and we must not unduly disparage our natural makeup, which is really quite incredible), but timewise it may not be so distant in view of our burgeoning progress.

The Singularity and Beyond

As we progress into our transhuman phase, we should gain experience from myriad experiments covering possible modes of existence and states of mind. A significant amount of this, we may imagine, will involve self-experimentation, and, indeed, we must embark on such a course to so much as tamper with our own aging process. There are bound to be bad effects along with the good, as we have noted, but either way we can learn. In time I think we will have largely determined what is more sensible and what is not, and choices will be made that set much of our course for future time.

By this point, then, we will have mapped out and largely brought about a mode of existence best suited to our ambitions as immortals. The Apocalypse will have given way to the Singularity, beyond which many current "givens" must no longer apply. Gone, probably, will be the biological housing that has been our home up to now, to be replaced by advanced computational hardware. We will not be human or even transhuman but what we should call posthuman. And yet, our humanity will endure in the carefully maintained recesses of our memories. Once again, remembering where we have been is vital to our survival, and I think this will be taken more seriously as the future unfolds. It should be a future of marvels, many of which we may be no more able to imagine than a sightless, small-brained earthworm can contemplate motion pictures. But some things must stay the same through all the changes, including information about our past, which we must preserve in some degree if "we" are to endure.

More than this, I think, will also stay the same, and we can be assured the future will not be utterly alien even if many unprecedented things must happen. Among these likely changes, which I think will still leave important things the same, is a great increase in our intelligence and raw processing speed. This alone boggles the mind. But I think at least improving our intelligence would be a desired option, along with more control over adverse mental states. Being joyful geniuses, as I think we can all become, will help considerably in making life both fun and meaningful.

As for simple speedups in our thinking process, certainly it should not be considered foregone that faster is better. With a slowdown, for example, other factors equal, you would presumably view the world like time-lapse photography, with more happening per subjective second, which could possibly make life more interesting. A slowdown, some might argue, would even be necessary if we want advantages such as more durable neurons or memories that are practical to "read out" into mass storage devices for backups in case of brain injury. I think instead, however, that we can probably "have our cake and eat it too," with circuitry that is more durable, more readable, and faster. Computer chips of today are much faster firing than neurons. And probably we will simply choose the best all-around circuitry that science can provide, after a careful process of thought, experimentation, and evaluation. In this way, if nothing else, we would remain competitive with our faster-paced comrades and machines, not requiring special treatment or protection, and better able to interact meaningfully with other immortals.

As one consequence, we might think a million times faster. To lend this some plausibility, neurons fire at millisecond rates, while today's high-speed computer chips clock around a million times faster and are getting faster still.[18] Other, now embryonic, technologies could play a pivotal role. The quantum computer in particular would be a massively parallel device running at electronic speeds or higher, which would open another avenue for progress. We do not know what the outcome of our progress will be, particularly as it could apply to our own mental processing, once we have taken advantage of the possibilities of brain enhancement. Perhaps big obstacles will appear. We could have to accept a slowdown after all, as a tradeoff for other advantages. (In a more distant future too, a cooling universe may force a slowdown to conserve energy.) I will not say the millionfold speedup is any sure thing, but let us consider it as a possibility.

We are computer programs, then, in sophisticated hardware of the future. On our subjective time scale, at the accelerated pace, light travels only 1,000 feet per second, about the speed of sound in the world today. It takes eighteen fast hours for a signal to travel to the most distant points on Earth, halfway around the surface. On the other hand, perhaps we will travel nearly as fast ourselves, as messages transmitted through optical fibers or by other means now unknown. We might want to travel like this to visit with friends who, of course, will also be speeded up.

Perhaps by then we will live in a global network of interconnected processing devices—an "Econet." The actual physical structures may be only an insignificant part of the environment. They could be largely underground, which would both protect them from the elements and intrude but little on the ecosphere. The earth could revert to the wild state so prized by today's environmentalists and much more completely than is possible with present civilization. (Certain valued monuments could perhaps be left in place, not taking inordinate space, each attended by caretaking nanites.) Unobtrusive surveillance cameras, posted at various places around the globe or in low Earth orbit, could provide "windows on the world" as a reality check to us, the fast-thinking denizens below, who in turn could inhabit virtual realities of our choice. For anything remotely open to our programming talents today would be ours—and far more.

With all the change would come the prospect of comforting familiarity, an endearing, enduring sameness, in computer software that interfaced with your mind and others' and provided realistic sensory impressions of desired surroundings. Virtual realities would seem as solid in every respect as the real thing does now, maybe more, since you would be smarter. You could, by choice, live in a Victorian mansion, warm yourself by the fire, eat grapes, and gaze out a big picture window. There you could watch your favorite movies in 3-D—or look at "stills," windows on the world, with information piped in from various points around the globe. For indeed the outside world, by comparison, would seem all but frozen solid, the fastest buzzing insect beating its tiny wings only three or four times an hour.[19]

A facility for manipulating objects in the outside world would not be ruled out either but instead, I think, would be essential to retain. (Indeed, there could be recognized dangers with too much disconnection from the outside world, with appropriate, remedial practices developed.) Special arrangements for outside contact could be provided while you remained in the Econet, or, alternatively, you could exercise "rights of emigration" and download into an individually controllable device or physical body. (If thoughts were greatly speeded up you would, of course, need more-than-human patience to deal with the glacially slow pace of moving objects, at least at the macroscopic level. But this superhuman attribute might be a natural accompaniment of enhanced intelligence.) You could then live on your own, undertake long journeys, and possibly, eventually, return and upload back into the Econet, leaving your body behind for later use by yourself or others.

I have been assuming that we would still inhabit the earth, but there would be no particular reason we could not move into space, and indeed it will no doubt be better or even necessary at some point. Our processors should work better under conditions of superconductivity, for instance, in the intense cold of deep space. (Ultimately we will also need more room for our growing stock of information.) This need not greatly affect our perceived surroundings, which could be information constructs made to order as we wished. The deep cold should certainly not feel "cold" or uncomfortable. And we would have whatever contacts we needed or wanted with the world outside. Our windows on the world could show blazing fields of galaxies, if we wanted to look that way, or scenes from our former earthly home, delayed a bit by the transmission but vivid as ever. Alternatively, it may be that many or most would prefer to go "solo" and live in individual bodies rather than together in an Econet—another of many things that would have to be worked out.

Posthumanity, on leaving Earth, may also return it to a fully pristine state. Our nanotechnology could help here, in ways we have considered. Recently extinct species, such as the once-abundant passenger pigeon, should be reconstructible from genomic remains. We might in this manner reverse some of the depredations our own species has inflicted in its upward struggle. We would have to face some remarkable moral issues too, however.

With the help of nanotechnology we could do many things to the world we now inhabit, and the question will always arise of whether we should. Should we eliminate all sentient, nonhuman life-forms in their natural habitats, for example? People today find this suggestion absurd and repugnant. But in the future we may consider it more than humane, since it would also eliminate predation, disease, pain, misery, and the endless, desperate struggles of a brief, mortal existence. (Long before this, such cruel sports as bull- and cockfighting will hopefully have been abolished.) We could even go so far as to capture each living thing in informational form, effectively immortalizing it then and there. But perhaps we will take a different view and leave the environment to its own devices so new species can evolve to intelligent immortals if they will.

If this idea is taken seriously, we can ask if it has happened already. An intelligent offshoot of the dinosaurs or cephalopods might be out there somewhere, waiting. Perhaps they used nanotechnology to doctor the fossil record and eliminate the telltale clues that we have so far failed to find, wanting instead to see us develop in "pure" form, untainted by the expectation of easy answers from a superior forerunner. Or perhaps they actually did leave a record but in an encrypted text we are not likely to read until we are further along ourselves. Such conjectures are fantasy and may be doubted on grounds that intelligent life does not evolve easily, even with plenty of unintelligent precursors. But in any case we are provided another interesting puzzle.

Meanwhile, we must not pass over the moral problems too lightly. In the past abuses were tolerated, such as slavery or the torturous execution of "heretics" that most today find intolerable and abhorrent. Indeed, we look back on those who did accept these things, who were also supposed to be wise, good, and well-intended, and wonder greatly. By the same token, there are things we accept today, such as animal predation, that may be viewed very differently in the future, when progress has also brought a considerable, additional refinement in sensibilities as well as powers to act. Values change with time. It is hard to predict or even imagine how some of these changes will go and what those in the future will think of many of the attitudes today considered respectable and honorable.[20]

Whatever the nearer-term adjustments in our values, more distantly we can expect vast changes in our surroundings and will have to adapt accordingly if we hope to endure. The sun will burn out. What will we do, in anticipation, to the earthly habitat? Keep it going somehow, long past the solar demise, or instead promptly retire it, taking care to translate any remaining, primitive life-forms to immortal computer programs? By then I expect we will have vast, accumulated wisdom, and whatever choices are made will be well advised—we should not worry over it now. Each individual should then be valued as part of a loving, enduring, cosmic community. Choices that are made should reflect both superhuman self-interest and an advanced desire for general benefit.

But as the universe evolves, and we along with it, earlier landmarks will disappear, to survive only in our growing information banks. The mechanisms of our processing will not matter so much as the processing itself. It is perhaps only during this time, billions of years hence or more, that we will turn serious thoughts to the sort of resurrections of past individuals we have considered, those who could not be preserved. By then I think the earth as we know it will be only a memory—resurrectees will be information constructs in places also part of virtual reality. Those who did not participate directly in the transition to more-than-human, who died too soon, will have missed something valuable but can still pick up the pieces and go on. Or such a project could happen much sooner, but still a person returning to life in this way, after a death interval, will face a void that must be filled over time.

Again, these thoughts boggle the mind. But through it all runs a constant theme, of creatures who are trying to survive and find meaning in existence. The humble earthworm has an inkling of this, at its primitive level. We, the hopeful masters of fate, may refine and modify it greatly, but with all the changes, something of its essence must remain the same.

It seems that, with all our present sophistication and the promise of greater things to come, in important ways we are still closer to the worm than to our distant future selves who, if all goes well, will master the fate of the universe. Certainly we have a long way to go, but great should be the rewards of success. Again, we have only ourselves to rely upon, and success or failure must depend on our efforts. But, to start, we must accept the goal of our immortalization as a worthy one. We can then direct our efforts wholeheartedly toward this goal. If we do, I am optimistic about the outcome: our progress will be our salvation.

COVER EMBLEM

The emblem on the cover shows the ankh (ancient Egyptian symbol of life) over an infinity symbol, enclosed in a heart, and expresses the hope that good will prevail in a future of everlasting life.

ILLUSTRATION CREDITS

Each chapter, and the Introduction, open with a title illustration, and some additional illustrations are distributed through the text. Art work is by the author, in some cases using photographs from the author's personal collection, with other credits as follows.

Title Illustrations:

Chapter 1. Image based on Signorelli's *The Elect* and mathematical work of Stokes.

Chapter 2. Based in part on images from the ancient Egyptian *Book of the Dead*.

Chapter 4. Detail from Raphael's *School of Athens*.

Chapter 5. NASA photo.

Chapter 8. Image based on detail from Da Vinci's *Mona Lisa*.

Chapter 9. Image from NASA-Ames Research Center.

Chapter 12. Image based on detail from Signorelli's *Resurrection of the Flesh*.

Chapter 13. Images based on detail from Raphael's *Sistine Madonna*.

Chapter 14. Image based on detail from Raphael's *Sistine Madonna*.

Chapter 18. NASA photo of Earth and unattributed image of the Andromeda Galaxy.

Other Illustrations:

The Gödel Sentence. Image based on flying eagle design by St. Gaudens for the U. S. $20 gold piece.

Lucretius Demonstrates Onticity. Image based on the ancient mosaic, *Virgil Writing the Aenid, Inspired by Two Muses*.

GLOSSARY

all-unity: as expounded by Fedorov, a state of universal harmony or kinship of the human race, generalized in Yuai to include all sentient beings.

anabiosis: [biological organism] a state of reversible suspended animation.

animism: belief in extracorporeal beings such as angels, demons, or gods.

Anthropic Principle: [cosmology] that the universe, to be observed, must provide for the existence of the observer. (This is the "weak" Anthropic Principle, "strong" enough for purposes here.)

Argument from Design: [theology] an argument that a divine or super-human agent was purposefully involved in creating the world or certain features of it.

assembler: predicted device for making arbitrary, stable structures out of atoms according to predetermined specifications; a possibility through **nanotechnology**.

B.C.E.: [calendar date] before the common era, or B.C.

biostasis: [biological tissue or organism] a state of arrested deterioration.

brain: in general terms, an **instantiation** of a **mind**.

C.E.: [calendar date] common era, or A.D.

Church-Turing thesis: the conjecture that all effectively doable procedures of the symbol-manipulation variety can be carried out by a device such as a Turing machine, hence by computers.

continuer: a more developed version of a person, as would normally occur at a later time, ignoring the problem of forgetting.

cryonics: the practice of freezing persons at death and storing them at low temperature in hopes of eventual reanimation.

day-person hypothesis: the hypothesis that a person dies each time a loss of consciousness occurs (e.g., in dreamless sleep) and a new, though similar, person "wakes up" when consciousness is regained.

death, structural or informational definition: irreversible loss of identity-critical, information-bearing structure in or pertaining to an organism or tissue.

diachronic self: the self as an entity persisting over the entire period of one's life.

disassembler: predicted device for breaking down a stable object and recording its detailed structure at the molecular level, so that an **assembler** could then create an atomically exact replica; a possibility through **nanotechnology**.

emulation: an exact simulation, e.g., of a person in a hypothetical, future computational device.

enontic: [information relating to past occurrences] derived from or implied by the historical record, as opposed to **hyperontic** or **xenontic**.

feeling content: [consciousness] the subjective experience of consciousness, involving perceptions, thoughts, and feeling, as distinguished from the objective experience or **information content**.

functionalism: a materialistic theory of mental states. A person (or other sentient being) is regarded as a mechanism that can be in one of a number of physical states, to each of which corresponds some mental state; more than one physical state may correspond to the same mental state. What distinguishes one mental state from another one is not the difference in physical states but the functional role played by each mental state in the conscious experience of the person.

God: [traditional, Western concept, with parallels in other traditions] a supreme, sentient being, generally held to be all-knowing, all-powerful, and perfectly good.

hyperontic: [information relating to past occurrences] consistent with the historical record but not necessarily derived from or implied in it, as opposed to **enontic** and **xenontic**.

ideal self: a being to which a developing, immortal person "converges" over the course of infinite time.

identity, conservation of: adequate preservation, in some form, of identity-critical information. See also **personal identity**.

identity, expression of: the living of one's life, as a conscious participant. See also **personal identity**.

Identity of Indiscernibles: the principle that two things are one and the same unless they exhibit some difference in their properties or features.

immortalism (modern definition): the philosophical position that human life span can be substantially extended scientifically, and ought to be. It is assumed that scientific approaches yet to be developed will be instrumental.

instantiation: a material construct such as a **brain** that, in its working, can be said to "run" or instantiate an entity such as a **mind** or, less directly, a person.

information content: [consciousness] the experience of consciousness regarded in purely informational or computational terms, under the assumption that consciousness can be so regarded or described, i.e., that consciousness is explained as an emergent property of certain information-processing systems. The latter is a principal implication of strong artificial intelligence (**strong AI**).

Interchangeability: the principle that "sufficiently" alike phenomena or things share identity, mainly applied to persons. Two persons are the same if their conscious experience is the same.

Interface: ties or connections between a person and external reality.

isomorphism: an equivalence between two functioning systems (or more generally, two mathematically definable entities) in which one system is obtained from the other by "renaming the parts." The principle of Interchangeability asserts that two, suitably isomorphic conscious systems are one and the same consciousness, multiply instantiated, rather than separate conscious individuals.

materialism (scientific): a doctrine holding that everything can be explained in terms of "matter and void"—particles and their interactions in space over time—rather than, e.g., invoking supernatural elements.

materialism (valuational): an attitude that what is important in one's life is material possessions or comforts; distinguished from **scientific materialism**.

medical criterion: [biostasis, cryonics] a standard that is met if a preserved individual can be recovered mentally intact, i.e., there is sufficient information-bearing structure in the remains to repair and reanimate the individual.

mind: (as understood here) a device or system that "runs" or supports a person, by analogy with a computer that runs or executes a program. A mind is instantiated in a **brain**, which thus indirectly instantiates the person.

mind-brain identity theory: a theory that identifies a mind with a particular brain; not consistent with **functionalism**, which allows that there could be more than one brain that "runs" or instantiates the same mind.

moral platform: a stance on what ought to be, used as a foundation or "springboard" for further deliberations, decisions, and actions.

mystical: as understood here, denoting or referring to a component of reality that is outside the bounds of rational understanding, i.e., incapable in principle of scientific explanation.

nanotechnology: the controlled manipulation of matter at the atomic and molecular scales.

ontic criterion: [biostasis, cryonics] a standard that is met if there is significant identity-critical information present in the preserved remains of a deceased individual or possibly in other physical artifacts. A weaker form of the medical criterion. Generally, meeting the ontic criterion will not allow the individual to be recovered intact from the preserved remains but will reduce the amount of guesswork needed to restore a functioning, "complete" individual.

ontic robustness: the twofold principle that (1) all persons who have died will be resurrected; and (2) every resurrection through guesswork is of a person who actually lived; both are implications of the **UI assumptions**.

paranormal: as understood here, any alleged phenomena of a fantastic character for which adequate confirming evidence has not been obtained. Examples range from visitations by extraterrestrial aliens, which might be explainable scientifically, to interventions of supernatural powers, which might not be.

parascientific: as understood here, synonymous with **mystical**, or **supernatural**

pattern-survival: a concept of personal survival through a duplicate or pattern. A person is held to survive or live on if a sufficiently accurate copy of the person is alive and functioning, irrespective of the physical connections between the copy and the original. The notion of a "sufficiently accurate" copy also extends to a suitable isomorphic image of the person that may be "running" in some device or construct, i.e., the person can survive through the image.

person-segment: a person regarded as a phenomenon persisting over a period or interval of time, whether long or short.

person-stage: a person at a particular point or stage in life; essentially, a **person-segment** in which the time interval approaches zero length.

personal identity: as understood here, a person survives through more advanced versions, or **continuers**. *P* is the "same" person as *Q* in case either *P* is a continuer of *Q* or vice versa, where *P* and *Q* are **person-stages** or **person-segments**. The continuer relation is transitive (if *P* is a continuer of *Q* and *Q* is a continuer of *R* then *P* is a continuer of *R*), but the relation of being the "same" person is not. This is because one person could in principle split into more than one person, providing two continuers of an original, neither of which is a continuer of the other.

physical continuity: the absence of sudden physical changes in an object or person over time, though gradual, accumulating changes are permitted.

physical reductionism: a doctrine that persons or other phenomena can be understood in terms of physical processes rather than, e.g., supernatural elements.

principal person-segment: a **person-segment** covering the period from the beginning of life up to some particular point in time.

Principle of Large Quantity: [philosophical position on computation and processing] the principle that unexpected or "impossible" effects could be anticipated to follow if a computational process is greatly expanded in length and complexity, though retaining its basic digital character. An example would be the emergence of consciousness and feeling in an "unconscious" discrete-state device.

psychological connectedness: similarities in mental features between person-segments or person-stages.

psychological continuity: the absence of sudden mental changes in a person over time, though gradual accumulating changes may occur.

psychological reductionism: a doctrine that persons can be understood in terms of mental events or conscious experience, without invoking **mystical** or **paranormal** elements.

q-episode: quasi-episode; a progression of events involving a person, which need not correspond to events as actually experienced. However, a q-episode will generally be "authentic" in that it corresponds to actual events somewhere in the multiverse. On this basis and for other reasons it may be reasonable and desirable, over a period of time, to edit and construe one's remembered experiences in terms of q-episodes, as delineated by **q-memories**.

q-memory: quasi-memory; a constructed "memory" of an event that may not record an actual happening but may yet have significance.

q-segment: quasi-segment; a person-segment in which a significant part of the remembered experiences are described in terms of **q-memories**.

q-stage: quasi-stage, analogous to **q-segment**. See also **person-segment**, **person-stage**.

reductionism: a doctrine that a system or phenomenon can be understood in terms of simpler systems or phenomena.

strong artificial intelligence (strong AI): a "digital view of reality" in which, in particular, true consciousness and feeling could emerge in a discrete-state device such as an advanced computer.

subperson: a "subordinate" personality that is expressed in a person's conscious experience over a restricted time interval, when more time would be needed to express the "complete" individual.

supernatural: as understood here, synonymous with **mystical**, or **parascientific**

Sufficiency of Information Content: [biostasis, cryonics] the principle that a person can eventually be restored to a state of consciousness and health if sufficient information survives in the preserved remains.

terror management theory: a theory that holds that attitudes about death are strongly tied to one's cultural affiliation. Culture provides an "anxiety buffer" to shield against the fear and despondency that would otherwise accompany the knowledge of one's mortality. When one is reminded of death, a natural response is to defend one's culture rather than look at the issue more rationally. This may account for the low level of interest shown by the general public in cryonics.

UI assumptions: Unboundedness + Interchangeability.

Unboundedness: the principle that all possible, finite histories actually happen.

Universalism: as understood here, in its weakest form, the theological or philosophical position that all human beings, including the deceased, will be able at their future discretion to enjoy eternal life and happiness. The "position" could refer to a **working hypothesis** rather than a dogma. Stronger forms take a more definite stand that all humans *will* enjoy eternal happiness or salvation, and sometimes additionally, as in Yuai, generalize "humans" to "all sentient beings."

Venturism: a non-supernatural, religious movement dedicated to the attainment of immortality scientifically, and in particular advocating cryonics or other biostasis procedures for hopefully restoring deceased persons to life.

weak artificial intelligence (weak AI): the point of view that digital or discrete-state devices can be "intelligent" though not necessarily conscious.

working hypothesis: a principle that is accepted provisionally rather than dogmatically.

xenontic: [information relating to past occurrences] contrary to or inconsistent with the historical record, as opposed to **enontic** or **hyperontic**.

Yuai (Universal Immortalism): a philosophical system built around the premise that the problem of death can be solved in its entirety through scientific means.

BIBLIOGRAPHY

Adams, Fred, and Greg Laughlin. *The Five Ages of the Universe: Inside the Physics of Eternity.* New York: The Free Press (Simon and Schuster), 1999.

Alcor Life Extension Foundation, *Cryonics: Reaching for Tomorrow.* 3d ed. Riverside, Calif., 1993.

Axelrod, Robert M. *The Evolution of Cooperation.* New York: Basic Books, 1984.

Barrow, John D., and Frank Tipler. *The Anthropic Cosmological Principle.* New York: Oxford University Press, 1988.

Beckmann, Petr. *A History of Pi.* 2d ed. New York: St. Martin's Press, 1974.

Bharati, Agehananda. *The Ochre Robe.* New York: Doubleday, 1970.

Bova, Ben. *Immortality: How Science Is Extending Your Life Span— and Challenging the World.* New York: Avon Books, 1998.

Brian, Denis. *Einstein: a Life.* New York: J. Wiley, 1996.

Broderick, Damien. *The Spike.* Victoria, Australia: Reed Books Australia, 1997.

Brown, David. *The Divine Trinity.* LaSalle, Ill.: Open Court Publishing Co., 1985.

Cetron, Marvin J. and Owen Davies. *Cheating Death: The Promise and the Future Impact of Trying to Live Forever.* New York: St. Martin's Press, 1998.

Codd, E. F. *Cellular Automata.* New York: Academic Press, 1968.

Cooper, E. See under Duhring, Nathan.

Croswell, Ken. *Planet Quest: The Epic Discovery of Alien Solar Systems.* New York: Free Press, 1997.

Davies, Paul C. W. *Are We Alone?: Philosophical Implications of the Discovery of Extraterrestrial Life.* New York: HarperCollins (Basic Books), 1995.

Davies, Paul C. W. *The Mind of God: The Scientific Basis for a Rational World.* 1992. Reprint, New York: Simon and Schuster, 1993.

Davis, Martin, ed. *The Undecidable: Basic Papers on Undecidable Propositions, Unsolvable Problems, and Computable Functions.* Hewlett, N.Y.: Raven Press, 1965.

Dawkins, Richard. *The Blind Watchmaker.* New York: Norton, 1986.

Delgado, José Manuel Rodríguez. *Physical Control of the Mind: Toward a Psychocivilized Society.* New York: Harper and Row, 1969.

Dennett, Daniel Clement. *Darwin's Dangerous Idea: Evolution and the Meanings of Life.* New York: Simon and Schuster, 1995.

Deutsch, David. *The Fabric of Reality: The Science of Parallel Universes—and Its Implications.* New York: Penguin, 1997.

Dewdney, A. K. *The Armchair Universe: An Exploration of Computer Worlds*. New York: W. H. Freeman, 1988.

Dewdney, A. K. *The Turing Omnibus: 61 Excursions in Computer Science*. Rockville, Md.: Computer Science Press, 1989.

Dewdney, Christopher. *Last Flesh: Life in the Transhuman Era*. Toronto: HarperCollins, 1998.

Drexler, K. Eric. *Engines of Creation*. Garden City, N.Y.: Anchor Press/ Doubleday, 1986.

Drexler, K. Eric. *Nanosystems: Molecular Machines, Manufacturing, and Computation*. New York: Wiley, 1992.

Douglas, John, and Mark Olshaker. *Unabomber: On the Trail of America's Most Wanted Serial Killer*. New York: Simon and Schuster (Pocket Books), 1996.

Du Charme, Wesley W. *Becoming Immortal: Nanotechnology, You, and the Demise of Death*. Evergreen, Colo.: Blue Creek Ventures, 1995.

Duhring, Nathan. (E. Cooper.) *Immortality: Physically, Scientifically, Now; A Reasonable Guarantee of Bodily Preservation, a General Discussion, and Research Targets*. 20th Century Books Foundation, 1962. Reprint, Society for Venturism, 1991.

Dyson, Freeman J. *Imagined Worlds*. Cambridge: Harvard University Press, 1997.

Dyson, Freeman J. *Infinite in All Directions: Gifford Lectures Given at Aberdeen, Scotland, April–November, 1985*. New York: Harper and Row, 1988.

Edwards, Paul, ed. *Immortality*. Amherst, N.Y.: Prometheus Books, 1997.

Epicurus. *Letters, Principal Doctrines, and Vatican Sayings*. Trans. Russel Mortimer Geer. New York: Macmillan Publishing Co., 1964.

Ettinger, Robert C. W. *Man into Superman: The Startling Potential of Human Evolution—and How to Be a Part of It*. New York: St. Martin's Press, 1972. Reprint, New York: Avon Books, 1974; Oak Park, Mich.: Immortalist Society, 1989.

Ettinger, Robert C. W. *The Prospect of Immortality*. Garden City, N.Y.: Doubleday, 1964. Reprint, London: Sidgwick and Jackson, 1965; Oak Park, Mich.: Immortalist Society, 1987.

Fossel, Michael. *Reversing Human Aging*. New York: W. Morrow, 1996.

Frankl, Viktor Emil. *Man's Search for Meaning: An Introduction to Logotherapy*. New York: Washington Square Press, 1985.

Frietas, R. *Nanomedicine Vol. 1: Basic Capabilities*. Austin, Tex.: Landes Bioscience, 1999.

Gosden, Roger G. *Cheating Time: Science, Sex, and Aging*. New York: W. H. Freeman, 1996.

Goswami, Amit. *The Self-Aware Universe: How Consciousness Creates the Material World*. 1993. Reprint, New York: Putnam's Sons, 1995.

Greenlees, D. *The Gospel of Zarathustra.* Wheaton, Ill.: Theosophical Publishing House, 1979.

Grosso, Michael. *The Millennium Myth: Love and Death at the End of Time.* Wheaton, Ill: Quest Books, 1995.

Gruman, G. "A History of Ideas about the Prolongation of Life." *Transactions of the American Philosophical Society* 56, no. 9 (December 1966).

Haldane, John B. S. *Fact and Faith.* London: Watts, 1934.

Halperin, James L. *The First Immortal.* New York: Ballantine Publishing Group, 1998.

Harrington, Alan. *The Immortalist.* New York: Random House, 1969. 2d ed. Millbrae, Calif.: Celestial Arts, 1977.

Harris, Marvin. *Our Kind: Who We Are, Where We Came From, Where We Are Going.* New York: HarperCollins, 1990.

Hart, L. S. "Guiding Principles of Sustainable Design." U.S. Dept. of Interior, National Park Service 1994. <http://www.nps.gov/dsc/dsgncnstr/> (25 August 1998).

Hartshorne, Charles. *The Logic of Perfection, and Other Essays in Neoclassical Metaphysics.* 1962. La Salle, Ill.: Open Court Publishing Co., 1991.

Herbert, Nick. *Elemental Mind: Human Consciousness and the New Physics.* New York: E. P. Dutton, 1993.

Herbert, Nick. *Quantum Reality: Beyond the New Physics.* Garden City, N.Y.: Anchor Press/Doubleday, 1985.

Hick, John. *Death and Eternal Life.* Louisville, Ky.: Westminster/John Knox Press, 1994.

Hillis, W. Daniel. *The Pattern on the Stone: The Simple Ideas That Make Computers Work.* New York: Basic Books, 1998.

Hodges, Andrew. *Alan Turing, the Enigma.* New York: Simon and Schuster (Touchstone), 1983.

Honderich, Ted, ed. *The Oxford Companion to Philosophy.* New York: Oxford University Press, 1995.

Horgan, John. *The End of Science: Facing the Limits of Knowledge in the Twilight of the Scientific Age.* Reading, Mass.: Addison-Wesley, 1996.

Howe, Charles A. *The Larger Faith: A Short History of American Universalism.* Boston: Skinner House Books, 1993.

Iqbal, Muhammad. *The Reconstruction of Religious Thought in Islam.* Ed. M. Saeed Sheikh. 1934. Reprint, Lahore: Institute of Islamic Culture, 1986.

Iserson, Kenneth V. *Death to Dust: What Happens to Dead Bodies?* Tucson, Ariz.: Galen Press, 1994.

Itô, Kiyosi, ed. *Encyclopedic Dictionary of Mathematics.* 2d ed. Cambridge: MIT Press, 1987.

Jaini, Padmanabh S. *The Jaina Path of Purification.* Dehli: Motilal Banarsidass Publishers, 1979. Reprint, Dehli: Motilal Banarsidass Publishers, 1990.

Kaufmann, Walter. *Nietzsche: Philosopher, Psychologist, Antichrist.* 4th ed. Princeton: Princeton University Press, 1974.

Kosko, Bart. *The Fuzzy Future: From Society and Science to Heaven in a Chip.* New York: Harmony Books (Random House), 1999.

Kurtz, Paul. *The Courage to Become: The Virtues of Humanism.* Westport, Conn.: Praeger Publishers, 1997.

Kurzweil, Ray. *The Age of Spiritual Machines: When Computers Exceed Human Intelligence.* New York: Viking, 1999.

Lamont, Corliss. *The Philosophy of Humanism.* 8th ed. Amherst, N.Y.: Humanist Press for the Half-Moon Foundation, 1997.

Leff, Harvey S. and Andrew F. Rex eds. *Maxwell's Demon: Entropy, Information, Computing.* Princeton: Princeton University Press, 1990.

Leslie, John. *The End of the World: The Science and Ethics of Human Extinction.* New York: Routledge, 1996.

Lewis, Dorothy Otnow. *Guilty by Reason of Insanity: A Psychiatrist Explores the Minds of Killers.* New York: Fawcett Columbine, 1998.

Livi-Bacci, Massimo. *A Concise History of World Population.* 2d ed. Trans. Carl Ipsen. Cambridge: Blackwell, 1997.

Locke, John. *An Essay Concerning Human Understanding.* Amherst, N.Y.: Prometheus Books, 1994.

Lucretius. *On the Nature of the Universe (De Rerum Natura)* Trans. R. E. Latham. 1951. New York: Penguin, 1979.

Macrae, Norman. *John von Neumann.* New York: Pantheon Books, 1992.

Magnusson, Magnus, ed. *Chambers Biographical Dictionary.* 1990. 5th ed. Edinburgh: W. and R. Chambers, 1996.

Medina, John. *Clock of Ages: Why We Age, How We Age—Winding Back the Clock.* Cambridge, Eng.: Cambridge University Press, 1996.

Mardia, Kanti V. *The Scientific Foundations of Jainism.* 2d ed. Dehli: Motilal Banarsidass Publishers, 1996.

Merton, Thomas. *New Seeds of Contemplation.* 1961. Reprint, Norfolk, Conn.: New Directions, 1972.

Minsky, Marvin L. *Computation: Finite and Infinite Machines.* Englewood Cliffs, N.J.: Prentice-Hall, 1967.

Minsky, Marvin L. *Society of Mind.* New York: Simon and Schuster 1986.

Moore, Thomas J. *Lifespan: Who Lives Longer—and Why.* New York: Simon and Schuster, 1993.

Moravec, Hans P. *Mind Children: The Future of Robot and Human Intelligence.* Cambridge: Harvard University Press, 1988.

Moravec, Hans P. *Robot: Mere Machine to Transcendent Mind.* New York: Oxford University Press, 1999.

More, Max. *The Diachronic Self.* Ph.D. diss., University of Southern California, 1995. (Available through UMI Press, Ann Arbor, Mich.)

Nagel, Ernest and James R. Newman. *Gödel's Proof.* New York: New York University Press, 1958.

Nietzsche, Friedrich. *Thus Spoke Zarathustra.* Trans. R. J. Hollingdale. New York: Penguin Books, 1969.

Niven, Larry. *Flatlander.* New York: Del Rey (Ballantine), 1995.

Nozick, Robert. *Philosophical Explanations.* Cambridge: Harvard University Press, Belknap Press, 1981.

Origen. *On First Principles.* Trans. G. W. Butterworth. London: Society for Promoting Christian Knowledge, 1936. Reprint, Gloucester, Mass.: Peter Smith, 1973.

Paine, Thomas. *The Age of Reason.* 1794. Buffalo, N.Y.: Prometheus Books, 1984.

Parfit, Derek. *Reasons and Persons.* Oxford: Clarendon Press, 1987. (Reprint with corrections of 1984 ed.)

Pearce, D. *The Hedonistic Imperative.* BLTC Research, 1997; <http://www.bltc.net/hedonism/>

Penrose, Roger. *The Emperor's New Mind: Concerning Computers, Minds, and the Laws of Physics.* Oxford: Oxford University Press, 1989.

Perry, Michael. *Introducing Venturism.* 6th ed. Scottsdale, Ariz.: Society for Venturism, 1994. (Available from the Society for Venturism or at <http://www.alcor.org/12.txt>.)

Pickover, Clifford A. *Strange Brains and Genius: The Secret Lives of Eccentric Scientists and Madmen.* New York: Plenum Trade, 1998.

Pool, J. Lawrence. *Nature's Masterpiece: The Brain and How It Works.* New York: Walker, 1987.

Posner, Richard A. *Aging and Old Age.* Chicago: University of Chicago Press, 1995.

Prehoda, Robert W. *Suspended Animation: The Research Possibility That May Allow Man to Conquer the Limiting Chains of Time.* Philadelphia: Chilton Book Co., 1969.

Price, Michael Clive. *The Everett FAQ.* By the author, 1995. <http://www.hedweb.com/everett/welcome.htm>

Reade, William Winwood. *The Martyrdom of Man.* New York: E. P. Dutton, 1926.

Regis, Edward. *Great Mambo Chicken and the Transhuman Condition: Science Slightly over the Edge.* Reading, Mass.: Addison-Wesley, 1990.

Rosenfeld, Albert. *Prolongevity: A Report on the Scientific Discoveries Now Being Made about Aging Dying, and Their Promise of an Extended Human Lifespan, without Old Age.* New York: Knopf, 1976.

Russell, Bertrand. *Why I Am Not a Christian, and Other Essays on Reli-*

gion and Related Subjects. Ed. Paul Edwards. New York: Simon and Schuster, 1957.

Sacks, Oliver W. *Awakenings*. New York: HarperPerennial, 1990.

Saddhatissa, H. *Life of the Buddha*. New York: Harper and Row, 1976.

Sagan, Carl. *The Demon-Haunted World: Science as a Candle in the Dark*. New York: Random House, 1995.

Saplosky, Robert M. *The Trouble with Testosterone: And Other Essays on the Biology of the Human Predicament*. New York: Scribner, 1997.

Shermer, Michael. *Why People Believe Weird Things: Pseudoscience, Superstition, and Other Confusions of Our Time*. New York: W. H. Freeman, 1997.

Smith, Huston. *The World's Religions: Our Great Wisdom Traditions*. San Francisco: HarperCollins, 1991.

Smith, Jonathan Z., ed. *The HarperCollins Dictionary of Religion*. San Francisco: HarperCollins, 1995.

Stenger, Victor J. *The Unconscious Quantum: Metaphysics in Modern Physics and Cosmology*. Amherst, N.Y.: Prometheus Books, 1995.

Stevens, Charles A. *Natural Salvation: The Message of Science*. New York: Arno Press, 1977.

Talbott, T. *The Inescapable Love of God*. Philadelphia: Universal Publishers, 1999.

Tipler, Frank J. *The Physics of Immortality: Modern Cosmology, God, and the Resurrection of the Dead*. New York: Doubleday, 1994.

Trigg, Joseph. W. *Origen: The Bible and Philosophy in the 3rd-Century Church*. Atlanta, Ga.: J. Knox, 1983.

Walford, Roy L. *The 120-Year Diet: How to Double Your Vital Years*. New York: Simon and Schuster, 1986.

Walls, Jerry L. *Hell: The Logic of Damnation*. Notre Dame, Ind.: University of Notre Dame Press, 1992.

Weinberg, Steven. *Dreams of a Final Theory*. New York: Vintage, 1994.

Wells, Herbert. G. *Three Prophetic Novels*. New York: Dover Publications, 1960.

Whitehead, Alfred North and Bertrand Russell. *Principia Mathematica*. 2d ed. New York: Cambridge University Press, 1925.

Wright, Lawrence. *Twins: And What They Tell Us about Who We Are*. New York: J. Wiley, 1997.

Young, Hugh D. *University Physics*. 8th ed. Reading, Mass.: Addison-Wesley, 1992.

Young, Thomas. *A Course of Lectures on Natural Philosophy and the Mechanical Arts*. London: Printed for J. Johnson, 1807.

Zakydalsky, Taras. *N. F. Fyodorov's Philosophy of Physical Resurrection*. Ph.D. diss., Bryn Mawr College, 1976. (Available through UMI Press, Ann Arbor, Mich.)

REFERENCES AND NOTES

For full reference information for shortened titles, please see Bibliography.

Introduction

1. That life should offer a "preponderance of satisfaction over dissatisfaction" has been a frequent observation of Robert Ettinger.

Chapter 1

1. Another possible term, *scientific theology*, is used by Horgan in *End of Science*, esp. chap. 10—"*teleology*" I think is more appropriate.

2. Tipler, *Physics of Immortality*, 17.

3. Ibid., 1.

4. Quoted from Russell, *Why I Am Not a Christian*, vii.

5. Sagan quoted in M. McDonough, "Star Stuff," *Skeptic* 4, no. 4 (1996):10.

6. See, for example, David Hume, *An Enquiry Concerning Human Understanding*, as quoted in Shermer, *Why People Believe Weird Things*, 45.

7. This is the principal theme in Horgan, *End of Science*.

8. Benjamin Franklin, Letter to Priestly, 1780, as quoted in Gruman, "History of Ideas about the Prolongation of Life," 74.

9. See, for example, Dewdney, *Last Flesh*, 115–16; Macrae, *John von Neumann*, 267–68.

10. See, for example, Vernor Vinge, "Technological Singularity," *Whole Earth Review* (10 December 1993).

11. See, for example, Fossel, *Reversing Human Aging*.

12. Tipler, *Physics of Immortality*, xi.

13. See, for example, Honderich, *Oxford Companion to Philosophy*, 482.

14. Nozick, *Philosophical Explanations*, 128, 670, as cited in Weinberg, *Dreams of a Final Theory*, 238.

15. See, for example, Barrow and Tipler, *Anthropic Cosmological Principle,* 106, 192.

16. Freeman J. Dyson, "Time without End: Physics and Biology in an Open Universe," *Reviews of Modern Physics* 51 (1979): 447–60.

17. Ettinger, *Man into Superman,* 247.

18. See, for example, Zakydalsky, *N.F. Fyodorov's Philosophy of Physical Resurrection.*

19. See, for example, Mikhail Soloviev, "Associations Relating to Priestly," *The Venturist* 1, no. 3 (3rd Qtr. 1997):8.

Chapter 2

1. Grosso, *Millennium Myth,* 36–37, based on Greenlees, *Gospel of Zarathustra.*

2. See, for example, Trigg, *Origen,* 115.

3. Honderich, *Oxford Companion to Philosophy,* 349. Talbott, *Inescapable Love of God,* offers a recent, well-argued case for Christian Universalism. Another interesting, if passing, reference to Universalism, in this case in twentieth-century Islam, is in Iqbal, *Reconstruction of Religious Thought in Islam,* 123.

4. Grosso, *Millennium Myth,* 34, based on Greenlees, *Gospel of Zarathustra.*

5. Smith, *HarperCollins Dictionary of Religion,* 545.

6. Honderich, *Oxford Companion to Philosophy,* 64, 240, 513–14.

7. Lucretius, *On the Nature of the Universe,* 122.

8. See, for example, Tipler, *Physics of Immortality,* 105.

9. Locke, *Essay Concerning Human Understanding,* 2.27.13.

10. See, for example, Gruman, "History of Ideas about the Prolongation of Life," 83–89.

11. Michael Perry, "For the Record," *Cryonics* 12, no. 10 (October 1991):7–8; Michael Perry, "For the Record," *Cryonics* 17 (2nd Qtr. 1996): 3–7.

12. Mikhail Soloviev, "Roots of the Scientific Resurrection Idea," *Venturist Monthly News* 8, no. 8 (August 1996): 6–7.

13. Zakydalsky, *N. F. Fyodorov's Philosophy of Physical Resurrection.*

14. Quotations in this paragraph are from Nietzsche, *Thus Spoke Zarathustra,* 41–44.

15. Robert Ettinger, "The Past, the Present, the Future, and Everything," *Cryonics* 15 (3rd Qtr. 1994): 27–32. See also Regis, *Great Mambo Chicken and the Transhuman Condition,* 85–87.

16. A good historical survey of work in anabiosis, or reversible suspension, of the life process (including both freezing and drying of organisms and tissues) is Mikhail Soloviev, "From Anabiosis to Cryonics," *Cryonics* 19 (3rd Qtr. 1998): 21–26.

17. One useful source for the early history of cryonics is the complete 60-issue edition of *Freeze-Wait-Reanimate* (originally *Life Extension Society Newsletter*), available from Alcor Life Extension Foundation.

18. *Cape Cod Times,* 30 November 1982, 2. "Ev Cooper," *Cryonics* 32 (March 1983): 7–9.

19. Michael Perry, "For the Record," *Cryonics* 19 (1st Qtr. 1998): 36–39.

20. Michael Darwin, "An Interview with Curtis Henderson," *Cryonics* 12 (July 1981): 22–28.

21. *Cryonics* 13, no. 4 (April 1992): inside back cover. Fred Chamberlain, "Talk at Alcor's 20th-Anniversary Celebration," *Cryonics* 13, no. 6 (June 1992): 15–19.

22. Michael Perry, "For the Record," *Cryonics* 15 (4th Qtr. 1994): 5–9.

23. Paul Segall, "Dog Survives Extended Period of Asanguinous Hypothermia," *Notebook* 3, no. 2 (American Cryonics Society [then affiliated with Trans Time]) (June 1986): 3–6.

24. "A Victory on February 1st," *Cryonics* 9, no. 2 (February 1988): 2–7.

25. Gates, acting J. P., "Mitchell v. Roe Decision," *Cryonics* 13, no. 7 (July 1992): 17–18.

26. "Thomas Donaldson et al. v. John Van De Kamp," *Cryonics* 13, no. 3 (March 1992): 13–16.

27. Paul Wakfer, CryoNet message #10420, 13 September 1998 (cryonet@cryonet.org).

28. Charles Platt, "The 21st Century Medicine Seminar: Amazing Breakthroughs in Cryobiology and Resuscitation," *Cryonics* 20 (1st Qtr. 1999): 7–16.

29. Ralph Merkle, "The Technical Feasibility of Cryonics," *Medical Hypotheses* 39 (1992): 6–16.

30. See, for example, Rosenfeld, *Prolongevity,* 143–44.

31. Dewdney, *Last Flesh,* 2.

32. Broderick, *The Spike,* 2.

33. Kurzweil, *Age of Spiritual Machines,* 2.

34. Kosko, *Fuzzy Future,* chap. 15 "Heaven in a Chip," 241–56.

35. See, for example, Robert Ettinger, CryoNet message #11453, 24 March 1999 (cryonet@cryonet.org).

Chapter 3

1. Sheldon Solomon, Jeff Greenberg, and Tom Pyszczynski, "A Terror Management Theory of Social Behavior: The Psychological Functions of Self-esteem and Cultural Worldviews," *Advances in Experimental Social Psychology* 24 (1991): 93–159.

2. Tim Freeman, "Terror Management," CryoNet message #7048, 19 October 1996 (cryonet@cryonet.org).

3. Solomon, Greenberg, and Pyszczynski, "Terror Management Theory of Social Behavior," 93–159.

4. Compare membership totals of Alcor Foundation, the largest cryonics organization, from the late 1980s, *Cryonics* 14, no. 12 (December 1993): 18; see also Hugh Hixon, "The Numbers," *Cryonics* 11, no. 6 (June 1990): 35–36.

5. Michael Perry, "For the Record," *Cryonics* 13, no. 4 (April 1992): 4–7.

6. See, for example, Livi-Bacci, *Concise History of World Population.*

7. Matthew 22:23–30. Michael Perry, "For the Record," *Cryonics* 15 (1st Qtr. 1994): 10. Jaime Wolf, "Freeze Your Mind," *Spin* (November 1995): 58.

Chapter 4

1. Gruman, "History of Ideas about the Prolongation of Life," 89.

2. Parfit, *Reasons and Persons,* chap. 10, 199–217.

3. Ibid., 237.

4. Something approaching this condition, in which mental patients awakened after decades of near-coma, is described in Sacks, *Awakenings.*

5. Compare Honderich, *Oxford Companion to Philosophy,* s. v. "Functionalism," 301–2.

6. See, for example, ibid., s. v. "Phenomenology," 658–60.

Chapter 5

1. Origen, *On First Principles* 1.7.3.

2. See, for example, Paul Kwiat, Harald Weinfurter, and Anton Zeilinger, "Quantum Seeing in the Dark," *Scientific American* (November 1996): 72–78.

3. Deutsch, *The Fabric of Reality,* 38–39; Herbert, *Quantum Reality,* 61–65.

4. See Young, *Course of Lectures on Natural Philosophy and the Mechanical Arts.*

5. The description of this experiment is based on Sharon Begley, "Faster Than What?" *Newsweek* (19 June 1995): 67, 69.

6. Young, *University Physics,* 1075–76.

7. One recent, interesting reference to work that upholds relativity despite some appearances to the contrary, is James Glanz, "Light Exceeds Its Own Speed Limit, or Does It?" <http://www.nytimes.com/library/national/science/053000/sci-physics-light.html>.

8. See, for example, Adams and Laughlin, *Five Ages of the Universe,* 2–9.

9. See, for example, Brian, *Einstein: A Life,* 163.

10. Compare Deutsch, *Fabric of Reality,* 3–15.

11. See, for example, Herbert, *Quantum Reality,* 19, 172.

12. Ibid., 242.

13. Compare, for example, John G. Cramer, "The Transactional Interpretation of Quantum Mechanics," *Reviews of Modern Physics* 58 (July 1986): 647–88, section A4, where many-worlds is incorrectly taken to task both for instantaneous splitting and time asymmetry.

14. A good discussion will be found in Herbert, *Quantum Reality,* chap. 12, 211–31, with the Aspect experiment on p. 227.

15. See, for example, Price, *Everett FAQ,* Q38 (1995).

16. See, for example, Honderich, *Oxford Companion to Philosophy,* s. v. "Ockham's Razor," 633.

17. Deutsch, *Fabric of Reality,* 39–53.

18. See, for example, Price, *Everett FAQ,* in addition to Herbert, *Quantum Reality,* which is several years older.

19. Tipler, *Physics of Immortality,* 170.

20. Philip Yam, "Rubbed Out with the Quantum Eraser," *Scientific American* (January 1996): 30–31.

21. See, for example, Tipler, *Physics of Immortality,* 170–72.

Chapter 6

1. See, for example, Honderich, *Oxford Companion to Philosophy,* 707.

2. Magnusson, *Chambers Biographical Dictionary,* 214.

3. See, for example, Deutsch, *Fabric of Reality,* chap. 11, 258–88.

4. Dennett, *Darwin's Dangerous Idea,* 107–11.

5. Jacob Bekenstein and Marcelo Schiffer, "Quantum Limitations on the Storage and Transfer of Information," *International Journal of Modern Physics* 1 (1990): 355–422, as cited in Moravec, *Robot,* 166.

6. Tipler, *Physics of Immortality,* 174–78.

7. See, for example, Tony Smith, "Solitons and the Proton Mass," 24 August 1998, <http://www.innerx.net/personal/tsmith/SolProton.html>.

8. One interesting discussion will be found in Stenger, *Unconscious Quantum,* 235–37; some earlier related ideas are summarized in Tipler and Barrow, *Anthropic Cosmological Principle,* 192–93.

9. See, for example, ibid., 237–39; see also Shermer, *Why People Believe Weird Things,* 263–64.

Chapter 7

1. See, for example, Beckmann, *History of Pi*, 172; see also Itô, *Encyclopedic Dictionary of Mathematics*, vol. IV: 1896.

2. Parfit, *Reasons and Persons*, 292–93.

3. Honderich, *Oxford Companion to Philosophy*, s. v. "Buddhist philosophy," 107.

4. Compare Nozick, *Philosophical Explanations*, 35.

5. Tipler, *Physics of Immortality*, 230–33.

6. Peter Forrest, s. v. "Identity of Indiscernibles" "The Impact of Quantum Mechanics," *Stanford Online Encyclopedia of Philosophy* (1996) <http:// plato.stanford.edu/entries/identity-indiscernible/#QM>.

7. Tipler, *Physics of Immortality*, 233.

8. Peter Forrest, s. v. "Identity of Indiscernibles" "The Impact of Quantum Mechanics," *Stanford Online Encyclopedia of Philosophy* (1996) <http:// plato.stanford.edu/entries/identity-indiscernible/#QM>.

9. Tipler, *Physics of Immortality*, 225–26.

10. Bernard Williams, *Problems of the Self*, 80–81, as cited in Parfit, *Reasons and Persons*, 293–94.

11. Tipler, *Physics of Immortality*, 228–29.

12. Antony Flew, *Logic of Mortality*, 12, as cited in Tipler, *Physics of Immortality*, 228.

13. Something along these lines is advocated in Herbert, *Elemental Mind*, and Goswami, *Self-Aware Universe*.

14. See, for example, Honderich, *Oxford Companion to Philosophy*, s. v. "Identity," 390; "Identity of Indiscernibles" 391.

15. See, for example, Price, *Everett FAQ*, Q22 (1995).

16. Robert Ettinger, "Probability and Cryonics" *The Venturist* 1 (1st Qtr. 1997): 7–8, reprinted as CryoNet message #7430, 7 January 1997 (cryonet@cryonet.org).

Chapter 8

1. Tipler, *Physics of Immortality*, 221–25.

2. See, for example, Kosko, *Fuzzy Future*.

3. See, for example, Chris Quigg, "Aesthetic Science," *Scientific American* (April 1999): 125–27, which reviews Brian Greene, *The Elegant Universe: Superstrings, Hidden Dimensions, and the Quest for the Ultimate Theory* (New York: W. W. Norton, 1999).

4. See, for example, Honderich, *Oxford Companion to Philosophy*, s. v. "Artificial Intelligence," 60–61.

5. Origen, *On First Principles*, 1.1.7.

6. Locke, *Essay Concerning Human Understanding*, 4.10.10, as quoted in Dennett, *Darwin's Dangerous Idea*, 26.

7. See, for example, Pool, *Nature's Masterpiece*, 90.

8. Some interesting work with "feeding" robots that recharge their batteries is summarized in Scott Jantz and Keith L. Doty, "Learning to Eat," <http://www.mil.ufl.edu/publications/#learning> (undated; about 1997).

9. Such ideas are a commonplace in science fiction; using the primes as a communication opener, for example, is seen in the movie *Contact*.

10. See for example, Hodges, *Alan Turing, the Enigma*, esp. 290–95.

11. Martin Gardner, "Mathematical Games—The Fantastic Combinations of John Conway's New Solitaire Game *Life*," *Scientific American* (October 1970): 120–23. See also, for example, Dewdney, *The Turing Omnibus*, chap. 41, 271–76 and chap. 43, 283–89; also Codd, *Cellular Automata*.

12. See Dewdney, "Three-Dimensional Life," in *The Armchair Universe*, 149–59.

13. Dewdney, *The Turing Omnibus*, chap. 41, 271–76 and chap. 43, 283–89; also Codd, *Cellular Automata*.

14. See, for example, Robert Wright, "Did the Universe Just Happen?" *The Atlantic Monthly* (April 1988): 29–44.

15. A good survey of these ideas will be found in Minsky, *Computation: Finite and Infinite Machines*.

16. For a good discussion of these ideas, see Tipler, "Can a Machine Be Intelligent?" in *Physics of Immortality*, 20–44.

17. See, for example, Umesh Vazirani, "Introduction to Special Section on Quantum Computation," *SIAM Journal on Computing* 26, no. 5 (1997): 1409–10.

18. For a good, accessible survey of quantum computing, see Deutsch, *Fabric of Reality*, chap. 9, 194–221.

19. See esp. ibid., 210; a technical reference is Seth Lloyd, "Universal Quantum Simulators," *Science* 273 (23 August 1996): 1073–79.

20. Alan Turing, "Computing Machinery and Intelligence," *Mind* 59 (October 1950): 433–62; an excellent, informal summary will be found in Hodges, *Alan Turing, the Enigma*, 415–26.

21. Tipler, "Can a Machine Be Intelligent?" in *Physics of Immortality*, 20–44.

22. Ibid., 38-43.

23. Here I have drawn on some ideas in loc. cit.

24. Corey S. Powell, "Kasparov vs. Deep Blue," <http://sciam.com/explorations/042197chess/042197powell.html>, with links.

25. A good general reference here is Honderich, *Oxford Companion to Philosophy*, s. v. "Frege," 294–97 s. v. "Gödel," 320; s. v. "Russell," 781–85 (and related topics).

26. Kurt Gödel, "On Formally Undecidable Propositions of the Principia Mathematica and Related Systems. I," in Davis, *The Undecidable*, 4–38 (Gödel's original paper in English translation; introduction is relatively non-technical and accessible). An accessible, useful summary of Gödel's results is Nagel and Newman, *Gödel's Proof.*

27. Dennett, *Darwin's Dangerous Idea*, chap. 15, 428–51.

28. William McCune, "Solution of the Robbins Problem," *Journal of Automated Reasoning* 19, no. 3 (1997): 263–76.

Chapter 9

1. "What Are Enzymes?" Novo Nordisk Biotech, Inc. 1445 Drew Ave., Davis, CA 95616, Tel. 1-916-757-8100, <http://www.nnbt.com/>.

2. Kurzweil, *Age of Spiritual Machines*, 137; Hugh Hixon, private communication with author. Drexler, *Engines of Creation*, 7–8.

3. Richard P. Feynman, "There's Plenty of Room at the Bottom," *Engineering and Science* 23 (1960): 22–36.

4. Elizabeth Pennisi, "Where's the Beef?" *Science* 279 (30 January 1998): 647.

5. Gina Kolata, "Japanese Scientists Report Success in Cloning

Calves," *New York Times*, reprinted in *Tribune* (Scottsdale, Ariz.), 9 December 1998, A9.

6. Sang-Hun Choe, "Advance Cited in Human Cloning," *Tribune* (Scottsdale, Ariz.), 17 December 1998, A12.

7. Janet Rossant and Andras Nagy, "In Search of the *Tabula Rasa* of Human Cells," *Nature Biotechnology* 17 (January 1999): 23–24.

8. Jennifer Markley, "Stroke Victim Feels Effect of Treatment," *Tribune* (Scottsdale, Ariz.), 11 April 1999, A1, A5.

9. Anthony Atala et al., "De Novo Reconstitution of a Functional Mammalian Urinary Bladder by Tissue Engineering," *Nature Biotechnology* 17 (February 1999): 149–55.

10. Eric S. Grace, "Better Health through Gene Therapy," *The Futurist* (January–February 1998): 39–42, excerpted from Eric S. Grace, *Biotechnology Unzipped: Promises and Realities* (Washington, D.C.: Joseph Henry Press, 1997).

11. See, for example, Elizabeth Pennisi, "After Dolly, a Pharming Frenzy," *Science* 279 (30 January 1998): 646–48.

12. See, for example, Rhonda Rowland, "New Gene Therapy Shows Promise for Heart Patients," <http://www.cnn.com/HEALTH/980105/heart.gene.treatment/> (January 5, 1998).

13. Janet Raloff, "New Gene Therapy Fights Frailty," *Science News* 154 (19, 26 December 1998): 388.

14. See, for example, Nicholas Wade, "Scientist Creates Smarter Mouse: Work on Formation of Memory May Someday Help People" <http://www.nytimes.com/ library/national/science/090299sci-ge-mice.html>

15. See, for example, Deborah Nelson and Rick Weiss, "Gene Therapy Seen as Risky," *Washington Post*, 30 September 1999, A7.

16. See, for example, Douglas Birch, "Scientists Draw Complete Map of Human DNA," *Baltimore Sun*, reprinted in *Tribune* (Scottsdale, Ariz.), 27 June 2000, A1, A14.

17. "Human Genome Project Information," Human Genome Program, U.S. Dept. of Energy <http://www.ornl.gov/hgmis>.

18. Kevin Berger, "Fantastic Voyage," *San Francisco Magazine* (November 1998) <http://www.sanfran.com/sf9811geron.html>.

19. Gregory M. Fahy, "Anti-aging Breakthrough Published in *Sci-*

ence," *Life Extension Magazine* (September 1999) <http://lef.org/magazine/mag99/sep99-interview1.html>.

20. "Tiny Australian Machine Gives Answers in a Nano," *Reuters*, 5 June 1997; B. A. Cornell et al., "A Biosensor That Uses Ion Channel Switches," *Nature* 387 (5 June 1997): 580–83.

21. Corinna Wu, "Polymer Buckyballs Combat Nerve Damage," *Science News* 152 (23 August 1997): 119.

22. Stu Borman, *Chemical and Engineering News* (30 June 1997): 35–36, as cited in Jeffrey Soreff, "Enzyme Design and Analysis," *Foresight Update* 30 (1 September 1997): 5 (web version <http://foresight.org/Updates/Update30/>).

23. Jonathan Knight, "The Engine of Creation," *New Scientist* (19 July 1999) <http:// www.newscientist.com/ns/19990619/theengineo.html>.

24. Thomas A. Bass, "Gene Genie," *Wired* (August 1995): 114–17, 164–68.

25. D. M. Eigler and E. K. Schweizer, "Positioning Single Atoms with a Scanning Tunnelling Microscope," *Nature* 344 (5 April 1990): 524–26.

26. See, for example, Joseph A. Stroscio and D. M. Eigler, "Atomic and Molecular Manipulation with the Scanning Tunneling Microscope," *Science* 254 (29 November 1991): 1319–26. Peter Weiss, "Atom Tinkerer's Paradise," *Science News* 154 (24 October 1998): 268–70.

27. Ivan Amato, "Trekking in the Molecular Forest," *Science News* 138 (10 November 1990): 300.

28. Elizabeth Corcoran, "Trends in Materials: Diminishing Dimensions," *Scientific American* (November 1990): 74.

29. Adam Rogers, "Making Something Out of Nothing," *Newsweek* (31 March 1997), 14.

30. David Keller, "A Nanotube Molecular Tool," *Nature* 384 (14 November 1996): 111. Sid Perkins, "Nanotubes: Metallic by a Twist of Fate," *Science News* 153 (10 January 1998): 22.

31. Sid Perkins, "Nanotubes: Metallic by a Twist of Fate," 22.

32. Based on Kurzweil, *Age of Spiritual Machines*, 138–39.

33. Sunny Bains, "Helical Beams Give Particles a Whirl," *Science* 273 (5 July 1996): 36.

34. David Rotman, "Will the Real Nanotech Please Stand Up?" *Technology Review* (March–April 1999): 47–53.

35. Graham P. Collins, "Quantum Sculpting," *Scientific American* (May 1999): 35–36.

36. Codd, *Cellular Automata.*

37. Simson Garfinkel and K. Eric Drexler, "Critique of Nanotechnology: A Debate in Four Parts," *Whole Earth Review* 67 (Summer 1990): 104–13.

38. Leff and Rex, *Maxwell's Demon: Entropy, Information, Computing.*

39. Ivars Peterson, "Microtools for Scaling Nanomountains," *Science News* 147 (1 April 1995): 207.

40. Robert F. Service, "Atomic Landscapes Beckon Chip Makers and Chemists," *Science* 274 (1 November 1996): 723.

41. David E. H. Jones, "Technical Boundless Optimism," *Nature* 374 (27 April 1995): 835–37.

42. Drexler, *Engines of Creation*, 8.

43. Gary Stix, "Waiting for Breakthroughs," *Scientific American* (April 1996) 94–99.

44. R. W. Keyes, "Miniaturization of Electronics and Its Limits," *IBM Journal of Research and Development* 32, no. 1 (January 1988): 24–28. Microsoft Corp. Hardware technology forecast Appendix 2 (1995) <http://www.research.microsoft.com/   ~gray/eos_dis/10_a2_hardware_technology_ forecast.doc>

45. See, for example, Broderick, *The Spike*, 34–35.

46. David Voss, "Chips Go Nano," *Technology Review* (March–April 1999): 55–57.

47. A general reference center for FPGAs and related technology is The Programmable Logic Jump Station <http://www.optimagic.com/index.shtml>.

48. See, for example, Lyle Burkhead, "Nanotechnology without Genies" <http://www.geniebusters.org/>.

49. Deutsch, "Quantum Computers," in *Fabric of Reality*, chap. 9, 194–221.

50. David P. DiVincenzo, "Real and Realistic Quantum Computers," *Nature* 393 (14 May 1998): 113–14.

51. Robert A. Freitas, Jr., "The Future of Computers," *Analog* (March 1996): 57–73.

52. Seth Lloyd, "Universal Quantum Simulators," *Science* 273 (23 August 1996): 1073–79.

53. *The Guinness Book of World Records 1998* (Stamford, Conn.: Guinness Publishing, Ltd., 1997), 134.

54. For an extended discussion of the possible dangers of nanotechnology, see Drexler, "Engines of Destruction," in *Engines of Creation*, chap. 11, 171–90.

Chapter 10

1. Compare, for example, Linwood Urban, *A Short History of Christian Thought*, rev. and enl. (New York: Oxford University Press, 1995), 45.

2. William Paley, *Natural Theology*, as quoted in Dawkins, *Blind Watchmaker*, 5.

3. See, for example, *Encyclopaedia Britannica*, 14th ed. (1948), s. v. "Deism," 7:144–45.

4. Tipler, *Physics of Immortality*, 326–27.

5. Compare, for example, George Ellis, "Piety in the Sky," *Nature* 371 (8 September 1994): 115.

6. Tipler, *Physics of Immortality*, xiv.

7. This position is explained in Barrow and Tipler, *Anthropic Cosmological Principle*; see esp. chap. 9, 576–612.

8. Tipler, *Physics of Immortality*, 7.

9. Ibid., 210–13.

10. See Deutsch, *Fabric of Reality*, chap. 14, 344–66.

11. Tipler, *Physics of Immortality*, 305.

12. Ibid., 3.

13. Ibid., 218.

14. Compare Smith, *Harpercollins Dictionary of Religion*, 437.

15. See especially Hartshorne, "Ten Ontological or Modal Proofs for God's Existence," in *Logic of Perfection*, chap. 2, 28–117.

16. Ibid., chap. 7, 191–215.

17. From Harris, *Our Kind*, 399, as noted by Chris Fedeli, CryoNet message #12318, 25 August 1999 (cryonet@cryonet.org).

18. Barrow and Tipler, *Anthropic Cosmological Principle*, 15–23.

19. See, for example, Barrow and Tipler, "The Weak Anthropic Principle in Physics and Astrophysics," in *Anthropic Cosmological Principle*, chap. 5, 288–366.

20. See Davies, *Mind of God*, esp. 215–22.

21. For a discussion of phase paths, see, for example, Tipler, *Physics of Immortality*, 174–78.

22. Compare Penrose, *Emperor's New Mind*, 328–45.

23. Tipler, *Physics of Immortality*, 177–78.

24. Compare Penrose, *Emperor's New Mind*, 343–45.

25. Merton, *New Seeds of Contemplation*, 1.

26. Compare, for example, Honderich, *Oxford Companion to Philosophy*, s. v. "Pantheism," 641.

27. Compare, for example, Honderich, *Oxford Companion to Philosophy*, s. v. "Taoism," 864–65.

28. Cecil Frances Alexander's famous poem, "All Things Bright and Beautiful," dates to 1848; a parody, "All Things Dull and Ugly" (author anonymous) will be found in *Venturist Monthly News* 7, no. 9 (September 1995): 6.

29. Tipler's viewpoint is discussed at length in Tipler, *Physics of Immortality*, 259–65.

30. See, for example, ibid., 188.

31. As noted in ibid., 3.

32. Schubert Ogden, *The Reality of God*, 37, as quoted in Brown, *Divine Trinity*, 16.

33. Mardia, *Scientific Foundations of Jainism*, 4, viii.

34. A good, general source on Jainism and its beliefs is Jaini, *Jaina Path of Purification*.

35. See, for example, Smith, *World's Religions*, 122–25.

36. See, for example, Smith, *Harpercollins Dictionary of Religion*, s. v. "Unitarianism," 1109–10.

37. A reference on Venturism is Perry, *Introducing Venturism*.

38. Ibid., 64–66.

39. Earles quoted in Lamont, *Philosophy of Humanism*, vii n.

40. Tipler, *Physics of Immortality*, 221.

Chapter 11

1. Compare, for instance, Axelrod, *Evolution of Cooperation*, 19–20.

2. Compare, for example, Honderich, *Oxford Companion to Philosophy*, 292–93.

3. See Leslie, *End of the World*.

4. See, for example, Carl Haub, "How Many People Have Ever Lived on Earth," *Population Today* 23, no. 2 (February 1995): 4–5, as cited by U.S. Census Bureau, The Official Statistics <http://www.census.gov/~rltaylor/email_test. html>.

5. U.S. Census Bureau World Population Profile (1996), 34.

6. Compare, for example, Leslie, *End of the World*, 98–99.

7. See, for example, Davies, "Against Aliens," in *Are We Alone?* Chap. 4, 66–87, which is a more general reference on possibilities for extraterrestrial life.

8. See, for example, Philip Klass, "A Field Guide to UFOs," *Astronomy* (September 1997): 30–35.

9. David S. McKay et al., "Search for Past Life on Mars: Possible Relic Biogenic Activity in Martian Meteorite ALH84001," *Science* 273 (16 August 1996): 924–30.

10. John Noble Wilford, "'Life on Mars' Theory Weakens in 2nd Look," *New York Times*, reprinted in *Tribune* (Scottsdale, Ariz.), 22 December 1996, A7.

11. Andrew H. Knoll, "A Martian Chronicle," *The Sciences* 38, no. 4 (July/August 1998): 20–26. John Noble Wilford, "Another Meteorite May Show Life on Mars, Scientists Report," *New York Times*, 19 March 1999 <http://www.nytimes.com/ subscribe/help/archsources.html>.

12. Such an opinion was aired by Robert Ettinger, CryoNet message #11195, 30 January 1999 (cryonet@cryonet.org).

Chapter 12

1. See Lucretius, *On the Nature of the Universe*, 74–75.

2. Epicurus, Letter to Herodotus 45b, *Letters, Principal Doctrines, and Vatican Sayings*, 13.

3. Lucretius, *On the Nature of the Universe*, 92.

4. Noted by Sagan, *Demon-Haunted World*, 206, based, a bit incorrectly, on Haldane, *Fact and Faith*, 60–65. (The latter does *not* consider the possibility of memories being recreated, though Sagan, appropriately, does.)

5. Tipler, *Physics of Immortality*, 157–58.

6. See Chap. 14 in this volume, notes 10, 17, 18.

7. See, for example, Ralph Merkle, "The Technical Feasibility of Cryonics," *Medical Hypotheses* 39 (1992): 12–13.

8. See, for example, Ralph Merkle, "Uploading: Transferring Consciousness from Brain to Computer," *Extropy* 5, no. 1 (Fall 1993): 5–8, as cited in Kosko, *Fuzzy Future*, 334 n. 12.

9. Tipler, *Physics of Immortality*, 224–25.

10. Nozick, *Philosophical Explanations*, 62–63.

11. See, for example, Pickover, *Strange Brains and Genius*, 266.

12. Tipler, *Physics of Immortality*, 210–13.

Chapter 13

1. Tipler, *Physics of Immortality*, 157–58.

2. Wells, "The Time Machine," in *Three Prophetic Novels*, 285.

3. Denise Babin, "Joy of Living and Commitment to Cryonics," *The Alcor Phoenix* (September 1995): 3–4.

4. See, for example, Howe, *Larger Faith*, 34–39.

Chapter 14

1. Russell, *Why I Am Not a Christian*, 107, as quoted in Tipler, *Physics of Immortality*, 69.

2. Ibid., 11, as quoted in Tipler, *Physics of Immortality*, 70.

3. Gruman, *History of Ideas about the Prolongation of Life*, 15.

4. Ibid., 14.

5. Saddhatissa, *Life of the Buddha*, 31.

6. Friedrich Nietzsche, *Untimely Meditations, Part II: Of the Use and Disadvantage of History for Life*, sect. 9, in Kaufmann, *Nietzsche: Philosopher, Psychologist, Antichrist*, as quoted in Tipler, *Physics of Immortality*, 80.

7. Tipler, *Physics of Immortality*, 119.

8. Ibid., 63.

9. Ibid., 117, 397–406.

10. Noted in ibid., 67.

11. See, for example, Brian, *Einstein: A Life*, 194–95.

12. See, for example, the series of articles under the heading "Revolution in Cosmology," *Scientific American* (January 1999): 45–69; see also Joshua Roth, "The Race to Map the Microwave Background," *Sky and Telescope* (September 1999): 44–48.

13. Freeman J. Dyson, "Time without End: Physics and Biology in an Open Universe," *Reviews of Modern Physics* 51 (1979): 447–60. Tipler, *Physics of Immortality*—the whole book is a presentation of his Omega Point Theory (including a technical appendix) for immortality in a closed universe.

14. Tipler, *Physics of Immortality*, 101.

15. Ibid., 70.

16. Dyson, *Infinite in All Directions*, 112.

17. Ibid., 109.

18. Ron Cowen, "The Cosmos' Fate: World without End," *Science News* 153 (3 January 1998): 4. James Glanz, "Exploding Stars Flash New Bulletins from Distant Universe," *Science* 280 (15 May 1998): 1008–9.

19. See, for example, Croswell, *Planet Quest*.

20. See Chap. 11 in this volume, notes 9, 10.

21. Tipler, *Physics of Immortality*, 116–19, critiques Dyson's open-universe model of immortality.

22. Lawrence M. Krauss and Glenn D. Starkman, "The Fate of Life in the Universe," *Scientific American* (November 1999): 58–65.

23. Michael C. Price, "Traversable Wormholes: Some Implications" *Extropy* 5, no. 1 (2nd half of 1993): 14–23.

24. Compare, for example, Tipler, *Physics of Immortality*, 450–56, where he offers a "proof" that "if life is to continue forever, the universe must be closed," versus Michael Price's review of Tipler's book in *Extropy* 7, no. 1 (1st Qtr. 1995): 42–45, which calls this argument into question.

Chapter 15

1. More, *Diachronic Self*, 188–91.

2. Locke, *Essay Concerning Human Understanding*, 2.27.9–29.

3. See, for example, Deutsch, *Fabric of Reality*, 263–66.

4. More, *Diachronic Self*, 42.

5. Tipler, *Physics of Immortality*, 190.

6. Parfit cites this example too, in *Reasons and Persons*, 205.

7. As quoted in Hick, *Death and Eternal Life*, 409.

8. Ibid., 410.

9. Quoted in Sagan, *Demon-Haunted World*, 156.

10. Tipler, *Physics of Immortality*, 188–204.

11. Deutsch, *Fabric of Reality*, 270–79.

12. Cited in Wright, *Twins*, 43–44.

13. Delgado, *Physical Control of the Mind*, 114–16.

14. See, for example, Tipler, *Physics of Immortality*, 201.

15. This brief survey is based on Tom Wolfe, "Sorry, But Your Soul Just Died," *Forbes ASAP* (Dec. 2, 1996): 211.

16. See, for example, Kurzweil, *Age of Spiritual Machines*, 122–23.

17. Wolfe, "Sorry, But Your Soul Just Died," 202.

18. Posner, *Aging and Old Age*, 28.

Chapter 16

1. These points are well-summarized in Smith, *World's Religions*, s. v. "Hinduism," chap. 1, esp. 12–21.

2. See, for example, Niven, "Death by Ecstasy," in *Flatlander*, 1–70.

3. Frankl, *Man's Search for Meaning*, 155.

4. Hick, *Death and Eternal Life*, 165.

5. Compare, for example, Honderich, *Oxford Companion to Philosophy*, s. v. "Kant and Post-Kantian Ethics," 589.

6. A point frequently made by Robert Ettinger.

7. One interesting modern example, by no means unique, is *The Ochre Robe* of Agehananda Bharati (né Leopold Fischer), an Austrian national who became a Hindu monk.

8. Zakydalsky, N. F. *Fyodorov's Philosophy of Physical Resurrection*, 7.

9. Hick, *Death and Eternal Life*, 410.

10. Zakydalsky, N. F. *Fyodorov's Philosophy of Physical Resurrection*, 124.

11. Tipler, *Physics of Immortality*, 249–50.

12. See, for example, Walls, "Hell and Human Freedom," in *Hell*, chap. 6, 113–38.

13. Locke, *Essay Concerning Human Understanding*, 2.27.6.

14. See, for example, Richard L. Gregory, ed., "Split Brain and the Mind," in *The Oxford Companion to the Mind* (New York: Oxford University Press, 1998), 740–47.

15. See, for example, Edwards, *Immortality*, 59–62.

16. Compare Zakydalsky, N. F. *Fyodorov's Philosophy of Physical Resurrection*, 11.

Chapter 17

1. See, for example, David Voss, "Moses of the Nanoworld," *Technology Review* (March–April 1999): 60–62; and also the web sites of Zyvex, <http://www. zyvex.com/>); and Nanotechnology Development Corporation, <http://www. developnanotechnology.com/>.

2. See, for example, Beth Baker, "Antiaging Humbug?" *AARP Bulletin* 38, no. 4 (April 1997): 1, 14–17.

3. Peter S. Eriksson et al., "Neurogenesis in the Adult Human Hippocampus," *Nature Medicine* 4 (November 1998): 1313–17. John Travis,

"Adult Human Brains Add New Cells," *Science News* 154 (31 October 1998) 276.

4. Leonard Hayflick, "The Limited *In Vitro* Lifetime of Human Diploid Cell Strains," *Experimental Cell Research* 37 (1965) 614–36, referred to in Fossel, *Reversing Human Aging*, 49–50.

5. Nicholas Wade, "Chromosomes Have a Loop at Each End, Scientists Find," *The New York Times on the Web*, 14 May 1999 <http://www.nytimes.com/>.

6. See, for example, Medina, *Clock of Ages*, 25–26.

7. Ibid., 275–79.

8. John Travis, "Tick, Tock, Enzyme Rewinds Cellular Clock," *Science News* 153 (17 January 1998): 37.

9. Dan Ferber, "Immortalized Cells Seem Cancer-Free So Far," *Science* 283 (8 January 1999): 154–55.

10. Summarized from Bova, *Immortality*, 22–26.

11. Ibid., 26–28.

12. Ibid., 62–66.

13. Fossel, *Reversing Human Aging*, 51.

14. David A. Sinclair and Leonard Guarente, "Extrachromosomal rDNA Circles—A Cause of Aging in Yeast," *Cell* 91, no. 7 (26 December 1997): 1033–42.

15. S. Jay Olshansky, Bruce A. Carnes and Douglas Grahn, "Confronting the Boundaries of Human Longevity," *American Scientist* 86 (January–February 1998): 60.

16. Bova, *Immortality*, 25.

17. Moore, *Lifespan*, 250–52.

18. Medina, *Clock of Ages*, 302–4.

19. Moore, *Lifespan*, 250–52.

20. Ibid.; Medina, *Clock of Ages*, 302–4; NIH National Task Force on the Prevention of Obesity, "Very Low-Calorie Diets," *Journal of the American Medical Association* 270, no. 8 (1993): 967–74. Cheol-Koo Lee et al., "Gene Expression Profile of Aging and Its Retardation by Caloric Restriction," *Science* 285 (27 August 1999): 1390–93. For those wishing to try calorie restriction, a basic reference is Roy Walford's *120-Year Diet*; as usual, check the Internet also.

21. Moore, *Lifespan*, 250–52.

22. For a discussion of the scientific basis and prospects for cryonics, see Alcor Life Extension Foundation, "The Cryobiological Case for Cryonics," *Cryonics Reaching for Tomorrow*, A-1–A-9.

23. Alcor Life Extension Foundation, *Cryonics: Reaching for Tomorrow*, 11.

24. See, for example, Alcor Life Extension Foundation, "Suspension Procedures," *Cryonics Reaching for Tomorrow*, chap. 9, 34–41.

25. Alcor Life Extension Foundation, *Cryonics: Reaching for Tomorrow*, A-38.

26. Tipler, *Physics of Immortality*, 157–58.

27. This illustration appears to have originated in the 1980s, possibly with Michael Darwin.

28. Alcor Life Extension Foundation, *Cryonics: Reaching for Tomorrow*, 28–29.

29. Ibid., 11.

30. Charles Platt, "Hearts, Brains and Minds," *CryoCare Report* 10 (January 1997): 4–14.

31. Alcor Life Extension Foundation, *Cryonics Reaching for Tomorrow*, A-5–A-6; see also Charles Platt, "Treating and Minimizing Ischemic Injury," *Cryonics* 20, no. 1 (1st Qtr. 1999): 9.

32. Alcor Life Extension Foundation, *Cryonics Reaching for Tomorrow*, A-3–A-7; see also Michael Perry, "For the Record," *Cryonics* 13, no. 4 (April 1992): 4–7. (Both have references to Suda's original papers.)

33. Yu. Pichugin, V. Marchenko, and A. Shilo, "Bioelectric Activity of Cryoconserved Brain Pieces of a Rabbit," *The Immortalist* 26, no. 9 (September 1995): 17–22; and 26, no. 11 (November 1995): 8–11.

34. Gregory Fahy, private communication, as cited in Michael Perry, "For the Record," *Cryonics* 13, no. 4 (April 1992): 6.

35. See, for example, "Total Body Washout #7," *Cryonics* 6, no. 5 (May 1985): 11–15.

36. See, for example, "The Art of Breath-Hold Diving," *Whole Earth Trekking Adventures*, 11 June 1998 <www.moreno-valley.com/wet/freediving/Freediving. html>.

37. Platt, "Treating and Minimizing Ischemic Injury," 9.

38. Saul Kent, CryoNet message #10385, 4 September 1998 (cryonet@cryonet.org).

39. Charles Platt, "The 21st Century Medicine Seminar: Amazing Breakthroughs in Cryobiology and Resuscitation," *Cryonics* 20, no. 1 (1st Qtr. 1999): 7–16.

40. See, for example, Geoffrey Cowley, and Anne Underwood, "Memory," *Newsweek* (15 June 1998): 48–49, 51–54, esp. 51, 54.

41. One reference on chemical fixation of medical cadavers is Iserson, *Death to Dust*, 88–89.

42. Ben Best, private communication with author.

43. Ralph Merkle, "The Technical Feasibility of Cryonics," *Medical Hypotheses* 39 (1992): 6–16, with a fuller treatment in Ralph Merkle, "Molecular Repair of the Brain," *Cryonics* 15, no. 1 (1st Qtr. 1994): 16–30; 15, no. 2 (2nd Qtr. 1994): 18–30.

44. Drexler, *Engines of Creation*, 136–38.

45. Gregory Fahy, "A 'Realistic' Scenario for Nanotechnological Repair of the Frozen Human Brain," in Alcor Life Extension Foundation, *Cryonics Reaching for Tomorrow*, A-10–A-26.

46. Merkle, "Molecular Repair of the Brain," *Cryonics* 15, no. 2 (2nd Qtr. 1994): 29.

47. Ibid., 21.

48. Based on U.S. Census Bureau, *World Population Profile: 1996*.

49. This was the U.S. rate at the largest cryonics organization, Alcor Foundation, during much of the 1990s.

50. *Le Monde Diplomatique* (April 1997): 16.

51. The first, passive form of the Golden Rule is found in such sources as the sayings of Confucius and Hillel; the second, proactive form is a principal tenet of Jesus (Matt. 7:12); Compare Honderich, *Oxford Companion to Philosophy*, s. v. "Golden Rule," 321–22.

52. Courage, reason, creativity, and hope I found emphasized in Kurtz, *Courage to Become*; love and the other values are from the list compiled by Rushworth M. Kidder and cited in Cetron and Davies, *Cheating Death*, 88–90.

53. The expression "inspired by love and guided by knowledge" is from Russell, "What I Believe," in *Why I Am Not a Christian*, 56.

Chapter 18

1. A short summary of progress in neural implants will be found in Kurzweil, *Age of Spiritual Machines*, 127–28.

2. See, for example, Douglas and Olshaker, *Unabomber*, which reprints Theodore Kaczynski, *Industrial Society and Its Future* (the "Unabomber Manifesto"). Quotations from the latter (which is also widely available on the Internet) are from paragraphs 1, 96, 178–81, 183. Also printed in this volume (and available on the Internet) is the Letter to the *New York Times*, 24 April 1995, from which the additional material is quoted. Another source I have used for biographical detail on Kaczynski is Pickover, "The Hermit from Montana," in *Strange Brains and Genius*, chap. 9, 157–82.

3. Hart, *Guiding Principles of Sustainable Design*, chap. 1. "Tropical Forests," World Wildlife Fund (WWF) Canada, 1998 <http://www.panda.org/kids/mntropic.html>. Julio Cesar Centeno, "Certification and Green Labelling: A View from the Tropics," International Conference on Sustainable Forest Management: Certification, Criteria and Indicators, Prince George, Canada. 21-26 September, 1997; <http://csf.colorado.edu/elan/nov97/0051.html>.

4. <http://www.columbiacolorado.com/topicareas/men/mensfertility.html> (28 May 1997); see also Gosden, *Cheating Time*, 341–42, 267-68.

5. See, for example, Bova, *Immortality*, 193, esp. n. 21.

6. See, for example, Richard Saltus, "Scientists Discover Replicating Human Cell," *Boston Globe*, reprinted in *Tribune* (Scottsdale, Ariz.), 6 November 1998, A1, A4, which notes funding of fetal cell research by Geron Corp.

7. See, for example, Lewis, *Guilty by Reason of Insanity*.

8. (As one reference out of many) Edward Hunter, "Experts Agree: Death Penalty Not a Deterrent to Violent Crime," 22 January 1997 <http://www.ucfn.aa.ufl.edu/ UFCN/ufnews/death.html>.

9. John Stuart Mill, *On Liberty*, Introductory, 342–46, as cited in Honderich, *Oxford Companion to Philosophy*, 569.

10. Iqbal, *Reconstruction of Religious Thought in Islam*, 12.

11. A viewpoint Tipler echoes; compare *Physics of Immortality*, 1–2,

127–28; it is also common among cryonicists: compare Ralph Merkle, CryoNet message #10624, 21 October 1998 (cryonet@cryonet.org).

12. Pearce, *Hedonistic Imperative*, Introduction <http://www.hedweb.com/ hedethic/hedonist.htm>.

13. See, for example, John Omicinski, "Japanese Haven't a Clue What to Do about Plummeting Birth Rate," *Gannet News Service*, printed in *Tribune* (Scottsdale, Ariz.) 8 August 1998, A17.

14. Constance Holden, "Gray Matter on a Chip," *Science* 278 (7 Novembr 1997): 1021.

15. This idea is explored at length in Joseph Strout, "Mind Uploading: An Alternative Path to Immortality," *Cryonics* 19, no. 2 (2nd Qtr. 1998): 26–30.

16. Kurzweil speculates on this possibility in *The Age of Spiritual Machines*, 124–26, after discussing current, relevant imaging techniques on pages 122–23.

17. Electronic telepathy is closely related to "radiotelepathy" as described in Dyson, *Imagined Worlds*, 132–37.

18. See, for example, Vadim Gerasimov, "Information Processing in the Human Body" <http://vadim.www.media.mit.edu/MAS862/Project.html>, referred to in Kurzweil, *Age of Spiritual Machines*, 332 n. 25.

19. Compare *The Guinness Book of World Records 1998* (Stamford, Conn.: Guinness Publishing, Ltd., 1997), 146.

20. This paragraph is based on Thomas Donaldson, CryoNet message #12205, 29 July 1999 (cryonet@cryonet.org).

ORGANIZATIONS

ANTIAGING RELATED

Advanced Cell Technology, Inc.
One Innovation Drive
Worcester, MA 01605
508-756-1212; fax 508-756-0931
<http://www.advancedcell.com>

American Academy of Antiaging Medicine
1341 West Fullerton, Ste. 111
Chicago, IL 60614
800-558-1267; fax: 773-528-5390
a4m@worldhealth.net; <http://www.worldhealth.net/>
Publication: *International Journal of Antiaging Medicine*

Geron Corporation
200 Constitution Avenue
Menlo Park, CA 94025
415-473-7700
info@geron.com; <http://www.geron.com/>

CRYONICS

Alcor Life Extension Foundation
7895 East Acoma Drive, Ste. 110
Scottsdale, AZ 85260
877-GO-ALCOR (877-462-5267); 480-905-1906; fax: 480-922-9027
info@alcor.org; <http://www.alcor.org/>
Publication: *Cryonics*

American Cryonics Society
1901 Old Middlefield Way, Ste. 17
Mountain View, CA 94043
800-523-2001; 415-254-2001; fax: 415-967-4444
cryonics@jps.net; <http://www.jps.net/>
Publishes in *The Immortalist*

CRYONICS (CONTINUED)

CryoCare Foundation
1013 Centre Road, Suite 301
Wilmington, DE 19805-1297;
800-TOP-CARE (800-867-2273)
cryocare@cryocare.org; <http://www.cryocare.org>

Cryonics Association of Australia
P.O. Box 57 Hampton
Victoria 3188 Australia
<http://www.pricom.com.au/caa/>

Cryonics Institute
24355 Sorrentino Court
Clinton Township, MI 48035
810-791-5961; fax: 810-792-7062
cryonics@cryonics.org; <http://www.cryonics.org/>
Publishes in *The Immortalist*

Cryonics Society of Canada
P.O. Box 788, Station A
Toronto, Ontario Canada M5W 1G3
<http://www.benbest.com/cryocdn.html>

Cryonics Society of Spain
<http://perso.wanadoo.es/Lmingorancem>

CryoSpan, Inc.
Three Christina Center
210 North Walnut Street, Ste. 1000
Wilmington, DE 19801
909-987-3883

Immortalist Society (promotional group associated with Cryonics
    Institute)
24355 Sorrentino Court
Clinton Township, MI 48035
810-791-5961; fax: 810-792-7062
<http://www.cryonics.org/info.html>
Publication: *The Immortalist*

Japanese Cryonics Association (discussion group)
chiron@biojapan.com; <http://www.kanon.to/jcaindex.html>

CRYONICS (CONTINUED)

Open Directory—Cryonics
<http://dmoz.org/Science/Biology/Cryobiology/Cryonics>

Trans Time, Inc.
3029 Teagarden Street
San Leandro, CA 94577
510-297-5577; fax: 510-297-5579

CRYONICS RESEARCH

Institute for Neural Cryobiology
238 Davenport Rd. #240
Toronto, ON M5R 1J6 Canada
416-968-6291; fax: 559-663-5511
wakfer@gte.net; <http://neurocryo.org/>

Twenty-first Century Medicine
10743 Civic Center Drive
Rancho Cucamonga, CA 91730
909-987-3883; fax: 909-987-7253
<http://www.21cm.com/>

DNA STORAGE

The Anthony Jones Foundation
The West House
West Ashling Road
Hambrook, West Sussex
PO18 8UP
England
01243-573668; fax: 01243-573668
<http://www.anthonyjonesfoundation.com/>

GENERAL SCIENTIFIC

Open Directory
<http://dmoz.org/Science/>

GENOMIC MAPPING AND GENE STUDIES

Celera Genomics
45 West Gude Drive
Rockville, MD 20850
877-723-5372
<http://www.celera.com/>

National Human Genome Research Institute (NHGRI)
9000 Rockville Pike
Bethesda, MD 20892
800-222-2225
<http://www.nhgri.nih.gov/>

INFORMATION STORAGE

Dr. Stephane de France
Recherches en Identigraphie
9-11, rue Clement Marot
F-82300 Caussade
France
StephanedF@aol.com

NANOTECHNOLOGY

Foresight Institute
P.O. Box 61058
Palo Alto, CA 94306
650-917-1122; fax: 650-917-1123
inform@foresight.org; <http://www.foresight.org/>
Publication: *Foresight Update*

IBM Thomas J. Watson Research Center
P.O. Box 218
Yorktown Heights, NY 10598
914-945-3000; fax: 914-945-2141

Institute for Molecular Manufacturing
555 Bryant Street, Ste. 253
Palo Alto, CA 94301
650-917-1120; fax: 650-917-1123
admin@imm.org; <http://www.imm.org/>

NANOTECHNOLOGY (CONTINUED)

Institute of Nanotechnology
<http://www.nano.org.uk/>

International Technology Research Institute: Nanotechnology Database
<http://itri.loyola.edu/nano/links.htm>
(has extensive listing of nanotechnology-related material covering major research centers, funding agencies, major reports, and books)

Lucent Technology (Bell Labs Innovations)
600 Mountain Avenue
Murray Hill, NJ 07974-0616
888-4-LUCENT (888-458-2368)
<http://www.lucent.com/>

Molecular Manufacturing Enterprises, Inc.
9653 Wellington Lane
St. Paul, MN 55125
612-288-0093
svetter@mmei.com; <http://www.mmei.com/>

Nanogen
10398 Pacific Center Court
San Diego, CA 92121
619-546-7000; fax: 619-546-7718
info@nanogen.com; <http:/www.nanogen.com/>

Nanologic, Inc.
4295 Walnut Boulevard
Walnut Creek, CA 94596
925-988-9650; fax: 925-988-9645
info@NanoLogicInc.com; <http://www.NanoLogicInc.com/>

Nanophase Technologies
453 Commerce Street
Burr Ridge, IL 60521
630-323-1200; fax: 630-323-1221
info-w@nanophase.com; <http://www.nanophase.com/>

NANOTECHNOLOGY (CONTINUED)

NanoTechnology (publication)
3 Degrees Kelvin Publishing Co.
4451 Sierra Drive
Honolulu, HI 96816
808-737-0629; fax: 808-735-0638
<http://www.nano-technology.com/>

Nanotechnology (publication)
Institute of Physics Publishing
The Public Ledger Building, Ste. 1035
150 South Independence Mall West
Philadelphia, PA 19106
215-627-0880; fax: 215-627-0879
<http://www.ioppublishing.com/>

Nanotechnology Development Corporation
1350 NASA Road One, NASA Building, Ste. 100
Houston, TX 77058
800-987-2001; fax: 281-333-5911
Info@DevelopNanotechnology.com;
    <http:www.developnanotechnology.com/>

Zyvex LLC
1321 North Plano Road, Ste. 200
Richardson, TX 75081
972-235-7881, fax: 972-235-7882
info@zyvex.com; <http://www.zyvex.com/>

SKEPTICISM

American Humanist Association
7 Hardwood Drive
P.O. Box 1188
Amherst, NY 14226-7188
716-839-5080; 800-743-6646; fax: 716-839-5079
humanism@juno.com; <http://www.infidels.org/org/aha>
Publication: *The Humanist*

SKEPTICISM (CONTINUED)

Atheist Alliance
P.O. Box 6261
Minneapolis, MN 55496
<http:///www.atheistalliance.org//>
Publication: *Secular Nation Magazine*

Council for Secular Humanism
P.O. Box 664
Amherst, NY 14226-0664
716-636-7571; fax: 716-636-1733
Publication: *Free Inquiry*

CSICOP [Committee for the Scientific Investigation of Claims of the
   Paranormal]
P.O. Box 703
Amherst, NY 14226-0703
716-636-1425; fax: 716-636-1733
<http://www.csicop.org/>
Publication: *The Skeptical Inquirer*

Skeptics Society
P.O. Box 336
Altadena, CA 91001
626-794-3119; fax: 626-794-1301
skepticmag@aol.com; <http://www.skeptic.com/>
Publication: *Skeptic*

TRANSHUMANISM

Extropy Institute
13428 Maxella Avenue, #273
Marina del Rey, CA 90292
310-398-0375
exi-info@extropy.org; <http://www.extropy.com/>
Publications: *Exponent, Extropy* (electronic)

TRANSHUMANISM (CONTINUED)

Immortalist Society
24355 Sorrentino Court
Clinton Township, MI 48035
810-791-5961; fax: 810-792-7062
cryonics@cryonics.org; <http://www.cryonics.org/>
Publication: *The Immortalist*

International Immortalist Movement Association
Via di S. Maria Ausiliatrice, 45
Rome 00181
Italy
Publication: *Longevita*

Periastron (publication of Thomas Donaldson)
12 Busby Street
O'Connor ACT 2602
Australia

Society for Venturism
15111 N. Hayden Road, Suite 160–169
Scottsdale, AZ 85260
mike@alcor.org; <http://www.venturist.org>
Publication: *The Venturist*

The Transhumanist Web Alliance
<http://www.aleph.se/>
Publication: *Homo Excelsior* (electronic)

Vita Longa
P.O. Box 301
St. Petersburg 196244
Russia
cryonics@chat.ru; <http://www.chat.ru/~cryonics>

World Transhumanist Association
<http://www.transhumanism.com/>
Publication: *Journal of Transhumanism* (electronic)

ACKNOWLEDGEMENTS

I especially thank Joe Hovey for his persistent interest and encouragement over the years that the book was in preparation. In addition to general support, Joe was very useful in bringing references to my attention that otherwise might have gone unnoticed. Michael Darwin gave encouragement in the very early stages, when I was studying Fedorov's work and hoping it could be adapted to a modern scientific picture. Thomas Donaldson and Robert Ettinger deserve special mention for their thought-provoking criticism that improved the philosophical content. I am grateful to Lisa Lock for her expert copyediting which helped bring the text up to scholarly standards and also made it more readable without altering its basic content.

Others with useful ideas, information, or criticism included Fred and Linda Chamberlain, Russell Cheney, John K. Clark, David Comos, Lee Corbin, Daniel Crevier, Andrzej Ehrenfeucht, Christopher Fedeli, Stanley Gerber, Scott Herman, Hugh Hixon, Peter Merrill, David Pizer, Mark Plus, Brian Shock, Anne and Robert Slaton, Mathew Sullivan, and Edgar Swank. I thank Jerry Searcy for reading and critiquing an early version of the manuscript. There are numerous others whose ideas influenced the writing, who unfortunately cannot be listed individually. I thank Alcor Foundation, my employer during the time that the book was written, for their kind indulgence and moral support. I also extend apologies to those on CryoNet who were offended by the sometimes protracted philosophical discussions relating to certain ideas in the book, during the time that others made contributions that improved it.

Finally, I must thank Aido my cat, who kept me company during many a long session with the book and offered his own insight into the mystery and wonder of living.

INDEX

abortion, 511, 549–50, 552
accelerating universe, 404, 408
Action, Philosophy of, 2, 4, 26, 412, 483, 501, 532, 535–36
afterlife, 1, 8, 11, 23, 29–30, 51–52, 56, 66, 98, 159–60, 195, 275, 287, 296, 303, 307, 494. See also resurrection
Age of Reason, The (Paine), 273
Age of Spiritual Machines, The (Kurzweil), 46
aging, 22, 503, 505, 541
  an imposition, 443
  elimination of, 2, 20, 31, 46, 97, 160, 247, 278, 444, 458, 472–73, 492, 528, 559, 561
  research, 49, 501–3, 536
  reversal, 19, 462, 506
agnosticism. See God: nonexistence of
Alcor (cryonics organization), 40, 42
all-unity (Fedorov), 467
alteration of race and gender, 539
Amazing Stories (science fiction periodical), 36
anabiosis (suspended animation), 37
animism, 12, 298
Anselm, 286
Anthropic Cosmological Principle, The (Barrow and Tipler), 9, 288
Anthropic Principle, 95, 154, 288–90, 292, 294, 305
  and Ockham's razor, 289
Apocalypse, 4–5, 7, 16, 18, 29, 44, 559, 563

Argument from Design (theology), 274, 282, 290–91
Aristotle, 131
artificial intelligence (AI), 254
  humans not to be outclassed, 70, 237, 264
  Robbins Problem, 235
  strong AI, 194–95, 199–200, 223, 225–26, 228, 234, 238, 244–45, 275, 308, 337, 406, 414–15
  weak AI, 224, 228
Aspect (twin-photon) experiment, 122–25, 128, 130
  Bell's inequality, 126
Aspect, Alain, 122
Aspiration, Philosophy of, 2, 412, 448, 455, 498–99
Assurance, Philosophy of, 2, 24, 412, 433, 445–47
atheism, 279, 296–99, 556, 557. See also God: nonexistence of
  traditional Western variety versus Yuai, 299
atheism versus agnosticism. See God: atheism versus agnosticism
atomic force microscope (AFM), 254
Axelrod, Robert, 313

Babel Picture Gallery, 149–50, 424
backward time travel, 11, 66, 426–27, 518
Bakhmetiev, Porfiry, 37
Barrow, John, 9, 288
basement universes, 410
Becoming Immortal (DuCharme), 501

Bedbug, The (Mayakovsky), 38
Bedford, James, 42
Beethoven, Ludwig, 202, 283
Bekenstein bounds, 219, 405
Bekenstein, Jakob, 150, 219
belief, 300
Bell, John Stewart, 125
benevolence, 4, 26, 28, 72, 100,
 286, 311–13, 316–17, 319, 323,
 326–29, 352, 398, 413, 437, 461,
 464, 475–76, 491, 494, 496, 536
biostasis, 2, 4–5, 20, 22, 27, 43, 45,
 47–48, 50, 52, 65, 73, 76, 85, 90,
 98, 160, 167, 278, 299, 302, 331,
 347, 351, 390, 394, 422, 447,
 482, 496–98, 500–1, 507–8, 510,
 527, 532, 534, 536, 556. See also
 cryonics
 advantages, 98–99, 356–58,
  362, 366, 369–70, 373–79,
  394, 482–83, 495–96, 500,
  507–8, 510, 514, 555, 557
 archeological argument, 361
 communitarian argument,
  359, 371–72
 conservatist argument, 363–
  65, 369, 372, 377
 coping with the unknown,
  356–57
 Darwinian argument, 369,
  371, 376
 forestalling irreversible loss,
  356–57
 libertarian argument, 371
 moral argument, 374
 summary of arguments, 375
 and capital punishment, 554
 biostatic versus nonbiostatic
  immortalist philosophy. See
  immortalism: biostatic versus
  nonbiostatic immortalist philosophy
 commitment desirable, 536
 future attitude toward, 559
 harmonization with different
  worldviews, 556, 558
 medical criterion, 508, 510,
  512–13, 524, 527, 533
 not superfluous. See biostasis:
  advantages
 ontic criterion, 510, 512, 524
 policy in regard to those unable
  to make informed, 555
 premortem procedure, 555
 problem of imperfect preservation, 21, 99, 376, 508, 533–34
Bohr, Niels, 118
Bova, Ben, 45
Boyle, Robert, 37
brain
 artificial augmentation, 561–62
 speedups, 463, 564–65
 brain death, 520–21
 computational analogy, 197–
  200, 223
 imaging, 441
 preservation, 532. See also biostasis; cryonics
 reanimation, 522
Broderick, Damien, 46
Brown, Robert, 144
Brownian motion, 144, 146, 311–
 12, 402
buckyball, 253
Buddhism
 doctrine of non-self, 162, 166,
  392, 451

calorie restriction (antiaging strategy), 506–7
capital punishment, 552–53
capital punishment and biostasis.
 See biostasis: and capital punishment
carbon nanotube. See nanotechnology: carbon nanotube
Carter, Brandon, 321

cellular spaces, 217–18, 220–22,
256, 383
Cetron, Marvin, 45
Chamberlain, Fred, 40
Chamberlain, Linda, 40
Cheating Death (Cetron and
Davies), 45
chemical preservation (fixation)
as alternative to cryonics, 21,
526
Chinese room experiment, 226–28,
239–41
human brain emulation, 239–40
Christianity, 10, 29, 32, 56, 279,
284, 287, 455, 558
Church, Alonzo, 213
Church-Turing Thesis, 213
Clark, John K., 46
classical physics, contrast with
quantum mechanics, 113, 119–
20
cloning, 67, 249–50, 511, 540
human, 250, 511, 541–42, 549
communism, 62
community as focus of interest,
464
complementarity of map and territory, 208
computer
as possible emulator of person,
88
developmental trend lines, 263
field programmable gate array
(FPGA), 263
molecular (DNA), 253
powers of, 210–12, 215
programmer as futurologist, 255
quantum. See quantum computing
universal, 213, 215, 217
computer viruses, 547
Condorcet, Antoine, 31
conscious experience. See con-

sciousness: conscious experience
consciousness, 30, 37, 68–69, 87,
91, 140, 161, 166, 171, 173, 175–
77, 179–81, 186–89, 194–95,
199–201, 209, 223–24, 226, 238,
241, 243, 245, 284, 292, 301–2,
310, 323, 339–40, 381–84, 389,
400, 413, 415–18, 421, 430, 442–
43, 474, 491, 496, 517, 561. See
also artificial intelligence (AI):
strong AI
conscious experience, 69, 87–
88, 96, 139, 166, 171–73, 176,
180–81, 209, 381, 383–85,
387, 390, 407, 418, 421, 429,
442, 454, 471, 486
feeling content, 384–85, 387
fused consciousness, 471
information content, 163, 384–
86, 421, 520
isomorphism, 225, 241–42, 243.
See also Interchangeability:
isomorphism
shared, 96, 172, 179, 384
strong AI. See artificial intelligence (AI): strong AI
conservation of identity, 209
contemplation as focus of interest,
464
continuer (personal survival), 76,
85, 93, 164, 195, 203, 301, 307–
11, 332, 334, 338–41, 344, 348,
351, 354, 359, 375, 380–81, 399,
403, 413, 415–16, 427, 433–34,
472, 474, 480, 486–89, 491–96,
509
and xenonticity, 353, 490
authenticity, 348
benefiting earlier stages
through, 475
closest continuer not essential,
163, 343

dangerous made benevolent, 329

exact duplication not necessary, 339

forgetting, false memories, 414, 418, 420, 421. See also memory: problem of forgetting

future advancement of, 314, 455

in multiverse, 425–26

intelligent creation of, 312, 314

joining (fusion) of, 434, 484. See also consciousness: fused consciousness; person: fusion

no survival except through, 302

not an instantiation, 164, 177

past lives problem, 350, 434

pattern-survival, 50, 163–67, 302, 331, 333, 422–24, 446, 475, 485, 487–88, 495, 508

pets and other creatures, 477–78, 481

recovery from amnesia, 487

rights of, 515

splitting (fissioning) of, 302, 339, 343, 485–86, 487. See also person: fissioning

suicide lottery, 329, 353

time precedence problem, 94, 114, 145–46, 151, 156, 341, 353, 426–27

transitivity, 342–44

Conway, John, 215

Cooper, Evan, 38–39

Copenhagen interpretation of quantum mechanics, 118–19, 132–35

Copernicus, Nicholas, 119

cosmological constant, 404

cosmology, 9, 196, 399, 410

cost not to vanish, 264

counterfactuality, 128

counterfactual definiteness, 128

counterfactual indefiniteness, 287, 425

CPT symmetry (quantum mechanics, determinism), 122, 135

Cramer, John, 120, 132

creativity as focus of interest, 25, 464

cryobiology, 37

cryonics, 2, 4–5, 21–23, 26, 29, 36–45, 48–49, 51, 58, 167, 269, 279, 299, 346, 356, 361, 365–66, 372, 374–75, 469, 473, 480, 483, 501–2, 507–10, 516–18, 520–27, 532–34, 536, 551, 555–57, 558. See also freezing of tissues

advantages. See biostasis: advantages

cost, 525

cryonicists, 21, 42, 49–51, 64, 78, 299, 363, 366, 373, 377, 469, 473, 477, 508–9, 512, 517, 528, 533, 556

difficulties over acceptance, 51–52, 59, 62–69, 73

difficulties over criteria of death, 517

failures, 40

first cryonic suspension, 39

harmonization with different worldviews. See biostasis: harmonization with different worldviews

head-only freezing, 40, 525, 535

legal challenges to, 41

medical criterion. See biostasis: medical criterion

ontic criterion. See biostasis: ontic criterion

opposition of cryobiologists, 517

pet freezing, 477

premortem suspension, 41, 555

procedures, 516

resuscitation, 473, 474. See also
  reanimation
  speculative repair scenario,
  527–31, 551
  right of refusal, 515
  workability of, 43, 66–69
  worldwide feasibility, 535
Cryonics Institute, 42
Cryonics Society of California, 40
Cryonics Society of Canada, 527
Cryonics Society of New York, 40

Darwin, Charles, 274
Darwin, Michael, 40
Darwin's   Dangerous   Idea
  (Dennett), 234
data-erasing experiment, 134, 136–
  37, 178, 427
Davies, Owen, 45
Davies, Paul, 282, 289
day-person concept, 161, 174
De Rerum Natura (Lucretius), 30,
  345
death, 1, 8, 30–32, 41–42, 51, 53–
  55, 66, 68, 70, 73, 92, 97–98,
  159–60, 162, 167, 174, 201, 203,
  209, 272, 278, 280, 289, 302–3,
  306, 308, 320, 341, 352, 356,
  371, 381, 392, 394–95, 397, 462,
  474, 495, 501, 506, 515, 517–18,
  542–43, 555, 561, 567
  a process not an event, 520
  acceptance, 50, 52, 56–57, 61,
    66, 166, 299, 392, 500, 542.
    See also death: terror manage-
    ment theory
  and transcendence, 450
  as detriment or imposition, 1, 44,
    47, 75, 332, 413, 549
  as solvable problem, 1–2, 10–
    11, 30, 33, 38, 48, 63, 161,
    195, 209, 299, 301–2, 310,
    329, 334, 337–39, 351–52,
    359, 412, 422, 446, 451, 470,

492, 499–500, 510, 558, 568.
    See also death: elimination of
  conflict of worldviews, 58
  continuer problem, 343
  conventional understanging, 510
  criteria, 509, 517–18
  definition, 517–18, 521
  elimination of, 2, 16, 19, 23, 28–
    29, 31, 44–47, 52–53, 57, 64,
    70, 75, 271, 278, 332, 381,
    395, 399, 444, 456–58, 460,
    472, 501, 535, 540, 560. See
    also death: elimination of
  materialistic hopes of reprieve
    from, 24
  preservation of remains at, 21–
    22, 27, 38–39, 42, 48, 65, 99,
    299, 369, 414, 482–83, 493,
    508, 520, 532, 535. See also
    biostasis; cryonics
  seriousness of problem, 160
  terror management theory, 55–
    59, 63, 64. See also death: ac-
    ceptance
Death and Eternal Life (Hick), 430,
  455
death penalty. See capital punishment
Deep Blue (chess program), 227
deism, 273–74, 352
Delgado, José, 440
Democritus, 30
Dennett, Daniel, 234
determinism, 49–50, 103, 113,
  122–23, 318–19, 437–38, 553
  accessible, 11, 49, 103, 214, 218,
    334–36, 340, 406, 414, 438
  forward, 334
  inaccessible, 50, 122
  reverse, 334–36
Deutsch, David, 3, 9, 119, 131,
  136, 145, 266, 277, 423, 425,
  437–38
Devil, 281

Dewdney, A.K., 3
Dewdney, Christopher, 46
diabolical choice, 498
diachronic self. See person: diachronic self
diamond (nanotechnology), 267–68
direction of time, 291–92
divinity, 279, 298–99, 557
DNA chips (aging research), 252, 507
Dolly (cloned sheep), 249
Donaldson, Thomas, 41, 555
Doomsday Argument, 321, 323
Drexler, Eric, 3, 43, 46, 248, 257, 528
drives
modification without sacrificing identity, 452, 454
Du Bois-Reymond, Emil, 32
DuCharme, Wesley M., 501
Duncan-Jones, Austin, 430
Dyson, Freeman, 9, 24, 303, 394, 405–8

Earles, Beverly, 300
Einstein, Albert, 80, 114, 136, 207, 283
Engines of Creation (Drexler), 3, 43, 248, 265, 528
enjoyment
as self-unifying force, 465
as unifying force, 466
enlightened self-interest, 26, 53, 99, 321, 332, 340, 413, 464, 466, 469, 473, 475, 481
Enlightenment, 13, 18, 31, 277
enonticity, 345–47, 350–53, 358, 369–71, 378, 380, 388, 390, 394, 397, 399, 401, 411, 422, 427, 435–36, 482–83, 490, 494, 496–97, 509. See also resurrection: enontic
entropy, 292, 401

environmental issues, 548
future, 463, 565, 567–68
future, morality, 567
enzymes, artificial, 253
Epicureanism, 30, 80, 333–34, 345, 392
Epicurus, 30, 333
episodic memories, 89–90, 388
eschatology, 16, 74
Essay Concerning Human Understanding, An (Locke), 31, 415
eternal life. See immortality
eternal punishment ruled out. See immortality: eternal punishment ruled out
Eternal Return, 35, 286, 334, 366–67, 393, 400–3, 409, 420, 430, 452–53, 460, 477
Ettinger, Robert, 3, 9, 24, 36, 38–39, 42, 49, 185
Everett, Hugh, 4, 97, 120, 133, 136, 151, 156, 174, 287
evil
diminishing persistence, 315
evil nature
as curable affliction, 32
evolution, Darwinian, 154, 158, 274, 282, 290, 324, 328, 370
Evolution of Cooperation, The (Axelrod), 313
expression of identity, 209
extraordinary claims, 13
extraterrestrials, 11
Extropy Institute, 44, 46

Fabric of Reality, The (Deutsch), 3, 9, 119, 131, 145, 277, 423
faith, 300
Faloon, Bill, 42
Fedorov, Nikolai, 24, 31–35, 42, 47–49, 57, 74, 92, 334, 336, 467, 477, 499
employment, 31
Fermi, Enrico, 322

Fermi paradox (failure to observe extraterrestrials), 250, 322
Feynman, Richard, 136, 249, 254
finite state machine, 218–20, 225, 244, 308, 318
  modeling of physical systems by, 219
Flew, Anthony, 175
forelife. See continuer (personal survival): past lives problem
Foresight Institute, 43, 501
four-slit photon experiment, 131
Frankl, Viktor, 454, 456
Franklin, Benjamin, 18, 31
free will, 318–19, 414, 437–40, 476, 478, 553
  brain studies, 440
  compatibilism, 318–19, 437–38, 440
  moral responsibility, 318
  twin studies, 439
Freeze-Wait-Reanimate (periodical), 39
freezing of tissues
  damage
    cracking, 523
Frege, Gottlob, 230
Frietas, Robert, 43
fullerene, 253
functionalism. See reductionism: psychological: functionalism
fusion of individuals, 484
future of the universe
  chaotic effects allow constructive change, 401
future scenario imagined, 467
Fuzzy Future, The (Kosko), 47

Game of Life (computation), 215
  generalizations, 217
Garbo, Greta (thought experiment), 84–86, 422
Garfinkel, Simson, 257

Gelisnger, Jesse (gene therapy casualty), 251
genetic engineering, 250, 260, 559
genomic preservation, 510–14, 524, 531, 533
geocentric model of the solar system, 119
Gibbs, J. Willard, 168
goals of life, 25, 449
  transcendence, 449–50
God, 10–12, 31, 57, 136, 153, 272–77, 279–81, 285, 287–88, 293–95, 297–99, 301, 410, 417, 429, 436–37, 445, 477–78, 552, 557
  advantages of absence of, 296
  atheism versus agnosticism, 297
  attributes of, 277, 280–81, 284, 286, 294
  conflict of beliefs in, 281
  consolation to believers in, 298
  Cosmic Community hypothesis, 285–86
  multiverse as alternative to, 95, 280, 288–89, 292–93
  nonexistence of, 10, 62, 154–55, 275–80, 282–87, 290–91, 294, 296–97, 437
  ourselves becoming a deity, 11, 17, 279, 295
  prayer, 282
  problem of evil, 280–81, 294, 437
Gödel, Kurt, 179, 190, 229, 231–33, 237, 315
Godwin, William, 31
Golden Rule, 312, 536
good
  prevailing in time, 301
Gott, Richard, 321
graphite (nanotechnology), 267–68
Grosso, Michael, 45
growing processes (as models of immortality), 209
Gruman, Gerald, 74

Haldane, J.B.S., 334
Halperin, James, 44
halting problem (unsolvable computation problem), 215, 218, 237, 258
Hanson, Robin, 46
happiness, 26, 71, 78, 91, 100, 270, 294, 316, 319–21, 372, 412, 433, 466, 470, 478, 495, 498–99, 556, 559
   eternal, 280, 316, 320
Harrington, Alan, 44–45, 48
Hartshorne, Charles, 286, 294
Hawking, Stephen, 136
Hayflick, Leonard, 502
Hayflick limit, 502–3
Heat Death of the universe, 49, 292–93, 380, 392–93, 395, 400–2, 406, 409
Heaven, 10, 16, 34, 276, 295, 298, 352, 459, 508, 544
Hedonistic Imperative, The (Pearce), 559
Hell, 295, 461, 478
Henderson, Curtis, 40
Herbert, Nick, 3, 121
Hick, John, 430, 455, 470, 472
Hilbert, David, 231
Hillis, Daniel, 3
Hinduism, 284, 449–50
history
   as computation, 225, 337
   different meanings of, 121, 140–41
   finite histories and Unboundedness, 14, 94, 138–47, 150–52, 154, 156, 174, 177, 222, 244, 294, 301, 316, 341, 424, 490, 567
Hitler, Adolf, 393, 455
Hixon, Hugh, 40
Holocaust, 393
human genome mapping, 251–52
human reproduction

   doomed as source of meaning, 457
Human Use of Human Beings, The (Wiener), 38
Humanism, 300
Hume, David, 13, 274
hunger, future of, 464
Hunter, John, 37
Hutchinson-Gilford syndrome, 505
hyperonticity, 345–47, 350–52, 358, 369, 377–78, 390, 480–81, 490, 509, 514, 534. See also resurrection: hyperontic

ideal self, 415. See also immortality: ideal self
identity
   pattern theory of, 14, 50, 88, 170, 174
Identity of Indiscernibles, 15, 170, 180, 423
immortalism, 1, 5, 16, 21–22, 24, 28, 30, 38, 44–45, 47–48, 50–51, 62–63, 89, 371, 458, 460, 496, 508, 533, 536–38, 543, 554–58
   apathy toward, 53
   biostatic versus nonbiostatic immortalist philoso, 48, 50
   cosmological philosophy versus transhumanist, 2, 19, 48
   immortalist philosophies, 48–50
   one-chance immortalist philosophy versus resurrectionist, 49
   roots, 71
Immortalist, The (Harrington), 44
immortalists
   as guardians of the future, 496
immortality, 9–11, 15, 19, 23, 26, 29–31, 33, 35, 44, 65, 78, 80, 97, 138, 142, 146, 152, 157, 162, 209, 214, 228, 243, 269, 277, 280, 284–86, 288, 299, 302, 309, 330, 351, 355, 358–59, 366, 370–71, 375–80, 387, 389–90, 411,

414, 422, 433–34, 446, 452, 462–
63, 466, 481–82, 484, 491–92,
499, 557, 561, 567–68
all to enjoy, 24, 354, 379, 455,
467, 470, 472, 474, 477–78,
480–81, 491, 493, 499, 511,
532, 537, 558. See also Universalism
almost enontic, 390
and cryonics, 21, 532
as goal of life, 5, 8, 17, 22, 25–
26, 28, 31, 45, 49–50, 52, 63,
71, 73–74, 76, 78, 89, 160,
237, 272, 287–88, 295, 297,
299, 301, 304, 320, 327, 352,
359, 385, 389, 391–94, 411,
413, 433, 436, 445–51, 455,
458–60, 464–65, 467–68, 470,
477–78, 480–81, 487–88, 490,
493, 496, 499, 532–36, 543–
44, 549, 553–54, 556, 569
benefits of successful immortalization, 461
cosmological models of, 24
cosmological requirements,
399–401, 403, 407, 411
phase space, 405–8
cross-purposes with biological
reproduction, 63, 561
early prospects for, 4, 45, 64,
247, 279, 414, 492, 501, 510,
526
enontic, 390
enontic seen as best, 394. See
also biostasis: advantages
eternal punishment ruled out,
316, 319
in Zoroastrianism, 29
experiences worth remembering, 90, 385, 391
hyperontic, 390
ideal self, 89, 415, 417, 419–21,
429, 432, 472–73, 487
immortal ego, 430, 471–73

immortalization as a moral
project, 499, 537
individual favored by, 394
inexhaustible opportunities, 315
information as backup, 395
meaning, 380–81, 386, 390–91
misery treated, 478
non-self ruled out, 386
not precluded by nonexistence
of God, 296, 299
not to be boring, 499
perils of failure to immortalize,
460–61
possible even if no universe is
eternal, 354
possible scientific pathways to,
5, 9, 15, 17, 22–23, 45, 64, 98,
195, 203, 244, 247, 275, 278–
79, 284, 292, 301, 305, 353,
388, 395, 398, 412–13, 427,
501, 507
problem of infrequent remembering, 429–30, 466, 470–72
psychological difficulties remedied, 472
requirements for, 386, 388, 397,
400, 470
resistance to ideas of, 3. See also
cryonics: difficulties over acceptance
suicides reversed, 478
transition from mortal status,
538
virtue rewarded, 473, 497
why desirable, 381, 391–92
world beyond oneself important,
473
wormholes, 410
xenontic, 390
Immortality (Bova), 45
incompleteness theorem (Gödel),
190, 229–37
individual, 22, 24, 26, 54–55, 61,
67, 76–77, 91, 100, 164, 178–79,

209, 283, 320, 328, 332, 366, 390, 394, 430, 434, 446, 460, 465, 478, 513, 520, 529, 534, 540
individuality, reasons for maintaining, 489
Industrial Society and its Future (Kaczynski), 545
Infinite in all Directions (Dyson), 9
information paradigm, 202–3, 208, 226–27, 308, 337, 472, 474, 551. See also Principle of Large Quantity
and fuzziness, 192
and relativity, 193
instantiation (functionalism). See person: instantiation
Interchangeability, 14–15, 23, 31, 34, 50, 88–89, 93, 95–96, 137–38, 145–46, 156, 163, 165, 167, 170, 173–81, 183, 186, 195, 203, 208, 225–26, 244–45, 302, 308, 333–34, 338, 342, 347–48, 352, 383–84, 413, 416, 423, 439, 442, 508, 557, 562. See also person: instantiation
in physics, 167–69
instantiation. See person: instantiation
isomorphism, 165, 166. See also consciousness: isomorphism
Iqbal, Muhammad, 557
Islam, 29, 273, 279, 281, 284, 287, 557
isomorphism. See consciousness: isomorphism; Interchangeability: isomorphism

Jainism, 29, 298
Jesus, 33, 73, 303, 314
Jews
persecution by Nazis and consequences, 393
Jones, David E.H., 259–60
Jones, Neil R., 36
Judaism, 10, 279, 284, 287

Kaczynski, Theodore, 544–47
Kant, Immanuel, 274, 455
Kasparov, Garry, 227
Kent, Dora, 40–42
Kent, Saul, 40, 42, 524
killing
as sometimes the lesser evil, 493
Klebanoff, Gerald, 40
Kosko, Bart, 47
Krauss, Lawrence, 409
Kurzweil, Ray, 47

labor of love (resurrection as). See resurrection: as labor of love
Last Flesh (Dewdney), 46
Leaf, Jerry, 40, 42
Leibniz, Gottfried, 180
Leslie, John, 321
Leucippus, 30
Lewis, David, 23, 142
Libet, Benjamin, 440
life after death. See afterlife; resurrection
life extension, 19, 21, 549
Life Extension Society (LES), 38
Linde, Andrei, 156
Lindemann, C.L.F., 159
Lloyd, Seth, 266
locality property, 114, 116–17, 128–29, 221
order of events, causality, 114, 116–17, 124, 126–28, 130
rescued by many-worlds, 114
twin photon polarization experiment, 118, 122, 125
Locke, John, 31, 174–75, 197, 415–17, 428–29, 485
Logic of Perfection, The (Hartshorne), 286
longterm preservation requirements, 523

loss of information sometimes desirable, 494
love, 32–33, 76, 280, 293, 354, 430, 467, 469, 471, 476, 498, 536–37
love, labor of (resurrection as). See resurrection: as labor of love
Lucretius, 30, 333, 345–46

Malthus, Thomas, 457
Malthusian population principle, 457, 560
Man Into Superman (Ettinger), 9
many-worlds, 4, 23, 50, 95–96, 110, 113–14, 118, 120–22, 126, 128, 130–38, 147, 151–52, 156, 174, 180, 182–84, 211, 217, 221–22, 286–87, 292, 294, 307, 335–36, 402, 438
    division model, 49, 182, 204, 503, 544
    generation model, 31–32, 182–83, 434, 510
    speciation model, 173, 183, 186
Mao Zedong, 394
Mars
    alleged fossils from, 324, 408
Martyrdom of Man, The (Reade), 31
materialism, 1, 10, 15, 24, 30, 65, 79–81, 87–88, 97, 139, 157, 162, 174–75, 179, 188–89, 195–97, 204, 208, 226, 275–76, 287, 296, 299, 303–4, 332–33, 345, 416, 439, 542, 552, 556
    central-state, 88
    Epicurean, 30, 80, 333–34
    reductive, 88
    valuational distinguished from scientific, 80
Maxwell, James Clerk, 258
Maxwell's Demon
    criticism and rebuttal. See nanotechnology: criticism and rebuttal: Maxwell's Demon

Mayakovsky, Vladimir, 38
McCay, Clive, 44
meaning in life, 1, 8, 15, 17, 21–22, 26, 34, 44, 54, 70, 77–78, 91, 98, 139, 158–59, 162, 179, 201, 208, 210, 270, 283, 294, 317, 319–20, 344, 360, 369–70, 384, 391–92, 399, 433, 445, 447, 449–52, 454, 456–58, 465–67, 474, 482, 495, 499, 543, 563–64, 568
medical criterion (biostasis, cryonics). See biostasis: medical criterion
meliorism, 16
memes, 462–63, 466
    evolution of, 463
memory, 11, 30, 67, 78, 90, 173, 175, 197, 201–2, 210, 219, 263, 383, 388–89, 397, 399, 415, 417–19, 421, 428–29, 431–32, 434, 455, 465, 470, 472, 487, 522, 524, 530, 561, 568
    episodic, 385, 387
    generalized, 385, 387
    memories
        role of synaptic connections, 525
        stored redundantly in the brain, 524
    problem of corruption of information, 388, 395
    problem of dissociation, 388, 470
    problem of false memories, 68, 89, 175, 181, 345, 414, 431–33, 445. See also continuer (personal survival): forgetting, false memories
    problem of forgetting, 89, 133, 164, 173, 175, 178, 181, 345, 387–88, 414, 417–18, 422, 428–30, 436, 445. See also continuer (personal survival): forgetting, false memories

problem of infrequent remembering. See immortality: problem of infrequent remembering

Merkle, Ralph, 43, 46, 336, 528–30

Merton, Thomas, 293

Mill, John Stuart, 554

Millennium Myth (Grosso), 45

mind, 197, 201

understanding, 62, 203

Mind Children (Moravec), 9

Mind of God, The (Davies), 282, 289

mind-body problem, 414

mind-brain identity theory. See reductionism: psychological: mind-brain identity theory

Minsky, Marvin, 484

modal realism, 23, 142

Mondragón, Carlos, 41

Moore, Gordon, 263

Moore's Law, 263, 264. See also Rock's Law

moral philosophy, 5, 32–33, 42, 74, 422. See also Yuai: moral philosophy (summary)

moral platform, 446–47, 499, 532

Moravec, Hans, 9, 24, 48–50, 152, 172

More, Max, 44, 46, 78, 86, 415

multiverse, 80, 94–96, 145–46, 149, 152, 156, 171, 174, 181, 185, 223, 244, 246, 273, 280, 286, 288–90, 292–94, 297, 301, 306–7, 309–10, 320, 332, 340–41, 343, 369, 380, 412, 423–25, 431, 438, 469, 478, 482, 486–87, 489, 538

snapshot model, 145, 423–25, 439, 441

mummification (ancient Egyptian practice), 29

mystical

defined, 12. See also mysticism; paranormal; supernatural

mysticism, 9, 11, 32, 51, 65, 79, 196, 201, 208, 303, 438–39, 442, 450, 500, 510, 542, 549–51, 557. See also paranormal; supernatural

Nagel, Thomas, 161

Nanomedicine (Frietas), 43

Nanosystems (Drexler), 43

nanotechnology, 4, 43, 58, 64, 67, 76, 93, 134, 202, 217, 246–49, 253, 255–59, 262–63, 265–66, 268–70, 299, 334, 347, 397, 479, 488, 501, 509–10, 517–18, 527, 530, 536, 559, 561, 567

assembler, 256–57, 259–60, 265–66, 270, 502, 530

carbon nanotube, 254–55, 268

criticism and rebuttal, 257–62

Maxwells Demon, 258, 260, 265

dangers of, 251, 271, 546

disassembler, 256, 266, 271

enzymes, 248, 263

functioning nanite (biosensor), 252

molecular shuttle, 253

nanobots, 265

recreation of extinct species, 269, 492, 567

restoration of ancient monuments, 269

nanotube (carbon). See nanotechnology: carbon nanotube

natural salvation, 74

Natural Salvation (Stephens), 31

naturalism, 80

Nazism, 36, 454, 493

Nelson, Robert, 39

Newton, Isaac, 34, 102, 211

Nietzsche, Friedrich, 35–36, 334, 393, 403

Niven, Larry, 452
Nozick, Robert, 23–24, 164, 343

observer
  weighted according to probabili-
    ties, 307
observer reality, 151, 178–79, 181,
  184, 287, 424, 538
Ockham, William, 131
Ockham's razor, 131, 183, 246,
  289–90
Omega Point, 24, 74, 92, 97, 275–
  77, 294–95, 335, 354, 518
one-chance immortalist philosophy
  versus resurrectionist, 508
ontic criterion (biostasis, cryonics).
  See biostasis: ontic criterion
ontic deficit, 482–83, 508–9, 511,
  513
ontic robustness, 348, 350, 435,
  508, 513, 534. See also resurrection: ontic robustness
onticity, 345–47, 390, 492, 497,
  513
ontology, 95, 184
optical spanner (nanotechnology),
  255
optical tweezers (nanotechnology),
  255
Origen, 29, 101, 197
overpopulation, 71, 457
  global threat unlikely, 457
Ovid, 37

pace of change, 538
pain, future of, 320
Paine, Thomas, 273, 351, 435
pantheism, 273, 284, 288, 293
paranormal, 11–12, 15, 66, 75, 79–
  80, 98, 147, 176, 296, 298–99,
  303, 311. See also mysticism;
  supernatural
  and brain pathology, 349
  defined, 12

parascientific
  defined, 12. See also mysticism;
    paranormal; supernatural
Parfit, Derek, 79, 84–86, 172, 422
past lives, problem of. See continuer (personal survival): past
  lives problem
Pattern on the Stone, The (Hillis),
  3
pattern-survival. See continuer
  (personal survival): pattern-survival
Pearce, David, 559
perfection, 17
person
  as computational process, 23,
    38, 165, 170, 190–91, 195,
    197–201, 223–24, 382, 462
  comparison with civilization, 90
  diachronic self, 78–79, 87, 89,
    164, 171, 209, 384, 421
  equivalence classes, 226
  fissioning, 93, 187, 485, 486.
    See also continuer (personal
    survival): splitting (fissioning)
    of
    split-brain patients, 485
  fissioning, social issues, 488
  fusion, 485. See also continuer
    (personal survival): joining
    (fusion) of
  instantiation, 88, 93–96, 164,
    169, 171–77, 179–81, 183–88,
    195, 208, 225–26, 307–10,
    337, 339–43, 347–48, 380,
    403, 416, 423, 431. See also
    Interchangeability
    hidden variable theory, 186
    principal instantiation, 171–
      72
  Interface, 60, 76, 98, 360, 369,
    482, 495
  persistence over time, 81, 83,
    85–86, 89, 164, 176, 195, 310,

337–42, 344, 381, 415, 418, 420, 422, 470, 472, 474–75, 487–88, 494, 514–15
  informational continuity not necessary for, 422–25, 427
  q-segment, 421
  q-stage, 420–21, 453, 472, 489
uploading, 38, 97, 222, 278, 531, 560, 562–63
person-segment, 78, 164, 384
  person-stage, comparison with, 171–72, 340
  principal person-segment, 171
person-stage, 78, 85, 87–88, 93, 156, 175, 416
  continuer, comparison with, 164
  knowledge of one person by another, 434
  not an instantiation, 164
  persistence of person over time. See person: persistence over time
  person-segment, comparison with, 171–72, 340
personal growth, 384
personal identity, 3–4, 31, 50, 163, 174–75, 202, 332, 343–44, 414–17, 422–23, 445, 485
  memory criterion, 175, 415, 417
  transitivity not necessary, 343
personhood, 44, 171, 344, 381–82, 412
phase conservation, 335
phase path, 291–92, 424
Philosophical Explanations (Nozick), 164, 343
photon detection experiments, 105–8
  two-slit experiment, 108–9, 121, 131
  two-slit experiment, quantum effects, 109–10

physical reductionism. See reductionism: physical
Physics of Immortality, The (Tipler), 3, 9, 23, 47, 50, 168, 274, 393
Pichugin, Yuri, 522
Pizer, David, 299
pleasure, 18, 91, 320, 449, 452, 456, 460, 464, 540, 559
  dangers and limitations, 452, 460
Pliny the Elder, 37
position of assurance (problem solving), 413, 420, 433, 435
posthumanity, 25, 27, 46, 72, 76–77, 278, 329, 434, 540, 547, 564
poverty, 18, 329, 457, 532, 539, 548
Price, Michael, 409
Principia Mathematica (formalized logical system), 230
principle of fecundity, 23
Principle of Large Quantity (computation, AI), 191, 198–99, 219, 223, 227, 238, 241, 382, 441. See also information paradigm
  and evolution, 191
problem of actualization, 184–86
progress, 1, 5, 9, 17–19, 30, 36–37, 43–44, 46, 56, 61, 64, 70, 74, 77, 91, 134, 158, 187, 209, 237, 247, 249, 253, 265, 283, 286, 295–96, 304, 314, 320, 350–51, 355, 393, 396, 402, 405, 413, 429, 433, 447, 450, 465, 467, 489, 500–1, 531–32, 535, 541–42, 548, 550, 552–53, 555, 560–61, 563, 565, 569
prolongevity, 74
Prometheus Project (suspended animation), 42
Prospect of Immortality, The (Ettinger), 3, 9, 38
psychoactive chemicals, 252, 554

psychological connectedness. See reductionism: psychological: psychological connectedness

psychological continuity. See reductionism: psychological: psychological continuity

psychological reductionism. See reductionism: psychological

Purgatory. See resurrection: possible future Purgatory

q-episode, 428
q-memory, 489
q-segment. See person: persistence over time: q-segment
q-stage. See person: persistence over time: q-stage
quantum computing, 130, 136, 215, 264–65
  universal devices, 222, 266
quantum logic (interp. of quantum mechanics), 120
quantum mechanics, 4, 23, 95, 106, 110–13, 118, 120, 130, 138, 141–43, 169, 190, 192, 393, 438
  quantum gravity, 130
Quantum Reality (Herbert), 3, 121
quantum sculpting, 255
quantum state, 96, 121, 168–70, 172, 176, 179–80, 186, 255, 264, 316, 337
quantum uncertainty, 92, 143

randomness
  explained by many-worlds, 120, 132
Reade, Winwood, 31, 45
reanimation, 21, 37–40, 48, 58, 331, 369, 474, 480, 482–83, 496, 508, 517–18, 523–24, 526, 528, 533–35, 551
Reasons and Persons (Parfit), 79
reductionism, 23, 79, 81–82, 172,

190, 196, 199, 288, 429, 437, 442, 509, 550
  physical, 81, 83, 85
    physical continuity, 81–84
  psychological, 4, 23, 81, 83, 85, 93, 166, 557
    functionalism, 2–4, 15, 23, 86–89, 93, 98, 164, 176, 188, 201, 238, 344, 414, 442, 445, 562
    mind-brain identity theory, 88, 163, 188
    psychological connectedness, 3, 85–86, 89, 98, 164, 175, 303, 311, 338, 341, 415–17, 420–22, 425, 427, 431, 433, 453
    psychological continuity, 85–86, 164, 341, 422
reformulation (problem solving), 159, 419
reincarnation, 303
relativity (physics), 112–14, 117–18, 122, 126, 130–31, 438
religion, 28–29, 33, 52, 55–57, 74, 271–74, 281, 283, 299, 303, 449, 458, 557–58
religious experience, 28–29, 52, 55–57, 74, 271–73, 283, 299, 449, 458, 557–58
Renaissance, 31
resurrection, 2, 4, 10, 15, 23–24, 32–34, 42, 44, 47, 49–50, 73–74, 76, 92–94, 96, 98–99, 146, 157, 167, 174–75, 184, 195, 203, 244, 247, 269, 271, 274–77, 288, 302, 305, 313–14, 329–30, 334, 336, 340–42, 344, 346, 348–49, 352, 356–59, 364–67, 369–70, 374–75, 377–81, 390, 422, 427, 446, 473, 475–89, 491, 495–96, 499–500, 509, 513–14, 561, 568. See also continuer (personal survival); survival

after justified self-sacrifice, 497
amnesiac problem, 487
and procreation, 314
as labor of love, 2, 474, 493
authenticity of, 94, 138, 151, 339, 347–48, 350, 512
creation of new beings, 474
dreams and brain pathologies, 350
early ideas on, 28
enontic, 346
exact replication unnecessary, 337–39, 341–42, 351
extraterrestrials not preferred for, 495
future interest anticipated, 99
hyperontic, 346, 534
immortalists favored, 98, 394
information necessary for, 202, 332, 336
information sufficient for, 509
logical requirements for, 338
non-biostatic delayed, 514
ontic robustness, 348
open to all, 2, 20, 166, 244, 294, 301–3, 333, 335, 352, 413, 424, 433, 470, 473, 495, 513
philosophical necessity of, 331–32, 413, 446
possibilities for advancement after, 314
possible future Purgatory, 28, 317, 327, 461, 476, 495, 511
in Zoroastrianism, 29
possible physical forms of, 473
problem of dreaming, 349
problem of past lives, 349
psychological reductionism required, 83
relative likelihood of different scenarios, 308, 310–13
scientific skepticism, 30–31, 92, 332

self-interested motives for carrying out, 314
time precedence problem. See continuer (personal survival): time precedence problem
traditional ideas versus scientific approach, 303
what if previously forbidden, 515
xenontic, 346, 353–54, 380, 390, 433
resurrectionist (immortalist philosophy), 49–50
resurrections
dreams and brain pathologies, 490
retrocreationism, 277, 354
ribosome, 248, 251
rights, limitations of, 515
RNA (aging research), 252
Rock's Law, 264. See also Moore's Law
rotifers (suspended animation), 37
Russell, Bertrand, 230, 392

Sagan, Carl, 13
salvation through science
hostility to idea, 541
Sandberg, Anders, 46
scanning probe microscope (SPM), 254–55, 259
scanning tunneling microscope (STM), 254–55, 259
scientific teleology, 9–10, 557
Searle, John, 226
Segall, Paul, 40
selection process, 53, 55–57, 60–62, 161, 282–83, 460, 462, 494
self-interest, 26, 72, 276, 305–6, 316, 368, 448, 455, 460, 464–65, 467, 470, 473, 487, 498, 533, 561, 568
self-sacrifice sometimes called for, 497–98

self-sustaining domicile, 560
senescence, 22, 502–3, 506–7, 535.
　See also aging
sentience, 63, 323, 490, 511, 548,
　551
sentient life
　preciousness of, 455, 532
sex
　as source of meaning, 457
　willing abandonment of, 458,
　561
Shakespeare, William, 311, 426
single-world ontology, 334, 336–
　37
Singularity, 18, 44, 46, 563
Smith, Huston, 449
Smolin, Lee, 156
social injustice, 539
Society of Mind (Minsky), 484
Solomon, Sheldon, 53
soul, 392, 557
　non-reductionist worldview, 23,
　33, 79, 197, 201, 416, 485,
　510, 550, 557
　reductionist worldview, 557
Spike, The (Broderick), 46
Spinoza, Baruch, 293
squaring the circle, 159, 214, 237,
　332
Stalin, Joseph, 394, 455
Starkman, Glenn, 409
Startling Stories (s.f. periodical),
　37
Stephens, C. A., 31, 45
Sternberg, Hal, 40
Stoicism, 392
subpersonality (subperson), 173,
　180, 187
Suda, Isamu, 39, 67, 522–23
Sufficiency of Information Con-
　tent, 517, 520
suicide lottery. See continuer (per-
　sonal survival): suicide lottery
supernatural, 1, 8, 15, 32–33, 51,

65, 76, 80, 92, 97, 101, 275, 281–
　83, 296, 299, 508. See also mys-
　ticism; paranormal
　defined, 12
　powers, 11, 32, 103, 107, 276,
　281–82, 296
Supramoralism, 35, 74, 92
survival, 17, 30, 45, 71, 78, 166,
　182, 195, 200, 278, 328, 341,
　343, 351–52, 357–61, 364, 369–
　71, 375–76, 381, 386–88, 396–
　98, 401, 407, 411, 419–21, 451,
　453, 456, 459, 462–63, 465–66,
　482, 492, 494, 498, 507–9, 541,
　555, 560–61, 564
　desirable adjustments in views
　of, 446
　disparagemet of ideas about, 52
　forms requiring informational
　continuity, 166
　imperfect survival, 413, 414.
　See also continuer (personal
　survival): forgetting, false
　memories
　intellect as instrument of, 54
　logical requirements for, 201
　of cultures, 55–56, 61, 283, 544
　of species, 53–54, 259–60, 282
　pattern-survival. See continuer
　(personal survival): pattern-
　survival
　personal, logical requirements
　for, 79, 160–63, 164. See also
　continuer (personal survival)
　role of religion, philosophy, 55
　seen as morally mandatory, 471
　works, et cetera not enough, 11

Taoism, 293
tardigrades (suspended animation),
　37
technocalypse, 45
Teilhard de Chardin, Pierre, 24,
　275

telomerase (possible rejuvenator), 252, 503, 506, 541
telomere, 22, 503–5, 541
terror management theory, 53, 56–58, 62. See also death: terror management theory
  cultural anxiety buffer, 55, 57–59, 61–64
  cultural drama, 55, 360, 368, 482
terrorism, 18, 461, 476, 539, 544, 546–47, 553–54
theism, 273–74, 296
Thermodynamics, Second Law of, 291–92, 380
Thorne, Kip, 409
time precedence problem. See continuer (personal survival): time precedence problem
Tipler, Frank, 3, 9–10, 23–24, 47–50, 74, 92, 97, 132, 136, 152, 168–69, 172, 175, 274–77, 288, 294, 301, 303, 335–36, 353–54, 393–94, 401, 405, 407–8, 427, 437–38, 442, 477
tissue engineering, 250
Trans Time (cryonics organization), 40
transcendence. See goals of life: transcendence
transhumanity, 1, 9, 16, 22, 25–26, 38, 46, 71, 90, 139, 191, 330, 347, 449–50, 461, 484, 510, 539–40, 543, 546, 559–61, 563–64, 568
  cosmological philosophy versus transhumanist. See immortalism: cosmological philosophy versus transhumanist
Tsiolkovsky, Konstantin, 32
Turing, Alan M., 212
Turing machine, 88, 212–13, 215, 217–18, 220–23, 239, 245, 318, 382–84, 389, 438

universal, 213, 215, 256, 477
Turing Omnibus, The (Dewdney), 3
Turing test, 224, 227, 240–41
Twenty-first Century Medicine, 42, 524
twin-photon experiment. See Aspect (twin-photon) experiment

UI assumptions, 15, 23, 68, 75, 97, 137, 139, 163, 181, 184–86, 287, 301, 306–8, 331–32, 336, 348, 352, 380, 413, 435, 508
Unabomber, 544
Unabomber manifesto, 545
Unboundedness, 4, 14–15, 23, 94–96, 101, 113, 132–33, 137–38, 142, 145–47, 150–54, 156, 174, 177, 179, 181–82, 223, 244, 286–87, 289, 292, 294, 301–2, 305, 307, 316, 329–30, 332–33, 336–37, 339, 346, 350–52, 354, 394, 413, 425, 431, 433
  alternatives to many-worlds, 156
  likelihood, 147–50, 152–56, 212, 220, 424
uncertainty
  not a cause of despair, 542
underlying reality, 151–52, 178–79, 184, 287, 423
  time does not flow, 145–46, 242, 320, 423, 438
Unitarianism, 299
unity and diversity both desirable, 484
Universal Immortalism, 75
universal language, 140, 204–7, 383
Universalism, 28–29, 32, 76, 276, 298, 319, 340, 370, 375–76, 436, 455, 476, 488, 556, 558
  impermanence of fortuitous advantages, 377

offenders redeemed, 476
Ultra-Universalism, 376

values, 47, 54, 56–57, 89, 344, 404, 421, 536, 556
change with time, 568
vegetarianism, 464, 537
Venturism, 44, 299
violence, 16, 18, 72, 398, 461–62, 543, 546–48
virtual reality, 566
Visser, Matt, 409
Vita Longa Society, 44
Vogel, Viola, 253
von Neumann automaton, 325, 328
von Neumann, John, 18, 325

Waitz, Harold, 40
war on drugs, 554
Washington, George, 39
wave-particle duality, 112, 120
Weinberg, Steven, 136
Whitehead, Alfred North, 23, 230
working hypotheses, 15–16, 75, 156, 244, 297, 331, 443, 455, 542–43
world
  information as territory, 204, 207–9
  matter as territory, 204
World's Religions, The (Smith), 449
worldview, 22, 55, 57–59, 61–63, 94, 161, 196, 293, 297, 304, 447, 469, 476, 516, 542, 544, 550, 552, 556, 558
wormholes (spacetime deformity), 118, 409–11
worms (suspended animation), 37

xenonticity, 345–46, 348–50, 352–54, 358, 369, 378, 390, 427, 431, 433, 490, 492. See also continuer (personal survival): and

xenonticity; resurrection: xenontic

Young, Thomas, 108
Yuai, 75–76, 91, 98–99, 288, 296–99, 331, 496, 513, 556–58
  as faith, 300
  as possible religion, 299
  moral philosophy (summary), 536–37
  Order of Universal Immortalism, 300
  problem of evil, 443

Zakydalsky, Taras D., 33
Zarathushtra (Zoroaster), 28–29, 32, 35
Zoroastrianism, 28–29, 558